OBSERVER'S HANDBOOK 2017

The Royal Astronomical Society of Canada is dedicated to the advancement of astronomy and its related sciences; this Handbook espouses the scientific method, and supports dissemination of information, discoveries, and theories based on that well-tested method.

EDITOR
JAMES S. EDGAR

ONE-HUNDRED-AND-NINTH YEAR OF PUBLICATION

203–4920 DUNDAS STREET WEST, TORONTO ON M9A 1B7
2016

ISSN 0080-4193
ISBN 978-1-927879-06-1

FSC
www.fsc.org
MIX
Paper from responsible sources
FSC® C004071

PRINTED IN CANADA
BY WEBCOM INC.

TABLE OF CONTENTS

N New content R Revised significantly

Key to Marginal Chapter Symbols

Basic Data

Time

Optics and Observing

The Sky Month by Month

Eclipses

The Moon

The Sun

Planets and Satellites

Dwarf & Minor Planets

Meteors, Comets, and Dust

Stars

The Deep Sky

LIST OF CONTRIBUTORS

JAY ANDERSON, Prairie Storm Prediction Centre, Winnipeg, Manitoba .... (Frequency of Nighttime Cloud Cover, Weather Prospects for the 2017 Solar Eclipses)

MICHELE ARENBURG, Brookside, Nova Scotia .... (Selected Observatories, *Star Parties*, and Planetaria, Index)

J. RANDY ATTWOOD, Mississauga, Ontario .... (Voyages in the Solar System)

CHRIS BECKETT, Regina, Saskatchewan .... (Feature Star Field, Wide-Field Wonders)

ROY BISHOP, Avonport, Nova Scotia .... (Astronomical Precession, Binoculars, Eclipse Patterns, Electromagnetic Spectrum, Expired Stars, Filters, Interplanetary Dust, Mars oppositions diagram, Map of the Moon, Maps of the Night Sky, Orbital Motion, Rainbows, Saturn Ring Diagram, Sky Brightness at Midnight, Some Astronomical and Physical Data, Telescope Exit Pupils, Telescope Parameters, Tides and the Earth–Moon System, Time and Time Scales)

LARRY D. BOGAN, Brooklyn Corner, Nova Scotia......... (Configurations of Jupiter's Galilean Satellites, Configurations of Saturn's Brightest Satellites)

DEREK BREIT (IOTA*), Morgan Hill, California .... (Planetary Occultations)

RANDALL BROOKS, Windsor, Nova Scotia .... (Astronomical Twilight and Sidereal Time)

PETER BROWN, Western University, London, Ontario .... (Meteors)

IAN CAMERON, University of Manitoba, Winnipeg, Manitoba .... (Finder Charts)

MARGARET CAMPBELL–BROWN, Western University, London, Ontario.............. (Meteors)

CHRIS CORBALLY, Vatican Observatory, Vatican City State .... (The Brightest Stars; Spectroscopy of Stars)

DAVID L. CRAWFORD, Tucson, Arizona .... (Light Pollution)

ROBERT DICK, Carleton University & University of Ottawa, Ottawa, Ontario .... (Light-Pollution Abatement in Canada)

SCOTT DONNELL (IOTA*), Elbert, Colorado .... (Planetary Occultations)

DAVID W. DUNHAM (IOTA*), Greenbelt, Maryland .... (Lunar Occultations, Planetary Occultations)

MICHEL DUVAL, Montréal, Québec .... (Coloured Double Stars)

ALAN DYER, Strathmore, Alberta .... (Deep-Sky Challenge Objects, Deep-Sky Observing Hints, The Finest NGC Objects, The Messier List)

LOUISE EDWARDS, California Polytechnique University, San Luis Obispo, California.................... (The Deep Sky—From Near to Far)

FRED ESPENAK, Portal, Arizona .... (Eclipses in 2017)

EDWIN GOFFIN (VVS†), Hoboken, Belgium .... (Planetary Occultations)

PAUL GRAY, South Greenwood, Nova Scotia .... (Dark Nebulae)

RICHARD GRAY, Appalachian State University, Boone, North Carolina ... (The Brightest Stars, Spectroscopy of Stars)

DANIEL W.E. GREEN, Harvard University, Cambridge, Massachusetts .... (Minor Planet Ephemerides, Comets in 2017)

KIM HAY, Yarker, Ontario .... (Solar Observing)

TODD J. HENRY, Georgia State University, Atlanta, Georgia .... (The Nearest Stars)

DAVID HERALD (IOTA*), Murrumbateman, Australia .... (Lunar Occultations, Planetary Occultations)

CHRISTOPHER D.K. HERD, Univ. of Alberta, Edmonton, Alberta .... (Meteorite Identification)

RICHARD K. HERD, Geological Survey of Canada, Ottawa, Ontario ...... (Meteorite Identification)

KATHLEEN HOUSTON, Saskatoon, Saskatchewan .... (Astronomical Sketching)

RICHARD HUZIAK, Saskatoon, Saskatchewan .... (Carbon Stars)

PETER JEDICKE, Fanshawe College, London, Ontario .... (Star Clusters)

*International Occultation Timing Association

†Flemish Astronomical Association

LEE JOHNSON, Vancouver, B.C. .... (Magnification and Contrast in Deep-Sky Observing)
STELLA KAFKA (AAVSO†), Cambridge, Massachusetts ....(Variable Stars)
TOOMAS KARMO, Richmond Hill, Ontario......... (The Brightest Stars, Spectroscopy of Stars)
PATRICK KELLY, Falmouth, Nova Scotia .... (Magnitudes of Naked-eye Planets, RAs of the Sun and Planets, The Sky Month by Month (events), Ephemeris of the Sun, Phenomena of Jupiter's Satellites)
DAVE LANE, Saint Mary's University, Halifax, Nova Scotia .... (Nebular Filter Transmission Chart, The Sky Month by Month (tables))
DAVID H. LEVY, Vail, Arizona ....(Deep-Sky Gems, Observing Comets)
ALISTER LING, Edmonton, Alberta ....(Deep-Sky Challenge Objects, The Sky Month by Month (lunar graphics))
BLAIR MACDONALD, Bedford, Nova Scotia ....(Polar Alignment)
BARRY F. MADORE, Caltech, Pasadena, California ....(Galaxies: Brightest and Nearest, Galaxies with Proper Names)
PAUL D. MALEY, Cave Creek, Arizona.. (Observing Artificial Satellites, Planetary Occultations)
PAUL MARKOV, Toronto, Ontario..(The Observing Logbook)
BRIAN D. MASON, U.S. Naval Observatory, Washington, D.C. ....(Double and Multiple Stars)
PHILIP MCCAUSLAND, Western University, London, Ontario..................................(Fireballs)
BRUCE MCCURDY, Edmonton, Alberta......(The Sky Month by Month text, Lunar Observing)
ANTHONY MOFFAT, Université de Montréal, Montréal, Québec....................... (Star Clusters)
ULISSE MUNARI (INAF††), Osservatorio Astronomico di Padova, Padova, Italy .(Variable Stars)
SYUICHI NAKANO, Sumoto, Japan ....(Comets in 2017)
PHILIP D. NICHOLSON, Cornell University, Ithaca, New York ...(Natural Satellites of the Planets)
RON OSTROMECKI, Erie, Pennsylvania .... (Carbon Stars)
MURRAY PAULSON, St. Albert, Alberta .... (The Planets in 2017)
HUGH PETT, Kelowna, British Columbia.......................(Radio Astronomy and Radio Sources)
DOUGLAS PITCAIRN, Dartmouth, Nova Scotia .... (Limiting Magnitudes)
STEVE PRESTON (IOTA*), Medina, Washington ....(Planetary Occultations)
ALLAN RAHILL, Canadian Meteorological Centre, Dorval, Québec... (Weather Resources on the Internet)
EBERHARD RIEDEL (IOTA*), München, Germany............. (Grazing Occultation Predictions)
WILLIAM ROBERTS, Vancouver, B.C. (Magnification and Contrast in Deep-Sky Observing)
RANDALL ROSENFELD, Toronto, Ontario.. (Feature Star Field)
JOSHUA ROTH, Amateur Telescope Makers of Boston, Arlington, Massachusetts.................... (Night Myopia and Stargazing Glasses)
JOHN SPRAY, University of New Brunswick, Fredericton, New Brunswick.............................. (Meteorite Impact Craters of North America)
JAMES STAMM (IOTA*), Tucson, Arizona ....(Planetary Occultations)
IAN STEER, Toronto, Ontario .... (Galaxies: Brightest and Nearest)
KEN TAPPING, Dominion Radio Astrophysical Observatory, Penticton, British Columbia........ (Radio Astronomy and Radio Sources, Solar Activity)
HEATHER THEIJSMEIJER, Kagawong, Ontario...... (Teaching and the *Observer's Handbook*)
TENHO TUOMI, Lucky Lake, Saskatchewan ....(Digital Astrophotography)
DAVID G. TURNER, Dartmouth, Nova Scotia .... (Astronomical Precession)
ELIZABETH O. WAAGEN (AAVSO†), Cambridge, Massachusetts .... (Variable Stars)
ALAN WHITMAN, Penticton, British Columbia................. (Southern Hemisphere Splendours)

*International Occultation Timing Association ....†American Association of Variable Star Observers
††Istituto Nazionale di Astrofisica

THE *OBSERVER'S HANDBOOK*

The *Observer's Handbook* is one of Canada's oldest scientific publications. Created by C.A. Chant, Professor of Astronomy at the University of Toronto, it first appeared over a century ago as *The Canadian Astronomical Handbook for 1907*, a small (13 × 17 cm), 108-page publication. A second edition covered the year 1908, but for the following two years most of the information that would have appeared was published instead in installments in the *Journal of the RASC*. The Council of the Society decided to return to a separate publication for 1911 with a new name—the *Observer's Handbook*—and it has been published annually ever since.

Each year, some 9000 copies of the Handbook are distributed to many countries throughout the world, to amateur and professional astronomers, to educators at school and university levels, and to many observatories, planetaria, and libraries. The Handbook is the main source of income for The Royal Astronomical Society of Canada. Since the first edition in 1907, the editorial team (see p. 8) and contributors (see p. 4) have voluntarily given their time and expertise every year to produce this unique book.

EDITORS OF THE *OBSERVER'S HANDBOOK*

		Position	**Editions**	**RASC President**
C.A. Chant	(1865–1956)	Editor	1907–1957	1903–1907
Frank S. Hogg	(1904–1951)	*Ass't Editor*	1939–1951	1940–1942
Ruth J. Northcott	(1913–1969)	*Ass't Editor*	1952–1957	1962–1964
		Editor	1958–1970	
John R. Percy	(1941–	Editor	1971–1981	1978–1980
Roy L. Bishop	(1939–	Editor	1982–2000	1984–1986
Rajiv Gupta	(1958–	Editor	2001–2006	2002–2004
Patrick Kelly	(1958–	Editor	2007–2011	
David M.F. Chapman	(1953–	Editor	2012–2016	
James S. Edgar	(1946–	*Ass't Editor*	2012–2016	2014–2016
		Editor	2017–	

The *Observer's Handbook* is intended to be "a companion which the observer would wish always to have in his pocket or on the table before him."

C.A. Chant, Toronto, 1906

"We believe that the *Observer's Handbook* is a truly significant contribution that Canadian astronomy in general and our Society in particular has been making to the dissemination of astronomical knowledge for half a century. I trust that it will still occupy the same position of respect after the first hundred years."

Ruth Northcott, Ottawa, 1964

"The more one knows, the more one can benefit from the Handbook. It inspires all who leaf through its pages to learn and question what the tables, graphs and data mean, perhaps to speculate on the mysteries of the Universe, and above all, to get out and look beyond our world. You have in your hands a key to the Universe—a key which will fit many doors. Please use it well and treasure it."

Peter Broughton, Toronto, 1992
Author of *Looking Up, A History of the RASC*

"The *Observer's Handbook* is the single most useful publication for the observational astronomer. Its combination of authoritative data, informative diagrams, and concise text is unique. Anyone interested in astronomy, beginner or expert, amateur or professional, student or teacher, will find the *Observer's Handbook* indispensable. Its international reputation for quality is a credit both to its many contributors and to Canadian astronomy."

Roy Bishop, Halifax, 2000

THE ROYAL ASTRONOMICAL SOCIETY OF CANADA

The beginnings of The Royal Astronomical Society of Canada go back to the mid-1800s. Then, in 1890, the Society was incorporated within the province of Ontario, received its Royal appellation from King Edward VII in 1903, and was federally incorporated in 1968. The Society Office (containing the business office and historical archives) is located at 203–4920 Dundas Street West, Toronto ON M9A 1B7; telephone: 416-924-7973 or 888-924-7272 from within Canada; email: nationaloffice@rasc.ca; website: www.rasc.ca.

The RASC has over 5000 members, who are from many countries and all walks of life. Members receive this *Observer's Handbook* (published every fall for the next calendar year) and electronic access to the bimonthly *Journal of the RASC*, which contains review articles, research papers on historical and contemporary topics, education notes, general notes of astronomical interest, book reviews, news items concerning the Society and its Centres, informal articles, and letters. (A print version of the *Journal* is available at a modest extra cost.) Also included in membership is *SkyNews*, Canada's popular bimonthly astronomy magazine.

Membership fees are $75 per year, with a reduced rate for persons under 21 years of age (under 25, if enrolled in post-secondary education). For members outside of Canada, these figures are to be read as U.S. dollars, and there is an additional fee ($18 for U.S. addresses; $48 for international addresses) to cover higher mailing costs. An applicant may affiliate with one of the Centres of the Society across Canada or join the Society directly as an unattached member. Membership in some Centres may require a higher membership fee.

The Society currently has 29 Centres located in Canada's major cities. Most Centres hold monthly meetings at which prospective members are welcome. For contact information and details on activities, please visit www.rasc.ca/locations-across-canada for the appropriate Centre website URL.

REPORTING OF ASTRONOMICAL DISCOVERIES

To report a possible significant discovery (**a new comet, nova, outburst of an unusual variable star, interesting meteor activity, or feature on a planetary surface**), email a *discovery report* to the International Astronomical Union (IAU) Central Bureau for Astronomical Telegrams (CBAT) at cbatiau@eps.harvard.edu or cbat@iau.org. You can also reach the Central Bureau for Astronomical Telegrams at Hoffman Lab 128, Harvard University, 20 Oxford St, Cambridge MA 02138, USA.

To report a possible **supernova** discovery, create a user account at the Transient Name Server wis-tns.weizmann.ac.il//user/register, then complete the Astronomical Transient Report form.

All discovery reports should include: your name, contact details, observation method (visual, CCD, etc.), a description of the instruments used, exposure details (if non-visual), and the observation site. If new to reporting discoveries, you should provide background information on your observing experience. Inexperienced observers should have their observation checked before contacting CBAT.

Regarding the object itself, report the date and time (UT) of observation, RA and Dec (with equinox) of the object, its estimated magnitude (with bandpass noted), and details of its physical appearance, depending on the type of object. Incomplete discovery reports may be ignored as not being truly serious. Please review the detailed instructions at www.cbat.eps.harvard.edu/DiscoveryInfo.html.

To avoid false alarms, before emailing CBAT, it is highly recommended to make one or more additional observations of the object over a time period of hours or a day. Such observations may be contributed by a privately notified independent observer.

Possible new **minor planets** should be reported to the IAU Minor Planet Center (www.minorplanetcenter.net/iau/info/TechInfo.html).

To report a **fireball** (a meteor brighter than magnitude –5), see p. 255.

EDITOR'S COMMENTS

This last year has been one of a very steep learning curve, trying to figure out four different software packages, learning layout and design, plus accumulating even more astro-knowledge from some very knowledgeable contributors.

We have a few contributor names to add and subtract: one very important person we lost is Geoff Gaherty, who suddenly passed away just as we were starting into the 2017 edition. Geoff wrote the left-hand pages of the SKY MONTH BY MONTH section for two Handbook editions—I dedicate this issue to his memory. Matthew Templeton of the AAVSO has gone on to other endeavours. We welcome new contributors: Michele Arenburg, taking over from me in the OBSERVATORIES, *STAR PARTIES*, AND PLANETARIA section, plus "doing" the INDEX and proofreading; Scott Donnell and Edwin Goffin (PLANETARY OCCULTATIONS); Hugh Pett (RADIO ASTRONOMY AND RADIO SOURCES); and Ulisse Munari (VARIABLE STARS). In addition, we have a new article on SPECTROSCOPY OF STARS by Chris Corbally, Richard Gray, and Toomas Karmo.

Honorary Member Dra. Julieta Fierro provided the GUEST EDITORIAL.

Thanks to all who so willingly give of their time and expertise for this wonderful enterprise. I must say Chris Malicki's proofreading skills are extraordinary! Welcome back to Betty Robinson—a very capable Copy Editor.

Finally, I couldn't have completed this undertaking on time without the helpful and ongoing hints, suggestions, and assistance of former editor, David M.F. Chapman. His automated spreadsheets are topnotch. Thank you, Dave XVII!

James S. Edgar
handbookeditor@rasc.ca
Melville, Saskatchewan
2017 Sep. 14

THE *OBSERVER'S HANDBOOK* EDITORIAL TEAM

EDITOR
James S. Edgar

EDITORIAL CONSULTANT
Roy Bishop

GRAPHICS CONSULTANT
Michael Gatto

COPY EDITOR
Betty Robinson

PROOFREADERS
Michele Arenburg
Chris Malicki
Bruce McCurdy

Several other individuals and organizations played a role in the production of this Handbook: Some of the data come from the publications *Astronomical Phenomena for the Year 2017* and *The Astronomical Almanac 2017*, both prepared jointly by the U.S. Naval Observatory's Nautical Almanac Office and Her Majesty's Nautical Almanac Office. Corrections or suggestions for improvement that were incorporated in this edition were provided by Rick Huziak, Jim Kaminski, Nicole Mortillaro, Walter Nissen, John O'Hanley, and James Wood.

Front cover: This is a crop from Alan Dyer's original image, where Orion rises on a January night over the famous Hoodoos near East Coulee, Alberta, in the Red Deer River valley. Clouds moving in added the photogenic glows around the stars. Obtained with a stack of 10-s exposures, using a Sigma 24-mm Art lens at f/2.8 and a Nikon D750 at ISO 3200.

Back Cover: This image is a composite of 13 photos taken by Judy Anderson during the Svalbard 2015 eclipse on Spitzbergen Island, Norway, and compiled by Alson Wong. Images were captured using a Canon EOS 60D at ISO 640 with a Canon EF 100–400-mm zoom lens at 275 mm and f/10. Exposures of the corona were in a series from 1/6400 to 1/15 during totality.

GUEST EDITORIAL: OUTREACH AS A GREAT JOB

BY DOCTORA JULIETA FIERRO

I am an astronomer, working at Mexico's national university, and doing outreach. When I was studying physics, more than half a century ago, I had been hired as a research assistant at the Institute for Astronomy. This enabled me to attend the weekly research seminars; I clearly remember the first time I heard about quasars and could not stop thinking about them. I also recall how miserable I felt when I saw the outstanding pictures of astronomical objects at the Institute's library books and realized so few people knew about their existence, so I set out to make a slide collection, in black and white! Soon after, I was asked to give a talk. At first, I thought the importance of a good lecture was to show images, state their names, and describe some of their characteristics. I soon realized that pointing out how the human mind is able to know so much about the Universe was far more exciting. After years of travelling all over the country, I began including demonstrations done by the public—these transform the magic of science into the understanding of nature. I have also included dance in my lectures in order to make them an artistic as well as scientific event. Some of the audiences were huge, for instance at the main square in Mexico city.

When I was working on my thesis, I realized there were no astronomy books in Mexican Spanish, so I began writing, at first very simple short texts with different coauthors. This was the beginning of a long series of books for all age groups. I have also written columns in newspapers and more recently in electronic bulletins, mainly about interesting things that happen to me, things I read, or ponder about, as well as scientific news. In my online book on how to do outreach, I suggest that readers work on a page or at least a paragraph every single day. I must admit I am getting old now, and am not following my own advice. I am currently working on a book about a proton; it tells its story, which began 13 800 million years ago. This particle currently lives in an extragalactic HII region and not only explains the way it converts starlight into beautiful colours, but tells about the time it spent inside several generations of stars. From its vantage point, the proton ponders upon the efforts humans make to understand its constitution and the physics that underlies the evolution of the Universe.

I belong to a prestigious organization, the Academy—the corporation dedicated to writing dictionaries, grammars, and to studying the evolution of Mexican Spanish.

I also began doing television and radio programs decades ago. In fact, I still do, recently appearing as an actor in a children's national television science series, where I was in charge of the scientific content. I still have a weekly 45-minute radio program. Participating in media regularly is quite exhausting since one is always thinking about the next program; nevertheless, it is worth the effort, since the media reaches millions.

I have also worked at astronomy exhibits. I am currently involved in building a large science centre in a park in Mexico City that will be dedicated to energy; the energy of the Universe will be one of the main topics.

I am at an age where one belongs to lots of committees, mainly on education, formal and informal, science-industry cooperation, women in science, innovation; I guess my main role is to encourage young people to come up with interesting ideas and to work at them.

When I began doing outreach it was frowned upon; conveying science to the public was considered something non-qualified people could carry out. I believe good popularization requires intelligence, creativity, and hard work. Fortunately, now, every state in Mexico sponsors specialists dedicated to promoting science for all.

I guess my success comes from being available, accepting all kinds of invitations and taking them seriously. I try to make science fascinating, accurate, and simple. I think my secret is my love for science and the urge I feel to share it with others.

Dra. Julieta Fierro is an Honorary Member of the RASC, a lifetime appointment. She is often described as "the Carl Sagan of Mexico," because of the vast amount of outreach she does and the popularization of science in her home country.

RECOMMENDED READING, ATLASES, AND SOFTWARE

Astronomy, a non-technical monthly magazine for amateur astronomers (Canada and U.S.: 800-533-6644; www.astronomy.com).

The Backyard Astronomer's Guide (3rd ed.), by Terence Dickinson and Alan Dyer. Firefly Books (Canada: 800-387-6192, United States: 800-387-5085; www.fireflybooks.ca), 2010. The best guide to equipment and techniques for amateur astronomers, by two experienced observers.

Catalog of the Astronomical Society of the Pacific, an excellent source of astronomical educational resources (415-337-1100; www.astrosociety.org).

Catalog of Sky Publishing, a good source of a variety of astronomical materials, including items listed on this page. (866-644-1377; www.shopatsky.com).

Exploring the Night Sky, by Terence Dickinson. Firefly Books (see above), 1987. A guide to stargazing, recommended for children.

A Field Guide to the Stars and Planets, by Jay M. Pasachoff. Houghton Mifflin Company, New York, 2015. In the Peterson Field Guides series, this classic work (also available as an e-book) is packed with star maps and accessible information.

Nightwatch (4th ed.), by Terence Dickinson. Firefly Books (see above), 2006. An excellent introductory observing guide.

Sky & Telescope, a monthly magazine widely read by both amateur and professional astronomers (866-644-1377; www.skyandtelescope.com).

SkyNews, the Canadian magazine of astronomy and stargazing, published bimonthly by the RASC (866-759-0005; www.skynews.ca).

Starlight Nights, by Leslie Peltier (1900–1980), 1999. Sky Publishing. Anyone who enjoys the night sky should read this book. Reprint of 1965 original.

Atlas of the Moon, by Antonín Rükl, Gary Seronik (Editor). Sky Publishing, 2007. A first-rate lunar atlas for amateur astronomers, currently out of print, but may return.

Millennium Star Atlas, by Roger Sinnott and Michael Perryman. A comprehensive atlas based on data from the *HIPPARCOS* satellite. Three volumes, each covering 8 hours in RA. Contains more than 1 000 000 stars to mag. 11 and more than 10 000 clusters, nebulae, and galaxies on 1548 charts (out of print).

***Sky & Telescope*'s Pocket Sky Atlas,** by Roger W. Sinnott, 2007. Introductory atlas containing 30 796 stars to mag. 7.6, many double stars, and the brighter deep-sky objects, on 80 charts. Spiral-bound, folds flat, great for a small telescope.

Sky Atlas 2000.0 (2nd ed.), by Wil Tirion and Roger Sinnott, 1998. Large format and well done. Contains 81 000 stars to mag. 8.5 and 2700 clusters, nebulae, and galaxies on 26 charts; laminated version available.

Uranometria 2000.0 Deep Sky Atlas, by Wil Tirion, Barry Rappaport, and Will Remaklus, 2001. A second edition of the popular atlas, with stellar data from the *HIPPARCOS* satellite. Contains more than 280 000 stars to mag. 9.75 and 30 000 clusters, nebulae, and galaxies on 220 double-page charts.

Computer-based Planetarium Programs: Available for a variety of platforms, e.g. *Coelix, ECU V6.0 (Earth Centered Universe), MegaStar5, Redshift 7, Starry Night, TheSkyX, Stellarium* (freeware), and *SkySafari*. For more information, see the catalogues listed above or do an Internet search at, for example, www.google.com.

Applications for Mobile Devices: There is a rapidly expanding universe of convenient "apps" for smart phones and tablets: star charting, lunar phase, observing logs, telescope controllers, and so on. See: Apple iTunes (www.apple.com/itunes); BlackBerry App World (appworld.blackberry.com); Windows Store (www.microsoft.com/en-us/windows/windows-10-apps); and Android Market (market.android.com). Also see Andrew Fraknoi's article at tinyurl.com/c63hk4a.

SELECTED OBSERVATORIES, *STAR PARTIES*, AND PLANETARIA

BY MICHELE ARENBURG

Observatories and *star parties* are ordered by longitude, planetaria are ordered alphabetically by city. Some *star party* dates are listed on p. 352.

Location	Lat.	Long.	Alt. (m/ft.)
Anglo-Australian Observatory—Siding Spring, Australia www.aao.gov.au	31°17′S	149°04′E	1164/3819
Mount Stromlo Observatory—Canberra, Australia rsaa.anu.edu.au/observatories	35°19′S	149°00′E	767/2516
Perth Observatory—Bickley, Australia www.wa.gov.au/perthobs	32°00′S	116°08′E	380/1247
Effelsberg Radio Telescope—Effelsberg, Germany www.mpifr-bonn.mpg.de/effelsberg	50°31′N	6°53′E	319/1046
Greenwich Observatory—Greenwich, England www.rog.nmm.ac.uk	51°29′N	0°00′	31/102
Lovell Radio Telescope—Jodrell Bank, England www.jb.man.ac.uk	53°14′N	2°18′W	89/292
Armagh Observatory—Armagh, Northern Ireland www.arm.ac.uk/home.html	54°21′N	6°39′W	43/144
"Leviathan" Great Telescope—Birr, Ireland birrcastle.com/telescope-astronomy	53°05′N	7°54′W	59/194
Isaac Newton Telescope—La Palma, Canary Islands www.ing.iac.es/Astronomy/telescopes/int	28°45′N	17°53′W	2336/7664
Butterpot Star Party—Butter Pot Prov. Park, Newfoundland www.stjohnsrasc.ca/star-party.shtml	47°23′N	53°04′W	164/538
Burke-Gaffney Observatory—Halifax, Nova Scotia www.smu.ca/academic/science/ap/bgo.shtml	44°38′N	63°35′W	93/300
Nova East—Smileys Provincial Park, Nova Scotia halifax.rasc.ca/ne/home.html	45°01′N	63°58′W	150/492
St. Croix Observatory—St. Croix, Nova Scotia halifax.rasc.ca/sco.html	44°57′N	64°02′W	65/213
Deep Sky Eye Observatory—Quinan, Nova Scotia www.deepskyeye.com	43°55′N	65°48′W	30/96
Arecibo Observatory—Arecibo, Puerto Rico www.naic.edu/general	18°21′N	66°45′W	307/1007
Paranal Observatory (ESO)—Cerro Paranal, Chile www.eso.org/paranal/site/paranal.html	24°38′S	70°24′W	2635/8645
Las Campanas Observatory—Cerro Las Campanas, Chile www.lco.cl	29°00′S	70°42′W	2282/7486
Gemini South Observatory—Cerro Pachon, Chile www.gemini.edu	30°14′S	70°44′W	2722/8930
La Silla Observatory (ESO)—Cerro La Silla, Chile www.eso.org/sci/facilities/lasilla.html	29°15′S	70°44′W	2400/7980
Cerro Tololo Inter-American Observatory—Cerro Tololo, Chile www.ctio.noao.edu	30°10′S	70°49′W	2200/7220
Mont Mégantic Observatory—Mont Mégantic, Québec omm.craq-astro.ca	45°27′N	71°09′W	1114/3654
Stellafane—Springfield, Vermont www.stellafane.com	43°16′N	72°31′W	393/1290
Bellevue Observatory—Montréal www.rascmontreal.org/moon/our-observatory	45°25′N	73°56′W	46/150
CAFTA—St-Timothée, Québec www.astrosurf.com/cdadfs/cafta.html	45°26′N	73°44′W	24/79

Location	Lat.	Long.	Alt. (m/ft.)
Helen Sawyer Hogg Observatory—Ottawa, Ontario www.sciencetech.technomuses.ca	45°24′N	75°37′W	70/230
David Dunlap Observatory—Richmond Hill, Ontario www.theDDO.ca	43°52′N	79°25′W	244/800
Green Bank Telescope—Green Bank, West Virginia science.nrao.edu/facilities/gbt	38°26′N	79°50′W	803/2634
Hamilton Centre Observatory—Waterdown, Ontario www.hamiltonrasc.ca/club-observatory	43°23′N	79°55′W	269/882
Allegheny Observatory—Pittsburgh, Pennsylvania www.pitt.edu/~aobsvtry	40°29′N	80°01′W	380/1247
Carr Astronomical Observatory—Collingwood, Ontario rascto.ca/content/ec-carr-astronomical-observatory-cao	44°30′N	80°23′W	422/1384
Starfest—Mount Forest, Ontario www.nyaa.ca/starfest.htm	44°04′N	80°50′W	400/1312
Sudbury Neutrino Observatory—Creighton, Ontario www.sno.phy.queensu.ca	46°28′N	81°11′W	−2073/−6800
Winter Star Party—Camp Wesumkee, Florida www.scas.org/winter-star-party	24°39′N	81°19′W	1/4
Manitoulin Star Party—Gordon's Park, Ontario gordonspark.com/astronomy-and-stargazing	45°40′N	81°58′W	235/771
Hallam Observatory—Comber, Ontario www.rascwindsor.com/pages/hallam-observatory.php	42°14′N	82°31′W	181/594
Prairie Skies Star Party— Bourbonnais, Illinois www.prairieskies.org	41°13′N	87°59′W	188/616
Yerkes Observatory—Williams Bay, Wisconsin astro.uchicago.edu/yerkes	42°34′N	88°33′W	314/1030
Texas Star Party—Fort Davis, Texas texasstarparty.org	30°36′N	103°57′W	1542/5057
McDonald Observatory—Fort Davis, Texas www.as.utexas.edu/mcdonald/mcdonald.html	30°40′N	104°01′W	2065/6773
Kalium Observatory—Regina, Saskatchewan www.regina.rasc.ca/node/9	50°26′N	104°36′W	577/1894
Apache Point Observatory—Sunspot, New Mexico www.apo.nmsu.edu	32°47′N	105°49′W	2788/9147
Sleaford Observatory—Saskatoon, Saskatchewan www.usask.ca/rasc/sleaford.html	52°06′N	105°57′W	565/1853
Very Large Array—Socorro, New Mexico www.vla.nrao.edu	34°05′N	107°37′W	2123/6965
Saskatchewan Summer Star Party—Cypress Hills Park, Sask. www.usask.ca/rasc/starparty.html	49°39′N	109°31′W	1272/4174
Steward Observatory—Tucson, Arizona skycenter.arizona.edu	32°26′N	110°47′W	2510/8230
Fred Lawrence Whipple Observatory—Amado, Arizona www.sao.arizona.edu/FLWO/whipple.html	31°41′N	110°53′W	2554/8379
Kitt Peak National Observatory—Tucson, Arizona www.noao.edu/kpno	31°57′N	111°36′W	2078/6816
Lowell Observatory—Flagstaff, Arizona www.lowell.edu	35°12′N	111°40′W	2206/7236

Location	Lat.	Long.	Alt. (m/ft.)
U.S. Naval Observatory—Flagstaff, Arizona www.nofs.navy.mil	35°11′N	111°44′W	2262/7421
TELUS World of Science—Edmonton, Alberta telusworldofscienceedmonton.ca/exhibits-events/observatory	53°34′N	113°34′W	677/2221
Wilson Coulee Observatory—Okotoks, Alberta calgary.rasc.ca/tourrequest.htm	50°46′N	114°02′W	1127/3697
Alberta Star Party—Starland Recreation Campground, Alta. calgary.rasc.ca/asp.htm	52°08′N	114°43′W	1072/3517
Riverside Telescope Makers Conference—Camp Oakes, Calif. www.rtmcastronomyexpo.org	34°14′N	116°45′W	2316/7600
Palomar Observatory—San Diego, California www.astro.caltech.edu/palomar	33°21′N	116°52′W	1706/5597
Mt. Wilson Observatory—Pasadena, California www.mtwilson.edu	34°13′N	118°03′W	1740/5700
Dominion Radio Astrophysical Observatory—Penticton, B.C. www.nrc-cnrc.gc.ca/eng/solutions/facilities/drao.html	49°19′N	119°37′W	545/1788
Mount Kobau Star Party—Osoyoos, British Columbia www.mksp.ca	49°07′N	119°40′W	1860/6102
Oregon Star Party—Ochoco National Forest, Oregon www.oregonstarparty.org	44°18′N	120°08′W	1499/4918
Fall Star Quest—Loon Lake, British Columbia www.merrittastronomical.com	49°53′N	120°30′W	1159/3802
Table Mountain Star Party—Ellensburg, Washington www.tmspa.com	47°15′N	120°35′W	1937/6357
Goldendale Observatory—Goldendale, Washington parks.state.wa.us/512/Goldendale-Observatory	45°51′N	120°47′W	640/2100
Pine Mountain Observatory—Pine Mountain, Oregon pmo-sun.uoregon.edu	43°47′N	120°57′W	1905/6250
Lick Observatory—San Jose, California mthamilton.ucolick.org	37°20′N	121°39′W	1290/4232
Prince George Centre Observatory—Prince George, B.C. www.vts.bc.ca/pgrasc/tour.html	53°45′N	122°51′W	691/2296
Gordon Southam Observatory—Vancouver, B.C. www.spacecentre.ca/gms	49°16′N	123°09′W	6/21
Dominion Astrophysical Observatory—Victoria, B.C. www.nrc-cnrc.gc.ca/eng/solutions/facilities/dao.html	48°31′N	123°25′W	238/780
RASCals Star Party—Malahat, British Columbia victoria.rasc.ca/events/rascals-star-party-2017	48°33′N	123°34′W	345/1132
James Clerk Maxwell Telescope—Mauna Kea, Hawaii www.eaobservatory.org/jcmt	19°49′N	155°28′W	4092/13 426
Canada-France-Hawaii Telescope—Mauna Kea, Hawaii www.cfht.hawaii.edu	19°49′N	155°28′W	4204/13 793
Gemini North—Mauna Kea, Hawaii www.gemini.edu/public	19°49′N	155°28′W	4213/13 824

Planetarium	Notes
Fiske Planetarium—Boulder fiske.colorado.eduZ/beta 303-492-5001	Evening shows and weekend matinees; observatory available following shows for stargazing; school groups welcome
TELUS Spark—Calgary www.sparkscience.ca/experience-telus-spark/the-dome-theatre 403-817-6800	TELUS Spark's all-new HD Digital Dome has 245 seats in a Digistar 4 theatre; new projectors, sound system, and presentations
Adler Planetarium—Chicago www.adlerplanetarium.org 312-922-7827	Historic, first in Western Hemisphere; large collection of historic instruments; Doane Observatory on-site

Planetarium	Notes
McAuliffe-Shepard Discovery Center—Concord www.starhop.com/plan-your-visit 603-271-7827	Dedicated to first "Teacher In Space" who tragically died in shuttle *Challenger* disaster 1986 Jan. 28
TELUS World of Science—Edmonton telusworldofscienceedmonton.ca/theatres 780-451-3344	Observatory; IMAX theatre; exhibit galleries; science camps and courses; planetarium shows; computer lab; robotics lab; gift shop
Halifax Planetarium—Halifax www.astronomynovascotia.ca 902-494-2314	Features a historic Spitz Model A-1 projector; great venue for small groups; teachers, group leaders, and individuals welcome
W.J. McCallion Planetarium—Hamilton, Ontario www.physics.mcmaster.ca/planetarium 905-525-9140	Shows are especially geared toward a younger audience and their family members; programs include solar and nighttime viewing
Burke Baker Planetarium—Houston www.hmns.org/see_do/planetarium.asp 713-639-4629	One of the Challenger Centres; dome is used for training astronauts to identify star fields; SkyScan digital stars; theatre seats 232
Samuel Oschin Planetarium—Los Angeles griffithobservatory.org/programs/soplanetarium.html 213-473-0800	Completely renovated with state-of-the-art technology; 300-seat theatre; Zeiss Mark IX star projector; and Digistar 3-laser system
ASTROLab du Mont Mégantic—Mont Mégantic www.astrolab-parc-national-mont-megantic.org 819-888-2941	Cosmic Rhythms multimedia show; dark skies; astronomy evenings; on-site lodging; open house for teachers; school programs
Planétarium de Montréal—Montréal espacepourlavie.ca/en/access/rio-tinto-alcan-planetarium 514-868-3000	The new Rio Tinto Alcan Planetarium offers an original and innovative approach to astronomy, with two theatres resembling telescopes
Mystic Seaport Planetarium—Mystic www.mysticseaport.org/visit/explore/planetarium 860-572-5315	Celestial navigation workshops; 30-foot dome; specialized group programs; history of navigation exhibit; GPS workshop
Hayden Planetarium—New York www.amnh.org/our-research/hayden-planetarium 212-769-5100	At American Museum of Natural History; programs, courses, and lectures; Zeiss Mark IX Universarium Star Projector
Harry C. Kendall Planetarium—Portland www.omsi.edu/planetarium 503-797-4610	Fifty-two-foot domed theatre with Digistar 3 projection; presentations on astronomy, space science, and lasers; school programs
James S. McDonnell Planetarium—St. Louis www.slsc.org 314-289-4400	The 80-foot dome houses a Zeiss Model IX; includes exhibits about living and working in space; camp-ins for the whole family
Doran Planetarium—Sudbury www.laurentian.ca/planetarium 800-461-4030	Largest planetarium in northern Ontario, features 10-metre dome, bilingual presentations, and media lectures.
Ontario Science Centre—Toronto www.ontariosciencecentre.ca/tour/live-planetarium-show 416-696-1000	In central Toronto; OMNIMax theatre; kids' sleepovers; summer day camps; home of the RASC Toronto Centre
MacMillan Planetarium—Vancouver www.spacecentre.ca 604-738-7827	Close to downtown Vancouver; special laser shows in summer; numerous programs for school groups of all ages; teacher packages
Albert Einstein Planetarium—Washington airandspace.si.edu/visit/mall/things-to-do/planetarium.cfm 202-633-1000	At National Air and Space Museum; café; IMAX theatre; planetarium upgraded to include Sky Vision™ dual digital projection
Northern Lights—Watson Lake, Yukon www.northernlightscentre.ca 867-536-7827	All-dome video planetarium; daily shows; programs concentrate on aurora borealis and northern experience
Aldrin Planetarium—West Palm Beach www.sfsciencecenter.org/planetarium-shows 561-832-1988	Laser shows; telescopes; exhibits; science camps; teachers' programs; birthday party programs
Manitoba Planetarium—Winnipeg manitobamuseum.ca/main/visit/planetarium/ 204-956-2830	In central Winnipeg; science centre, museum, and planetarium in one site; school programs; new Digistar 5 All-Dome projector

SELECTED INTERNET RESOURCES

The World Wide Web is an important source of astronomical information. A selection of websites together with a reference to a page number in this Handbook (if any) is given below. A listing of all websites mentioned in this Handbook, with URL links to the various sites, is available at www.rasc.ca/web-links.

URL	Description
www.aavso.org	American Association of Variable Star Observers (p. 298)
www.alpo-astronomy.org	Association of Lunar and Planetary Observers (p. 221)
www.astrosociety.org	Astronomical Society of the Pacific (p. 18)
www.astronomy.com	*Astronomy* magazine (p. 10)
www.cascaeducation.ca	Canadian Astronomical Society's education website (p. 16)
www.space.gc.ca	Canadian Space Agency
www.cleardarksky.com/csk	Clear Sky Chart, by Attilla Danko (p. 78)
www.rasc.ca/david-h-levy-logbooks	David H. Levy Logbooks (p. 324)
www.MrEclipse.com	Eclipse photography and safety (p. 142)
heritage.stsci.edu	Hubble Heritage Site, access to HST images
www.cbat.eps.harvard.edu/index.html	International Astronomical Union Central Bureau for Astronomical Telegrams (p. 7)
www.darksky.org	International Dark-Sky Association (p. 79)
www.imo.net	International Meteor Organization (p. 254)
www.lunar-occultations.com/iota	International Occultation Timing Association (p. 162)
www.jpl.nasa.gov	Jet Propulsion Laboratory, activities for adults and kids
miac.uqac.ca	Meteorites and Impacts Advisory Committee, Canadian Space Agency (p. 255)
cdsads.u-strasbg.fr	NASA Astrophysics Data System (ADS); bibliographic database, access to millions of articles
eclipse.gsfc.nasa.gov	NASA eclipse site (p. 142)
nedwww.ipac.caltech.edu	NASA/IPAC Extragalactic Database (p. 334)
spaceflight.nasa.gov	NASA space flight site giving current information on *ISS* activities and human space flight
www.rasc.ca/observers-handbook	*Observer's Handbook* website (inside front cover)
planetary.org	Planetary Society—contains over 2000 pages of information about space exploration
www.rasc.ca	The Royal Astronomical Society of Canada (p. 7)
www.saguaroastro.org	Saguaro Astronomy Club, includes observing list database (p. 87)
www.heavens-above.com	Satellite tracking information, including *International Space Station*
simbad.u-strasbg.fr/simbad	SIMBAD astronomical database
www.skyandtelescope.com	*Sky & Telescope* and Sky Publishing (p. 10)
www.skynews.ca	*SkyNews*—Canada's astronomy magazine, published by the RASC (p. 10)
www.stsci.edu	Space Telescope Science Institute; access to Digitized Sky Survey
seds.org	Students for the Exploration and Development of Space
vizier.hia.nrc.ca/viz-bin/VizieR	VizieR service; access to most astronomical catalogues

TEACHING AND THE *OBSERVER'S HANDBOOK*

BY HEATHER THEIJSMEIJER

You are holding in your hand a valuable resource for teaching astronomy. Every user of this Handbook, whether amateur or professional astronomer, or teacher in any setting, at any level, can contribute to education in astronomy; see *JRASC, 96* (October 2002), p. 196, for information on how you can, too.

The RASC, in partnership with the Canadian Astronomical Society and other organizations, has recently embarked on several major education and public outreach initiatives. These include www.rasc.ca/education-public-outreach (the RASC astronomy education website), and the RASC publication *Skyways*, by Mary Lou Whitehorne, an excellent astronomy guide for teachers. A French version, *Explorons l'astronomie*, is also available.

Countering Misconceptions

Surveys show that many basic astronomical concepts are misunderstood by most people. Examples of common misconceptions include the relative sizes and distances within the Solar System, the "reason for the seasons," and the cause of lunar phases. Poor understanding of these physical systems is often based on false logic (e.g. it is warmer in the summer because the Earth is closer to the Sun) and misleading diagrams (with a poorly chosen, or no existing scale) in common reference books. There is an excellent review and explanation of these and other misconceptions at the Private Universe Project: www.learner.org/teacherslab/pup—certainly worth checking out.

Many of these concepts are so basic that it is worth taking the time to teach them correctly. During learning activities, students' preconceptions can be monitored through conversations and observations. As teachers, we can make sure that these concepts are understood, and that the students can explain them from personal understanding—not just from memorization. This section of the Handbook is designed to do just that.

Igniting Creativity

Nearly every topic in astronomy fires up the imagination and engages a student's creativity. At first glance, while you may be uncertain how a handbook of historical facts and observing data could help you teach space science, the wealth of information found here can easily serve as a jumping-off point for delving into the curriculum. Each topic below is divided into two sections: **Minds-on** will show you where to get information and background pertaining to the specific topic for the classroom, and how it relates to teaching; **Hands-on** will suggest teaching activities to reinforce the concepts discussed in Minds-on, along with other resources.

The Sun

Minds-on: Students are often amazed to learn that the surface of the Sun is quite turbulent and always changing. The SOLAR OBSERVING section (p. 186) describes in detail the types of "blemishes" that can be seen on the surface of the Sun, as well as safe methods of observing the Sun. The SOLAR ACTIVITY section (p. 189) explains the effects that an unstable solar atmosphere can have on the Earth, while Roy Bishop's section on rainbows, halos, etc. (p. 194) examines some of the more common visual phenomena caused by the interaction of sunlight with water droplets and ice crystals in our own atmosphere.

Hands-on: Students can track the motion of the Sun throughout the course of the day, or the position of the Sun at the same time of day throughout the year. Likewise, sunrise and sunset times can be charted to try to find patterns (the times can be found on p. 205), and senior students can apply concepts of periodic motion. Building a sundial (see www.sundials.co.uk/projects.htm) can give students a sense of how the Sun is linked to our 24-hour clock. Viewing the Sun by projection is an easy way to search for sunspots in a classroom setting. See the link above or the Handbook section VIEWING A SOLAR ECLIPSE–A WARNING (p. 145) for a description of these methods. However, **NEVER** observe the Sun directly, especially by looking through binoculars or a telescope; permanent eye damage could result. Daily images of the Sun are available at sohowww.nascom.nasa.gov.

The Moon

Minds-on: Four hundred years ago, the Moon was one of Galileo's first telescopic targets. It is one of the easiest objects to observe as a class, and can often be found in the daytime sky! A detailed map of the Moon can be found on p. 148, with historical and geographical details. The sections on TIMES OF MOONRISE AND MOONSET (p. 150) and LUNAR OBSERVING (p. 158) can be used to help determine when the Moon can best be seen. The sections ECLIPSES IN 2017 (p. 126) and THE SKY MONTH BY MONTH (p. 98) can be consulted to learn if there are any special celestial events involving the Moon. Finally, the section TIDES AND THE EARTH-MOON SYSTEM (p. 179) gives an excellent review of the Moon's effects on Earth, to which many Canadian students can relate.

Hands-on: As for the Sun during the day, the appearance of the Moon can be sketched from night to night throughout the lunar month. Using the maps in this Handbook, students can learn to identify the prominent lunar features they saw and drew. With a light source to act as the Sun, a scale model of the Moon can be used to explain eclipses and the phases of the Moon (www.exploratorium.edu/ronh/solar_system). Pairing-up widely separated groups of students (education.skype.com), when a lunar eclipse is visible to one group but not the other, connects youth globally and provides an opportunity to share experiences of celestial events. Extending the modelling to the entire Solar System allows comparison of the size of the Moon with that of the satellites of other planets (p. 24) and even the planets and dwarf planets themselves (p. 22). Earth's satellite is one of the largest!

The Night Sky

Minds-on: In a sense, astronomy is the easiest strand of science to practice—simply go outside at night and look up! Star charts may be found in many books and magazines (see p. 10), as well as in the MAPS OF THE NIGHT SKY section (p. 339). Aside from finding the Moon, many people can identify constellations, a listing of which can be found on p. 270, and with images at www.dibonsmith.com/constel.htm. THE SKY MONTH BY MONTH (p. 98) will also give you a concise overview of what's up in the night sky during a particular time of the year.

Hands-on: Have the students create a planisphere, which they can use to locate objects in the sky ((National Research Council of Canada has a good one—see p. 5 of http://goo.gl/xl50hj). This can also be used to teach the proper way to read a star chart. Students can practice the science of observation by drawing what they see in the night sky, including the horizon and compass points, and by keeping an observing logbook (p. 86). Even the study of light pollution (p. 79) can be an educational experience, relating astronomy to the environment; see *JRASC, 96* (February 2002), p. 24, and the Astronomical Society of the Pacific (tinyurl.com/4ygwrgu).

The Solar System, Including Comets, Dwarf Planets, and Minor Planets

Minds-on: The Solar System is our celestial neighbourhood. Our planetary neighbours are introduced below, but who else resides in the 'hood? The PRINCIPAL ELEMENTS OF THE SOLAR SYSTEM (p. 22) and the VOYAGES IN THE SOLAR SYSTEM (p. 36) are an excellent introduction to the history of exploration of the Solar System, as well as what types of objects are believed to be typical in stellar systems. THE DWARF PLANETS (p. 241) and THE BRIGHTEST MINOR PLANETS (p. 244) can be helpful in finding those bodies in the night sky (most only need binoculars), while a table of brightness, sizes, and distances from the Sun can be found on p. 23. The section on METEORITE IMPACT CRATERS OF NORTH AMERICA (p. 260) brings the idea of meteorite impacts a little closer to home for students.

Hands-on: The "Toilet-paper Solar System" (www.nthelp.com/eer/HOAtpss.html) and the "Earth as a Peppercorn" model (Guy Ottewell, see tinyurl.com/2ooch5) are both excellent, hands-on activities for modelling the vast distances in the

Solar System. Likewise, students can design their own scale model using www.exploratorium.edu/ronh/solar_system. Students can simulate meteoric impacts in the class with the "craters-in-the-classroom" activity (see http://goo.gl/RIVAMx) and can even build a comet out of dry ice, sand, and other organic materials, with instructions found at www.noao.edu/education/crecipe.html.

The Planets

Minds-on: Learning about "another world" in the classroom and then seeing that planet in the night sky serves to stimulate student interest and fire up their imaginations. THE SKY MONTH BY MONTH (p. 98) tells us when the various planets are visible, and these are sure to be the highlight of any outdoor observing session with students. THE PLANETS FOR 2017 (p. 211) gives more information about each planet, as does the tabular data starting on p. 22. A history of the theories pertaining to the motion of the planets is provided in the ORBITAL MOTION section (p. 27).

Hands-on: Using the information summarized from THE PLANETS IN 2017 (p. 211), students can "design an alien" that could live on a particular planet, given the surface temperature, atmospheric composition, surface features, etc. This could also be adapted for older students by having them design a human colony on another planet. It is certainly true that a picture can be worth a thousand words—many of the resources listed on p. 10 and p. 15 help bring these other worlds into the classroom. Finally, Exploratorium has calculators for one's age and weight on other planets at www.exploratorium.edu/ronh, as well as other activities.

Is a Telescope Necessary?

Binoculars and telescopes can be useful but are not essential; much interesting astronomy can be done with the unaided eye. However, binoculars are often available and should be used when helpful. See the section BINOCULARS (p. 60) for a guide to their selection and use. The inexpensive, make-it-yourself *Project STAR* telescopes and *Galileoscopes* (www.galileoscope.org) are highly recommended. See TELESCOPE PARAMETERS (p. 49) and the pages following for more on observing with telescopes.

Resources

In addition to the list of reading material below, and the RASC's *Skyways*, you may be able to make use of the following:

(1) See the SELECTED OBSERVATORIES, *STAR PARTIES*, AND PLANETARIA section in this Handbook (p. 11). Take your students to visit one of these.

(2) The Royal Astronomical Society of Canada is the largest organization of amateur astronomers in Canada. Their 29 Centres across Canada (see the section THE ROYAL ASTRONOMICAL SOCIETY OF CANADA on p. 7) offer a wide variety of activities that might be interesting to you and your students. For example, a member of the RASC might be willing to visit your class and demonstrate a telescope. The Astronomical Society of the Pacific's *Project ASTRO How-To Manual* can facilitate such visits. See www.astrosociety.org/edu/astro/astropubs/how_to.html.

Astronomical Society of the Pacific, 390 Ashton Ave, San Francisco CA 94112, USA; 415-337-1100. In addition to their excellent educational material, the ASP publishes a free quarterly teachers' newsletter; download current and back issues from www.astrosociety.org/publications/universe-in-the-classroom.

Project STAR Hands-on Science Materials, Science First/STARLAB, 86475 Gene Lasserre Blvd, Yulee FL 32097, USA; 800-537-8703; www.starlab.com. Unique, high-quality, low-cost materials for introducing students (and teachers) to astronomy.

SkyNews, 203–4920 Dundas Street W, Toronto ON M9A 1B7; 866-759-0005; www.skynews.ca, published bimonthly by the RASC and included as a membership benefit. General astronomy from a Canadian perspective.

The Universe at Your Fingertips, and *More Universe at Your Fingertips*, edited by Andrew Fraknoi et al., Astronomical Society of the Pacific, 390 Ashton Ave, San Francisco CA 94112, USA. Another excellent collection of teaching activities and resources for grades 3–12. See also www.astrosociety.org/education/activities/astroacts.html.

BASIC DATA

TERMINOLOGY AND SYMBOLS

COORDINATE SYSTEMS

Astronomical positions are usually measured in a system based on the *celestial poles* and *celestial equator*, the intersections of Earth's rotation axis and equatorial plane, respectively, and the infinite sphere of the sky. *Right ascension* (RA or α) is measured in hours (h), minutes (m), and seconds (s) of time, eastward along the celestial equator from the vernal equinox (see below). *Declination* (Dec or δ) is measured in degrees (°), minutes (′), and seconds (″) of arc, northward (N or +) or southward (S or –) from the celestial equator toward the north or south celestial pole.

Positions can also be measured in a system based on the *ecliptic*, the intersection of Earth's orbital plane and the infinite sphere of the sky. The Sun appears to move eastward along the ecliptic during the year. *Longitude* is measured eastward along the ecliptic from the vernal equinox; *latitude* is measured at right angles to the ecliptic, northward or southward toward the north or south ecliptic pole. The *vernal equinox* is one of the two intersections of the ecliptic and the celestial equator; it is the one at which the Sun crosses the celestial equator moving from south to north.

An object is *in conjunction with the Sun* if it has the same longitude as the Sun and *at opposition* if its longitude differs from that of the Sun by 180°. Mercury and Venus are in *superior* conjunction when they are more distant than the Sun and in *inferior* conjunction when they are nearer than the Sun (see the diagram on the next page). An object is *stationary* when it reaches an extreme longitude.

Two *nonsolar* objects are in conjunction if they have the same RA. Generally, but not always, close mutual approaches correspond to conjunctions; following Jean Meeus, we use the term *quasi-conjunction* to denote close (< 5°) nonconjunctional approaches.

If an object crosses the ecliptic moving northward, it is at the *ascending node* of its orbit; if it crosses the ecliptic moving southward, it is at the *descending node*.

Elongation is the geocentric angle between an object and the Sun, or between a satellite and its primary, measured in the plane formed by Earth and the other two bodies.

SYMBOLS

Solar System Objects

☉ Sun	♀ Venus	♃ Jupiter	♆ Neptune
☾ Moon	⊕ Earth	♄ Saturn	♇ Pluto
☿ Mercury	♂ Mars	♅ Uranus	

Signs of the Zodiac

♈ Aries ......0°	♌ Leo ......120°	♐ Sagittarius ......240°
♉ Taurus ......30°	♍ Virgo ......150°	♑ Capricornus ......270°
♊ Gemini ......60°	♎ Libra ......180°	♒ Aquarius ......300°
♋ Cancer ......90°	♏ Scorpius ......210°	♓ Pisces ......330°

The Greek Alphabet

Α, α.....alpha *(alfa)**	Η, η........eta	Ν, ν...... nu *(niu)*	Τ, τ....... tau
Β, β.....beta	Θ, θ, ϑ....theta *(teta)*	Ξ, ξ...... xi *(ksi)*	Υ, υ...... upsilon
Γ, γ......gamma	Ι, ι..........iota	Ο, ο...... omicron	Φ, φ...... phi
Δ, δ.....delta	Κ, κ........kappa	Π, π...... pi	Χ, χ...... chi *(khi)*
Ε, ε......epsilon *(eps)*	Λ, λ........lambda	Ρ, ρ....... rho	Ψ, ψ..... psi
Ζ, ζ......zeta	Μ, μ.......mu *(miu)*	Σ, σ...... sigma	Ω, ω..... omega

**Variant spellings are used in some online search databases* (see www.aavso.org/greek-letters).

SOLAR SYSTEM GEOMETRY

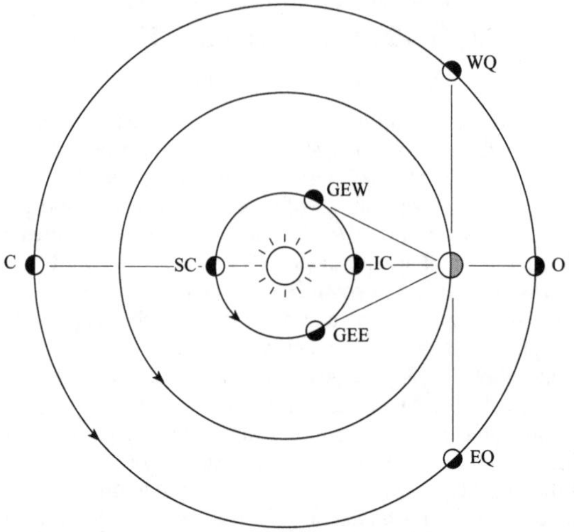

The diagram is a simplified view of the Solar System, from the north side. Earth is shown (middle orbit) together with an inferior planet (i.e. Mercury or Venus) and a superior planet (e.g. Mars). Four special geometrical configurations of the inferior planet relative to Earth are shown; in counterclockwise chronological sequence they are inferior conjunction (IC), greatest elongation west (GEW), superior conjunction (SC), and greatest elongation east (GEE). Four special configurations of the superior planet relative to Earth are also shown; in clockwise chronological sequence they are opposition (O), eastern quadrature (EQ), conjunction with the Sun (C), and western quadrature (WQ).

HANDY SKY MEASURES

Angular measure in the sky can be quickly estimated using the fingers of an outstretched arm, or by comparing with the star separations in the Big Dipper.

(Adapted from *Nightwatch* by Terence Dickinson, see Handbook p. 10.)

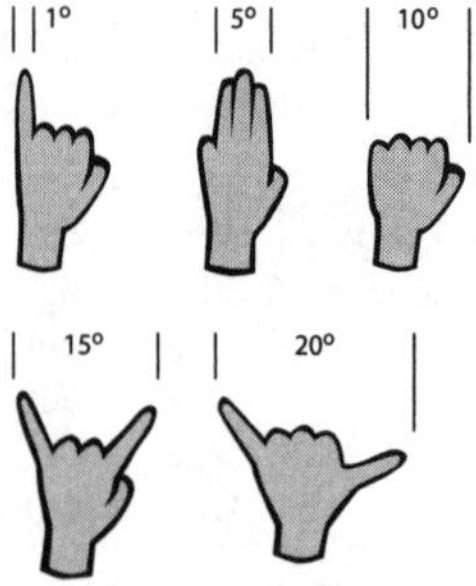

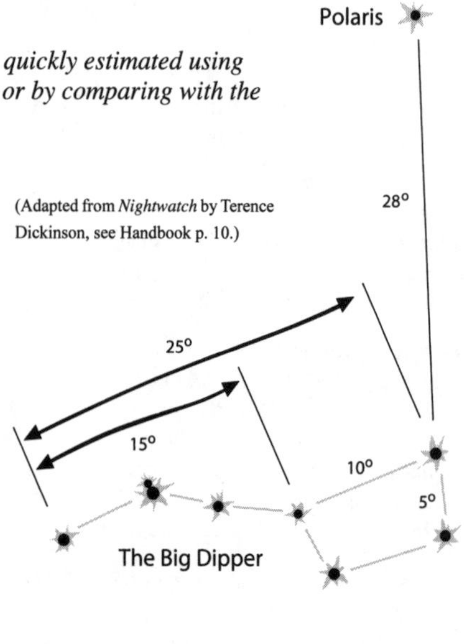

ASTRONOMICAL PRECESSION

BY DAVID G. TURNER AND ROY L. BISHOP

Physical causes of precession: In addition to causing oceanic tides, the Moon and (to a lesser extent) the Sun exert a tidal torque on Earth's equatorial bulge, tending to align Earth's equatorial plane with the Moon and Sun. The axis of the spinning Earth responds, not by tilting to achieve that alignment, but by slowly moving in a conical path, a motion called *precession*. The precession of a rotating body, be it a toy top or planet Earth, appears strange or counterintuitive only because we naively tend to assume that the body should behave in the same way that it would if it were not spinning. Once the spin is acknowledged, it becomes apparent that the various parts of the body are moving as expected, according to Newton's second law of motion. The off-centre support force on a tilted, spinning, toy top on a table applies a torque tending to increase the tilt, and the resulting precession is in the same rotational sense as the spin. The tidal torque on Earth tends to decrease the tilt, so Earth's precession is opposite to its spin. Although the other planets have an almost negligible tidal effect on Earth, they do cause the plane of Earth's orbit, the ecliptic, to wobble a small amount (see **Earth's rotation relative to the equinox**, p. 40). As a result of the combined precession of the equator and precession of the ecliptic, the equinoxes (the intersection points of the celestial equator and the ecliptic) drift westward (retrograde) about 50.29″ per year (a period of approximately 25 800 years).

Coordinates of celestial objects: As a consequence of precession, the locations of the celestial poles continually move along circles of radius 23.4° around the north and south ecliptic poles; consequently, the RA and Dec coordinates of even a "fixed" celestial body continually change, and must be referred to the *epoch* (i.e. Julian year date) of the equatorial grid used. Most of the positions in this Handbook are referred to J2000.0 for compatability with current star charts and atlases. In the event that a conversion of coordinates is required from one epoch to another, use the precession formulae found in ANGULAR RELATIONS, p. 32. To the accuracy that amateur computer-controlled or Go To telescopes are capable of pointing, precession may not be a significant factor, although it is always advisable to keep software and firmware up to date.

Precession and the constellations: The vernal equinox was located in the constellation Gemini 7500 years ago, in Taurus 4500 years ago, and in Aries 3000 years ago. It moved into Pisces from the "first point of Aries" around the beginning of the Christian era 2000 years ago, at roughly the same time as Hipparchus discovered precession of the equinoxes.

Precession causes stars to apparently move almost parallel to the ecliptic, relative to the vernal equinox, but our civil calendar (since the inception of the Gregorian calendar) is regularly adjusted so that the annual seasons are synchronized with the months. Consequently, *where* and *when* the constellations appear in the sky slowly change over the years. The faint stars in the 105-degree-long constellation of Hydra, the Water Snake, lay along the celestial equator 4600 years ago, but are inclined more than 30° away from the celestial equator today. With so few stars of any significance, it could only have originated as a navigational aid, helping ancient sailors steer an east-west course. In 12 000 years, the "summer" constellation Sagittarius will appear high in Northern Hemisphere winter skies, while Orion will barely rise in the summer sky.

The *shape* of a constellation is affected mainly by the relative proper motions of its member stars in the sky, and this effect on sky lore can be more interesting. The bright stars of Ursa Major, for example, bore a resemblance to the outline of a bear's head 125 000 years ago; and 4000 years ago, the bright star Arcturus was located near the centre of Boötes rather than at its southern tip.

PRINCIPAL ELEMENTS OF THE SOLAR SYSTEM

PHYSICAL ELEMENTS

Object (Pronun.)	Equatorial Diameter km	Oblateness	Mass Earth=1*	Density t/m³	Gravity† Earth=1	Escape Speed† km/s	Rotation Period d	Inclination‡ °	Albedo
Sun	1 392 530	0	332 946.0	1.41	27.9	617.5	25–35††		
Mercury (mûr′kū-rē)	4 879	0	0.055 274	5.43	0.38	4.2	58.6462	0.0	0.11
Venus (vē′nŭs)	12 104	0	0.815 01	5.24	0.90	10.4	–243.0185	2.6	0.65
Earth (ûrth)	12 756	1/298	1	5.513	1.00	11.2	0.99727	23.4	0.37
Moon	3 475	0	0.012 300	3.34	0.17	2.4	27.32166	6.7	0.12
Mars (märz)	6 792	1/170	0.107 45	3.93	0.38	5.0	1.02596	25.2	0.15
Ceres[A] (cē′rēz)	952	1/15	0.000 157	2.08	0.028	0.5	0.3781	10.6	0.07
Jupiter (jo͞o′pĭ-tẽr)	142 984 ‡‡	1/15	317.83	1.33	2.53	59.5	0.4135†††	3.1	0.52
Saturn (săt′ûrn)	120 536 ‡‡	1/10	95.161	0.69	1.06	35.5	0.44401	26.7	0.47
Uranus[B] (yûr′ȧ-nŭs)	51 118 ‡‡	1/49	14.536	1.27	0.90	21.3	–0.71833	82.2	0.51
Neptune[C] (nĕp′tyo͞on)	49 528 ‡‡	1/59	17.148	1.64	1.14	23.5	0.67125	28.3	0.41
Pluto[A] (plo͞o′tō)	2 390	0?	0.002 184	1.82	0.067	1.3	–6.3872	60.4	0.30
Eris[A] (ēr′ĭs)	2 400	0?	0.002 795	2.52	0.08	1.4	1.0800	44.0	0.86

*5.972×10^{24} kg †At the equator ‡Inclination of equator to orbital plane †† Depending on latitude
‡‡At 1 atmosphere (101.325 kPa) †††For the most rapidly rotating part, the equatorial region

[A]*Dwarf planet* (see 2006 IAU Resolution B5). *Ceres* discovered by Giuseppe Piazzi, 1801 Jan. 1; *Pluto* discovered by Clyde Tombaugh, 1930 Feb. 18; *Eris* discovered by M. Brown et al., 2005 Jan. 5
[B]Discovered by William Herschel, 1781 Mar. 13
[C]Position predicted by Le Verrier (independently by Adams) and located by Johann G. Galle, 1846 Sep. 23
Pronunciation guide: ȧ gȧgȧ; ē wē; ĕ mĕt; ẽ makẽr; ĭ bĭt; ō gō; o͞o mo͞on; ū ūnite; ŭ sŭn; û ûrn

OSCULATING ORBITAL ELEMENTS FOR 2017

The tables at the right give the orbital elements of the planets, three dwarf planets, and the 25 brightest minor planets, from the *Astronomical Almanac*. At any given time or "epoch," six basic quantities determine each body's elliptical orbit, for example:

(1) the mean distance from the Sun, a, equal to the semimajor axis of the ellipse;
(2) the eccentricity e of the ellipse;
(3) the inclination i of the orbital plane to the ecliptic;
(4) the longitude Ω of the ascending node of the orbital plane on the ecliptic;
(5) the longitude $\tilde{\omega}$ of perihelion;
(6) the body's mean longitude L at the given epoch.

The date of the ecliptic and equinox used to measure the last four quantities must also be specified, and may be different from the given epoch. Other, equivalent, parameters may be substituted: the distance q of perihelion in place of a; the argument of perihelion, $\omega = \tilde{\omega} - \Omega$, in place of $\tilde{\omega}$; or the mean anomaly, $M = L - \tilde{\omega}$, or time T of perihelion in place of L. Once six fundamental quantities are known, all other attributes of the orbit of the body, such as the sidereal period P and synodic period S, can be derived.

If the body followed a perfectly elliptical orbit as predicted by classical orbital mechanics, then for a fixed ecliptic and equinox the first five quantities above would be constant over time. However, because of perturbations caused by the gravitational influence of other bodies, the orbits are not perfectly elliptical; hence the orbital elements depend on the epoch. The given *osculating* elements can be used to determine an elliptical orbit that is a close approximation to the actual path of the body for times near the given epoch. Elements for two epochs are provided for each planet, 240 days (roughly 8 months) apart; the elements can be linearly interpolated to other epochs in 2017 for precision of a few arcseconds (typically 1″ or 2″), noting that multiples of 360° must be added to the second value of L if the planet completes one (or more) orbits between those dates. For selected *dwarf planets* and minor planets, elements for one epoch (2017 Sep. 4) are given, with resulting precision of about 1′ (for more information, see **ssd.jpl.nasa.gov**).

HELIOCENTRIC OSCULATING ORBITAL ELEMENTS FOR 2017
REFERRED TO THE MEAN ECLIPTIC AND EQUINOX OF J2000.0

Planet	Epoch Julian Date 245...	Mean Distance* a au	Eccentricity e	Inclination i °	Long. of Asc. Node Ω °	Long. of Perihelion $\tilde{\omega}$ °	Long. at Epoch L °	Sidereal Period P y	Synodic Period† S d
For Julian Date 245 7800.5 (2017 Feb. 16.0) and Julian Date 245 8040.5 (2017 Oct. 14.0)									
Mercury	7800.5	0.387 099	0.205 627	7.004	48.3092	77.4799	291.8769	0.2409	115.9
	8040.5	0.387 098	0.205 638	7.004	48.3084	77.4839	194.0359	0.2409	
Venus	7800.5	0.723 331	0.006 746	3.3944	76.6331	131.6533	124.1110	0.6152	583.9
	8040.5	0.723 328	0.006 786	3.3945	76.6285	131.3854	148.6197	0.6152	
Earth‡	7800.5	1.000 001	0.016 701	0.0022	172.4	102.9137	145.9405	1	—
	8040.5	0.999 998	0.016 694	0.0024	173.9	102.9015	22.4884	1	
Mars	7800.5	1.523 692	0.093 504	1.8484	49.5071	336.1677	33.5343	1.8809	778
	8040.5	1.523 644	0.093 489	1.8484	49.5068	336.1245	159.3104	1.8809	
Jupiter	7800.5	5.202 158	0.048 896	1.3037	100.5130	14.2689	194.1602	11.8600	398.9
	8040.5	5.202 169	0.048 893	1.3037	100.5133	14.2429	214.1084	11.8594	
Saturn	7800.5	9.559 738	0.052 963	2.4873	113.5851	93.8056	259.2040	29.5004	378.1
	8040.5	9.564 689	0.052 387	2.4869	113.5898	93.6714	267.2352	29.5283	
Uranus	7800.5	19.108 196	0.050 844	0.7719	73.9838	173.5173	26.6258	83.5410	369.7
	8040.5	19.108 903	0.050 454	0.7716	74.0114	174.0900	29.3841	83.4951	
Neptune	7800.5	29.963 210	0.006 354	1.7723	131.8204	68.0064	342.1299	163.6933	367.5
	8040.5	29.996 402	0.006 013	1.7721	131.8154	57.0098	343.5104	163.8366	

*1 au = 1.496×10^{11} m † Synodic period = (product of *P*s of two planets) ÷ (difference of the *P*s)
Tabular values are relative to Earth ‡ Values are actually for the Earth–Moon barycentre

Dwarf Planet or Minor Planet	Absolute Mag.*	Diam. km	Mean Distance a au	Eccentricity e	Inclination i °	Long. of Asc. Node Ω °	Long. of Perihelion $\tilde{\omega}$ °	Long. at Epoch L °	Sidereal Period P y
For epoch Julian Date 245 8000.5 (2017 Sep. 4.0)									
Eris	*−1.20*	*2400*	*67.781*	*0.440*	*44.204*	*151.549*	*73.024*	*23.506*	*561.4*
Pluto	*−0.80*	*2390*	*39.519*	*0.250*	*17.128*	*110.296*	*113.960*	*287.366*	*252.7*
4 Vesta	**3.20**	**512**	**2.3618**	**0.0892**	**7.140**	**103.836**	**254.779**	**187.489**	**3.6297**
1 Ceres	*3.34*	*952*	*2.768*	*0.075*	*10.593*	*80.309*	*73.024*	*98.505*	*4.603*
2 Pallas	**4.13**	**524**	**2.7731**	**0.2306**	**34.838**	**173.087**	**123.079**	**54.730**	**4.6181**
15 Eunomia	**5.28**	**320**	**2.6449**	**0.1867**	**11.733**	**293.141**	**30.898**	**177.549**	**4.3017**
3 Juno	**5.33**	**274**	**2.6685**	**0.2569**	**12.990**	**169.858**	**58.065**	**317.300**	**4.3593**
10 Hygiea	**5.43**	**444**	**3.1399**	**0.1127**	**3.832**	**283.218**	**235.257**	**281.449**	**5.5639**
7 Iris	**5.51**	**211**	**2.3858**	**0.2314**	**5.523**	**259.565**	**44.879**	**24.728**	**3.6852**
6 Hebe	**5.71**	**190**	**2.4249**	**0.2028**	**14.737**	**138.648**	**18.509**	**308.076**	**3.7763**
16 Psyche	5.90	239	2.9257	0.1349	3.098	150.263	17.809	189.307	5.0046
9 Metis	**6.28**	**209**	**2.3872**	**0.1221**	**5.575**	**68.917**	**75.117**	**191.819**	**3.6887**
14 Irene	6.30	180	2.5867	0.1668	9.119	86.129	184.171	206.690	4.1603
22 Kalliope	6.45	181	2.9096	0.0991	13.717	66.065	61.004	139.821	4.9632
8 Flora	**6.49**	**138**	**2.2014**	**0.1570**	**5.887**	**110.901**	**36.211**	**49.972**	**3.2664**
20 Massalia	6.50	145	2.4092	0.1424	0.709	206.103	102.676	62.410	3.7396
18 Melpomene	6.51	138	2.2951	0.2188	10.134	150.467	18.288	115.642	3.4771
11 Parthenope	6.55	153	2.4525	0.1005	4.630	125.559	321.425	86.023	3.8409
13 Egeria	6.74	208	2.5769	0.0838	16.540	43.237	123.792	168.390	4.1367
5 Astraea	6.85	120	2.5733	0.1915	5.368	141.583	140.340	279.403	4.1280
23 Thalia	6.95	108	2.6250	0.2353	10.114	66.851	127.552	324.310	4.2531
24 Themis	7.08	175	3.1373	0.1252	0.752	35.943	142.829	31.685	5.5573
19 Fortuna	7.13	225	2.4419	0.1587	1.574	211.143	33.240	75.543	3.8159
12 Victoria	7.24	113	2.3340	0.2200	8.373	235.411	304.999	272.567	3.5659
21 Lutetia	7.35	98	2.4345	0.1645	3.064	80.878	330.867	159.529	3.7985
26 Proserpina	7.40	95	2.6558	0.0908	3.564	45.782	239.477	208.258	4.3281
17 Thetis	7.76	90	2.4711	0.1326	5.590	125.557	261.683	52.840	3.8848
25 Phocaea	7.83	75	2.4001	0.2543	21.606	214.137	304.382	318.273	3.7186

*Ordered by absolute magnitude, which is the hypothetical magnitude at zero phase angle with both Earth and Sun at 1 au distance. At opposition, the body will appear dimmer than this value by 2–20 mag., depending on the actual distance. Note that the largest are not always the brightest. **Bold** = opposition in or near 2017 at mag. 9.7 or brighter (see p. 245 for the ephemerides of these and some others).

NATURAL SATELLITES OF THE PLANETS

BY PHILIP D. NICHOLSON

Of the 173 known natural satellites of the 8 Solar System planets, all but 3 orbit the giant planets. At latest count, Jupiter has 67, Saturn has 62 (though one reported in 2009 may be no more than a temporary dust cloud in the rings), Uranus has 27, and Neptune has 14. With a few exceptions, these moons may be divided into three groups, which presumably reflect their different origins. Closest to the planets are small ring moons, less than 200 km in diameter and with strong evolutionary and dynamical connections to the planetary ring systems. Many of these objects were discovered during the Voyager flybys of 1979–1989, and all are very difficult to observe from Earth. They include the Saturnian shepherd satellites Prometheus and Pandora, and the co-orbital satellites Janus and Epimetheus, all of which have been photographed from Earth (or by the *Hubble Space Telescope*) when the rings turn edge-on.

Next come the larger "regular" satellites in near-circular orbits in or near their planets' equatorial planes, thought to have been formed in situ via accretion in circumplanetary disks at the dawn of the Solar System. This group extends out to Callisto, Iapetus, Oberon, and Proteus, but does not include Triton, which is now thought to have been captured. There are numerous orbital resonances among the regular satellites, for example, Io:Europa:Ganymede (1:2:4), Mimas:Tethys (1:2), Enceladus:Dione (1:2), and Titan:Hyperion (3:4); the origin of these resonances is generally ascribed to orbital expansion driven by tidal interactions with Jupiter or Saturn. Temporary capture in similar resonances in the past may have been responsible for the anomalously large inclinations of Miranda and (perhaps) Naiad. Tidal-energy dissipation within Io is responsible for this moon's spectacular volcanic activity, and similar heating at a lower level may still occur within Europa and Enceladus.

The third and outermost group—and the group whose numbers have increased so much in recent years—comprises the "irregular"satellites. These generally small bodies (2–200 km in diameter, except for 340-km Nereid) move in quite eccentric orbits at large inclinations. Their orbits are not random; rather, they fall into several more-or-less tight clusters in semimajor axis and inclination: three or four at Jupiter (all but one retrograde), and three at Saturn (one retrograde). These clusters are believed to be due to collisional disruptions of a smaller number of original objects captured from heliocentric orbits. The situation at Uranus and Neptune remains unclear, although there are now nine Uranian irregulars (all but one retrograde) and six Neptunians (three retrograde). The orbits of the irregular satellites, along with that of Earth's Moon, are subject to strong solar gravitational perturbations, and thus maintain approximately fixed inclinations to their respective planet's orbital planes rather than to their equators.

Of the five officially recognized dwarf planets, three have satellites, for a total of eight: Pluto has five, Haumea has two, and Eris has one.

The *New Horizons* spacecraft flew by the Pluto system in July 2015 and continues to transmit data acquired during the rapid flyby. The current diameter estimates of Pluto (2380 ±2 km) and its satellites are Charon (1210 km), Hydra and Nix (55 & 50 km in longest direction, respectively), Kerberos and Styx (19 & 16 km in longest direction, respectively). In late 2015, *New Horizons* was directed toward Kuiper belt object 2014 MU69, with an anticipated flyby date of 2019 Jan. 1.

The following table OBSERVABLE SATELLITES OF THE PLANETS (updated by Chris Malicki for 2017) contains only those satellites considered to be visually observable using typical amateur telescopes. The level of difficulty ranges from "easy" to "very challenging." For up-to-date orbital and physical elements of all the planetary satellites, see ssd.jpl.nasa.gov/?satellites.

OBSERVABLE SATELLITES OF THE PLANETS

Name (pronunciation)[1]	Mean Diameter km	*GM* [2] km³/s²	Density gm/cm³	Visual Mag.[3]	Albedo	Mean Dist. from Planet 10³ km	Orbital Period d	Eccen-tricity	Orbital Incl.[4] °	Discovery
Satellite of Earth										
Moon (mo͞on)	3475	4902.801 (1)	3.34	−12.7	0.12	384.4	27.322	0.055	5.16	—
Satellites of Mars[5]										
I Phobos (fō′bŏs)	22	0.000 711 (1)	1.9	11.4	0.07	9.38	0.319	0.015 1	1.08	A. Hall, 1877
II Deimos (dī′mŏs)	12	0.000 099 (2)	1.5	12.5	0.07	23.46	1.262	0.000 2	1.79	A. Hall, 1877
Satellites of Jupiter										
V Amalthea[6] (ăm′′l–thē′ȧ)	167	0.14 (3)	0.85	14.1	0.09	181.4	0.498	0.0032	0.38	E. Barnard, 1892
I Io[7] (ī′ō)	3643	5959.92 (1)	3.53	5.0	0.63	421.8	1.769	0.0041	0.04	Galileo, 1610
II Europa[7] (ū–rō′pȧ)	3122	3202.74 (1)	3.01	5.3	0.67	671.1	3.551	0.0094	0.47	Galileo, 1610
III Ganymede[7] (găn′ĕ–mēd′)	5262	9887.83 (2)	1.94	4.6	0.43	1070.4	7.155	0.0013	0.18	Galileo, 1610
IV Callisto (kȧ–lĭs′tō)	4821	7179.29 (1)	1.83	5.7	0.17	1882.7	16.689	0.0074	0.19	Galileo, 1610
VI Himalia[8] (hĭm′ȧ–lĭ–ȧ)	170	0.45	2.6	14.2	0.04	11 460.0	250.6	0.159	28.6	C. Perrine, 1904

[1] Pronunciation guide: ă tăp; â câre; ā dāte; ȧ gȧgȧ; ē wē; ĕ mĕt; ī īce; ĭ bĭt; ō gō; ŏ hŏt; ô ôrb; o͞o mo͞on; ŭ ŭp; ū cūte; û ûrn
For some background on the names of the satellites, visit **planetarynames.wr.usgs.gov/Page/Planets**.

[2] The satellite's *standard gravitational constant*. Divide by *G* for mass in kg. The numbers in parentheses are uncertainties in the last digit.

[3] Visual magnitude at mean opposition distance.

[4] Inclinations are relative to the *Laplace Plane*, which for inner satellites (those closer than 100 planetary radii) is close to the planet's *equator*, but for most outer satellites (such as Himalia) is close to the planet's *orbital plane*. For our Moon, the inclination relative to Earth's orbital plane is 5°; relative to Earth's equator it varies between 18° and 29° in an 18.61-year cycle.

[5] The Martian satellites are so close to the primary, the use of an *occulting bar eyepiece* is recommended. For instructions on how to modify an eyepiece in this way, see **www.skyandtelescope.com/observing/the-martian-moons-in-200708**.

[6] Amalthea, the last satellite to be discovered visually, is but one example of a *very challenging* visual object, owing to its proximity to Jupiter. Amateurs using large professional telescopes have observed Amalthea and other challenging natural satellites not shown in this table.

[7] The revolutions of this trio of Jovian satellites form a *Laplace resonance*; longitudes satisfy L(Io) – 3L(Europa) + 2L(Ganymede) ≈ 180°. Also, the mean motions are such that the three periods are nearly 1:2:4.

[8] Himalia is an *irregular satellite* with a highly inclined and highly eccentric orbit that carries it well out of Jupiter's equatorial plane.

OBSERVABLE SATELLITES OF THE PLANETS (continued)

Name (pronunciation)	Mean Diameter km	*GM* km^3/s^2	Density gm/cm^3	Visual Mag.	Albedo	Mean Dist. from Planet 10^3 km	Orbital Period d	Eccen-tricity	Orbital Incl. °	Discovery
Satellites of Saturn										
I Mimas[9, 10] (mī′măs)	396	2.5026 (6)	1.15	12.8	0.6	185.5	0.942	0.0196	1.57	W. Herschel, 1789
II Enceladus[10] (ĕn–sĕl′ȧ–dŭs)	504	7.20 (1)	1.61	11.8	1.0	238.0	1.370	0.0000	0.00	W. Herschel, 1789
III Tethys[10] (tē′thĭs)	1066	41.207 (4)	0.97	10.3	0.8	294.7	1.888	0.0001	1.10	J. Cassini, 1684
IV Dione[10] (dī–ŏ′nē)	1123	73.115 (2)	1.48	10.4	0.6	377.4	2.737	0.0022	0.03	J. Cassini, 1684
V Rhea (rē′ȧ)	1529	153.943 (4)	1.23	9.7	0.6	527.1	4.518	0.0002	0.33	J. Cassini, 1672
VI Titan (tī′t′n)	5149[11]	8978.138 (2)	1.88	8.4	0.2	1221.8	15.945	0.0288	0.31	C. Huygens, 1655
VII Hyperion (hī–pēr′ĭ–ŏn)	270	0.37 (1)	0.54	14.4	0.3	1500.9	21.277	0.0232	0.62	Bond et al.[12], 1848
VIII Iapetus[13] (ī–ăp′ĕ–tŭs)	1471	120.504 (8)	1.08	11.0v	0.05–0.5	3560.9	79.330	0.0293	8.30	J. Cassini, 1671
Satellites of Uranus[14]										
I Ariel (âr′ē–ĕl)	1158	86. (5)	1.59	13.7	0.39	190.9	2.520	0.0012	0.04	W. Lassell, 1851
II Umbriel (ŭm′brē–ĕl′)	1169	82. (5)	1.46	14.5	0.21	266.0	4.144	0.0039	0.13	W. Lassell, 1851
III Titania (tī′tā′nē–ȧ)	1578	228. (5)	1.66	13.5	0.27	436.3	8.706	0.0011	0.08	W. Herschel, 1787
IV Oberon (ō′bȧ–rŏn)	1523	192. (7)	1.56	13.7	0.23	583.5	13.463	0.0014	0.07	W. Herschel, 1787
Satellites of Neptune										
I Triton (trī′t′n)	2707	1428. (2)	2.06	13.5	0.72	354.8	5.877	0.0000	156.9	W. Lassell, 1846

[9] Mimas is another *very challenging* object, best observed when Saturn's rings are edge-on, so their glare is reduced.

[10] The orbital periods of the pair Mimas:Tethys show a near-1:2 resonance, as do Enceladus:Dione.

[11] As seen in the eyepiece, Titan's cloud-top diameter is 5550 km.

[12] W. Bond, G. Bond, and W. Lassell

[13] The highly variable magnitude of Iapatus is due to its dark and bright hemispheres, tidally locked to Saturn (see p. 237).

[14] Best within 6 weeks of opposition. An occulting-bar eyepiece is recommended for Ariel and Umbriel.

ORBITAL MOTION

BY ROY BISHOP

Whether you are observing a distant galaxy, the stars in a globular cluster, the waltz of Jupiter's Galilean satellites, the drift of the Moon during an occultation, or merely uttering an expletive as an artificial satellite passes through the field of your camera, an understanding of orbital motion is central to an appreciation of the heavens.

Among early cosmologies were those of **Aristotle** (340 BC) and **Ptolemy** (published as the *Almagest*, c. AD 150), and the superior heliocentric model proposed by **Copernicus** (*De revolutionibus*, 1543). These attempts at modelling the heavens used complex systems of circles upon circles, of eccentric deferents and epicycles. John Milton, a contemporary of Galileo, wrote the following lines in his epic poem "Paradise Lost" (1674), possibly expressing his discontent with the Ptolemaic and Copernican systems of compounded circles:

From Man or Angel the great Architect
Did wisely to conceal, and not divulge
His secrets to be scann'd by them who ought
Rather admire; or if they list to try
Conjecture, he his Fabric of the Heav'ns
Hath left to thir disputes, perhaps to move
His laughter at thir quaint Opinions wide
Hereafter, when they come to model Heav'n
And calculate the Stars, how they will wield
The mighty frame, how build, unbuild, contrive
To save appearances, how gird the Sphere
With Centric and Eccentric scribbl'd o'er,
Cycle and Epicycle, Orb in Orb.

Kepler, using observations accumulated by Tycho Brahe, broke with the 2000-year preoccupation with circles when he discovered that the planets move in an elegantly simple way along elliptical paths (*Astronomia nova*, 1609). Although he had discovered *how* the planets move, Kepler was unable to explain quantitatively *why* they move in this way.

Galileo strongly supported the Copernican heliocentric Universe (*Dialogue on the Two Chief World Systems*, 1632) and achieved brilliant insights concerning the motion of objects (*Two New Sciences*, 1638); however, he ignored Kepler's ellipses and did not apply his mechanics to the sky.

Newton united the heavens and Earth by showing that the laws governing motions on Earth also apply to the heavens. In his *Principia* (1687), the greatest book in the physical sciences, Newton presented his three laws of motion and the first ever physical force law, his law of gravitation. He used these to explain the motions not only of bodies on Earth, but also of the planets, comets, stars, equinoxes, tides, etc. Newton was the first to realize that the Moon is falling toward Earth just as freely as does an apple, and that the elliptical orbit of the centre of mass of the Earth–Moon system is the path that results (as he described it) as these two bodies free-fall under the action of the Sun's gravitational force.

In popular-level explanations of phenomena involving rotary motion, such as spinning wheels, automobiles on corners, tides, and orbital motion, "centrifugal force" is usually invoked. That is unfortunate because centrifugal force is a fiction, and its use in a popular description of motion obscures understanding.*

*Brief descriptions of tides in the Newtonian context (without invoking the obfuscating centrifugal force!) and in the context of the general theory of relativity appear on p. 179 and p. 183, respectively.

In the case of orbits, the common misconception is that the inward gravitational force is balanced by an outward "centrifugal force." Newton's view is simpler: There is only one force, the inward pull of gravity. There is *no physical agent* to cause an outward force. (Note that forces cause accelerations, not vice versa.) Also, if there *were* an outward supporting force, the two forces would cancel and, as Galileo realized, the body would then move along a straight line. If you choose a rotating reference frame and then ignore the rotation (mistake no. 1), you have to pretend there is a "centrifugal force" (mistake no. 2) in order to make sense of motions occurring within this frame. The two mistakes effectively cancel, but the description has been made needlessly complicated, and if you do not realize what you have done, you do not understand the motion.

Einstein's general theory of relativity (GTR) of 1915 superseded Newton's description of gravity. The arbiter of which is a good theory and which theory is wrong is nature. Newton's laws are accurate enough for most of NASA's calculations, but they do not work exactly. For example, if the computer programs used in the Global Positioning System (GPS) were based on Newton's gravitation, the system would be a multibillion-dollar boondoggle. Einstein's conception of gravitation is essential to the operation of this satellite-based navigation system. In the case of strong gravitation and/or speeds approaching the speed of light, Newton's laws fail dramatically. The GTR may be wrong too, but so far it has passed all experimental tests. Science does not hie after ultimate explanations or "truth"; its goal is a rational, coherent description of the measurable physical world, a description that has beauty in its simplicity, a description that makes sense. In the courtroom of nature, any aspect of science is falsifiable. Modern technology is making possible increasingly precise tests of general relativity (for instance, see **einstein.stanford.edu**, and also *Sky & Telescope*, July 2004, p. 22, and August 2010, p. 29).

According to Einstein's GTR, gravitation is not a mysterious force that one mass exerts upon a distant mass; gravitation is the geometry (non-Euclidean) of the 4-dimensional spacetime within which we and the stars exist. Golf balls (if air friction is ignored), satellites, planets, stars, and light follow *geodesics*, the straightest possible, force-free paths through a spacetime whose geometry is shaped by mass–energy. The difficulty in intellectually grasping a non-Euclidean spacetime originates with us. Common sense is inadequate. That is not surprising, given that our common sense is based on the Euclidean, three-dimensional geometry of straight lines, rectangles, and spheres we learned in the crib by age two. The underlying cause of our delusion is that our senses and thought processes are constrained by the speed of neuron signals. Compared to light, neuron signals ooze along at a very slow rate, about one ten-millionth the speed of light. Consequently, to us a second of time is brief, light looks instantaneous, relativistic effects seem foreign, and time appears to be independent of space.

Gravitation is geometry. That is why no one has ever felt a force of gravity. Like the centrifugal force, it never did exist. A force of gravity was the glue Newton invented to make his naïve, Euclidean, space-plus-time model of the Universe approximate reality. Newton himself was well aware of the unsatisfactory nature of several of his assumptions, far more so than most people who came after him.

When you release a coin from your hand, you see the coin "fall" because the contact force of the ground on your feet (the *only* force you feel) accelerates you the other way. An orbiting astronaut experiences no such force, so he or she remains beside a released coin. Orbital motion could not be simpler—*no* forces are involved.

What would Milton have written had he been familiar with the conjectures of Newton and Einstein?

SOME ASTRONOMICAL AND PHYSICAL DATA

BY ROY BISHOP

Many of the numbers listed below are based on measurement. Exceptions include defined quantities (indicated by ≡), quantities calculated from defined quantities (e.g. m/ly, au/pc), and numbers of mathematical origin such as π and conversion factors in angular measure. Of those based on measurement, some are known to only approximate precision and the equal sign is reduced to ≈. Many others are known to quite high precision (the uncertainties occur after the last digit given), and several are from "the 2014 CODATA recommended values of the fundamental physical constants" (see physics.nist.gov/cuu/Constants). The units (Système International (SI) where possible), symbols, and nomenclature are based on recommendations of the International Astronomical Union and the International Union of Pure and Applied Physics.

LENGTH

1 metre (m) ≡ the distance travelled by light in a vacuum in $(299\,792\,458)^{-1}$ s

1 astronomical unit (au)	≡ 1.495 978 707 × 10^{11} m = 499.004 783 8 light-s	
1 light-year (ly)	= 9.460 730 × 10^{15} m (based on average Julian year)	
	= 63 241 au (63 360 inches = 1 mile)	
1 parsec (pc)	= 3.085 678 × 10^{16} m = 206 264.8 au = 3.261 564 ly	
1 mile*	≡ 1.609 344 km	
1 micron*	≡ 1 μm	*Indicates deprecated unit;
1 angstrom*	≡ 0.1 nm	unit on right is preferred

TIME

1 second (s) ≡ 9 192 631 770 periods of the radiation involved in the transition between the two hyperfine levels of the ground state of the ^{133}Cs atom at mean sea level

Day:	Mean sidereal (equinox to equinox)	= 86 164.0921 s
	Mean rotation (fixed star to fixed star)	= 86 164.1005 s
	Day (d)	≡ 86 400. s
	Mean solar	= 86 400.0016 s
Month:	Draconic (node to node)	= 27.212 221 d
	Tropical (equinox to equinox)	= 27.321 582 d
	Sidereal (fixed star to fixed star)	= 27.321 662 d
	Anomalistic (perigee to perigee)	= 27.554 550 d
	Synodic (new Moon to new Moon)	= 29.530 589 d
Year:	Eclipse (lunar node to lunar node)	= 346.620 075 d
	Tropical (equinox to equinox) (y)	= 365.242 190 d
	Average Gregorian	≡ 365.242 5 d
	Average Julian	≡ 365.25 d
	Sidereal (fixed star to fixed star)	= 365.256 363 d
	Anomalistic (perihelion to perihelion)	= 365.259 635 d

EARTH

Mass, M_E = 5.972 × 10^{24} kg   Age ≈ 4.6 Gy   Central T ≈ 5000 K to 6000 K

Geocentric gravitational constant, GM_E = 3.986 004 42 × 10^{14} m^3/s^2

Radius: Equatorial, a = 6378.14 km   Polar, b = 6356.75 km

Mean = $(a^2b)^{1/3}$ = 6371.00 km   Of metallic core = 3475 km

Solar parallax = 8.794 143″ (Earth equatorial radius ÷ 1 au)

1° of latitude = 111.132 95 − 0.559 82 cos 2ϕ + 0.001 17 cos 4ϕ km (at latitude ϕ)

1° of longitude = 111.412 88 cos ϕ − 0.093 50 cos 3ϕ + 0.000 12 cos 5ϕ km

1 knot = 1 nautical mile (≈ 1′ of latitude) per hour ≡ 1.852 km/h = 0.51444 m/s
Distance of sea horizon for eye *h* metres above sea level
(allowing for refraction) ≈ $3.9h^{1/2}$ km ≈ $2.1h^{1/2}$ nautical miles
Atmospheric pressure: 1 atm ≡ 101.325 kPa (There is ≈ 1 kg of air above 1 cm^2.)
Density of air at sea level (1 atm, 20 °C) = 1.2 kg/m^3
Values of atmospheric refraction for various elevations (assuming 1 atm, 10 °C):
90°: 0′; 44°: 1′; 26°: 2′; 18°: 3′; 11°: 5′; 6°: 8′; 4°: 12′; 2°: 18′; 0°: 34′
Speed of sound in standard atmosphere = 331 m/s ≈ 1 km/3 s ≈ $10^{-6}\,c$
Magnetic field at surface ≈ 5×10^{-5} T (**B** field comes out of a N-seeking pole)
Magnetic dip poles: 86°N, 187°E; 64°S, 136°E (as of 2017)
Standard acceleration of gravity ≡ 9.806 65 m/s^2
Meteoritic flux ≈ 1×10^{-15} $kg/(m^2s)$ ≈ 10^4 t/y over entire Earth
Obliquity of ecliptic = 23.4371° (2017.0) Constant of aberration = 20.495 52″
Annual general precession = −50.29″ (2000.0); Precession period ≈ 25 800 y
Escape speed from Earth = 11.2 km/s Mean orbital speed = 29.786 km/s
Escape speed at 1 au from Sun = 42.1 km/s (= √2 × orbital speed)

SUN

Mass = 1.9891×10^{30} kg Radius = 695 660 km Eff. temp. ≈ 5780 K
Output: Power = 3.85×10^{26} W, $M_{bol} = 4.79$
Luminous intensity = 2.84×10^{27} cd, $M_v = 4.82$
At 1 au outside Earth's atmosphere:
Energy flux = 1.37 kW/m^2, $m_{bol} = -26.78$
Illuminance = 1.27×10^5 lx, $m_v = -26.75$
Inclination of the solar equator on the ecliptic of date = 7.25°
Longitude of ascending node of the solar equator on the ecliptic of date = 76°
Period of rotation at equator ≡ 25.38 d (sidereal), 27.2753 d (mean synodic)
Solar wind speed near Earth ≈ 450 km/s (travel time, Sun to Earth ≈ 4 d)
Solar velocity = 19.4 km/s toward α = 18.07h, δ = +30° (solar apex)
Location in Milky Way Galaxy: ≈ 27 kly from centre, ≈ 50 ly N of galactic plane, on the inner edge of the Orion arm

MILKY WAY GALAXY

Mass ≈ 10^{12} solar masses Diameter ≈ 300 kly (including the galactic halo)
Centre: α = 17h 45.7m, δ = −29°00′; N pole: α = 12h 51m, δ = 27°08′ (2000.0)
Rotation speed at Sun ≈ 230 km/s, period ≈ 200 My
Velocity relative to 3 K background radiation ≈ 400 km/s toward α ≈ 14h, δ ≈ −30°

CONSTANTS

Speed of light, c ≡ 299 792 458 m/s (This, in effect, defines the metre.)
Planck's constant, $h = 6.626\,070 \times 10^{-34}$ J·s = $4.135\,668 \times 10^{-15}$ eV·s
Gravitational constant, $G = 6.674 \times 10^{-11}$ $N{\cdot}m^2/kg^2$
Elementary charge, $e = 1.602\,177 \times 10^{-19}$ C
Constant in Coulomb's law ≡ $10^{-7}\,c^2$ (SI units) (This defines the coulomb.)
Avogadro constant, $N_A = 6.022\,141 \times 10^{26}$ $kmol^{-1}$
Boltzmann constant, $k = 1.380\,65 \times 10^{-23}$ J/K = 8.6173×10^{-5} eV/K ≈ 1 eV/10^4K
Stefan–Boltzmann constant, $\sigma = 5.6704 \times 10^{-8}$ $W/(m^2K^4)$
Wien's Law: $\lambda_m T = 2.897\,77 \times 10^{-3}$ m·K (per dλ)
Hubble constant, $H = 68 \pm 1$ km/(s·Mpc) Age of Universe = 13.80 ± 0.04 Gy
−273.15 °C (degree Celsius) = 0 K (kelvin) (lowest thermodynamic temperature)
Volume of ideal gas at 0 °C, 101.325 kPa = 22.4140 m^3/kmol
Water: fusion at 0 °C: 0.333 MJ/kg vapourization at 100 °C: 2.26 MJ/kg
specific heat and density (near 20 °C): 4.18 kJ/(kg·C°) and 1.00 t/m^3
surface tension (near 20 °C): 0.073 N/m

MASS AND ENERGY

Mass is a measure of sluggishness of response to a net force. (SI unit: kg)
Weight (≠ mass) is the magnitude of the force required to support a body. (SI unit: N)
(1 pound-mass* = 0.453 59 kg) (1 pound-force* = 4.4482 N)

1 kilogram (kg) ≡ mass of a platinum-iridium cylinder stored in Paris, France
1 atomic mass unit (u) ≡ 1/12 of the mass of an atom of ^{12}C
= $1.660\,539 \times 10^{-27}$ kg = N_A^{-1} = 931.4941 MeV
1 joule (J) ≡ work done by a force of 1 N acting through a distance of 1 m
≈ the kinetic energy gained by this Handbook in falling freely 0.3 m
1 electron-volt (eV) ≡ the kinetic energy gained by a particle carrying one unit of elementary electrical charge *(e)* in falling through an electrical potential difference of one volt (V)
= $1.602\,177 \times 10^{-19}$ J

Electron mass = $9.109\,38 \times 10^{-31}$ kg = 548.579 909 μu = 0.510 998 9 MeV
Proton mass = $1.672\,622 \times 10^{-27}$ kg = 1.007 276 467 u = 938.2721 MeV
Neutron mass = $1.674\,927 \times 10^{-27}$ kg = 1.008 664 916 u = 939.5654 MeV

Some atomic masses: ^{1}H (1.007 825 u) ^{2}H (2.014 102 u) ^{4}He (4.002 603 u)

Thermochemical calorie* (cal) = 4.184 J
1 erg*/s = 10^{-7} J/s = 10^{-7} W
1 BTU*/h = 1054.35 J/h = 0.292 88 W
1 horsepower* = 745.7 W
*Indicates deprecated unit; unit on right is preferred.
1 eV per event = 23 060 cal/mol
$C + O_2 \rightarrow CO_2$ + 4.1 eV $4\,^{1}H \rightarrow {}^{4}He$ + 26.73 MeV

Highest cosmic-ray energy (carried by protons) ≈ 10^{20} eV
Power output (average) of an adult human ≈ 100 W
1 kg of TNT or milkshake releases 4.2 MJ ≈ 1000 kcal ≈ 1 kWh
Fuel oil: 6.36 GJ/barrel (1 barrel ≡ 42 U.S. gallons = 35.0 Imp. gallons = 159 L)

Relation between rest mass *(m)*, linear momentum *(p)*, total energy *(E)*, kinetic energy *(KE)*, and $\gamma \equiv (1 - v^2/c^2)^{-0.5}$, where c is the speed of light and v is the speed of the object: $E = \gamma mc^2 = mc^2 + KE = [(mc^2)^2 + (pc)^2]^{0.5}$

MAGNITUDE RELATIONS (See also p. 49 and p. 54.)

Log of light intensity ratio ≡ 0.4 times magnitude difference
Distance modulus *(D)* ≡ apparent magnitude *(m)* – absolute magnitude *(M)*
Log of distance in ly = $0.2D + 1.513\,435$ (neglecting absorption)
Magnitude of sum of magnitudes m_i is equal to $-2.5 \log \Sigma_i 10^{-0.4 m_i}$

Moon's apparent visual magnitude at phase angle P degrees (0° = full Moon) when at its average distance from Earth: $-12.7 + 0.026\,|P| + (4 \times 10^{-9})P^4$

A light source of apparent visual magnitude m provides an illuminance E (lux) where $E = 10^{-0.4\,(m\,+\,13.99)}$ or $m = -13.99 - 2.5 \log E$
A diffuse (matte) surface with albedo A subject to illuminance E (lux) will have luminance L (visual surface brightness): $L = AE \div \pi$ (cd/m²)
To convert luminance S (magnitude/arcsecond²) to luminance L (cd/m²): $L = 10^{0.4(12.59-S)}$ or $S = 12.59 - 2.5 \log L$

DOPPLER RELATIONS FOR LIGHT

α ≡ angle between velocity of source and line from source to observer
$\beta \equiv v/c$ $\gamma \equiv (1 - \beta^2)^{-0.5}$
Frequency: $f = f_0\, \gamma^{-1}(1 - \beta \cos \alpha)^{-1}$ $z \equiv (\lambda - \lambda_0)/\lambda_0 = \gamma\,(1 - \beta \cos \alpha) - 1$
For $\alpha = \pi$ radians: $z = (1 + \beta)^{0.5}(1 - \beta)^{-0.5} - 1$ (≈ β if β << 1)
$\beta = [(1 + z)^2 - 1][(1 + z)^2 + 1]^{-1}$

OPTICAL WAVELENGTH DATA

Bright-adapted (photopic) visible range ≈ 400 – 750 nm ($L \approx 0.005 - 10^5$ cd/m^2)
Dark-adapted (scotopic) visible range ≈ 400 – 620 nm ($L \approx 1 - 5000$ μcd/m^2)
Wavelength of peak sensitivity of eye: ≈ 555 nm (photopic), 507 nm (scotopic)
Mechanical equivalent of light: 1 lm ≡ 1/683 W at 540 THz ($\lambda \approx 555$ nm)
i.e. 1.46 W/klm (A 60-W incandescent light bulb emits about 1 klm = 1000 lm. Compared to an optimum light source that delivers all its energy as light at 540 THz, a 60-W incandescent light bulb is 1.46/60 ≈ 2.4% efficient.)
Colours (representative wavelength, nm):
violet (420), blue (470), green (530), yellow (580), orange (610), red (660)

Some useful wavelengths (element, spectral designation or colour and/or (Fraunhofer line)):

H Lyman α	121.6 nm	N_2^+ blue†	465.2	Hg yellow	577.0
Ca (K solar)	393.4	Hβ (F solar)*	486.1	Hg yellow	579.1
Ca (H solar)	396.8	O^{++} green*	495.9	Na (D_2 solar)	589.0
Hg violet	404.7	O^{++} green*	500.7	Na (D_1 solar)	589.6
Hδ (h solar)	410.2	Green laser	532.	O red†	630.0
Hγ (g solar)	434.0	Hg green	546.1	O red†	636.4
Hg deep blue	435.8	O yel.-green†	557.7	Hα (C solar)	656.3

* Strong contributor to the visual light of gaseous nebulae   † Strong auroral lines

ANGULAR RELATIONS

2π radians = 360° $\pi = 3.141\,592\,653\,589\,793\,2\ldots \approx (113 \div 355)^{-1}$
Number of square degrees on a sphere = 41 253

For 360° = 24 h, 15° = 1 h, 15′ = 1 min, 15″ = 1 s (Earth turns 360° in 86 164.1 s)

Relations between sidereal time t, right ascension α, hour angle h, declination δ, azimuth A (measured east of north), altitude a, and latitude ϕ:

$$h = t - \alpha$$
$$\sin a = \sin\delta \sin\phi + \cos h \cos\delta \cos\phi$$
$$\cos\delta \sin h = -\cos a \sin A$$
$$\sin\delta = \sin a \sin\phi + \cos a \cos A \cos\phi$$

Annual precession in α (in seconds) ≈ $3.0748 + 1.3361 \sin\alpha \tan\delta$
Annual precession in δ (in seconds of arc) ≈ $20.042 \cos\alpha$
(Convert α to degrees for the trigonometric functions above.)
e.g. for RA 4h 20m, Dec +40°, the annual change is $\Delta\alpha = 4.091$ s and $\Delta\delta = 8.470''$

SOME SI SYMBOLS AND PREFIXES

m	metre	N	newton (kg·m/s^2)	a	atto	10^{-18}
kg	kilogram	J	joule (N·m)	f	femto	10^{-15}
t	tonne (10^3 kg)	W	watt (J/s)	p	pico	10^{-12}
s	second	Pa	pascal (N/m^2)	n	nano	10^{-9}
min	minute	A	ampere	μ	micro	10^{-6}
h	hour	C	coulomb (A·s)	m	milli	10^{-3}
d	day	V	volt (J/C)	c	centi	10^{-2}
y	year (tropical) (*not SI*)	Ω	ohm (V/A)	h	hecto	10^2
Hz	hertz (s^{-1})	F	farad (C/V)	k	kilo	10^3
rad	radian	Wb	weber (V·s)	M	mega	10^6
sr	steradian	T	tesla (Wb/m^2)	G	giga	10^9
K	kelvin (temperature)	lm	lumen	T	tera	10^{12}
L	litre (10^{-3} m^3)	cd	candela (lm/sr)	P	peta	10^{15}
ha	hectare (10^4 m^2)	lx	lux (lm/m^2)	E	exa	10^{18}

THE ELECTROMAGNETIC SPECTRUM
BY ROY BISHOP

The Scottish physicist James Clerk Maxwell (1831–1879) was the first to understand the nature of light. In 1865, with elegant mathematics, Maxwell predicted that light is a self-sustaining electromagnetic wave, a quivering linkage of electric and magnetic fields in which a changing electric field generates a magnetic field, and vice versa, sustaining each other as they travel at a prodigious speed.

Four decades later Albert Einstein (1879–1955) revealed three more remarkable properties of light: (1) unlike water waves and sound waves, electromagnetic waves require no medium whatsoever in which to travel; (2) the speed of electromagnetic waves is the same for all observers, irrespective of any motion of the source of the waves; (3) when electromagnetic waves interact with matter, they do so as if composed of discrete particles, photons, whose individual energy E is proportional to the frequency f of the wave: $E = hf$, where h is Planck's constant (see p. 30).

The product of wavelength λ and wave frequency is the speed of a wave: $\lambda f = c$, where c is the usual symbol for the speed of an electromagnetic wave. The frequency (or photon energy, or wavelength) range of electromagnetic waves is unlimited, but our eyes see only a very narrow slice of this spectrum. Vision has a range of less than an octave, $\lambda \sim 400$ to 750 nm (see p. 32). We are almost blind! Nevertheless, once the physics was understood, the technologies to generate and detect all parts of the electromagnetic spectrum were soon developed. The first step in this direction occurred prior to Maxwell's work, in 1800 when astronomer William Herschel (1738–1822) discovered *infrared* radiation beyond the red end of the visible spectrum.

The diagram at the end of this article summarizes the electromagnetic spectrum. The various named parts of the spectrum overlap to some extent. One part is defined by the source of the radiation rather than by wavelength or photon energy: *gamma rays* refer to electromagnetic radiation emitted by radioactive atomic nuclei. *X-rays* overlap with gamma rays but are produced by sources other than atomic nuclei—an arbitrary distinction based on the historical origins of these two terms. A detector defines another part of the spectrum: *light* is usually restricted to human vision, although occasionally this term is extended to include the adjacent *ultraviolet* portion of the spectrum.

The importance of the particle aspect at high frequencies and of the wave aspect at low frequencies is implied by the names; for instance, gamma **rays** and radio **waves**. Photon energy, not wavelength, dominates the behaviour of gamma rays. At the other end of the spectrum, the energy of individual photons is very small, obscuring the granular nature of the radiation, and frequency is usually the measured characteristic of the radiation. Vision operates between these two extremes where *both* particle and wave properties play significant roles. Events in the retina are triggered by individual photons, and wave diffraction is relevant for minimum eye pupil size and the spacing of retinal photoreceptors. For the infrared and microwave regions, wavelength has a convenient range and is usually cited. The transition across the spectrum from photon through wavelength to frequency domination is indicated in the diagram by the range of the units on the left side of each of the three scales.

Photon energy determines how electromagnetic radiation interacts with matter. Chemistry and biology involve changes in atomic and molecular structure, the energies involved being typically a few *electron-volts* (eV) per reaction (see p. 31). Retinal photochemistry operates over a very limited energy range, and thereby determines the narrow visual window on the electromagnetic spectrum. For $\lambda > 750$ nm, the photon energy is insufficient (<1.6 eV) to alter the structure of light-sensing protein molecules in the retina, so we cannot see the infrared. For $\lambda < 400$ nm, the photon energy is high enough (>3.1 eV) to damage these delicate molecules; however, the cornea and lens of the eye absorb that radiation before it can reach the retina. Thus, we cannot see the ultraviolet.

Although the energy of an infrared photon is too weak to stimulate vision, infrared photons are readily absorbed by many types of molecules, such as water, causing the molecules to move more rapidly, thereby increasing the temperature of the substance. In this manner, infrared radiation from the Sun, a fire, or a hot stove warms us. Hence infrared is often called heat radiation, although it is *not* heat that is being radiated. The heating is a secondary effect, generated in our bodies subsequent to the absorption of the photons.

Confusion of sensation with electromagnetic radiation also occurs with visible light. For instance, almost invariably we speak of colours as if they were a property of light, or of the bodies emitting the light, rather than being indescribable hue sensations arising in the brain. As Sir Isaac Newton cautioned us three centuries ago: "The rays, to speak properly, are not coloured." The light reflected by a leaf is not green, and neither is the leaf; green exists only in the neuron-based representation of the leaf in the observer's consciousness, and then only if the light is not too dim. The electromagnetic radiation from a leaf is characterized by a particular spatial and spectral distribution of radiant power. A CCD or CMOS chip finds only photons. It is we who create the colour and the brightness. The distinction between our internal visual world and the external physical world is profound but rarely appreciated. It is the distinction between how the world *looks* to us, and how it *is*.

Visual perception aside, what *is* light, a wave or a particle? Light travels like a wave (Maxwell was right) and interacts like a particle (Einstein was right). A detector finds photons, but *where* the detector finds photons is determined by a wave. When a typical backyard telescope is aimed at an average star in the night sky, at any instant there is seldom more than one photon from that star in transit through the telescope. Yet the distribution of light in the star's image at the focal plane is determined by an aperture-filling wave. In the case of a Newtonian telescope with a four-vane spider support for the secondary mirror, in some real sense, each photon passes through all four quadrants of the spider. But it is not that the spider quarters the hapless photon like a cleaver quarters a steak in a butcher shop; whole photons, not quartered photons arrive at the detector. The message of physics revealed during the first half of the last century is that it is simply *wrong* to speak of the path of a photon while in transit to a detector. Light is queerer than we can imagine. Matter is equally queer, for it too displays a wave-particle duality, a duality that is particularly obvious on the subatomic scale. Just as it is wrong to speak of the path of a photon, it is wrong to speak of the path of an electron in an atom—as if, for example, it were in orbit about the nucleus. The wave-particle puzzle is of our own making, for we try to apply naïve concepts abstracted from crude sensory experiences on the macroscopic scale of everyday life to the subatomic world. Pure waves or pure particles never did exist. Reality is more subtle.

Despite the strange behaviour of electromagnetic radiation, we know how to describe its interaction with matter quantitatively and with astounding accuracy. The theory encompasses the work of Maxwell and Einstein, and was completed in the mid-20th century by Richard Feynman (1918–1988) and Julian Schwinger (1918–1994) of the United States, and Sin-Itiro Tomonaga (1906–1979) of Japan, for which they shared the Nobel Prize in Physics in 1965. The theory is called quantum electrodynamics. With the exception of gravitation and things that go on inside atomic nuclei, quantum electrodynamics appears to describe all phenomena in the physical world—in principle, if not in actuality, in the case of complex systems because of the complexity.

THE ELECTROMAGNETIC SPECTRUM

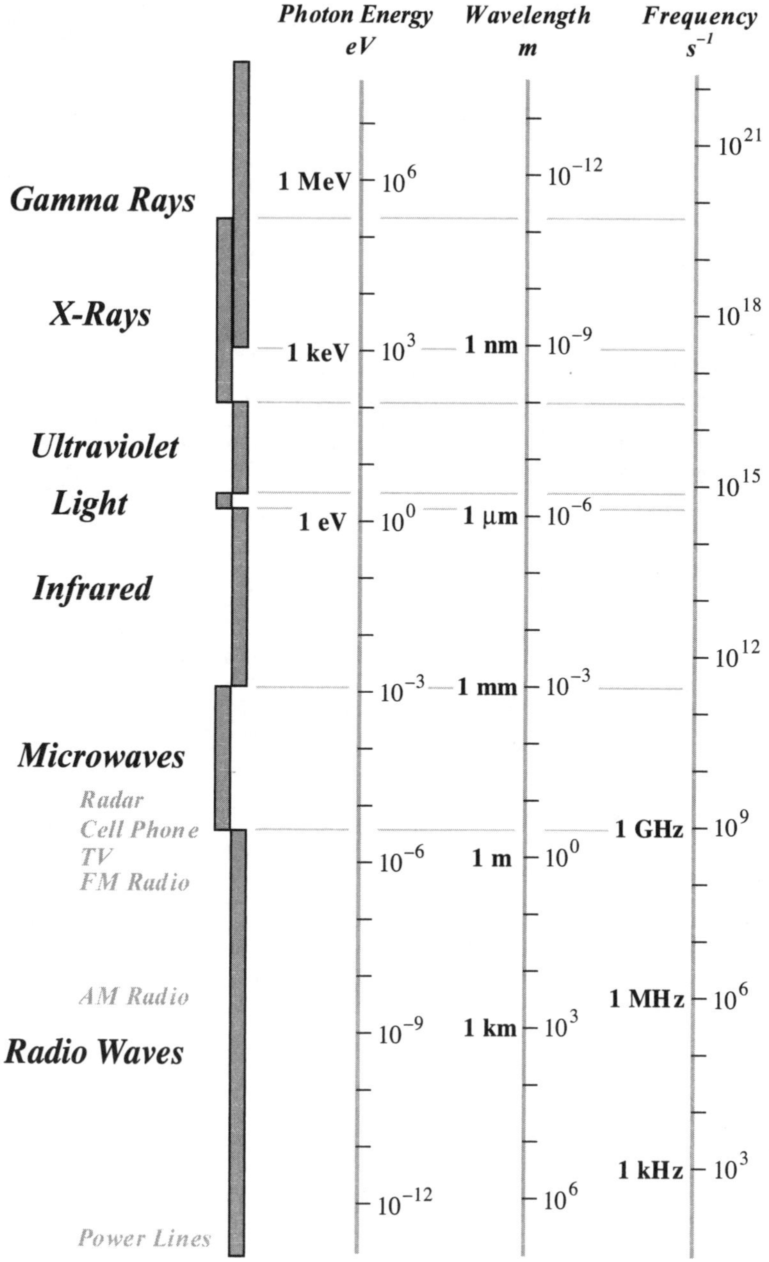

Diagram by Roy Bishop

VOYAGES IN THE SOLAR SYSTEM

BY J. RANDY ATTWOOD

During the second half of the 20th century, humankind began its reconnaissance of the Solar System. Although people have travelled only as far as the Moon, robotic space probes have been sent to all the major planets plus a few minor planets and comets. Our understanding of the solar neighbourhood is increasing at a tremendous pace as a result of the improving sophistication of these spacecraft.

The following is a list of some of the important firsts in the short history of the exploration of the Solar System. Note that all space missions are not recorded, not even all the space firsts. A short list of upcoming missions to watch for is also included.

Year	Name	Significance
1957	*Sputnik 1*	First artificial satellite of Earth (Oct. 4); USSR
1957	*Sputnik 2*	First living being in Earth orbit (a dog named Laika); USSR
1959	*Luna 1*	First to escape Earth's gravity; USSR
1959	*Luna 2*	First to impact on the Moon; USSR
1959	*Luna 3*	First to image the far side of the Moon; USSR
1961	*Vostok 1*	First human in Earth orbit (Yuri Gagarin, Apr. 12); USSR
1961	*Freedom 7*	First American in space (Alan Shepard, May 5); USA
1962	*Friendship 7*	First American in Earth orbit (John Glenn, Feb. 20); USA
1962	*Mariner 2*	First to fly by another planet, Venus; USA
1962	*Alouette 1*	First Canadian satellite placed in Earth orbit
1963	*Vostok 6*	First woman to fly in space (Valentina Tereshkova, Jun. 16); USSR
1965	*Voshkod 2*	First astronaut to take a spacewalk (Alexei Leonov, Mar. 18); USSR
1965	*Mariner 4*	First to fly by Mars and take pictures; USA
1966	*Luna 9*	First soft landing on the Moon; USSR
1966	*Venera 3*	First to impact on another planet, Venus; USSR
1966	*Luna 10*	First to orbit the Moon; USSR
1967	*Apollo 1*	Astronauts perish in a fire during a launch-pad test (Grissom, White, and Chaffee, Jan. 27); USA
1967	*Soyuz 1*	First astronaut to die during spaceflight (Vladimir Komarov, Apr. 24); USSR
1968	*Apollo 8*	First human voyage to the Moon (orbit without landing); USA (Frank Borman, James Lovell, and William Anders, Dec. 24)
1969	*Apollo 11*	First humans to land and walk on the Moon; USA (Neil Armstrong and Edwin Aldrin, Jul. 20)
1970	*Apollo 13*	Moon mission cancelled after onboard explosion (Apr. 14); USA
1970	*Venera 7*	First soft landing on another planet, Venus; USSR
1971	*Mariner 9*	First to orbit another planet, Mars; USA
1971	*Mariner 9*	First close views of outer satellites Phobos, Deimos; USA
1972	*Anik A1*	First Canadian communications satellite placed in Earth orbit
1972	*Apollo 17*	Last two of 12 men to walk on the Moon; USA
1973	*Pioneer 10*	First to fly by Jupiter, reach solar escape speed; USA
1974	*Mariner 10*	First to fly by and study Mercury; USA
1975	*Venera 9*	First to return surface pictures of Venus; USSR
1976	*Viking 1*	First to softly land on Mars, return pictures; USA
1979	*Voyager 1*	First close-up study of Jupiter and its moons; USA
1979	*Pioneer 11*	First to fly by Saturn; USA
1980	*Voyager 1*	First close-up study of Saturn and its moons; USA
1981	STS 1	First launch of the reuseable *Space Transportation System* (Space Shuttle); USA
1983	STS 7	First American woman to fly in space (Sally Ride, Jun. 18); USA
1984	*Soyuz T–7*	First woman to walk in space (Svetlana Savitskaya, Jul. 25); USSR
1984	STS 41G	First Canadian to fly in space (Marc Garneau, Oct. 5); Canada
	"	First American woman to walk in space (Kathy Sullivan); USA
	"	First time two women in space at the same time (Kathy Sullivan, Sally Ride); USA

Year	Name	Significance
1985	ICE	*(International Cometary Explorer)* First to study a comet; USA
1986	*Voyager 2*	First close-up study of Uranus and its moons; USA
1986	*Challenger*	First American astronauts to die during spaceflight (Jan. 28); USA
1986	*Giotto*	First images taken of a comet nucleus, Halley; ESA
1989	*Voyager 2*	First close-up study of Neptune and its moons; USA
1989	*Magellan*	First radar maps made of Venus from orbit; USA
1989	COBE	First precise data on cosmic microwave background radiation; USA
1990	*Hubble*	Launch of the *Hubble Space Telescope*
1991	*Galileo*	First flyby, closeup photos of a minor planet, 951 Gaspra; USA
1992	STS 42	First Canadian woman in space (Roberta Bondar, Jan. 22); Canada
1994	*Clementine*	First images of perma-shadowed areas at the Moon's south pole; USA
1994	*Hubble, Galileo*	Images of comet fragments of Shoemaker–Levy 9 impacting Jupiter
1994–5	*Mir*	Longest single spaceflight: 437 days in Earth orbit (V. Polyakov); USSR
1995	*Ulysses*	First flyby above the Sun's south/north poles; ESA
1995	*Galileo*	First to orbit Jupiter and 1st to send probe into Jupiter's atmosphere; USA
1996	*Pathfinder*	First rover on Mars (Sojourner); USA
1998	*Deep Space 1*	First test of ion propulsion; navigates to Comet Borelly (2001); USA
1999	*Chandra*	Launch of the *Chandra X-Ray Observatory*; USA
2001	*Soyuz TM-32*	First private citizen to pay for a spaceflight (Dennis Tito)
2001	NEAR *Shoemaker*	First to orbit and land softly on a minor planet, 433 Eros; USA
2001	*Genesis*	First solar-wind sample return; USA
2003	*Columbia*	Second Space Shuttle disaster; crew of 7 lost (Feb. 1)
2003	MOST	First Canadian space telescope launched into Earth orbit
2003	*Shenzhou V*	First Chinese taikonaut to orbit Earth (Yang Liwei)
2004	*Mars Rovers*	First long-range surface exploration of Mars; USA
2004	*Stardust*	First collection and return of cometary material, Wild 2; USA
2004	*Cassini*	First to orbit Saturn; USA
2004	*Gravity Probe B*	First test of Einstein's general theory of relativity in space; USA
2005	*Huygens*	First to land on Titan; USA/ESA
2005	*Deep Impact*	First to impact on and study the interior of a comet, Tempel 1; USA
2008	*Mars Phoenix*	First to examine Martian arctic soil; discovered water ice; USA
2009	ISS	Most people (13) together in one spacecraft: (Expedition 20/21 and STS 127), including two Canadians (Robert Thirsk, Julie Payette)
2009	*Kepler*	First to verify Earth-sized planets at nearby stars; USA
2010	*Hayabusa*	First minor-planet-sample return mission(rendezvous in 2005); Japan
2010	ISS	Four women in space at one time: Expedition 23, STS 131
2011	*Messenger*	First spacecraft to orbit and study Mercury; USA
2011	*Atlantis*	135th and last Space Shuttle flight
2011	*Dawn*	First to orbit a minor planet (4 Vesta) and a dwarf planet (1 Ceres), in 2015; USA
2011	*Juno*	First mission to study Jupiter from a polar orbit (July 2016); USA
2012	*Mars Science Laboratory*	Carrying Curiosity, the first nuclear-powered rover on Mars; USA
2012	*NEOSSat*	First to look for objects on a potential Earth-collision course; Canada
2014	*Rosetta/Philae*	First to soft land on a comet (67P/Churyumov–Gerasimenko); ESA
2014	*Enterprise*	SS2 class, lost in test flight, with fatality; Virgin Galactic, UK
2015	*New Horizons*	First to fly by and closely image the Pluto system; USA
2016	OSIRIS-*Rex*	First NASA/CSA mission to sample an asteroid (101955 Bennu)

As of August 2017, a total of 549 people have travelled into space.

Upcoming Missions

2018+	JWST*	Launch of the *James Webb Space Telescope*: USA/ESA
2019+	*New Horizons*	First to fly by Kuiper Belt Objects; USA
2020	*Euclid**	First mission to map the Dark Universe; ESA
2022	JUICE*	First mission to primarily study JUpiter's ICEy moons; ESA

* Mission not yet launched

OBSERVING ARTIFICIAL SATELLITES

BY PAUL D. MALEY

Watching satellites for fun can lead to more important things. Because the "satellite universe" is dynamic, there are special sights happening all the time that few people ever see. To amateurs who observe deep-sky objects, the Moon, Sun, comets, or meteors, these man-made bodies traipse through a field of view and interrupt briefly or possibly ruin a photograph. But satellites offer a wide-open field of discovery since most are not observed after being left in orbit, or if they are, observations are few.

This author made a discovery on 2016 Mar. 28, after an initial report that the Japanese ASTRO-H (Hitomi) satellite experienced a problem. My video observations showed the object designated as the satellite was rotating every once 23.14 seconds. A couple of days later, a second object was recorded rotating once every 1.54 seconds. These optical signatures indicate that what should have been a single stable, non-varying object, was indeed at least two bodies tumbling out of control. Attempted observations of still more pieces associated with this payload proved unsuccessful as those pieces were quite small. It appears the satellite broke up due to some disturbance, resulting in two major pieces With just this cursory information one can very accurately conclude that this important $270 million X-ray research satellite is likely broken beyond repair.

In the past, both my random and targeted observations of specific satellites have provided similar information that was used by both NASA and the Japanese Space Agency; the primary tools used were as simple as a pair of 7 × 50 binoculars, stopwatch, audio recorder, star charts, and shortwave time signal receiver. In 1999, I made numerous observations of the German ABRIXAS X-ray astronomy satellite. The telescope's battery was accidentally overcharged and destroyed three days after the mission started. When attempts to communicate with the satellite when its solar panels were illuminated by sunlight failed, the $20 million project was abandoned. During the investigation period, I was asked to monitor its behaviour with those simple tools; I was able to draw light curves over time revealing its rotation pattern, which was then modelled based on the known spacecraft shape to help construct rotational axis orientation. This data was then folded into a formal technical paper presentation at an aerospace conference.

Some 16 years ago, while jogging early in the morning in Noordwijk, Holland, I noticed a flashing satellite above me. It turns out that it was a member of the Iridium satellite constellation that had suffered an attitude failure. Instead of providing reliable "Iridium flares," it was rotating out of control indicating a failure. This was an accidental discovery.

The night sky reveals some of these unusual reflections, provided you are aware and have an interest to wonder what they are. A random bright flash in the sky might be due to a specular mirror glint of sunlight from a satellite hundreds or even thousands of miles from Earth. Such reflections may recur after seconds or even minutes. Other flashes may come from geostationary orbit 22 000 miles above the Earth as an errant communications satellite that has lost attitude control drifts from east to west instead of being located in its designated spot at an assigned longitude.

Optical observation has been of great help in my past observations where a satellite's telemetry failed in analyzing rotation of the Japanese ADEOS payload in 1998, and the failure of WIRE observatory in 1999. When some satellites are launched either secretly or with minimum mission information, watching where they should appear can provide some gross insight into their apparent size and stability, and also if there are other objects in close proximity associated with the launch.

It is well to remember that virtually every object we can see in the sky with the eye or optics, regardless of the aperture, is in motion. And in space, things can happen randomly without warning. After weeks, months or even decades in orbit satellites can leak residual fuel, undergo an explosion, flake off paint fragments, collide with other satellites, etc. You might be able to be the first one to spot one of these cosmic events.

TIME

TIME AND TIME SCALES

BY ROY BISHOP

Time has been said to be nature's way of keeping everything from happening at once. In 1687, Sir Isaac Newton (1642–1727) perceived time as being separate from and more fundamental than the spinning of changeable planets or the oily mechanisms of clocks: "Absolute, true, and mathematical time, of itself, and from its own nature flows equably without regard to anything external." That is the common sense or intuitive view most people have of time.

Albert Einstein (1879–1955) was the first to understand that time is but an abstraction that does not exist independently of clocks. In his special theory of relativity (1905) Einstein predicted that clocks moving relative to an observer run slower, a phenomenon called time dilation or the second-order Doppler effect. For example, relative to a clock fixed beside a road, the wristwatch of a person driving past at a speed of 100 km/h loses 0.26 ps per minute (ps = picosecond = 10^{-12} s; see p. 32). A decade later, in his theory of gravitation, the general theory of relativity, Einstein predicted that clocks lower or higher than the observer in a gravitational field run slower or faster, respectively, than the observer's clock. In the case of a lower clock, it is called the gravitational redshift. For example, an alarm clock on the floor a metre below your bed loses 3.1 ps per 8-h night relative to a watch on your wrist. These counterintuitive effects are not only real, but in recent years they have found their way into the consumer marketplace in the form of GPS (Global Positioning System) receivers. These handheld units receive signals from orbiting atomic clocks and rely on programs that allow for time dilation and gravitational redshift (see *Physics Today*, May 2002, p. 41). In astronomy, the general theory of relativity was mostly ignored until the last few decades of the 20th century, when increasing precision of clocks and advances in theoretical astrophysics and cosmology demanded its use.

As to understanding time, Lord Kelvin (1824–1907) said that you know a physical quantity if you can measure it. Time can indeed be measured, with mind-boggling precision. For those who feel compelled to state "We still don't know what time actually is," perhaps the mystery resides merely in the meaning of this statement.

The essence of time is that isolated material changes occur in invariant ratios one with respect to another. That is, as Sir Hermann Bondi (1919–2005) put it: "Time is that which is manufactured by clocks." Thus, to deal with time, clocks must be devised and units and time scales established. Readers who wish to pursue this topic beyond the brief overview presented here should consult *The Measurement of Time*, by C. Audoin and B. Guinot, Cambridge University Press, 2001, and the *Explanatory Supplement to the Astronomical Almanac, 3rd ed.*, by S.E. Urban and P.K. Seidelmann (eds.), University Science Books, 2013. For less-technical descriptions of many aspects of time see *A Matter of Time*, a special edition of *Scientific American* (vol. 21, no. 1, 2012).

Periodic Time Intervals and Clocks

There are three obvious, natural, periodic time intervals on Earth: the seasonal cycle (year), the cycle of lunar phases (month), and the day–night cycle (day). The cycle of the seasons is called the *tropical year* and contains 365.242 190 days. The cycle of lunar phases is known as the *synodic month* and equals 29.530 589 days. The average day–night (diurnal) cycle is the *mean solar day* and presently contains approximately

86 400.0016 s. Other types of year, month, and day have been defined and are listed along with brief definitions and durations on p. 29.

The problem of accurately subdividing these natural intervals to make time locally available at any moment (i.e. timekeeping) was satisfactorily solved in 1657 by Christiaan Huygens, who invented the first practical pendulum clock. Through successive refinements, the pendulum clock reigned supreme for nearly three centuries, until it was surpassed in precision by the quartz oscillator in the 1940s. Within another 20 years the quartz clock was, in turn, superseded by the cesium atomic clock, which by the year 2000 reached a precision of about 1 part in 10^{15}. Today, clocks based on single ions of other elements are approaching a short-term stability of one part in 10^{17} (one second in 3 billion years), and optical-lattice clocks are exceeding that figure (see *Physics Today*, March 2014, p. 12).

Earth's Rotation and Time Scales

Of the three obvious, natural, periodic time intervals on Earth (year, month, and day), the day dominates our lives and determines the various time scales we have created. The day is caused primarily by Earth's rotation on its axis. To count rotations, a reference or fiducial point is required. Four such points are of interest, and three of these are the basis of five time scales:

(1) Earth's rotation relative to the distant stars: Although the distant stars (or better, extragalactic sources) provide a reference frame to determine the "true" period of Earth's rotation (presently about 86 164.1005 s), because of Earth's orbital motion and its rotational precession, this true period is not that of either the solar day or the RA/Dec coordinate grid used to specify astronomical positions. Hence no time scales are based on Earth's true rotational period.

(2) Earth's rotation relative to the equinox: The equator and poles of the RA/Dec celestial coordinate grid are aligned with Earth's mean equator and poles. ("Mean" denotes that small, periodic variations caused by the nutation of Earth's axis have been averaged out. Nutation involves the true pole moving relative to the mean pole with an amplitude of about 9″ and a variety of short periods up to 18.6 years.) Hence the RA/Dec grid slowly shifts relative to the distant stars as Earth's rotation axis and equator precess, a motion caused primarily by the torques exerted by the Moon and Sun on Earth's equatorial bulge. The other planets make a smaller contribution to this *precession of the equator* and also cause a *precession of the ecliptic*. The sum of these two precessions is called *general precession*. General precession causes the zero point of right ascension (the "Greenwich of the skies," the vernal equinox, or "first point of Aries") to drift westward (retrograde) along the ecliptic about 50″ per year. As a result, Earth's rotation period relative to the equinox (called the *mean sidereal day*, currently 86 164.0921 s) is 8.4 ms shorter than the time for one rotation (see p. 29). At any longitude on Earth, the RA of a star on the meridian (corrected for nutation) is the ***Local Mean Sidereal Time*** **(LMST)** at that instant. At the Greenwich meridian (0° longitude), this is called ***Greenwich Mean Sidereal Time*** **(GMST)**. LMST may be used to set a telescope on an object of known right ascension. The hour angle of the object equals the sidereal time less the RA. LMST may be available from a sidereal clock, or it can be calculated as explained in the middle of p. 47. Because Earth makes one more rotation with respect to the other stars than it does with respect to the Sun during a year, sidereal time gains relative to time scales linked to the Sun (see below) by about 3 min 56 s per day, or 2 h per month.

(3) Earth's rotation relative to the real Sun: A common misconception is that the Sun is highest in the sky and lies on the local north–south meridian at 12:00 noon. However, time based on the position of the Sun in the sky, known as local ***apparent solar time*** or *sundial time*, can differ by up to an hour or more from civil time (the time that we normally use). There are two reasons for this discrepancy. One reason is that the Sun's eastward annual apparent motion around the sky is far from uniform both because of Earth's elliptical orbit and because of the inclination of the celestial equator to the ecliptic. Thus apparent solar time does not have a uniform rate (see the next paragraph). The second reason for the difference between sundial time and civil time is the use of standard time zones (see the penultimate paragraph of this article).

(4) Earth's rotation relative to the mean Sun: If the Sun is replaced by a fictitious mean sun moving uniformly along the celestial equator, Earth's rotation relative to this mean sun defines ***Local Mean (solar) Time*** **(LMT)**. Apparent solar time can differ by up to 16 min from LMT depending upon the time of year (see the diagram on p. 185). Small, periodic shifts of Earth's crust relative to the axis of rotation *(polar motion)* affect astronomical time determinations through the resulting east–west shift in the meridian at latitudes away from the equator. LMT at the Greenwich meridian (0° longitude), when corrected for this polar motion, is called ***Universal Time*** **(UT1**, or often simply **UT)**. UT1 is determined using very-long-baseline interferometry, satellite laser-ranging data, lunar laser-ranging data, and GPS data (via the International GPS Service).

All the above mean time scales (LMST, GMST, LMT, and UT1), being based upon Earth's rotation, are only as uniform as that rotation. By the mid-19th century, discrepancies between theory and the observed motion of the Moon indicated that, over the long term, Earth's rotation is slowing down. However, not until clocks became better timekeepers than the spinning Earth (c. 1940, when crystal-controlled clocks exceeded precisions of 1 in 10^{10}) was it realized how complex is the variable rotation of our planet. There are (i) long-, (ii) medium-, and (iii) short-term accelerations:

(i) Over many centuries there is a *secular* slowing caused by tidal friction of about 8 parts in 10^{13} per day (i.e. the day becomes one second longer about every 40 000 years).

(ii) Over a few decades there are *random* accelerations (positive and negative), apparently caused by core–mantle interactions and possibly by changes in ocean currents. These are about 10 times larger than the tidal deceleration and thus completely obscure the latter effect over time intervals of less than a century or so.

(iii) The largest accelerations in Earth's rotation rate are short-term ones: *periodic components* are associated mainly with lunar-induced tides (over two-week and monthly intervals) and seasonal meteorological factors (over semiannual and annual intervals); *nonperiodic* (chaotic) high-frequency variations are associated mainly with the global atmospheric wind and pressure distributions. These short-term accelerations are typically one or two orders of magnitude larger again than the random, decadal fluctuations on which they are superimposed (see the article by John Wahr in the June 1986 issue of *Sky & Telescope*, p. 545).

Uniform Time Scales

(1) Based on orbital motion: Although Earth's axial rotation is not sufficiently predictable to serve as a precise clock, the orbital motions of our Moon, Earth, and the other planets are predictable to high accuracy. Through the dynamical equations describing these motions plus extended astronomical observations, a uniform dynamical time scale can be derived. Such a scale, known as *Ephemeris Time* (ET), was for several years (1952–1984) the basis of astronomical ephemerides. The ephemeris second, defined in 1955 as a certain fraction of the tropical year 1900.0, was the fundamental unit of time. Early in the 20th century, the UT1 and ET scales coincided, but because Earth's rotation rate has been generally slower than the ET rate, by 1984

UT1 was 54 s behind ET and was losing about half a second per year. Between 1984 and 2015, Earth's rotation rate has varied (part of the random decadal fluctuations), losing between 0.2 and 0.8 s per year relative to ET (actually TT, see below).

(2) Based on atomic transition frequency: The quantum nature of matter gives atoms a permanence and stability that macroscopic objects such as quartz crystals, planets, and pendulums do not possess. The idea of an atomic clock was proposed by the Austrian–American physicist Isidor Rabi in 1945. In 1967, the second was given an atomic definition: 9 192 631 770 periods of the radiation involved in the transition between the two hyperfine levels of the ground state of the cesium 133 atom. This is known as the SI (for Système International) second (abbreviation s, *not* sec). The number 9 192 631 770 was chosen so that on the rotating geoid (i.e. for clocks fixed on Earth at mean sea level), the SI second is identical to the older ET second to within the precision of measurement.

The previous sentence implies that clocks on the geoid run at the same rate. What about Earth's rotation? Clocks nearer the equator move faster, so does time dilation not make them run slower relative to clocks at higher latitudes? Ignoring the Moon and Sun, if Earth did not rotate and had an isotropic density distribution, its geoid (mean sea-level surface) would be spherical, and clocks fixed on this geoid would, by symmetry, all run at the same rate (they would all be at rest and have similar positions in Earth's gravitational field). For a rotating Earth, the equatorial bulge is such that clocks away from the poles are just enough higher in Earth's gravitational field that the resulting gravitational blueshift exactly cancels the time dilation associated with their rotational speed. This simple, elegant, and convenient result is a consequence of Einstein's principle of equivalence: A body at rest in a gravitational field is equivalent to a body being accelerated in a field-free space. As described by general relativity, gravitation is geometry, not a force, which is why no one has ever felt a force of gravity. The only force acting on Earth-based clocks, or on any stationary Earth-based objects, is the electromagnetic contact force supporting them. Any two nearby clocks located on the same surface perpendicular to the direction of this contact force (the plumb-bob direction) will have identical rates. Thus *all* clocks on the geoid run at the same rate. Whether or not the planet beneath is rotating is immaterial.

Five SI-second-based time scales are in use today. One of these (UTC) merely differs an integral number of seconds from one of the other four and is described in the last section. The fundamental time scale for unambiguously dating events within the Solar System and beyond (e.g. planet and interplanetary spacecraft motions, and pulsar signals) is **Barycentric Coordinate Time (TCB)**. TCB is the time base of a non-rotating coordinate system with its origin located at the centre of mass of the Solar System, and it is not influenced by the gravitational fields of any bodies in the Solar System. It is as if the Solar System were not present.

The fundamental time scale for unambiguously dating events in the vicinity of Earth (e.g. motions of Earth-orbiting satellites) is **Geocentric Coordinate Time (TCG)**. TCG is the time base of a non-rotating coordinate system with its origin located at the centre of mass of Earth, and it is not influenced by the gravitational field of Earth. It is as if all bodies of the Solar System except Earth were present.

TCG runs at a slower (and slightly variable) rate relative to TCB because of both time dilation associated with Earth's orbital motion and gravitational redshift associated with Earth's location within the Sun's gravitational well, and (to a much lesser extent) the gravitational wells of all the other bodies in the Solar System (except Earth). Relative to TCB, TCG loses about 467 ms per year.

One might expect that TCG would be the time scale of choice for Earth-based observers (e.g. for dealing with apparent geocentric ephemerides); however, cesium atomic clocks at Earth's surface are deep within Earth's gravitational well and lose about 22 ms per year relative to TCG. To avoid this inconvenience, a second geocentric coordinate time scale has been devised, **Terrestrial Time (TT)**. TT is defined as having a rate exactly $1 - 6.969290134 \times 10^{-10}$ as large as the TCG rate so that the unit of the TT scale is very close to the SI second on the rotating geoid, matching the rate of Earth-based atomic clocks. Thus TT is an idealized atomic time scale on the geoid, and is a derived scale, not fundamental. The TT rate definition is based upon TCG and not the geoid because of uncertainties surrounding the realization of the geoid (the geoid would coincide with Earth's sea surface *if* the waters of the oceans were homogeneous and at rest). TT loses about 22 + 467 = 489 ms (nearly half a second) per year relative to TCB.

TCB, TCG, and TT are theoretical, ideal time scales. Real clocks are needed for measurements. To this end in 1972, ***International Atomic Time*** (**TAI** = Temps Atomique International) was introduced. TAI is based on a weighted average of more than 200 atomic clocks in more than 30 countries and presently is the most precise *achievable* time scale. Not even atomic clocks are perfect time keepers (they drift randomly one with respect to another), so TAI shifts unpredictably relative to the ideal TT rate by about 0.1 μs/year (a few parts in 10^{15}). The TAI scale was set to agree with UT1 on 1958 Jan. 1, which led to the definition that TT be exactly 32.184 s ahead of TAI on 1977 Jan. 1.0 (TAI) to ensure continuity of TT with ET, TT's predecessor for geocentric ephemerides.

TCB, TCG, and TT are defined to have had the same reading on 1977 Jan. 1.0 (TAI) at Earth's centre of mass, all three being exactly 32.184 s ahead of TAI at that point in spacetime. At the beginning of 2017, TT is about 0.9 s behind TCG, and 20 seconds behind TCB. TCB, TCG, and TT are realized via TAI.

Three time scales no longer in use are associated with the SI second: ET, TDT, and TDB. ET and TDT have been abandoned, and TDB is deprecated. Unfortunately they still appear in some publications so they must be mentioned. *Ephemeris Time* (ET), introduced in section (1) above, was defined and adopted by the International Astronomical Union in 1952. The transition from ET to the modern TT took place in three steps: (i) Because of several difficulties surrounding both the original concept of ET and its determination (the most serious being that it ignored relativity), and because atomic clocks had become readily available, in 1984 ET was abandoned in favour of *Terrestrial Dynamical Time* (TDT). The unit of TDT was the SI second on the rotating geoid, and its scale was chosen to agree with the 1984 ET scale; (ii) In 1991, the general theory of relativity was explicitly adopted as the theoretical background for spacetime reference systems. To emphasize that TDT was no longer derived from observations of the dynamical aspects of Solar System bodies, TDT was renamed simply Terrestrial Time (TT); (iii) Because of uncertainties surrounding the realization of the geoid (mentioned above), TT was redefined in terms of TCG in 2000.

In 1976, *Barycentric Dynamical Time* (TDB) was introduced when it became necessary to acknowledge relativistic effects but before the general theory of relativity was accepted by astronomers. It was similar to TCB except its scale unit was adjusted to approximate ET (currently TT). TDB was needlessly complex and confusing; however, it was used extensively by the Jet Propulsion Laboratory for ephemerides in planetary exploration, so was not completely abandoned when TCB was introduced in 1991. This unsatisfactory situation was resolved in 2006 when TDB was redefined by a simple linear relation in terms of TCB. Although redundant and deprecated, TDB is now an alternative way to express TCB, with the minor convenience that it keeps nearly in step with TT at Earth's centre.

(3) Based on pulsars: Millisecond radio pulsars (old, rapidly spinning neutron stars) display extraordinary stability in their rotation. Their stability, after allowing for spin-down, is almost as good as the best atomic clocks. However, uncertainties in

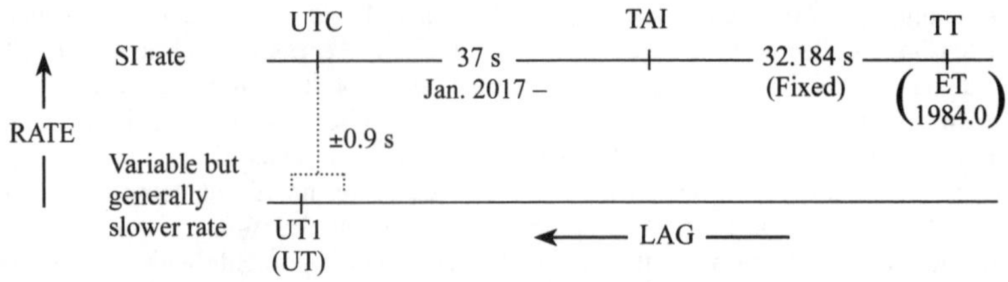

This diagram displays the rate and scale relations between Earth-based time scales that run at or near the SI rate at sea level and that are not longitude dependent.

predicting the spin-down rate of a pulsar and in Earth's motion relative to a pulsar, the elaborate equipment needed to observe a pulsar, and the complex data analysis required all make it unlikely that a pulsar will ever replace cesium clocks as the basis for a uniform time scale. Like quartz crystals, planets, and pendulums, pulsars do not possess the permanence and stability of atoms.

Uniform Time Scales with Steps (to track the mean Sun)

Closely related to UT1 (which follows Earth's variable rotation relative to the mean Sun) is ***Coordinated Universal Time*** **(UTC)**, introduced in its present form in 1972. UTC, the basis of the world system of civil time, runs at the TAI rate and is offset an integral number of seconds from TAI so that it approximates UT1. When required (usually on Jun. 30 or Dec. 31), "leap seconds" are inserted into (or, if necessary, deleted from) UTC so that the difference UT1 – UTC = ΔUT1 does not exceed ±0.9 s. The most recent insertion of a leap second occurred at the beginning of 2017, making the difference TAI – UTC = ΔAT = 37 s. Hence TT – UTC = 37 s +32.184 s = 69.184 s exactly (see the diagram above). When the next leap second may be required will depend upon Earth's rate of rotation during the coming months. UTC is readily available via radio time signals and GPS receivers. (Note: The term *Greenwich Mean Time* (GMT) over the years has had three different meanings: the same as UT1, UTC, and mean solar time at the Greenwich meridian with 0 h corresponding to noon. To avoid confusion, the term *Greenwich Mean Time* should not be used.)

The website maia.usno.navy.mil/search/search.html provides Earth orientation data, including daily values of the difference (UT1 – UTC) = ΔUT1. See also TIME SIGNALS on p. 47. Anyone can see how Earth's rotation has been varying by going to the website maia.usno.navy.mil which gives a link to values of (TT – UT1) = "Delta T" at monthly intervals since 1973. A graph of Delta T versus time is interesting.

Local Mean (solar) Time (LMT) would suffice for the inhabitants of an isolated village, but with the advent in the 19th century of rapid travel and communication (railways, steamships, and the telegraph), it became essential that clocks over a range of longitudes indicate the same time. To keep these clocks reasonably in phase with the day–night cycle and yet avoid the inconvenience to travellers of a local time that varies continuously with longitude, in 1884, Earth was divided into 24 ***Standard Time*** zones, adjacent zones generally differing by one hour and each ideally 15° wide (see the time-zone map on p. 46). All clocks within the same zone read the same time. The Canadian railway surveyor and construction engineer Sir Sandford Fleming (1827–1915) was instrumental in establishing this system of standard time zones. The zero zone is centred on the Greenwich meridian (longitude 0°), and, since 1972, standard time in that zone is UTC. Thus the world system of civil time is based on UTC and includes the "leap seconds," which keep UTC near UT1. Depending upon an observer's location within his or her standard time zone, standard time may differ by up to an hour or so from LMT (see the third paragraph on p. 205). That is the second reason why the Sun seldom, if ever, is on the observer's meridian at 12:00 noon, standard time.

Humans generally have an awake/asleep cycle that is delayed by a few hours relative to the day/night cycle. Consequently, in higher latitudes during the spring and summer, when the Sun rises before humans do, more energy is needed for lighting in the evening than would be the case if the two cycles coincided. To shift the lifestyles of their citizens more in phase with the day/night cycle, many countries adopt ***Daylight Saving Time***, advancing clocks by one hour during the spring and summer (a better term would be *Energy Saving Time* because it is energy that is being saved, not daylight). For most of Canada and the United States[1], clocks are advanced by one hour at 02:00 local time on the second Sunday in March, and return to standard time at 02:00 local time on the first Sunday in November: *spring ahead, fall back*.

[1] Some regions, such as northwestern Ontario, Saskatchewan, northeastern and southeastern British Columbia, Hawaii, and most of Arizona, do not observe Daylight Saving Time. For more information see webexhibits.org/daylightsaving.

STANDARD TIME ZONES

The map on the following page shows the world system of standard time zones. It was prepared and provided by Her Majesty's Nautical Almanac Office. Over the open oceans, the time zones are uniformly spaced and are bounded by lines of longitude 15° apart. In populated regions, political and other considerations have considerably modified the ideal geometry.

The standard time zones are generally designated by letters of the alphabet. The zero time zone, centred on the longitude 0° meridian passing through the Airy Transit Circle at the Old Royal Observatory in Greenwich, England, is denoted Z. Standard time within this zone is Coordinated Universal Time (UTC). Zones A, B, C,…, M (J excluded), increase eastward at one-hour intervals to the International Date Line (where, continuing eastward, the day of the week jumps discontinuously back by one day), while zones N, O, P,…, Y decrease westward at one-hour intervals to the same boundary (where, continuing westward, the day of the week jumps discontinuously ahead by one day). Zones M and Y are only one-half hour wide. Also, as indicated on the map, there are several partial zones that are one-half hour different from the adjacent main zones.

In North America, there is one partial zone and six standard time zones. In terms of their name (and letter designation, hours behind the Greenwich zone, and the west longitude of the reference or standard meridian), these are:

(1)	Newfoundland	(P*,	3 h 30 min,	52.5°)
(2)	Atlantic	(Q,	4 h,	60°)
(3)	Eastern	(R,	5 h,	75°)
(4)	Central	(S,	6 h,	90°)
(5)	Mountain	(T,	7 h,	105°)
(6)	Pacific	(U,	8 h,	120°)
(7)	Alaska	(V,	9 h,	135°)

Note: Caution is advised when relying on the time-zone information given in this map. The zones are drawn based on the best information available as of August 2016 and are subject to change. Also, local jurisdictions, especially those near depicted zone boundaries, often adopt a different time. For current official Canadian and U.S. time zones visit www.nrc-cnrc.gc.ca/eng/services/inms/time-services.html and www.time.gov respectively.

WORLD MAP OF TIME ZONES

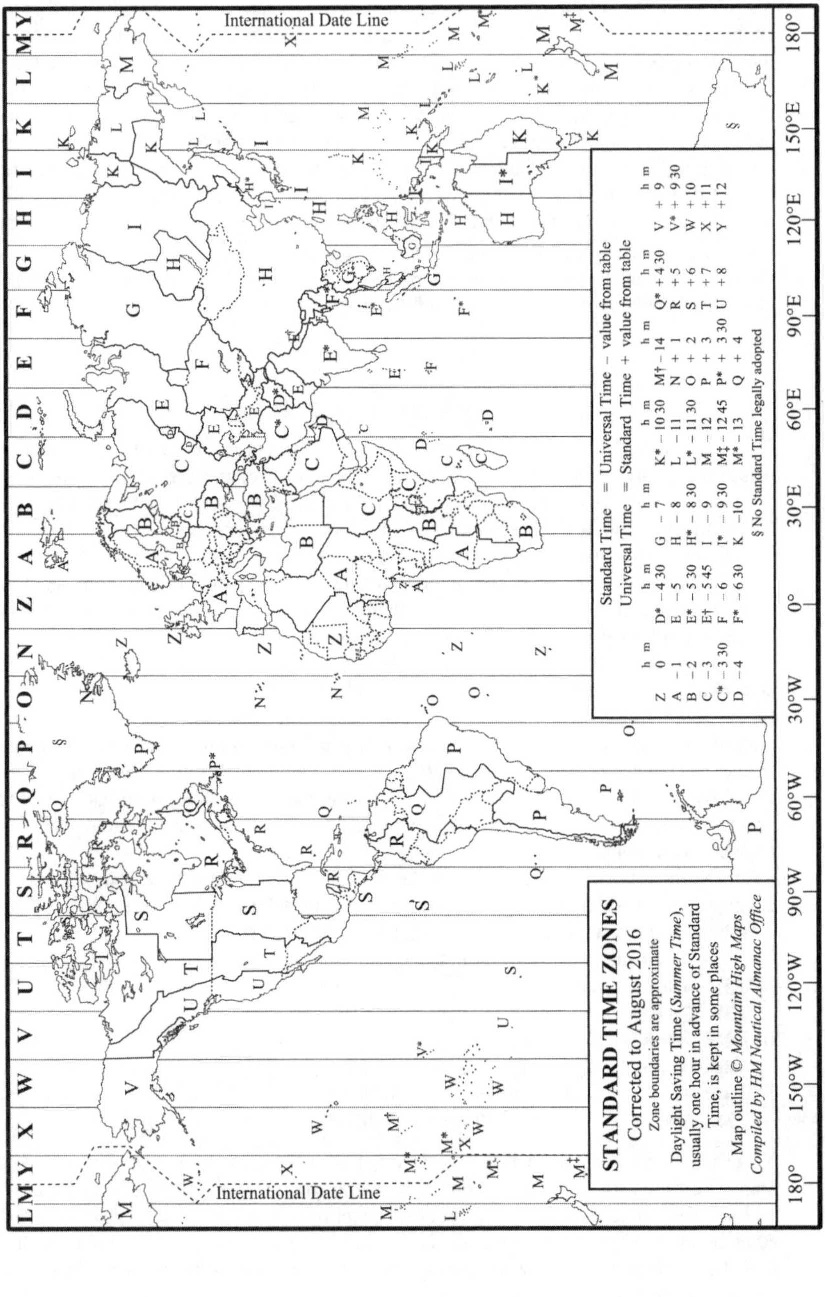

TIME SIGNALS

National time services distribute Coordinated Universal Time (UTC). UTC is coordinated through the Bureau International des Poids et Mesures (BIPM) in Sèvres, France, so that most time services are synchronized to a tenth of a millisecond. Radio time signals available in North America include:

CHU Ottawa, Ontario, Canada 3.330, 7.850, 14.670 MHz
WWV Fort Collins, Colorado, USA 2.5, 5, 10, 15, 20 MHz

For CHU, each minute starts at the *beginning* of the tone following the voice announcement, the tone for the 29th second is omitted, and the tones for seconds 31 through 39 have a different sound from the others.

The difference ΔUT1 = UT1 – UTC to the nearest tenth of a second is coded in the signals. If UT1 is ahead of UTC, second markers beginning at the 1-second mark of each minute are doubled, the number of doubled markers indicating the number of tenths of a second UT1 is ahead of UTC. If UT1 is behind UTC, the doubled markers begin at the 9-second point.

Time signals are also available by telephone from the National Research Council in Ottawa. Call 613-745-1576 for English, and 613-745-9426 for French; the call may be routed via one or two communications satellite hops, being delayed by 0.25 seconds per hop. Internet time services can be found at time5.nrc.ca and www.nist.gov/pml/div688/grp40/its.cfm.

MEAN SIDEREAL TIME, 2017

The following is the Greenwich Mean Sidereal Time (GMST) in hours on day 0 at 0h UT of each month ("day 0" is the last day of the previous month):

Jan. 6.6568	Apr. 12.5707	Jul. 18.5503	Oct. 0.5956
Feb. 8.6938	May 14.5420	Aug. ... 20.5873	Nov. 2.6326
Mar. 10.5337	Jun. 16.5790	Sep. 22.6243	Dec. 4.6039

GMST (in hours) at hour t UT on day d of the month =
GMST at 0h UT on day 0 + $0.065710d + 1.002738t$
LMST (Local Mean Sidereal Time) = GMST – west longitude (or + east longitude)

LMST computed by this method is accurate to ±0.2 s provided t is stated to ±0.1 s or better and the observer's longitude is known to ±1″. Note that t must be expressed in decimal hours UT and longitude in hours, not degrees. Also, to achieve ±0.1 s accuracy in t, the correction ΔUT1 must be applied to UTC. See TIME SIGNALS above.

JULIAN DATE (JD), 2017

The Julian Date (JD) is commonly used by astronomers to refer to the time of astronomical events, because it avoids some of the annoying complexities of the civil calendar. Julian Date 0.0 was the instant of Greenwich mean noon on 4713 Jan. 1 BC (see "The Origin of the Julian Day System" by G. Moyer, *Sky & Telescope*, April 1981, and en.wikipedia.org/wiki/Julian_day#Julian_Date).

The Julian day **commences at noon** (12h) UT. To find the JD at any time during 2017, determine the day of the month and time at the Greenwich meridian, convert this to a decimal day, and add it to one of the following numbers according to the month (these numbers are the JD for 0h UT on the 0th day of each month):

Jan. ... 245 7753.5	Apr. ... 245 7843.5	Jul. 245 7934.5	Oct. 245 8026.5
Feb. ... 245 7784.5	May ... 245 7873.5	Aug. .. 245 7965.5	Nov. ... 245 8057.5
Mar. .. 245 7812.5	Jun. ... 245 7904.5	Sep. ... 245 7996.5	Dec. ... 245 8087.5

For example, 21:36 EDT on May 18 = 1:36 UT on May 19 = May 19.07 UT = 245 7873.5 + 19.07 = JD 245 7892.57.

The JD for 0h UT Jan. 0 for the five proximate years are 245 0000.5 plus: 6657 (2014), and 7022 (2015), and 7387 (2016), and 8118 (2018), and 8483 (2019).

ASTRONOMICAL TWILIGHT AND SIDEREAL TIME

BY RANDALL BROOKS

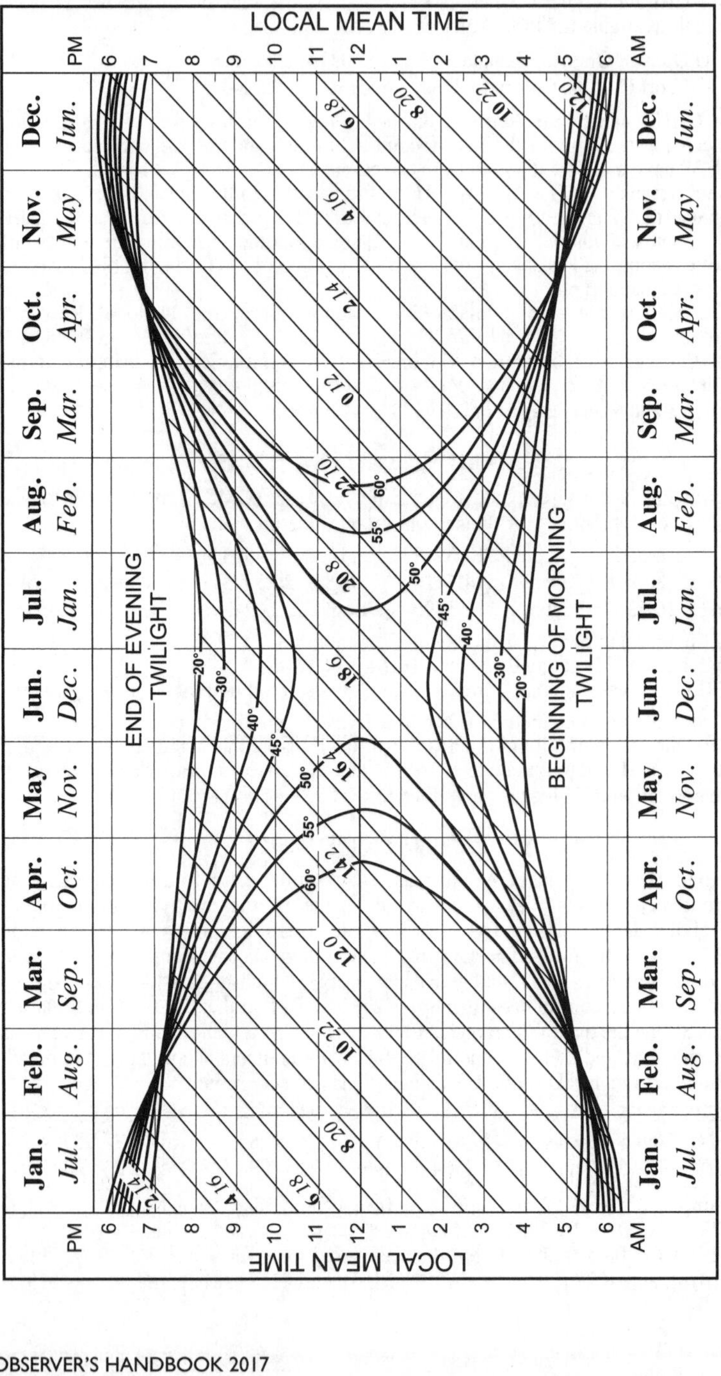

The diagram gives for any day of the year: **(1)** *the LMT of the end and beginning of astronomical twilight at seven specified latitudes (curved lines);* **(2)** *the (LMST = right ascension at the observer's meridian) as a function of LMT (diagonal lines). Months and right ascensions shown in* **boldface** *are for observers in the Northern Hemisphere, those in italics are for observers in the Southern Hemisphere.*

OPTICS AND OBSERVING

TELESCOPE PARAMETERS

BY ROY BISHOP

Equations

Objective: f_o = focal length
D = diameter
FR = focal ratio

Eyepiece: f_e = focal length
d_f = diameter of field stop
θ_p = apparent angular field

Whole Instrument: M = angular magnification
d_p = diameter of exit pupil
θ_c = actual angular field

$$M \equiv \tan(\theta_p/2)/\tan(\theta_c/2) = f_o/f_e = D/d_p \approx \theta_p/\theta_c \quad \text{FR} = f_o/D$$

$$d_f = 2f_o \tan(\theta_c/2) = 2f_e \tan(\theta_p/2) \approx f_o\theta_c{}^* \approx f_e\theta_p{}^*$$

*(θ_c and θ_p must be expressed in radians.)

Performance

D is assumed to be expressed in millimetres.

Light Grasp (LG) is the ratio of the light flux intercepted by a telescope's objective lens or mirror to that intercepted by a human eye having a 7-mm-diameter entrance pupil.

Limiting Visual Magnitude $m \approx 2.7 + 5 \log D$, assuming transparent, dark-sky conditions and magnification $M \geq 1D$ (see *Sky & Telescope, 45*, 401, 1973; *77*, 332, 1989; *78*, 522, 1989).

Smallest Resolvable Angle $\alpha \approx 116/D$ seconds of arc (Dawes's limit). However, atmospheric conditions seldom permit values less than 0.5″.

Useful Magnification Range ≈ 0.2D to 2D. The lower limit (0.2D) guarantees that, for most observers, all the light exiting a telescope can reach the retina. (The reciprocal of the coefficient to D is the diameter (in mm) of the telescope's exit pupil. Also, see the next section concerning exit pupils and magnification.) The upper limit (2D) is determined by the wave nature of light and the optical limitations of the eye, although atmospheric turbulence usually limits the maximum magnification to 400× or less. For examination of double stars, detection of faint stars, and studying structure in bright nebulae, magnifications of up to 3D are sometimes useful.

Chapman's Magnification Rule: For any telescope, an eyepiece of focal length FR mm provides $M = D$ and a 1-mm exit pupil.

Values for some common apertures

D (mm):	60	100	125	150	200	250	330	444
LG:	73	200	320	460	820	1300	2200	4000
m:	11.6	12.7	13.2	13.6	14.2	14.7	15.3	15.9
α:	1.93″	1.16″	0.93″	0.77″	0.58″	0.46″	0.35″	0.26″
0.2D:	12×	20×	25×	30×	40×	50×	66×	89×
2D:	120×	200×	250×	300×	400×	500×	660×	890×

TELESCOPE EXIT PUPILS

BY ROY BISHOP

The performance of a visual telescope is constrained by Earth's atmosphere, the wave aspect of light, the design of the telescope and imperfections in its optical system, and the properties of the human visual system. Telescope and eye meet at the *exit pupil* of the telescope, which is the image of the telescope's objective lens or mirror formed by its eyepiece. When a telescope is pointed at a bright area, such as the daytime sky, the exit pupil appears as a small disk of light hovering in the space just behind the eyepiece. (Insert a small piece of paper in this vicinity to prove that this disk of light *really is* located behind the eyepiece.) Since the exit pupil is the narrowest point in the beam of light emerging from the telescope, it is here that the observer's eye must be located to make optimum use of the light passing through the telescope.

The diagram on p. 52 may be used to display the relation between the diameter of the exit pupil (d_p) of a telescope and the focal lengths (f_e) of various eyepieces. Both d_p and f_e are expressed in millimetres. The numbered scale around the upper right-hand corner of the diagram indicates the focal ratio (FR) of the objective lens or mirror of the telescope. (The FR equals the focal length of the objective divided by its diameter; see p. 49.) To prepare the diagram for a particular telescope, locate the FR of the telescope's objective on the FR scale, and draw a straight diagonal line from there to the origin (the lower left-hand corner). The diagram provides a visual display of the standard relation $d_p = f_e/\mathrm{FR}$. One can see at a glance what range of eyepiece focal lengths is suitable for a particular telescope. Concerning the "AGE" scale on the diagram, see the section Very Low (RFT) Magnifications below.

To determine, for example, the eyepiece focal length required to produce a 3-mm exit pupil on a certain telescope, locate $d_p = 3$ on the ordinate, run horizontally across to the diagonal line corresponding to the FR of that telescope, and from there drop vertically downward to the abscissa to find f_e. This procedure may, of course, be reversed: for a given f_e, find the corresponding d_p.

Magnification Ranges

The ranges H, M, L, and RFT blocked off along the ordinate of the diagram break the d_p scale into four sections, starting at 0.5 mm and increasing by factors of 2. Although this sectioning is somewhat arbitrary, it does correspond closely to what are usually considered to be the high (H), medium (M), low (L), and "richest-field telescope" (RFT) magnification ranges of any visual telescope—and the associated d_p ranges are easy to remember. Note that these magnification ranges are defined by d_p, not by the numerical value of the magnification; for example, a magnification of 100× is "high" for a telescope of aperture $D = 70$ mm, "medium" for $D = 150$ mm, "low" for $D = 300$ mm, "very low (RFT)" for $D = 600$ mm, and "ultra-low" for D larger than 0.8 m.

High Magnifications: In the case of the Moon, the planets, and all but the dimmest stars, the highest useful magnification is the point at which blurring due to diffraction (caused by the wave nature of light) becomes noticeable. That corresponds approximately to $d_p = 0.5$ mm, assuming good optics and negligible atmospheric turbulence (i.e. excellent "seeing"). Higher magnifications will not reveal any more detail in these images and will cause reductions in four desirable features: sharpness, brightness, field of view, and eye relief (the space between the eye and eyepiece). However, for double stars and for some objects requiring the use of averted vision (e.g. faint stars) very high magnifications ($d_p < 0.5$ mm) can sometimes be used to advantage.

Medium Magnifications: A problem with high magnifications is that exit-pupil diameters of about 1 mm and smaller cause "floaters" (mobile debris in the vitreous humour of the eye in front of the retina) to interfere with vision. That problem increases with the age of the observer and with decreasing d_p. To avoid the distraction of floaters, an observer might choose to keep exit-pupil diameters no smaller than 1.5 mm (i.e. in the "medium" magnification range). For this lower limit the diagram indicates a minimum eyepiece focal length of, for example, 7 mm for a FR = 4.5 telescope, 15 mm for a FR = 10 telescope, and 24 mm for a FR = 16 telescope. With this restriction, to achieve a magnification of 250× for observing planets, a telescope would need an aperture of at least $D = M \times d_p = 250 \times 1.5 = 375$ mm. Hence, in addition to providing more light and greater resolution, a large-aperture telescope makes floaters less noticeable and magnifications in the "high" range less necessary.

With magnifications greater than very low (RFT) magnifications and also possibly greater than low magnifications, structure in dim, extended objects, such as galaxies and bright and dark nebulae, will be more easily seen. To see such objects, observers use averted vision, which places the image on the peripheral retina, which is composed primarily of the very sensitive "rod" photoreceptor cells. However, the number of rod cells far exceeds the number of nerve axons available to carry the signals to the visual centres in the brain. To accommodate this limitation and to cope with spontaneous thermal noise in the rod cells, the cells are grouped into detector units of various sizes (analogous to binning of pixels in a CCD chip). Because of the thermal noise, only those signals triggered by almost simultaneous photon hits in several rod cells are allowed to produce a conscious sensation. Thus in very dim light only large retinal detector units receive enough photon hits to respond. As a consequence, our ability to see detail is greatly reduced in dim light. Hence extra magnification helps to reveal structure in galaxies and nebulae.

Low Magnifications: Low magnifications have several advantages over certain other magnification ranges:

(1) For most observers an exit-pupil diameter between 2 mm and 4 mm results in the sharpest optical image because the combined influence of optical aberrations in the eye of the observer (which increase with increasing d_p) and blurring due to diffraction (which decreases with increasing d_p) is at a minimum. Assuming, for example, that the optimum d_p for a "typical observer" is 2.5 mm, then to realize this and achieve a magnification of 250× for observing planets, a telescope needs an aperture of $D = M \times d_p = 250 \times 2.5 = 625$ mm. Once again, the superiority of a large telescope (by amateur standards) is apparent. Another example: the reason for the crisp images provided by Canon's image-stabilized binoculars is that their d_p is in the "low magnification" range, and their optical quality is up to the challenge.

(2) Low magnifications provide greater luminance than high or medium magnifications, enabling the eye to discern contrast variations over a wider range of spatial frequencies.

(3) Viewing is more comfortable than with very low (RFT) magnifications, since the observer can move a bit (move the head and/or scan the field) without cutting into the light beam and dimming the image. As mentioned below, ultra-low magnifications have the same advantage, but light is wasted.

(4) Light entering near the edge of the pupil of the dark-adapted eye is not as effective in stimulating the rod cells in the retina—the "scotopic Stiles–Crawford effect" (see VanLoo and Enoch, *Vision Research, 15* (1975), p. 1005). Thus low magnifications make more effective use of the light than very low (RFT) magnifications.

(5) Low magnifications provide a darker sky background than very low (RFT) magnifications, producing views that some observers consider to be aesthetically more pleasing.

EXIT-PUPILS DIAGRAM

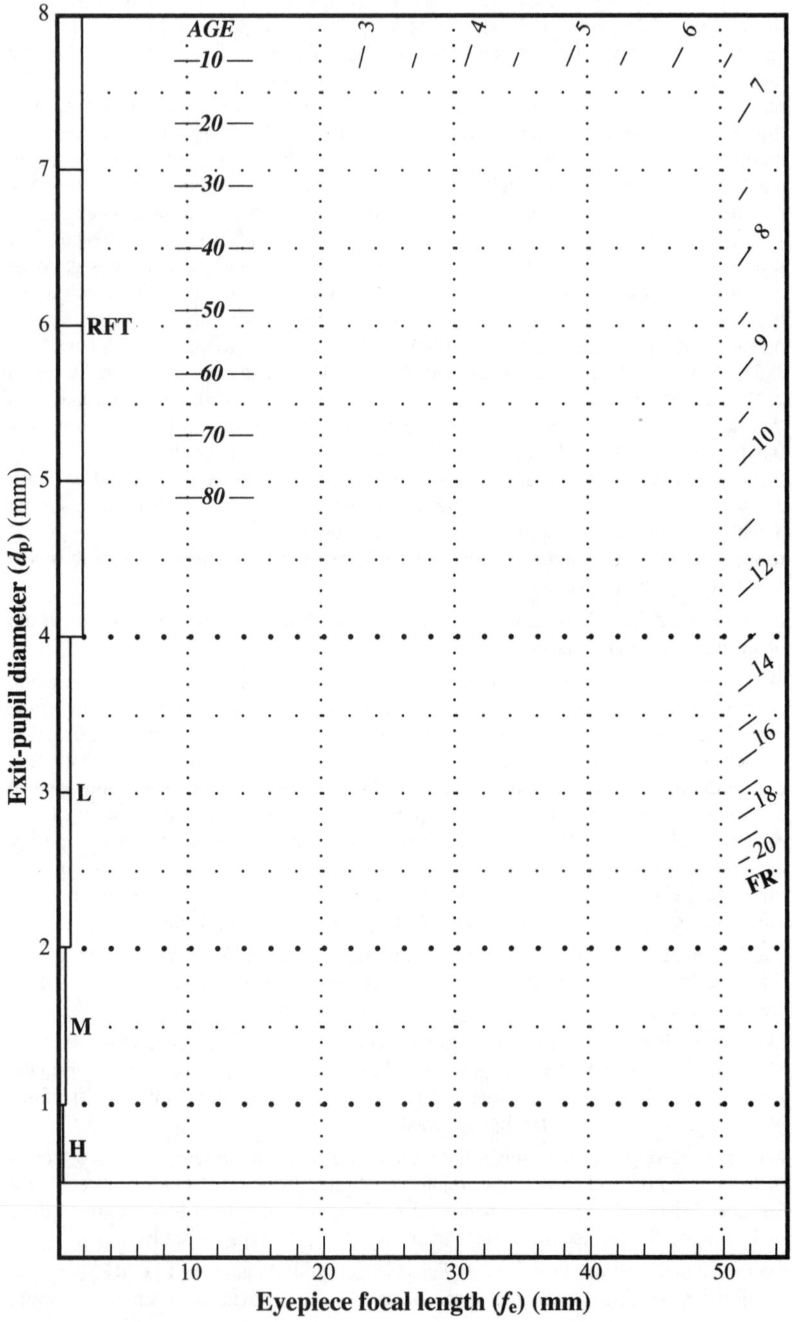

Diagram by Roy Bishop

Very Low (RFT) Magnifications: Magnifications in the RFT range are useful because they yield wide fields of view, the brightest (greatest luminance) images of extended objects, and for common telescope apertures, the most stars visible in one view (hence the term *richest field*). The lowest magnification that still makes use of the full aperture of a telescope is determined by the point at which the diameter of the telescope's exit pupil matches the diameter of the *entrance pupil* of the observer's eye.

For the dark-adapted eye, the entrance-pupil diameter seldom equals the often-quoted figure of 7 mm, but depends, among other things, upon the age of the observer as indicated by the scale in the upper-left portion of the diagram (see Kadlecová et al., *Nature, 182* (1958), p. 1520; *Sky & Telescope*, May 1992, p. 502). Note that this scale indicates *average* values; the maximum diameter of the entrance pupil of the eye of any *one* individual may differ by up to a millimetre from these values. A horizontal line should be drawn across the diagram corresponding to the maximum diameter of one's own entrance pupil. This line will be an upper bound on d_p in the same sense that the line at $d_p = 0.5$ mm is a lower bound. Note that in daylight, the entrance pupil of the eye has a diameter in the range of 2 mm to 4 mm. Thus for daylight use of telescopes, the upper bound on d_p will be correspondingly reduced.

Ultra-Low Magnifications: If a d_p value larger than the entrance pupil of the eye is used, the iris of the observer's eye will cut off some of the light passing through the telescope to the retina; that is, the iris will have become the light-limiting aperture *(aperture stop)* of the system rather than the edge of the telescope's objective. In this case, the cornea of the eye together with the lenses of the telescope's eyepiece form an image of the observer's iris at the objective of the telescope; to the incoming starlight, a highly magnified image of the iris hovers as an annular skirt covering the outer region of the objective of the telescope! A telescope can be used at such "ultra-low" magnifications, but obviously a telescope of smaller aperture would perform as well. However, ultra-low magnifications have two advantages:

(1) A wider actual field of view, assuming the field stop of the eyepiece will permit this (an eyepiece having a 2-in. barrel diameter is usually necessary).

(2) Ease of alignment of the entrance pupil of the eye with the exit pupil of the telescope, an aspect of viewing that is usually troublesome when these two pupils are nearly the same size. An oversize exit pupil provides "slop," making alignment less critical. That is particularly helpful when using binoculars during activities involving motion, such as boating or bird watching, and is one advantage of using 7 × 50 (= $M \times D$) binoculars rather than 7 × 35 binoculars for daytime activities, although less than half of the light entering the larger binoculars can reach the observer's retinas.

Some examples using the diagram:

(1) Consider the common 8-in. Schmidt–Cassegrain telescopes. These have $D = 200$ mm and (usually) FR = 10. The diagram indicates that eyepieces with focal lengths from 5 mm to 55 mm are usable for most observers. With a 32-mm eyepiece, the diagram gives $d_p = 3.2$ mm, in the L magnification range, and the magnification $M = D/d_p = 200/3.2 = 62\times$.

(2) If an observer wishes to use the full aperture of an FR = 4.5 telescope, a 40-mm eyepiece is ruled out. Similarly, a 70-year-old observer should probably not use even a 27-mm eyepiece on such a telescope and should not bother with 7 × 50 or 11 × 80 binoculars, unless ease of eye/exit-pupil alignment is the main consideration.

(3) There is no point in using extremely short focal length eyepieces, especially when combined with Barlow lenses, on telescopes having large FRs. That is a common fault (among many others!) with camera/department store "junk telescopes."

MAGNIFICATION AND CONTRAST IN DEEP-SKY OBSERVING

BY LEE JOHNSON AND WILLIAM ROBERTS

For visual observation of point sources (stars), magnitude limits of common telescope apertures are given in TELESCOPE PARAMETERS (see p. 49). Additional challenges attend the observation of faint, extended, deep-sky objects. This article explores methods to determine the visibility of diffuse objects such as galaxies, dense star clusters, and gaseous nebulae. The main variables governing the visibility of such an object are its average luminance ("surface brightness" in older sources), its angular dimensions, the sky luminance, the telescope aperture, and the magnification used (or, equivalently, the exit pupil of the telescope). Additional factors include the effects of filters, atmospheric extinction, and the limitations of monocular vision. Addressing all these factors, this article builds on seminal research on visual contrast thresholds (Blackwell, 1946), and concludes by linking to an online **Magnification and Contrast Calculator** for estimating the visibility of deep-sky objects. (For an alternative treatment of the same research, especially in relation to the structure of the eye, see Clark, 1990.)

Luminance and Exit Pupils

Table 1 shows the magnitude, size, and luminance of two representative deep-sky objects, with luminance expressed in units of magnitude per square arcsecond (mag/arcsec^2). (For more details on these two objects, see the referenced pages in this Handbook.) When these luminance values are compared to those of skies corresponding to mountain-top observatories (22), dark country sites (21), sites with 5th-mag. stars visible (19.5), and a suburban setting with 4th-mag. stars visible (18.5), it is clear that an object can be dimmer than the sky background; that is, the contrast between the object and the sky is very low. A Sky Quality Meter (unihedron.com) provides a baseline luminance measurement for such a comparison.

TABLE 1—MAGNITUDE, SIZE, AND LUMINANCE

Object	Type	m_V	Size (arcmin)	Luminance (mag/arcsec^2)	OH Page Ref.
NGC 7317	galaxy	13.6	0.5×0.5	20.7	p. 337
Jones 1	planetary nebula	12.1	5.5×5.5	24.4	p. 323

Size, magnitude, and luminance (surface brightness) of deep-sky objects can be found in *The Deep Sky Field Guide to Uranometria 2000.0* and (for a few objects) in A DEEP-SKY SELECTION (see p. 309). In addition, most tables in THE DEEP SKY (see p. 307) include magnitudes and sizes of objects. For any extended deep-sky object, the luminance, S, in mag/arcsec^2, can be estimated from size and magnitude by

$$S = m_V + 2.5\log(2827ab),$$

where a and b are, respectively, the object's major and minor diameters in arcminutes, assuming an elliptical shape. (Subtract 8.9 to convert units to mag/arcmin^2.)

The exit pupil of a telescope (objective diameter divided by magnification) determines the luminance of the image of both the object and the sky as viewed through the eyepiece (see TELESCOPE EXIT PUPILS, p. 50). When an extended object is magnified to the extent that the telescope exit pupil becomes smaller than the entrance pupil of the eye—nominally 7 mm—its luminance decreases relative to the naked-eye view. The decrease is the same for both the object and the sky; in other words, **magnification does not alter contrast**. Table 2 gives the reduction in luminance of both object and sky as the exit pupil decreases.

TABLE 2—DIMMING WITH RESPECT TO A 7-MM EXIT PUPIL

Exit Pupil (mm)	7	6	5	4	3	2	1	0.5
Dimming (mag)	0.0	0.3	0.7	1.2	1.8	2.7	4.2	5.7

Human binocular vision has a lower luminance limit of approximately 1 μcd/m^2, which, when adjusted for monocular vision, is about 27 mag/arcsec^2. When the dimming due to reduced exit pupils (from Table 2) is combined with the sky luminance, it is apparent that the luminance of a magnified dark sky may approach the detection limit of the eye; for example, a 1-mm exit pupil in a 22.0 mag/arcsec^2 sky reduces the apparent sky luminance to 26.2 mag/arcsec^2, which is near the limit of the eye.

The Relation Between Size and Threshold Luminance

Blackwell (1946), in a massive World War II study that is still the only one of its kind, analysed approximately 450 000 observations of threshold contrast over a wide range of background illumination. Table 3, derived from Blackwell's data, gives the minimum detectable luminance of an object for various combinations of object size and background luminance. The values are corrected for monocular vision and assume a 50% probability of detection; for 90% probability, subtract 0.5 from the entries in the table.

TABLE 3—THRESHOLD LUMINANCE OF EXTENDED OBJECTS

Object	Background Luminance (mag/arcsec^2)							
Size (′)	26	25	24	23	22	21	20	19
360	26.3	26.0	25.6	25.0	24.4	23.7	23.0	22.3
240	26.1	25.8	25.4	24.8	24.2	23.5	22.8	22.2
120	25.5	25.3	24.9	24.4	23.7	23.1	22.4	21.8
60	24.7	24.5	24.2	23.7	23.1	22.5	21.9	21.3
30	23.8	23.8	23.3	22.8	22.3	21.7	21.1	20.6
15	22.5	22.3	22.0	21.6	21.1	20.6	20.1	19.7

The table confirms that low-luminance objects of a given size are more easily seen against darker backgrounds. For a given background luminance, large objects are more easily detected than small ones of equal luminance. Applied to the case of an object viewed through a telescope, as magnification increases, one moves up in the table (larger apparent size) and also to the left (smaller exit pupil = darker sky). Hence, detectability benefits from higher magnifications, in agreement with observing experience. However, note that this benefit is smaller toward the upper-left corner of the table. As magnification increases, a point may be reached where the decreasing exit pupil reduces the object luminance faster than the increasing size raises the threshold luminance. Thus the object would become more difficult to detect, but the increased magnification might make it easier to identify bright detail within the object.

It is important to note that the table values are guidelines only. If Table 3 suggests that the detection of an object is marginal, do not be discouraged; try anyway. Other factors that affect object detection are: atmospheric extinction, light loss in the telescope optics, the difference between the nighttime and daytime response of the eye (see FILTERS, 64), and the observer's visual acuity. Typically, the cumulative effect of these factors is between –0.5 and +0.5 mag.; see Schaefer (1990) for further details.

An example using Table 3: Consider the galaxy NGC 7317 in a 21.0 mag/arcsec^2 sky. A magnification of 148× with a 445-mm telescope gives an apparent object size of 74′ with a telescope exit pupil of 3 mm. From Table 2, a 3-mm exit pupil dims both object and sky by 1.8 mag., resulting in luminance values of 22.5 (object) and 22.8 (sky). The entry in Table 3 for background luminance 23 and object size 60′ gives a threshold luminance of 23.7. That is more than one magnitude dimmer than the image of NGC 7317, which should therefore be clearly visible under the specified conditions. On the other hand, a smaller, 130-mm telescope with a magnification of 43× gives a reduced object size of 22′ with a 3-mm exit pupil, hence the values of object and sky luminance are the same as before. Again from the fourth column of Table 3, the interpolated threshold luminance of this smaller image is 22.2, so the object will likely not be visible in this smaller instrument at this magnification. Alternatively, finding the object luminance in that column, we see that the minimum apparent size is almost 30′, and since 22′ is less than this, the object is unlikely to be seen.

The Relation between Minimum Detectable Size and Contrast

Figure 1 shows another way of interpreting Blackwell's data, a graphical representation of Table 3, whose columns are now a set of curves (odd-valued sky luminance values are shown with dashed lines for clarity). The vertical axis represents the minimum detectable size of an object, and the horizontal axis is the object–sky magnitude contrast, that is, the magnitude difference between object luminance and sky luminance. Whereas Table 3 emphasizes detectability as a function of object luminance and size, Figure 1 emphasizes detectability as a function of the object–sky magnitude contrast and size.

FIGURE 1—MINIMUM DETECTABLE SIZE VS. CONTRAST

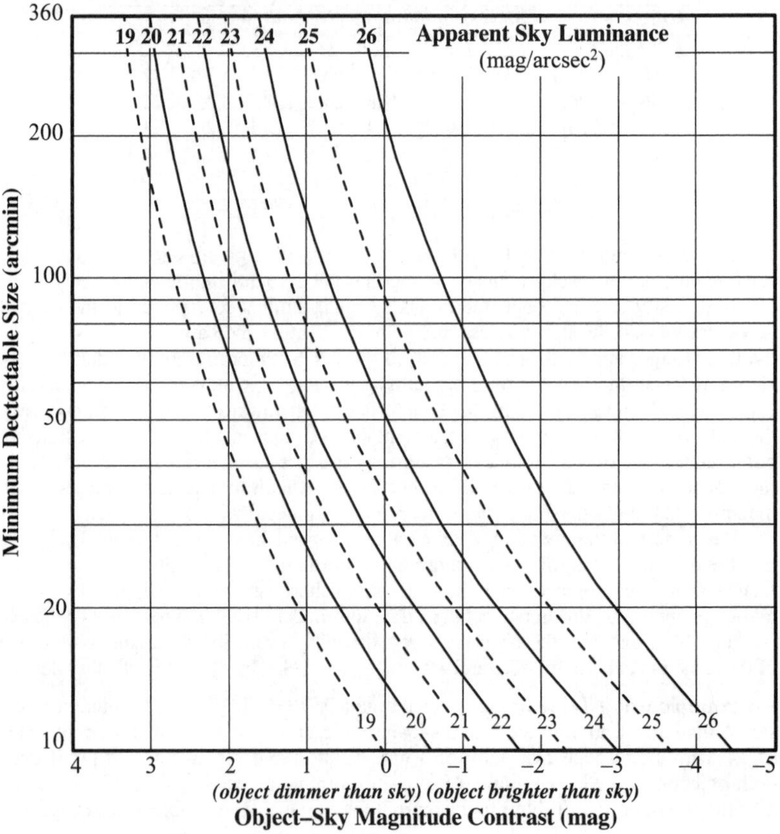

An example using Figure 1: Emission and planetary nebulae are special cases, as contrast can be improved using filters (see FILTERS, 64). Bandpass filters such as the UHC, OIII, and Hβ improve contrast by passing light near the emission wavelengths and rejecting broad-spectrum light from light pollution and natural skyglow at other wavelengths, effectively reducing the sky luminance by about 1.6 mag. through the UHC filter and about 2.6 mag. through the OIII and Hβ filters. The visible light from emission nebulae is mainly in the OIII and Hβ wavelengths, which lie close to the peak response of the dark-adapted eye. Filters such as the UHC pass all the light from these lines and do not significantly dim the nebulae. These filters therefore do not require an increase in exit pupil in order to maintain the object luminance. On the other hand, OIII filters—and especially Hβ filters—may pass only a portion of the light from an emission nebula, hence dimming the nebula. Here, restoring the object's luminance requires an increase in exit pupil and thus a decrease in magnification. The OIII filter passes most of the light from a typical planetary nebula and thus does not require an increase in exit pupil; it is therefore the filter of choice for these objects. The situation for other emission nebulae is not so clear.

Consider viewing Jones 1, a dim planetary nebula of luminance 24.4 mag/arcsec^2, in a sky of luminance 21.0, a magnitude contrast of +3.4. An exit pupil of 2 mm or smaller would reduce the object luminance below the eye's absolute threshold of 27. In a 250-mm aperture, a magnification of 50× gives an exit pupil of 5 mm, which results in a sky luminance of 21.7 and an object size of 275′. Figure 1 shows the minimum detectable size at a contrast of 3.4 to be greater than 360′, so Jones 1 would not be visible under these conditions. An OIII filter would reduce the sky luminance by 2.6 mag. without dimming Jones 1 appreciably and results in a sky luminance of 24.3. The magnitude contrast would be +0.8 mag., and the minimum apparent size is approximately 40′. The planetary nebula should be visible when viewed in that telescope with the filter.

Magnification and Contrast Calculator

Table 3 has been incorporated into a **Magnification and Contrast Calculator** spreadsheet, available online at www.rasc.ca/handbook/supplements. When data for an object, the sky, the telescope, and possible filters are entered, the spreadsheet calculates the observed image parameters and makes a detection prediction of YES, NO, or MAYBE.

Summary

Generally, experienced deep-sky observers select eyepieces that produce exit pupils in the range 2–3 mm when viewing a faint deep-sky object. This range of exit pupils corresponds to the middle of both Table 3 and Figure 1. Larger exit pupils correspond to the lower right of the table, where small, faint objects may fall below the threshold of visibility; and smaller exit pupils to the upper left, where excessive magnification may dim the object to invisibility. At any fixed apparent size, moving from right to left across the table results in a decrease in threshold brightness, which shows the benefit of observing in increasingly dark skies or with the aid of a filter.

References and Resources

- Blackwell, H.R., "Contrast thresholds of the human eye," *J. Opt. Soc. Am. 36*, 624–643 (1946).
- Clark, Roger N., *Visual Astronomy of the Deep Sky*, Sky Publishing Corp., Cambridge, Mass., 1990, p. 13 *ff.* Also see www.clarkvision.com/visastro
- Schaefer, Bradley "Telescopic Limiting Magnitudes," *Publ. Astron. Soc. Pac. 102*, 213–215 (February, 1990).
- Mel Bartels' Internet page *Visual Astronomy*: www.bbastrodesigns.com/visual.html

NIGHT MYOPIA AND STARGAZING EYEGLASSES

BY JOSHUA ROTH

For most of human history, visual astronomy relied on one and only one optical instrument: the human eye. For the past four centuries, though, we have taken to scrutinizing the heavens with optical aid, and the telescope—once a rarity—is attainable by nearly everyone in the developed world who wishes to own one. With its ability to provide more light and magnify the rings of Saturn, gaseous nebulae, and Milky Way beyond what our own eyes can do, telescopic viewing understandably has displaced naked-eye observing as the *modus operandi* of the modern visual astronomer. Nevertheless, there are many observations, some purely aesthetic, others of scientific value, that are best made with the unaided eye.

Unaided, that is, except for eyeglasses or contact lenses; and then only when warranted. But when exactly is such "unit-magnification" optical aid warranted? Most of us get glasses or contacts only when an eyecare professional diagnoses a vision defect. However, even those who were born with decent daytime vision may need eyeglasses or contact lenses to best see the stars by night; and those who *do* use eyeglasses or contact lenses by day may need a different prescription for stargazing. Are you one of those people? In what follows, I will tell you how to find out, but first, a little background on the eye as an optical instrument.

Using its varied layers and components, the eye functions like a converging lens. This means that it brings numerous light rays from a star—or any other point in the field of view—to focus at a single point in space. In practice, of course, not all of the rays that enter the eye from one point can be brought to a single focus: various aberrations conspire against this. Still, at its best the eye brings much of the light from a star to focus at a single point.

Unfortunately, in many cases that point fails to land on the retina: the pad of light-sensitive cells that functions as the eye's "CCD." In many cases, the light is focused in front of the retina, and it spreads out anew before reaching our rods and cones. We call this condition *myopia*, or nearsightedness, because a person so afflicted can see nearby objects well, even though distant ones are blurred, sometimes beyond recognition.

Needless to say, those of us who suffer from myopia typically wear our eyeglasses or contact lenses when looking at the constellations or watching for meteors. If we are purely near- or farsighted, we can do without them at the telescope, since a twist of the focus knob can correct for these visual defects. Astigmatism, on the other hand, requires us to keep using our eyeglasses or contacts at the eyepiece.

Still, many of us have been less than satisfied with our "unit-magnification" views of the night sky, straining to see 6th-magnitude stars or large, diffuse objects like the Beehive Cluster. In many cases, this is because our eyes are not bringing starlight to a focus on our retinae *even if our daytime vision is essentially perfect (be it with or without glasses or contacts)*. Rather, in many cases (though by no means all), humans become more nearsighted as their pupils dilate. This *night myopia* requires correction—above and beyond any correction that may already be in use for daylight hours—if we are to use our eyes to the fullest at night.

Eyecare professionals have debated the causes of night myopia for decades. One theory attributes the effect to the notion that humans tend to focus on their immediate surroundings when startled, frightened, or deprived of adequate visual stimulus. In recent years, it has become possible to measure the human eye's optical figure precisely. In doing so, researchers have found that many peoples' eyes evince significant amounts of spherical aberration when their pupils are dilated.[1]

As a practical matter, one quick way to probe any night myopia you may have would be to borrow eyeglasses from a friend who is more myopic than you, but a better probe—and one that will quantify the effect—is to use a set of optometrists' "flippers": a pair of mounted lenses that can be held in front of your eyes (or your eyeglasses) and quickly flipped in and out of position.[2] Do-it-yourselfers can use biconcave or plano-concave lenses with focal lengths of one metre or greater (corresponding to powers of one diopter and below). Alternatively, an astronomy club could split the (admittedly modest) cost of a set of flippers.

Once you have your flippers in hand, how will you use them to establish whether or not you suffer from night myopia (and, if so, to what degree)? Ideally, lie out for at least half an hour in a setting free of light pollution, and periodically assess your night myopia as you become increasingly dark adapted. Targets such as Ursa Minor and the Pleiades, with their well-established sequences of apparent magnitudes, are ideal, but any star field you are familiar with will do. View the field through your existing eyeglasses or contact lenses (if any), then insert the various flipper lens pairs between your eyes and the night sky and take careful note of any change in limiting magnitude or image quality. Consider allowing for the possibility that each eye may have a different amount of night myopia.

If indeed you find that a particular flipper lens pair best shows you the stars, you may find that looking at the stars through your flipper is all you need to enhance your experience of the night sky. (Certainly it would suffice for a quick look through a reflex sight (e.g. *Telrad*) or to determine limiting magnitude for one's observing log.) On the other hand, you may find that you prefer to obtain a set of eyeglasses dedicated to "naked-eye" stargazing, so that you can gaze heavenward with your arms at rest. These stargazing glasses should be made of a material that separates different colours of light as little as possible (above all, do not use polycarbonate, which is very impact-resistant but also "prisms" points of light into little rainbows, especially near the edges of one's field of view). Many aficionados recommend antireflection coatings.

Anecdotal reports on Internet discussion boards suggest that correcting for night myopia has enabled many visual observers to gain a half magnitude or more in their ability to see faint stars. Such reports also suggest that the typical observer who does order a pair of stargazing eyeglasses finds him/herself correcting for ½ to ¾ diopter of night myopia (above and beyond any daytime nearsightedness that they already may be correcting with glasses or contacts). My own stargazing eyeglasses (one extra diopter) enabled me to spot Uranus "naked-eye" and a dozen or so NGC star clusters for the first time. More importantly, they improved the definition of dark nebulae and lanes in the Milky Way. I now consider them by far my most important piece of optical equipment. Systematic research on this topic by active observers among the RASC membership would be a valuable addition to the literature of visual astronomy.

References:

[1] See "Spectacles for Spectacular Skies" p. 30 in the September 2005 issue of *Sky & Telescope* for details and illustrations. As of this writing it is available free of charge in PDF at www.skyandtelescope.com/howto/visualobserving.

[2] Ontario-based Optego Vision Inc. (optego.com) sell two affordable sets of Night Myopia Diagnostic Flippers (one with ¼ and ½ diopter of myopia correction, and another with ¾ and 1 diopter). Between these two sets, you can correct for night myopia as strong as 1½ diopters, as the flippers can be stacked. Optego also offer flippers with other diopter settings. 341 Deloraine Ave., Toronto ON M5M 2B7. Tel: 416-780-1289 or toll free 800-678-3464

BINOCULARS

BY ROY BISHOP

For an experienced observer, binoculars are indispensable. For a beginning observer, binoculars are preferable to an astronomical telescope. For a beginner unfamiliar with the large-scale features of the sky, who cannot yet identify a dozen constellations on any clear night, a telescope's narrow field of view, confusing image orientations, and unfamiliar controls will quickly cause more frustration than fun. The beginner is at a double disadvantage because he or she also does not know enough about astronomical telescopes to distinguish those that are worthy of the name from the common camera/department-store "junk telescopes"—the $299 wonders with poor optics and wobbly mounts. How many such telescopes are gathering dust in closets, their young owners turned off astronomy and their parents a few hundred dollars poorer? Far better had the same investment been made in a good pair of binoculars. With their ease of use, wide field of view, and unreversed, upright images, binoculars are a great help in finding one's way around the sky, and provide many unique views of the heavens.

Binoculars magnifying 6 to 10 times are ideal for locating planets in the twilight, scanning the constellations, studying the larger dark nebulae and star fields of our galaxy, and viewing bright comets. Binoculars magnifying 10 to 20 times provide the best views of objects spanning a few degrees, such as the Hyades, the Pleiades, the North America Nebula, and the Andromeda Galaxy; they also give the finest view of the slender crescent Moon, or of the full Moon with broken clouds blowing by.

Binoculars permit us to view the Universe with both eyes, thereby providing more advantages: an improved sense of reality and depth (although parallax is negligible when viewing the heavens); more relaxed viewing; a complete view in the sense that the blind areas of one eye (associated with blood vessels and the region where the optic nerve attaches to the retina) are compensated by the field provided by the other eye; and dim objects appear brighter when viewed with two eyes.

Sizes: Binocular sizes are specified by numbers, for example, 7 × 50 and 8 × 30. The first number, including the "×," is the angular magnification or "power"; the second number is the diameter of the front (objective) lenses in millimetres. That is, in the notation on p. 49: $M \times D$. Thus the exit-pupil diameter is easily calculated from $D \div M$ (e.g. 7 × 35 binoculars have exit pupils of $35 \div 7 = 5$ mm). Another important parameter is field of view. Binoculars have apparent angular field diameters of about 50° when equipped with standard eyepieces, to near 70° with wide-angle eyepieces. The actual field of view on the sky (typically 3° to 10°) equals approximately the apparent field divided by the magnification. Thus the area of sky visible decreases rapidly with higher magnifications, making aiming binoculars at an object of interest more difficult.

What is the best binocular size for astronomical use? There is no simple answer. Almost *any* pair of binoculars will show far more than can be seen with the unaided eyes; however, for astronomical use the objective lenses should be at least 30 mm in diameter. Also, small binoculars of high quality are more enjoyable to use than a large pair of low quality.

Caveat emptor! Low-quality binoculars (and telescopes) are common. Images seen through low-quality binoculars are slightly fuzzy (usually not apparent to the inexperienced observer), one's eyes will be strained in trying to compensate for imperfectly aligned optics, and the focusing mechanism is usually flexible and crackling with an excess of grease used to mask poor workmanship. Avoid both zoom (variable magnification) binoculars and binoculars that do not have an adjustable focus—invariably these are of low quality.

Considering that binoculars contain at least 14 pieces of glass with 36 optical surfaces, antireflection coatings on (hopefully) all air-to-glass surfaces, plus two focusing mechanisms and an interpupillary adjustment, it is not surprising that top-quality instruments cost about $1000 or more. Such prices buy crisp, high-contrast images, accurately aligned optics, precise, rugged, dust- and moisture-proof construction, and pleasurable service for a lifetime. Nevertheless, there is a big market for $99 binoculars and $299 telescopes, and manufacturers are happy to satisfy the demand. When it comes to optical equipment, quality usually matches price.

Stability: One aspect of binocular use not often appreciated is how much more can be seen if the binoculars are mounted on a stable support, such as a camera tripod. This eliminates the constant jiggling associated with hand-holding and also supports the weight of the instrument. Adapters for attaching binoculars to a tripod are available, although usually it is not difficult to make your own. A recent major advance in binocular design is "image stabilization," an active optical system built into binoculars that compensates for the tremor associated with hand-holding. For example, the Canon company has introduced microprocessor-controlled binocular image stabilization that gives almost tripod-like stability with the convenience of hand-holding (see *SkyNews*, July/August 1998, p. 12; and *Sky & Telescope*, July 2000, p. 59). The Canon 10 × 42L model in particular, with its superb optics, convenient 6.5° diameter actual field, and close focusing ability, is the single best, hand-held set of binoculars ever created for both general daytime use and astronomy. It accepts 52-mm camera UV filters to protect the objective lenses.

Rating Binoculars

A frequently cited figure for binocular performance is "Relative Brightness," which equals the square of the diameter (in millimetres) of the instrument's exit pupils. For example, for 7 × 50 binoculars this figure is $(50 \div 7)^2 \approx 51$. Although this is a measure of the surface brightness *(luminance)* of an extended object seen through the binoculars under nighttime conditions, it is a totally inadequate measure of binocular performance on the night sky. For instance, using this figure of merit, large 14 × 100 binoculars have practically the same rating as the unaided eyes (which, when young and in dim light, are effectively 1 × 7 binoculars)!

Since seeing depends upon light, and the amount of light passing through a pair of binoculars depends primarily upon the *area* of the objective lenses (diameter D), a D^2 dependence appears reasonable. However, although the amount of light going into the point images of stars increases as D^2, assuming constant magnification the increase in the luminance of the background sky as D increases leads to a somewhat slower improvement in the visibility of these stars. A similar muted improvement occurs for dim extended images, resulting in an approximately D^1 dependence, rather than D^2.

Also, for constant D the detail that can be seen in the night sky increases with the magnification M. The resulting lower luminance of the background sky allows fainter stars to be seen, and the visibility of structure in extended images improves as M increases because the image is larger and of fixed contrast relative to the sky background.

The simplest figure of merit for the performance of binoculars in low-light conditions that combines both variables is the mathematical product $M \times D$ (which happens to look the same as the binocular size specification). In the case of two pairs of binoculars, one having twice the M and twice the D of the other, $M \times D$ indicates that "four times as much" should be visible in the larger instrument (e.g. 16 × 60 versus 8 × 30 binoculars). That is to be expected, since in the larger instrument stars will be four times brighter and extended images will have four times the area from which the eyes can glean information, with luminances being the same in both instruments.

For many decades the venerable Carl Zeiss optical company has cited $\sqrt{(M \times D)}$ as a "Twilight Performance Factor" for binoculars, its value said to be proportional to the distance at which various binoculars will show the same detail. That is equivalent to $M \times D$ being proportional to *the amount of detail that can be seen at the same distance*. The latter situation is relevant for astronomy since, unlike a bird or other object on Earth, a star or a galaxy is always at essentially the *same distance* from the observer. $M \times D$ could be called the *visibility factor.*

Binocular Performance Diagram

The diagram on the following page enables one to quickly compare binoculars in terms of their ability to reveal detail in the night sky. The vertical axis is magnification M; the horizontal axis is aperture D. The uniform grid of small dots is a guide to reading the diagram. The five straight lines indicate constant exit-pupil diameters of 3, 4, 5, 6, and 7 mm, as indicated both by numbers and by circles of these diameters near the top ends of the lines. The five curved arcs indicate constant values of $M \times D$ (the visibility factor), increasing by successive powers of 2 toward the upper right (100, 200, 400, 800, and 1600). Each large dot represents a common size of binoculars. The arrows in the lower-right corner indicate the directions on the diagram in which various quantities increase most rapidly.

Each straight line (constant exit-pupil diameter) also corresponds to constant luminance of extended areas, such as the Orion Nebula or the background sky glow, with the luminance being proportional to the square of the exit-pupil diameter (provided the entrance pupils of the observer's eyes are large enough to accommodate the exit pupils of the binoculars). However, exit pupils of 3 to 5 mm ensure that (i) all the light transmitted by the binoculars can enter the dark-adapted eyes no matter what the observer's age; (ii) alignment of exit pupils with dark-adapted eye pupils is relatively easy to achieve; (iii) the background sky glow will be subdued; and (iv) star images will be less distorted by aberrations in the observer's eyes (see TELESCOPE EXIT PUPILS, p. 50).

Examples (see the diagram): for viewing the night sky 10 × 50 binoculars will show about twice as much detail as 7 × 35s; 11 × 80 and 15 × 60 binoculars are equally capable, as are 8 × 30s and 6 × 42s (assuming one's eye pupils can accommodate the exit pupils of the instrument with the larger D); 10 × 50 binoculars are appreciably better than 7 × 50s for visibility (although, assuming equal apparent angular fields, 7 × 50s will show about twice as much sky area as will 10 × 50s). Canon's image-stabilized 15 × 45 binoculars are nearly equivalent to tripod-mounted 10 × 70s, with the *triple* advantage of smaller size, accommodating observers whose pupils will not open to 7 mm, and not requiring a tripod!

The visibility factor ($M \times D$) is applicable to the usual range of binocular sizes (exit pupils between about 2 mm and 7 mm), but should not be extrapolated indefinitely. For instance, as the magnification is increased on a telescope and the exit pupil approaches 1 mm or less, a point will be reached (dependent upon the darkness of the sky) where the background sky glow is imperceptible. Also, stars will begin to show either seeing disks or diffraction disks. A further increase in M will not cause a noticeable improvement in the visibility of stars, and the perceived contrast between an extended object and the sky will decrease. In addition, the angular size of an extended object must be kept in mind. Once M is increased to the point at which the object fills the field of view of the instrument, the object may not be visible at all! For example, a large, dim comet coma may be visible in 15 × 60 binoculars ($M \times D = 900$) but *invisible* in a 45 × 200 telescope ($M \times D = 9000$).

BINOCULAR PERFORMANCE DIAGRAM

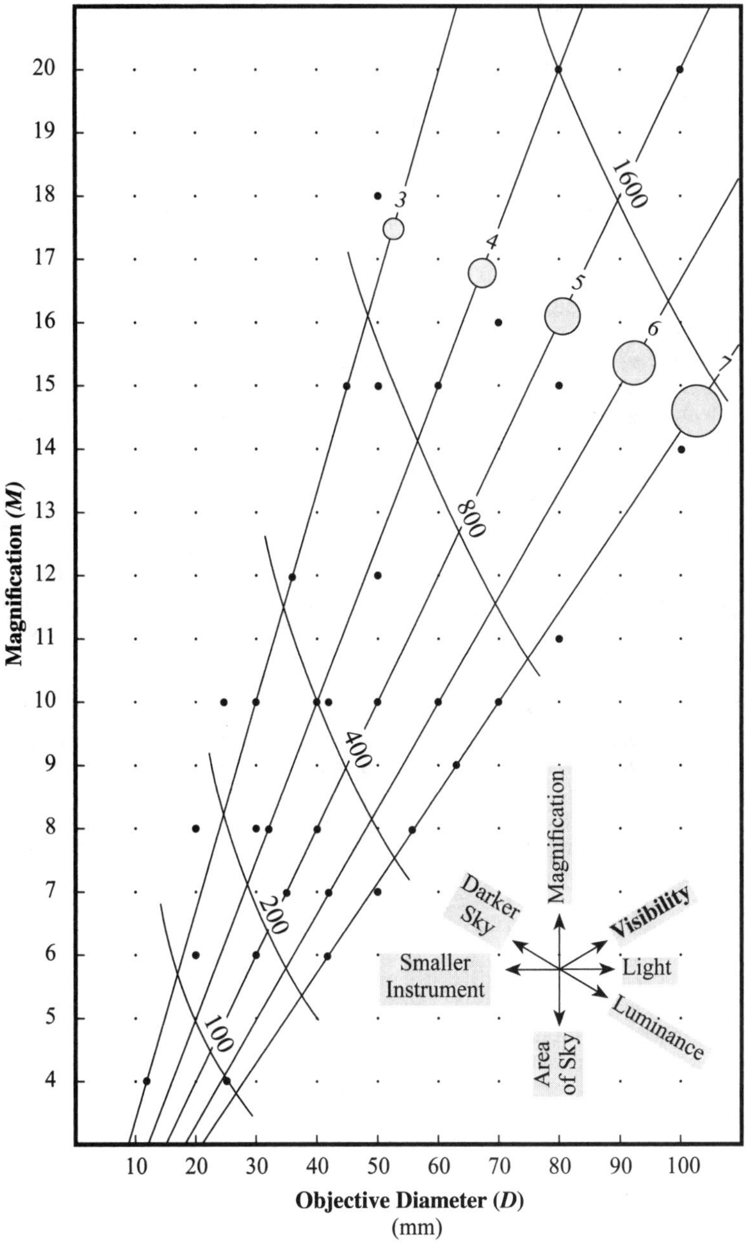

Diagram by Roy Bishop

FILTERS

BY ROY BISHOP

Optical filters reflect and absorb some portion of the incident light. *Neutral-density filters* reflect and absorb light more or less uniformly across the visible spectrum. *Coloured (dye) filters* typically pass only one or two moderately broad portions of the spectrum. *Interference filters* are more selective and typically pass only one or two well-defined, narrow segments of the spectrum. All three types of filter are invaluable in astronomy.

In addition to categorization by physical type, filters may be categorized according to their intended use: lunar and planetary (neutral-density and dye filters), solar (neutral-density and interference filters), and nebular (interference filters).

Lunar and Planetary Filters

As viewed in a telescope, the Moon and the planets Venus, Mars, and Jupiter are often uncomfortably bright. A neutral-density filter, which passes only 13%–25% of the light, solves this problem while avoiding the loss in resolution that would accompany stopping down the aperture of the telescope to decrease the brightness to the same level. With a less-glaring image, light scattering in the observer's eye is reduced and fine details are easier to see. A neutral-density filter is typically about 26 mm in diameter and is attached to the forward-facing end of an eyepiece.

Dye filters can enhance the visibility of various planetary features. For instance, a red or yellow filter will absorb bluish light scattered by the Martian atmosphere and thereby improve the contrast of features on the surface of Mars. A green filter will increase the visibility of pale red and blue areas in the atmosphere of Jupiter (although the entire image will then appear green). Also, since they absorb an appreciable fraction of the light, dye filters or polarizing filters have the same advantage as a weak neutral-density filter when viewing bright objects.

Solar Filters

A filter is essential when observing the Sun. Solar filters must be designed not only to reduce the brightness of the solar surface to a comfortable level, but to block out the invisible but damaging infrared and ultraviolet radiation. Just because a filter makes the Sun dim enough to view comfortably is no guarantee that it is not transmitting damaging amounts of invisible radiation! This is no place to experiment with do-it-yourself filter designs—use only a proper solar filter from a reputable manufacturer. *Failure to use a proper filter when observing the Sun can cause immediate and irreversible damage to vision.*

A special warning: Heavy atmospheric haze near sunrise or sunset often dims the Sun so that it appears as a dull red disk, not uncomfortably bright to the eye. At such times resist the temptation to view the Sun with a telescope without using a solar filter. The atmosphere at such times is still relatively transparent in the invisible infrared portion of the spectrum, and the great light grasp of a telescope can result in thermal retinal damage! With the unaided eyes the retinal solar image, although just as bright, is much smaller and the eye can better dissipate the heat. Also, with unaided vision, one is less apt to fixate on the Sun for a prolonged period.

For white-light views of the Sun a dark, broad-spectrum, neutral-density solar filter is needed. Aluminized Mylar and metal-coated glass are common designs, although they usually do not attenuate light uniformly across the visible spectrum (i.e. they are not perfect neutral-density filters). Aluminized Mylar gives a bluish colour to the solar image, while metal-coated glass filters usually give an orange colour.

The filter should be 50 mm or more in diameter and must be positioned to cover the *front* of the telescope. Ensure that the filter is *securely attached* so that a gust of wind or a bump cannot dislodge it. (Some small telescopes are sold with a "Sun filter" designed to attach to the eyepiece, just before the observer's eye. Sunlight concentrated by the telescope can overheat and shatter a filter of this design. Such filters should be thrown in the garbage!)

For direct viewing of the Sun (not using binoculars or a telescope) shade #14 (no other shade) rectangular welder's glass may be used; this is available for a few dollars at welding supplies shops. These filters are not suitable for attaching to the front of binoculars or a telescope simply because their poor optical quality results in a fuzzy image.

Red, flame-like prominences at the Sun's limb and much structure in its chromosphere across the solar disk can be seen in hydrogen-alpha (Hα) light, a strong spectral line emitted by atomic hydrogen. This light is totally overwhelmed by the rest of the solar spectrum, so a neutral-density filter will not work. Advances in vacuum thin-film technology have made possible interference filters, filters that operate on the same principle as Fabry–Perot interferometers, involving the interference of multiply reflected beams of light. These filters can be constructed so they are transparent only to light having an extremely narrow range of wavelengths, typically 0.15 to 0.05 nm for solar viewing, although band-passes of up to 1 nm are used in solar-prominence viewers designed to occult the solar disk. If this band-pass is centred on the Hα wavelength (656.3 nm), nearly all the Sun's light will be blocked, leaving an image in Hα light.

Hα filters are expensive, particularly for band-passes near 0.05 nm that are needed for high-contrast images of the solar disk. These filters may be located either in front of the objective of a telescope or between the objective and the eyepiece. In the latter case, because the wavelength of the centre of the narrow band-pass varies with the angle at which light rays enter the filter (a characteristic of interference filters), the focal ratio of the imaging telescope must be near *f*/20 for 0.15-nm band-pass filters and *f*/30 or higher for filters with narrower band-passes. Temperature control is usually required to keep the band-pass centred on the Hα wavelength, although some Hα filters are designed to be tilted in order to tune them to the Hα wavelength (the wavelength of peak transmittance is shifted toward shorter wavelengths when the filter is tilted away from 90° incidence).

Hα filters require a broadband "energy-rejection prefilter," located at the front of the telescope. The prefilter has a band-pass of about 100 nm in the red part of the spectrum and blocks essentially all the infrared, ultraviolet, and much of the visible part of the solar radiation from entering the telescope.

Nebular Filters

From the surface of Earth, the night sky is not completely dark. Even in the absence of light pollution (human-made and lunar), the air itself emits a feeble light called airglow. In higher latitudes, aurorae can also contribute to the glow of the atmosphere. Two other components of the light of the night sky are the zodiacal light and background starlight. The diffuse glow from all four sources reduces the contrast of celestial objects and, in the case of dim comets, galaxies, and nebulae, the object may be completely obscured by the brightness of the sky.

Filters transmit only a fraction of the incident light. Thus employing them to see faint objects may seem counterproductive. However, there are objects in the heavens that emit light only at certain wavelengths. This behaviour is characteristic of plasmas—excited gases, matter composed of separate atoms energized either by ultraviolet radiation from nearby hot stars or by collisions such as occur in supernova explosion shock fronts. Such regions are called emission nebulae and include star-forming regions, planetary nebulae, and some supernova remnants. A filter that selectively blocks most of the background sky glow but is transparent to the wavelengths at which such objects emit most of their visible light will darken the sky background without appreciably dimming the object of interest. With narrow-band-pass interference-type filters the effect can be dramatic, improving contrast and revealing details that otherwise are completely invisible. It is the next best thing to observing these objects from above Earth's atmosphere!

Dark-adapted (scotopic) human vision responds to light having wavelengths from approximately 400 to 620 nm. In bright light (photopic vision) the spectral range extends to somewhat longer wavelengths, about 750 nm. For both types of vision the response curve (sensitivity vs. wavelength) is "bell-shaped," the wavelength of maximum sensitivity being in the middle of the visible range—near 507 nm for scotopic vision and 555 nm for photopic vision (see the figure "Nebular Filter Transmission" on the following page). The photopic sensation produced by 555-nm light is green; for scotopic vision colour is not produced, but at photopic levels 507-nm light appears blue-green.

Hydrogen is the predominant element in the Universe. Atomic hydrogen, when excited by ultraviolet radiation from a nearby hot star, emits light in the visible spectrum at only four discrete wavelengths: 656, 486, 434, and 410 nm (designated as Hα, Hβ, Hγ, and Hδ, respectively, part of the *Balmer spectrum* of hydrogen). Scotopic vision is blind to 656-nm (Hα) light and relatively insensitive to the less intense 434- and 410-nm light. However, 486 nm (Hβ) lies near the 507-nm peak sensitivity of scotopic vision, and an Hβ ("H-beta") filter having a narrow band-pass at this wavelength will greatly reduce the surrounding sky brightness and reveal Hβ-emitting nebulae.

The classic example is the Horsehead Nebula, a dark, silhouetted column of dust just southeast of the east end of Orion's belt. The surrounding hydrogen gas, excited probably by the nearby hot star ζ Orionis, fluoresces dimly with Hβ light. If the obscuring airglow is blocked by an Hβ filter, the dark Horsehead can distinctly be seen in a telescope having an aperture of 400 mm or greater and an eyepiece giving an exit pupil near 5 mm (see pp. 50–53). However, the number of objects that can be viewed advantageously with an Hβ filter is very limited, apparently because few nebulae emit strongly in Hβ light.

Two other strong nebular emission lines lie at 496 and 501 nm, nearly at the peak sensitivity of scotopic vision. Originally detected in 1864 by the British astronomer William Huggins, the origin of these lines was unknown at that time, and they were attributed to a hypothetical new element, "nebulium." In 1927, the American astrophysicist Ira Bowen identified the lines as due to doubly ionized oxygen (O^{++} or OIII), which glows brightly when very low-density nebular gas is strongly excited (high temperature). A filter that has a narrow band-pass spanning these two wavelengths gives striking views of highly excited nebulae. A good example is the Veil Nebula, a supernova remnant in eastern Cygnus. Through an OIII filter on a dark, transparent night, the direct view of the Veil in a large amateur telescope is more spectacular than any photograph or CCD image. Planetary nebulae (fluorescing, low-density shells of gas surrounding hot central stars) also show up well with an OIII filter; examples include the Helix Nebula, the Owl Nebula (M97), the Dumbbell Nebula (M27), and the Ring Nebula (M57).

Because of their narrow band-passes, Hβ and OIII filters are sometimes called *line filters*, although their band-passes are much wider than that of an Hα filter. Filters encompassing both the Hβ and OIII lines, such as the Lumicon Ultra High Contrast (UHC) filter, are termed *narrowband filters*. These filters also enhance views of many emission nebulae, although with the wider band-pass the sky background is brighter. With a large telescope under dark skies, I find that the single most useful filter is the

NEBULAR FILTER TRANSMISSION

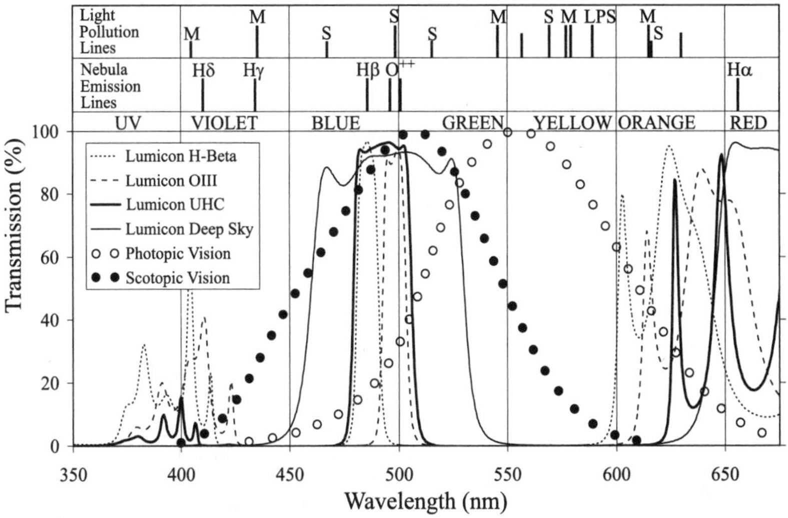

The dotted, dashed, and continuous curves show the transmission versus wavelength characteristic of four interference filters (in descending order in the legend): two line filters, a narrowband filter, and a broadband filter. The bell-shaped curves composed of small open and solid circles show the relative response of bright-adapted (photopic) vision and dark-adapted (scotopic) vision. In ascending sequence above the curves are spectral colours, nebula emission lines, and light-pollution lines (M = mercury, S = high-pressure sodium, and LPS = low-pressure sodium). High-pressure sodium light sources emit an additional broad continuum spectrum that is not shown. The two unlabelled light-pollution lines are strong airglow/auroral lines produced by atomic oxygen. (Dave Lane used a "Varian Model Cary 50 Conc UV-Visible Spectrophotometer" owned by the Chemistry Department at Saint Mary's University to obtain the filter curves; he also prepared the diagram.)*

OIII line filter. With smaller apertures (less than about 200 mm), the narrowband Lumicon UHC filter (or equivalent filter from other manufacturers) may be preferable since it dims the stars less.

Some other nebulae that are greatly enhanced by OIII and narrowband filters include the Omega or Loon Nebula (M17), the Trifid Nebula (M20), the Lagoon Nebula (M8), the Rosette Nebula, the Eagle Nebula (M16), the North America Nebula, and the Carina Nebula (NGC 3372).

Stars emit light across the entire visible spectrum. Thus line filters and narrowband filters impair views of single stars, reflection nebulae, star clusters, and galaxies. Filters with wide band-passes extending from about 450 to 530 nm are called *broadband filters*. Examples are the Lumicon Deep Sky filter, the Orion SkyGlow filter, and the Meade Broadband filter. These decrease the airglow somewhat and block several of the brighter wavelengths emitted by sodium- and mercury-vapour streetlights, without dimming stars and galaxies too much. Thus they provide a modest improvement in the visibility of some objects from light-polluted sites. Because of their wide band-pass and high transmission at the Hα line, they are also useful for photography of emission nebulae. However, under dark skies an unfiltered view is preferable to that through a broadband filter.

(See p. 32 for basic information on optical wavelength and colour.)

LIMITING MAGNITUDES

BY DOUGLAS PITCAIRN

Limiting Visual Magnitude

One of the many difficulties with visual observing from the surface of our planet is the variability of the atmosphere. In any record of observations it is important to note the condition of the sky. Parameters such as brightness and contrast are greatly affected by the transparency of the sky and the presence of light pollution or aurorae.

One of the simplest ways to quantify local sky conditions is to note the magnitude of the faintest star visible with the unaided eye: the *limiting visual magnitude* (LVM). (See www.rasc.ca/lpa/sky-quality-measurement-project for an alternative method using an electronic *sky quality meter* that measures sky brightness in units of *magnitude per square arcsecond*.) Although individuals differ in their ability to detect faint stars, these differences are generally small, and for any one observer such observations provide a consistent measure of sky quality. The chart at the left shows a 9° field in the vicinity of Polaris (the brightest star on the chart) and is useful for observers at latitude 20°N or higher. For orientation, the solid lines mark the beginning of the handle of the Little Dipper (see MAPS OF THE NIGHT SKY, p. 339). Several stars have their visual magnitudes indicated (with decimal points omitted). Using this field to determine your LVM has several advantages: it is always above the horizon in mid-northern latitudes; its altitude does not change with the time of night or year, so the variation of atmospheric extinction with altitude is not a consideration; there are no bright stars or planets in the field to dazzle the eye; the faint stars are quite well spaced and therefore easy to identify; and being a simple field, it can be memorized. Especially note the dashed spiral of descending magnitudes labelled "A" through "F."

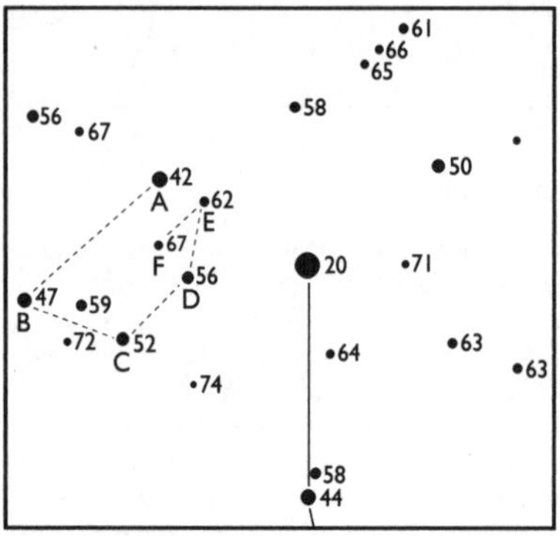

Limiting Telescopic Magnitude

Aperture, telescope design, eyepiece design, magnification, and the quality of optical surfaces are a few of the many variables that will determine the faintest stars visible through a given telescope and eyepiece. By determining an instrument's limiting magnitude—the *limiting telescopic magnitude* (LTM)—you can effectively assess the effect of these variables. The quality of the night sky will also affect the LTM. Therefore, changes in the LVM should be taken into account when determining the LTM. (The relationship between LTM and LVM is complex; readers may explore it using the excellent web-based calculator at www.bogan.ca/astro/optics/maglimit.html.) The LTM is a useful guide when attempting faint targets (Pluto in a 150-mm scope?), comparing the performance of different instruments, or determining whether a mirror or lens needs cleaning (many people clean their optics too often, assuming that dust degrades optical performance more than it actually does). For a study on sky brightness, telescope magnification, and contrast in deep-sky observing, see p. 54.

To help determine the LTM of your instrument, use the charts on the next page, which show an 8′-wide section of the northwest quadrant of M67 centred at RA 8 h 50.1 m and Dec +11° 53′. This old open cluster lies 8° south-southeast of M44, Cancer's famous Beehive Cluster. The accompanying table lists the visual magnitudes

STAR	VISUAL	B – V
A	10.60	1.10
B	11.19	0.43
C	11.59	0.42
D	12.01	0.57
E	12.26	0.68
F	12.57	0.59
G	13.04	0.85
H	13.35	0.59
I	13.61	0.59
J	13.96	0.62
K	14.34	0.56
L	14.66	0.67
M	14.96	0.69
N	15.30	0.79
O	15.58	0.84
P	16.06	0.74
Q	16.31	0.99
R	16.62	0.81
S	17.05	1.26
T	17.38	1.17
U	17.64	1.31
V	18.04	1.27
W	18.38	0.76
X	18.69	1.17
Y	19.07	1.56
Z	19.29	0.61
a	19.42	1.34
b	20.10	0.00
c	20.35	0.83
d	20.61	1.55
e	21.03	0.32

M67 Limiting Telescopic Magnitude Chart

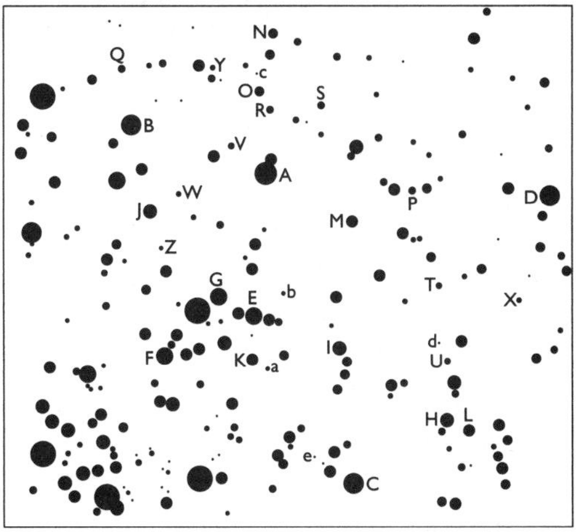

as above, mirror-reversed view

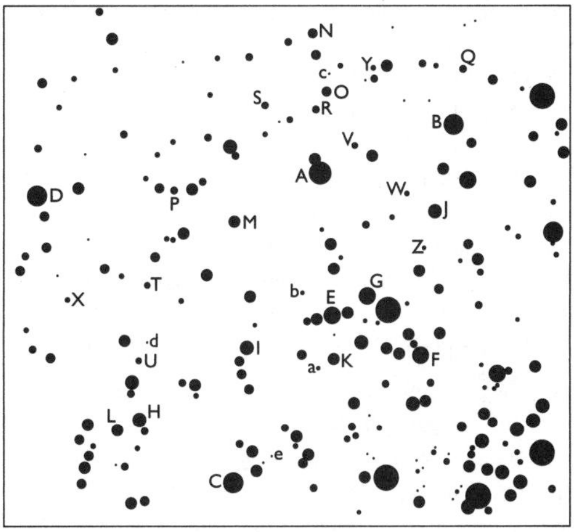

The upper chart is for telescopes with an even number of reflecting surfaces (e.g. Newtonian reflectors) and the "mirror-reversed" chart is for telescopes with an odd number of reflecting surfaces (e.g. a refractor with a diagonal). North is at top in both of these charts.

and the *B* – *V* colour indices of the labelled stars. The diagram was constructed from a photograph taken by René Racine of the Université de Montréal, who exposed a 103a-D plate at the *f*/3.67 focus of the Hale Reflector. The magnitudes are based on work by Racine and Ronald Gilliland of the Space Telescope Science Institute.

Correction for Atmospheric Extinction

Atmospheric extinction varies with altitude above the horizon. To normalize observations to the zenith (altitude 90°), the following values should be added to estimates of faintest visible magnitude obtained using the charts. The format is: (altitude range) **correction:**

(18°–20°) **0.5** (20°–24°) **0.4** (24°–29°) **0.3** (29°–36°) **0.2** (36°–52°) **0.1** (52°–90°) **0.0**

These corrections are for near sea level and would be reduced at higher elevations. Also, excellent sky conditions are assumed; under less-than-ideal conditions, the corrections are generally larger and can be quite uncertain, especially when the target area is closer to the horizon.

POLAR ALIGNMENT

BY BLAIR MACDONALD

Beginning observers are often confused by the concept of telescope mount alignment. With the advent of Go To mounts, this confusion is compounded by the fact that the *computer* of such a mount must also be oriented to the sky. Polar alignment applies only to equatorial mounts; it is an independent physical alignment of the polar axis of the mount with the north celestial pole (NCP) or the south celestial pole (SCP).

Ideally, the polar axis is parallel to Earth's rotational axis and therefore must point at a celestial pole. The required alignment accuracy depends on the observing goals. For casual visual observing, it is usually sufficient to align the polar axis of an equatorial mount with Polaris (in the Northern Hemisphere) or σ Octantis (in the Southern Hemisphere). The charts on the facing page show the location of the NCP and SCP in their surrounding star fields, and the caption describes the alignment procedure.

For long-exposure astrophotography or for an automated observing program, significantly more accurate polar alignment is necessary. A dedicated polar axis telescope with a Polaris-offset reticle on a German equatorial mount, makes it simple to achieve polar alignment. However, any equatorial mount can be polar aligned by the straightforward *drift alignment* method. As outlined below, the drift alignment method uses a reticle eyepiece and the viewing of two stars on the celestial equator, one near the meridian and the other near the eastern horizon. The method also works in the Southern Hemisphere: simply interchange north and south, clockwise and counterclockwise.

1. Roughly level the mount and point the polar axis at Polaris. A simple eyeball alignment is sufficient, but the closer you get now, the fewer drifting iterations you will have to make later. The rough alignment described above is usually good enough.

2. Install a reticle eyepiece with the lines aligned to the right ascension (RA) and declination (Dec) axes directions as follows: First, centre a star on one of the lines. Then move the telescope slightly in RA and rotate the eyepiece until the star moves parallel to the line.

3. Point the telescope at a star on the celestial equator in the south near the meridian.

4. With the drive engaged, centre the star on a reticle line aligned with the RA direction. Ignoring RA drift, note the Dec drift of the star over several minutes.

5. If you must move the telescope north to recentre the star, then adjust the mount clockwise in azimuth as seen from above. If you must move the telescope south to recentre the star, then adjust the mount counterclockwise in azimuth.

6. Repeat Steps 4 and 5 until there is no visible drift over several minutes.

7. Now point the telescope at a star near the eastern horizon on the celestial equator.

8. Centre the star on a reticle line aligned with the RA axis as in Step 4. Ignoring RA drift, note the Dec drift of the star over several minutes.

9. If you must move the telescope north to recentre the star, then tilt the polar axis downward. If you must move the telescope south to recentre the star, then tilt the polar axis upward.

10. Repeat Steps 8 and 9 until there is no visible drift over several minutes.

Repeat Steps 3–10 for improved accuracy, because adjusting the elevation often requires further adjustment in azimuth and vice versa. The longer it takes to detect Dec drift, the more accurate the polar alignment. For a star near the equator, a Dec drift of d arcseconds over time t minutes indicates a polar axis misalignment of $p \approx 3.8\ d\ /\ t$

arcminutes. For example, a 10″ drift over 1 min indicates a polar axis misalignment of 38′, while a 5″ drift over 5 min indicates a polar axis misalignment of only 3.8′.

The drift method produces very accurate alignment even when the optical tube is not exactly aligned with the mount.

See www.backyardastronomy.com/Backyard_Astronomy/Downloads.html for a comprehensive treatment of polar alignment.

FINDER CHARTS FOR THE NORTH AND SOUTH CELESTIAL POLES

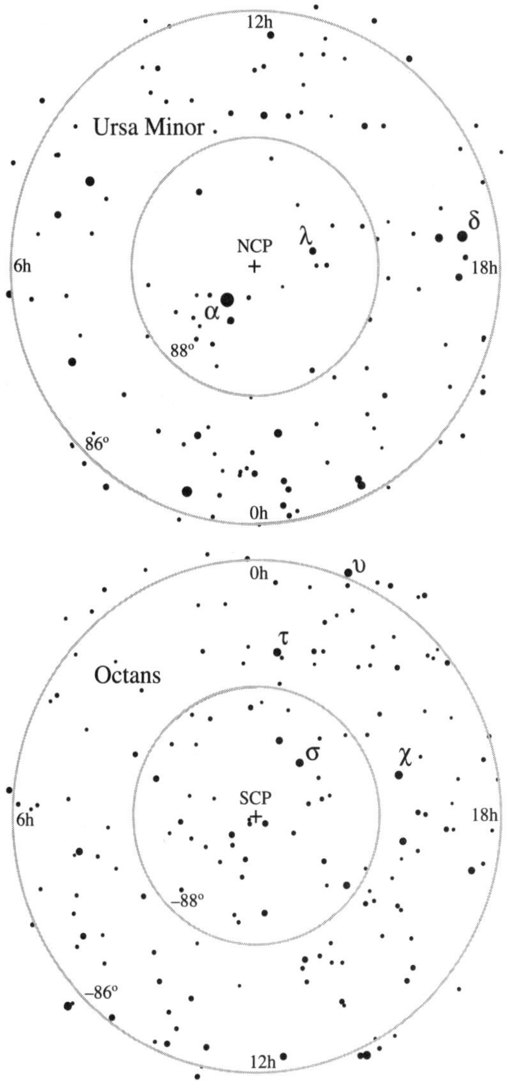

The finder charts depict mirror-correct fields of view with circles of diameter 4° and 8° centred on the celestial poles (Dec is indicated on the circles). Stars are shown to magnitude 9. δ UMi is the penultimate "handle" star in Ursa Minor.

For casual visual observing, it is sufficient to align the polar axis of an equatorial mount to Polaris (α UMi, magnitude 2.0), near the NCP, or to σ Oct (magnitude 5.5), near the SCP, as follows:

Roughly level the mount and orient the RA axis to true north (south) in azimuth. Set the RA axis elevation to the observing latitude. Lock the Dec axis to +90° (−90°). While viewing through the finder or telescope at low magnification, adjust the azimuth and elevation to centre the pole star. For finer alignment, align to the estimated position of the NCP (SCP) relative to the star field.

For accurate polar alignment, the drift alignment method (described on the facing page) is recommended and works for all equatorial mounts.

(Finder charts were derived from sky charts generated with Voyager III*, a product of Carina Software.)*

Diagram by Dave Chapman

FREQUENCY OF NIGHTTIME CLOUD COVER

BY JAY ANDERSON

FEBRUARY–MAY MEAN NIGHTTIME CLOUD COVER IN PERCENT

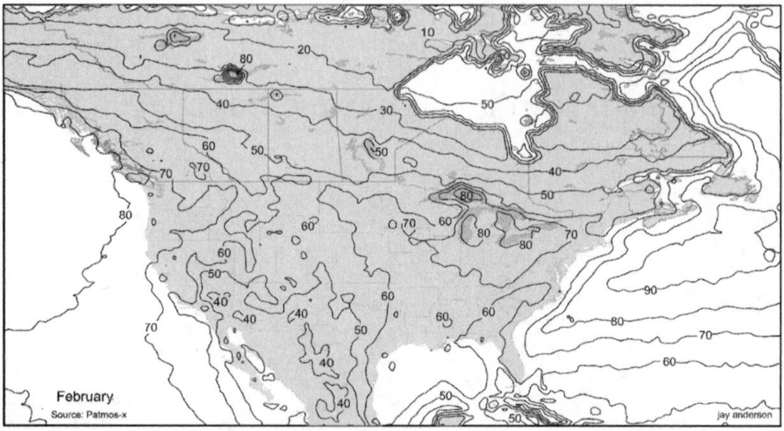

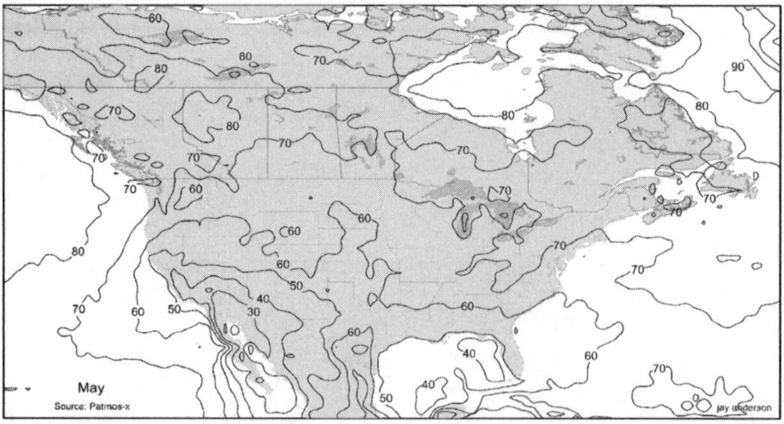

The maps on these pages are constructed from observations taken from 16 years of satellite observations ending in 2009. These sensors detect emitted and reflected radiation in several wavelengths and use a statistical, climatological, model-based algorithm to determine the amount of cloud in a 1-degree longitude by 1-degree latitude bins. The Patmos-x dataset used in these maps is one of the best of several approaches to cloud measurement.

The months chosen give a good year-round depiction of annual cloud climatology, while avoiding June and July. Several notable trends are shown: the clearer skies over western Canada that come with frigid winter temperatures, the heavy winter cloudiness around the Great Lakes, the sunny Prairie summers, the higher cloud amounts in mountainous terrain, and the onset and decay of the mid-summer Southwest Monsoon of Arizona and New Mexico.

February cloud amounts follow a quasi-latitudinal pattern across Canada, interrupted by the very high cloudiness across the Great Lakes. The situation in the U.S. is more complex, with more cloud over the northern Rockies, Appalachians, and the northeast U.S, where the influence of the Great Lakes and east-coast storms dominates. The southwest states have the least cloudiness, mostly because their low latitude takes them out of the path of the major winter storms, along with the shelter provided by the mountain chains in the area. That protective topography has an influence farther north, creating a zone of low cloud that extends northward along the Front Range of the Rockies as far north as the Canadian border.

AUGUST–NOVEMBER MEAN NIGHTTIME CLOUD COVER IN PERCENT

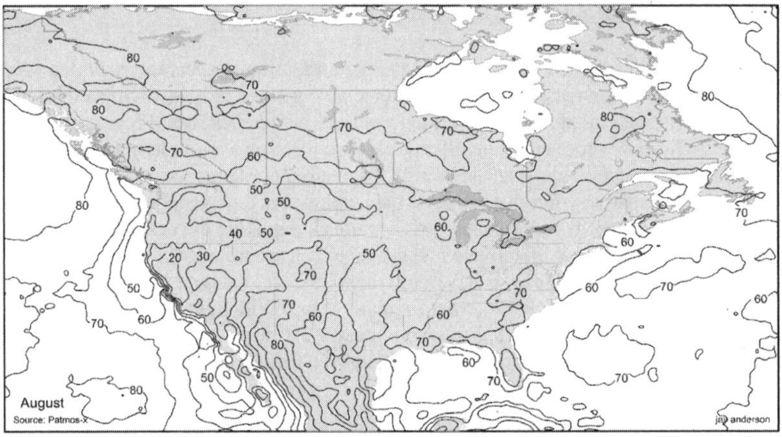

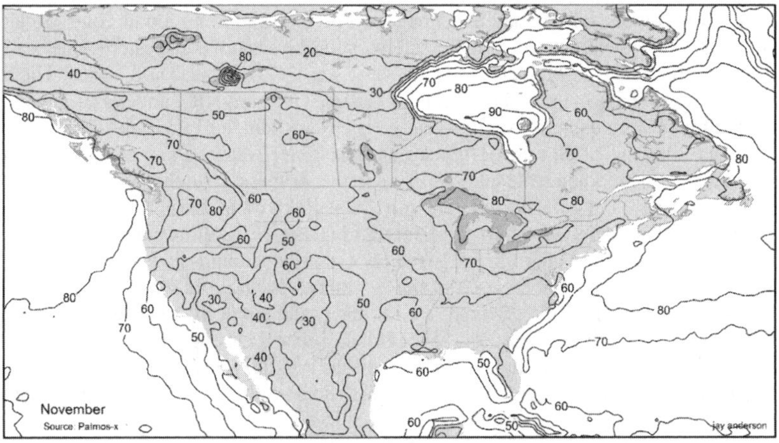

In May, the cold air retreats northward and much of Canada returns to a cloudier climatology. The protection provided by the Rockies fades away, leaving a broad band of moderate cloudiness across the Great Plains. The Appalachians north of Georgia retain their reputation for high cloudiness, but in the American Southwest May is the sunniest month, sandwiched between the winter months with their occasional low-latitude snows and the summer's onset of convective thunderstorms.

In August, the Southwest becomes one of the cloudiest regions, as Gulf of California moisture spreads north. Noteworthy is the very low cloud amount in central California. The plains retain a modest amount of cloud—it's still thunderstorm season, but the protection of the Rockies is still evident in the arc of below-50% contours from southern Saskatchewan and Alberta to Texas. The Appalachian states still hold onto high cloud frequencies, but eroded from earlier maximums.

November brings a hint of winter, though the low cloud amounts that come with freeze-up are still limited to the Northwest Territories. The monsoon season is long gone over the southwest, the Great Lakes have begun their role as winter cloud-makers, but winter has not reached the south; the Appalachians enjoy their sunniest season of the year. Rocky Mountain cloudiness has increased over British Columbia as the first of the fall storms arrive onshore, and the Prairies are gradually losing their sunny disposition.

Additional maps of global cloudiness may be found on the author's website at www.eclipsophile.com. Data source: Patmos-x/CIMMS/SSEC.

WEATHER RESOURCES ON THE INTERNET

BY ALLAN RAHILL

Despite public skepticism, weather forecasts are in fact quite accurate, provided they are from informed sources. Specialized weather services—usually involving a fee—are available for aviation, agriculture, forestry, and marine applications. Previously, there was no such service for astronomy, likely because there was no directly related economy. However, the Canada-France-Hawaii Observatory at Mauna Kea has been using a seeing and transparency forecast for more than eight years to "queue schedule" observing activities. Currently, professional observatories are making the best use of weather conditions and are able to effectively manage activities accordingly.

Similar information has been freely available to amateur and professional astronomers worldwide on the Internet for many years. With light pollution becoming more and more pervasive, amateur astronomers must drive long distances to get to dark skies. They can avoid frustration by using the information and URLs below to plan their observing sessions.

Satellite Images

Many astronomers rely on satellite images to predict nighttime cloud cover. Real-time images are available from GOES satellites for the eastern and western Americas; other satellites such as Meteosat give the same service for Europe and Africa. These satellites give three main types of images: visible, infrared (IR), and water vapour. Visible images are easy to interpret, but they are available only during the day; for nighttime tracking of clouds, IR images are available. Water-vapour images do not track clouds; they indicate the total moisture in the air mass. Usually the darkest areas in those images have good correlation with the best sky transparency.

Particularly useful for short-term forecasting are IR satellite loops, which are available at many websites. IR images show the radiance emission from Earth and indicate the temperature of the ground and/or clouds. During cold seasons, the ground can be as cold as, if not colder than, the air mass, and single IR satellite images are not very helpful in identifying low-level clouds such as stratocumulus. One way to separate clouds from the ground in these situations is to use a time-lapse loop and look for motion: the ground doesn't move, but clouds do. People in northern latitudes from late fall to early spring should keep this trick in mind.

There are many IR image enhancements available at various websites, and you should be aware that many of them do not display *any* low clouds, even with the trick mentioned above. One way to familiarize yourself with low-cloud detection is to compare visible GOES images to IR enhancements in the early morning, when the ground is still cold. In some situations, you may be surprised by the amount of low cloud not displayed in the IR satellite images. By comparing IR and visible images, you can select a website that you feel gives accurate images and one that you are comfortable with. I recommend the following website for IR satellite images because it provides the ability to zoom into your region, to choose different satellite-image enhancements, and to do animation easily weather.unisys.com/satellite/infrared.php.

To make the best use of weather-satellite images, you also should be aware of the behaviour of certain types of cloud. Low-level clouds such as stratus usually develop locally and generally move much more slowly than high clouds. These clouds appear during the night and usually get burned off by the Sun during the day. Coastal regions will usually see the low clouds moving inland in the evening and out to sea in the morning.

In addition, cumulus, towering cumulus, and cumulonimbus clouds arise with daytime convective heating if the air mass is unstable. The depth or height of the cloud structure is related to the level of instability and can reach up to 20 000 m for severe thunderstorms. On satellite loops, these clouds appear as clear areas that are gradually filled with clouds during the day and that slowly vanish in the evening. In the summer, some of the most unstable cumulonimbus clouds will survive at night. Even though thunderstorms, associated with cumulonimbus clouds, can be far from your location, cirrus blowoff from these cells may reach you quite quickly, depending on the upper wind direction, and thus ruin your observing session. Satellite and radar loops are good ways to keep track of these thunderstorm lines.

Radar

Remote-controlled observatories, where the operator is not physically present, and star parties, where telescopes are often left set up and exposed, are becoming more popular. When the sky conditions are variable, there is one common worry: is there a fast-moving precipitation band approaching the observing site? The best way to track precipitation in the short term is with radar. The radar network is extensive across the United States; it also covers populated regions of Canada.

Radar images require careful interpretation. During the night, the air cools near the ground and creates a temperature inversion. On some nights with strong inversions, radar signals are refracted, or bent, toward the ground and scattered back to the radar, thus appearing as precipitation on the graphical displays. Similar situations occur in mountainous areas, where higher terrain interrupts the radar signal. A radar loop will help you distinguish these areas: sometimes they are nearly motionless; at other times they shift around in a chaotic jumble. Precipitation moves in a smoother fashion, at times linearly. The best websites for access to radar loops for Canada and the United States, respectively, are weather.gc.ca/radar and www.intellicast.com (click on "radar").

Weather Forecasts for Astronomy

Cloud Forecasts: Local media and television "experts" cannot always be relied upon when conditions are uncertain. Usually their forecasts cover a large area, and the weather can be quite different within the region. Also, for most people, including many local weather forecasters, skies are considered clear despite thin, high cloudiness that may interfere with observing.

The best forecasts for clouds are from the direct output of numerical models. Weather models are not perfect, but they are surprisingly good at capturing local effects and predicting cloud formation and dissipation. The biggest problem with numerical forecasting is convection (thunderstorms): it is like trying to predict the next bubble in boiling water. Complex thunderstorm cells can be forecast much farther away than they actually appear, leading to poor cloud progression forecasts for regions hundreds of kilometres ahead.

Some weather channels and websites use animated forecasts to show cloud progression for the next day, but these animations generally have low resolution and are not very useful for astronomy. The only North American high-resolution cloud forecast I still know of is produced at the Canadian Meteorological Centre (CMC) and is at weather.gc.ca/astro/clds_vis_e.html.

Occasionally, especially in the fall when low clouds (stratocumulus) are omnipresent, a weather balloon can be launched into a cloud hole, and the resulting cloud forecast may be too optimistic for the surrounding regions. To avoid a bad forecast, always compare the cloud-cover forecast with the latest satellite picture. In these situations, an old forecast may be a better choice. This is why the most recent old forecast, in addition to the current forecast, is available at this website; hourly forecasts are now available.

Sky Transparency Forecasts: For deep-sky observing, sky transparency is critical because it largely determines how dark the sky will be. Aerosols—particles suspended in the atmosphere—and moisture reduce sky transparency and brighten the sky by diffusing the light in the sky. Aerosols include volcanic ash, pollen, sea salts, and smoke from forest fires. Spectacular examples of events that introduced aerosols into the atmosphere are the Mount St. Helens volcanic eruption, which spread roughly 540 million tonnes of ash into the atmosphere in 1980, and the more recent large forest fires: in summer 2003 over British Columbia, which spread smoke over large areas, and in 2002 in northern Québec, which spread smoke over all of northeastern North America. Specialized weather numerical models handle aerosol phenomena; websites that track aerosol envelopes with up to five-day forecasts across the world are ozoneaq.gsfc.nasa.gov and www.nrlmry.navy.mil/aerosol/#currentaerosolmodeling.

Moisture is the only weather element affecting sky transparency that can be forecast with confidence. For many northern-latitude residents, moisture is the most important contributor to reduced sky transparency; despite clear skies, very often, high-level ice crystals (extremely thin clouds) are present and can be seen only at sunset and sunrise. In addition, moisture from open waters, vegetation (evapotranspiration), or moist soil can keep the low-level atmosphere humid.

Over the years, I have compared water-vapour satellite images to various observers' estimates of background sky brightness. The resulting hourly sky transparency forecasts can be found at weather.gc.ca/astro/transparence_e.html.

There is a good correlation between the darkest areas in water-vapour images and the darkest observed sky conditions. There are some cases where the sky background is brighter than expected due to moisture trapped by a temperature inversion. Based on this observation and others, the forecasts in the above website emphasize humidity near the surface and also near the tropopause (cirrus heights).

Seeing Forecasts: Seeing conditions determine the steadiness of images through a telescope and are relevant for planetary as well as deep-sky observing. When highest resolution is necessary for planetary imaging or visual observing, seeing should be at its best.

Conditions are favourable when the atmosphere is turbulence-free all across the path of the light. The best weather pattern is weak wind circulation at all levels. These conditions occur more frequently over the southeastern United States than any other region of North America, with Atlantic Canada generally having the worst conditions among populated North American regions. Canadian and U.S. central prairies often experience blocking weather systems that give weak upper wind circulation and excellent seeing conditions.

Another pattern for excellent seeing takes place when moderate winds blow from the same direction at all levels, that is, when horizontal and vertical wind shear are weak at all levels. In other words, no jet stream (strong winds reaching 200 km/h–400 km/h at an altitude of 10 km–12 km) or sudden shifts or increase in wind speed with height are present.

At locations downwind from mountains when winds are moderate, it is best to be far away from the mountains, since "gravity waves"—vertical air-mass oscillations caused by the mountains—can downgrade seeing. In general, topography is quite important because rough terrain increases the wind shear in the low-level atmosphere, due to friction and gravity waves.

Temperature variation at the surface also plays a role in seeing conditions. Nights of excellent wind conditions as described above may nevertheless have marginal seeing. On such nights, temperatures quickly and steadily fall, and large telescopes have trouble cooling at the same rate as the surrounding air. This creates what is called "local seeing": thermal heat released from the optics (despite good ventilation) ruins the seeing despite the excellent weather pattern. The opposite is also true: the best planetary observations with a large telescope often take place just before thick clouds roll in or when looking through thin cirrostratus cloud. Under these conditions, the temperature usually rises a few degrees before the clouds appear. Thin cirrostratus clouds usually keep the temperature steady, eliminating any negative local seeing effects. Thin clouds also play the role of a neutral-density filter, increasing fine detail and contrast on bright planets. Ground fog can also be associated with excellent seeing conditions (until the fog thickens), if you can keep your optics dry.

Predicting favourable seeing conditions requires the ability to interpret weather charts, something that is difficult for most observers to do. The Canadian weather service has a seeing forecast, available at their astro-weather website, which attempts to simulate wind shears, topography, and temperature effects; it is at weather.gc.ca/astro/seeing_e.html.

Some Tips to Get the Most Out of Your Telescope: "Local seeing" is the term used to describe the effects of heat radiating from the components of a telescope (e.g. its optics) or from the immediate surroundings (e.g. observatory walls and floor, trees, flowing water, neighbouring houses). If the local seeing is bad, the telescopic viewing will be significantly deteriorated. However, in contrast to atmospheric seeing, the effects of local seeing can be controlled.

Tube currents in particular will dramatically deteriorate telescopic images. Mirror-type instruments are more sensitive to such currents than refractors. Large mirrors can take hours to cool down during the night and in fact may never reach full thermal equilibrium. However, the amateur astronomer can accelerate the cooling of the primary mirror by installing one or more battery-type fans behind it. Their use will cool down the mirror to near the ambient temperature in one or two hours. Another approach is to use a high-quality but thin primary mirror. Many manufacturers offer mirror blanks of thickness 2.5 cm for mirror diameters up to 400 mm, in addition to the traditional mirrors of thickness 5–8 cm. The thinner mirrors will reach thermal equilibrium 2–3 times faster[*] than the thicker ones. Many amateurs also ventilate the front of their primary mirror with two fans placed on either side of the mirror, separated by 180°. One fan pulls air into the tube while the other pushes it out. Such ventilation has two benefits: it breaks up the thermal boundary layer near the mirror surface (and therefore reduces convective-type turbulence) and it cools the mirror up to 50% more quickly than without the fans[*].

The popular Schmidt–Cassegrain telescopes do not come with cooling fans and they are known to suffer from internal turbulence, especially at large apertures. Only a few advanced amateur astronomers will have the courage to add fans to those telescopes. Any telescope, and particularly the Schmidt–Cassegrain type, should always be brought outside to cool it down at least two hours before the observing session. Better yet is to keep a telescope permanently outside in a backyard observatory.

To minimize the occurrence of poor local seeing, one must avoid all potential sources of heat in the surroundings. For example, concrete structures and buildings or houses have the capacity to retain daytime heat and then release it during the night. Even trees during the growing season can release heat at night, and so deteriorate the local seeing for astronomical objects found just above their canopy. Ideally, the amateur should choose an environment free from all these elements. If you are lucky enough to have an observatory, then remember that all the outside walls must be white, since even pale colours will allow the walls to heat up during the day and then create local seeing problems when they release the heat at night.

The local geography can also be used to one's advantage: observing can be better at the top of a hill than at its base. It appears that the local seeing is improved at the top of a hill, due to nighttime katabatic winds that drain air down the slope of the hill

[*] *Sky & Telescope*, June 2004, p. 122 (Improving the Thermal Properties of Newtonian Reflectors—Part 2)

to its base. This means that air above the hill must also move downward to replace the air that moved away. This descent creates a dry subsidence inversion that, combined with the cool surface temperature at the top of the hill, stabilizes the air locally. This results in good seeing. Many of my best planetary observations took place on hill tops.

One final tip: near dusk and dawn, if you can spot planets, then there will often be a 20–60-min window during which the seeing will be one or two notches better than during the night. This seems to be related to large-scale tidal motions in the atmosphere that create more-stable conditions at those times, but the effect is not well understood. Give it a try in the early morning and the early evening.

The Clear Sky Chart

The Canadian Meteorological Centre's numerical weather forecasts, given in the URLs above, are unique because they are specifically designed for astronomers. They can be found on the "Weather forecast for astronomy" page of the Environment Canada website at weather.gc.ca/astro. There are several products for the astronomy community, including hourly forecast images of cloud cover, sky transparency, seeing, and near-ground weather. However, they include 842 forecast images per day, covering all of North America, so it can be a chore to find the precise one you need. All the above astronomical weather forecasts can be viewed at a glance for any particular observing site in North America using Attilla Danko's excellent Clear Sky Chart at www.cleardarksky.com/csk.

Editor's Note: Attilla Danko, a member of the Ottawa Centre of The Royal Astronomical Society of Canada, received the Ken Chilton Prize from the Society in 2005 for his creation of the Clear Sky Chart, which uses the Canadian Meteorological Centre's forecasts for astronomers created by Allan Rahill. Most popular observing locations in North America now have an associated chart, and many amateur astronomers rely on these forecasts to plan their observing sessions. Several websites give useful information similar to the Clear Sky Chart. The spatial resolution of these sites is quite low compared to the Canadian Meteorological Centre's products.

For the UK:	www.weatherweb.net/wxwebastronomy.php
For Australia:	www.philhart.com/content/cloud-forecasts-astronomers
For the U.S.:	www.accuweather.com (Click the + sign and choose "Astronomy.")

Sagittarius and the Milky Way in a clear, dark sky, free of light pollution. (photo: Dave Chapman)

LIGHT POLLUTION
BY DAVID L. CRAWFORD

A Lost Heritage: Most people on Earth have now lost the spectacular view of the Universe that our ancestors enjoyed on clear, dark nights. The development of electrical lighting in the last century and the increase in urban population have caused a rapid increase in sky glow above towns and cities. As a result, fewer and fewer members of the general public have ever seen a prime dark sky; our children and grandchildren may never. It seems that the night now exists for watching television and for discos, not for nature. For urban dwellers, star-studded nights are limited to planetaria. Even in rural areas, poorly designed yard lights often obscure the splendour of the night sky. As Leslie Peltier, one of the most famous amateur astronomers of the 20th century, stated eloquently in his autobiography *Starlight Nights:*

> *The Moon and the stars no longer come to the farm. The farmer has exchanged his birthright in them for the wattage of his all-night sun. His children will never know the blessed dark of night.*

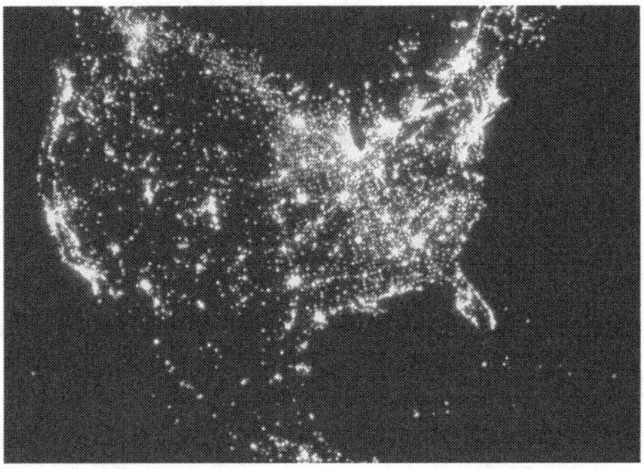

A nighttime satellite view of central North America

The increased sky glow that adversely affects the environment is a major part of what is called *light pollution.* Light pollution originates from excess light that does nothing to increase useful night-time illumination. It is light that sprays horizontally and upward into the sky from ill-conceived lighting fixtures. It is light that glares into the eyes of motorists and homeowners, compromising visibility, safety, and security. It is light that depresses property values by reducing the aesthetic quality of a neighbourhood. It is light that can seriously affect the circadian rhythm of all living things, including humans, as well as creating other hazards for many species (birds, sea turtles, etc.). In the United States and Canada, billions of dollars (plus large amounts of energy) are lost annually in generating this wasted light. It makes for increased air pollution and CO_2 emissions. Any night lighting that causes such light pollution is neither effective nor efficient. Unfortunately, such adverse lighting is still in a growth stage, even with the increasing emphasis on improved, energy-efficient night lighting. There is a great lack of awareness by users of lighting.

A Threat to Astronomy: Light pollution poses special perils to astronomy. Many observations, including most of those of cosmological interest, can be made only from prime observing sites, far removed from centres of population. Some older observatories, such as the David Dunlap in Ontario and Mount Wilson in California, are severely affected by light pollution from nearby urban centres. Newer observatories usually are located at remote sites, and amateur astronomers routinely drive long distances to escape the glare of towns and cities. The argument that all astronomy can be done from space is incorrect because it does not make sense to do in space, at much higher costs, what can be done from the ground. There are observations that can only be done from space, but the recent decades of space astronomy have greatly increased the need for ground-based observatories.

Solutions: There are solutions to the problem of light pollution. Outdoor lighting ordinances or policies have been instituted in many locales by governmental agencies,

Inefficient street lighting

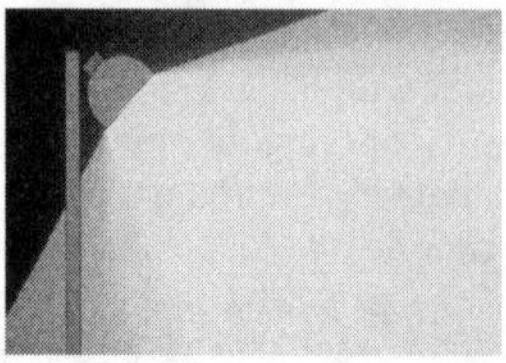

particularly near large observatories, such as: near Tucson, Arizona; San Diego, California; and in Hawaii. The solutions involve several methods to control light output. The first is the use of lighting fixtures that direct the light output only where it is needed, well below the horizontal, not upward and sideways, hence less overall output than older generation fixtures use and less power is required.

The type of light source also makes a difference: it should be an energy-efficient lamp. Worldwide, quite a few cities are realizing substantial savings each year through extensive use of efficient outdoor lighting, including the use of LED and low-pressure sodium (LPS) street lighting. For example, replacing a 175-W mercury-vapour lighting fixture with a fully-shielded, 35-W LPS fixture produces the same amount of useful light with none of the glare and light trespass. The energy saving is remarkable. In addition to providing illumination at the lowest cost, LPS lights are nearly monochromatic, with the result that most of their light can be filtered out by astronomers. Low-pressure-sodium lights are especially good for street lighting, parking-lot lighting, security lighting, and any application where colour rendering is not important. A number of cities are converting their street lighting to either LED or induction lamps, also rather energy efficient, especially when used at lower wattages than existing facilities. It is essential to reduce the wattage to realize power savings, and not to confuse power consumption (watts) with actual light output. **It is critical to avoid the use of bluish-looking LED or induction lamps, sold often in the name of energy efficiency.** Such night lighting can badly affect the circadian rhythms of humans, other fauna, and flora, compromising the health of our bodies and of the ecosystem. It also scatters more in the atmosphere and hence adds much to the artificial sky glow.

Common Types of Outdoor Lights
(in increasing order of efficiency)

Type	**Power** (W/klm)
incandescent	50
mercury vapour	20
compact fluorescent	15
metal halide	13
LED and induction	13
high-pressure sodium (orange-gold)	12
low-pressure sodium (yellow)	8

A full-cutoff, efficient light fixture

It is essential to use no more light than is required, and local ordinances usually regulate the maximum amount of light that can be used for different tasks. Too much light (and poorly shielded luminaires) will create glare and ruin adaptation to night lighting, blinding us just when we need to see. When we go from too-bright to too-dark environments, or vice versa, "transient adaptation" is impaired, and we suffer poor visibility for a while. Do not exceed lighting levels recommended by the Illuminating Engineering Society of North America (IESNA, see www.iesna.org). Overkill never helps; it usually just adds glare, and it always wastes energy. In addition, lights should be used only when necessary (timers are useful for controlling lights). Curfews are usually included in lighting ordinances.

Another common inclusion in lighting ordinances is the use of lighting zones. Different areas have different requirements for lighting; downtown Toronto is not the same as rural Ontario. In addition, some locales have officially been declared Dark-Sky Preserves or Urban Sky Parks, regions where lighting is strictly controlled or prohibited. A number of these are located in Canada, and the RASC has been instrumental in helping establish these. (See LIGHT-POLLUTION ABATEMENT IN CANADA, overleaf.)

Lighting Myths: Increased lighting levels are generally perceived to provide higher security, yet there is no statistically significant evidence that increased lighting leads to reduced crime. Criminals need light, and they are more likely to be up and about at 3 a.m. than the property owner. Furthermore, security lights may draw attention to a house or business that would otherwise go unnoticed, and mask any unusual light that criminals may need to do their work. Our cities and towns are more brightly lit than ever, yet there has been little or no reduction in the crime rate. Security can best be provided by shielded, motion-activated luminaires that light up only when triggered by nearby movement. These serve to startle criminals, alert others that there is a potential problem, and provide glare-free visibility (when properly installed); they also use insignificant amounts of energy. The *Myth of the More the Better* is just that: a myth.

Lack of Awareness: The biggest problem in controlling light pollution is lack of awareness rather than resistance. After all, it costs money to pollute with light. Unlike the case with many other forms of pollution, simple solutions are available; moreover, *everyone benefits* in applying these solutions. Most people are not yet aware of the expense, the waste, and the harm associated with excess lighting. They put up with distant lights that shine directly into their eyes, not realizing that not only does this do *nothing* to illuminate the area near the light but that it also produces a veiling glare. The pollution usually involves not only the light itself but also other forms of environmental pollution associated with the production of the wasted light: the extraction, transportation, and burning of coal and oil. This general lack of awareness has been summarized nicely by Doug Pitcairn, an astronomy teacher in Nova Scotia:

> *"It surprises me how someone who would never think of leaving a plastic bottle on the ground at a picnic site will pay extra money each month to illuminate half the neighbourhood with unnecessary, distracting light."*

Education: Educating the public, government officials, lighting professionals, and astronomers is a major thrust of current programs. These efforts have helped. Most committees in the IESNA and the International Commission on Illumination (CIE) have been addressing these issues, and Recommended Practices and other documents reflect these concerns. As they are issued, one will see them implemented, albeit on a slow time schedule. Astronomers and environmentalists should do all they can to both learn from these documents and to help publicize them and thereby get them into existing practices in our communities.The International Dark-Sky Association (IDA) is another source of good information (see www.darksky.org). Members receive a regular newsletter, have access to members-only material on the website, and may join one of several local Sections worldwide. For effective visual images that celebrate the night sky, also see The World at Night (www.twanight.org) and APOD (apod.nasa.gov).

In summary: Educate everyone you can, everywhere you can, by any means you can about the value of both dark skies and quality night-time lighting. There are solutions to control the light output: use light only where needed (shine it down), only when needed (turn it off), only the level needed (more is not better), and use energy-efficient (but not blue-white) light sources. It can be done, and it must be done if we are to improve the value of our night environment, for ourselves and for everyone, everywhere.

Within Canada: The RASC has an active Light-Pollution Abatement Committee (LPAC, see www.rasc.ca/light-pollution-abatement-committee). You may also contact the RASC Society Office directly for information (see p. 7) or one of the local RASC Centres, some of which have local LPACs that have taken effective action to address poor lighting practices in their areas. **Get involved!**

LIGHT-POLLUTION ABATEMENT IN CANADA

BY ROBERT DICK

The RASC's broadly based program of Light-Pollution Abatement (LPA) involves collaboration with governments and private property owners. Governments rarely act on the needs of an individual; however the RASC, with the support and participation of its 5000 members, wields considerable influence, which is applied diplomatically. However local citizens are critical in implementing and monitoring the programs. To reduce light pollution, we must understand its three components: *glare*, *light trespass*, and *sky glow*. All three affect astronomical observing sites as well as the ecological balance of a region.

Glare is the main contributor to light pollution, and its removal is the first remedy. Glare is light concentrated within our field of view, typically shining directly into our eyes from an unshielded source. Glare impedes our eyes from adapting to darkness, hampering our night vision overall. Although shadowing by buildings may limit the extent of artificial lighting, poorly illuminated areas are effectively masked by glare, making it difficult to identify hazards.

Light Trespass and Scotobiology is the second component of light pollution. It can be a consequence of glare, because unshielded light can easily shine onto neighbouring properties. Light trespass was once considered only a nuisance, but now it is recognized as a detriment to human and environmental health. Artificial outdoor lighting "fools" our bodies into believing it is still daytime, and alters our biological processes accordingly. The wealth of medical research on this topic has resulted in the American Medical Association and the World Health Organization recognizing artificial light at night (ALAN) as a health risk.

The design life of our bodies is about 40 years, after which the warranty expires! As the average age of the population increases, problems arise that we can no longer ignore. These are exacerbated by ALAN. For guidance, we need to explore the relatively recent bio-medical and animal studies to ascertain the ecological limits to artificial lighting. The study of the biological need for periods of darkness is called *scotobiology*, a term coined in 2003 by Dr. R.G.S. Bidwell (Professor Emeritus, Queen's University).

Our bodies have evolved to repair minor damage at night, when it is dark and we are asleep. Hormones ebb and flow on a schedule under the control of our internal body clock (the circadian rhythm) and help heal our bodies after a busy day. The clock is kept in phase with our activity by nightfall, compensating for the varying length of the day through the seasons. Artificial lighting that extends our day well into the night delays or aborts these repairs, resulting in the erosion of our physical health (encouraging diabetes, obesity, and other conditions). ALAN also affects our ability to cope during the day, and compromises our mental health (increased irritability, dementia, and stress, and all the problems they entail). Deteriorating vision is another form of degradation we experience with age. Our eyes begin to develop incipient cataracts, a clouding of the lens. For most of us, they do not affect our daytime seeing, but at night it is a different story. When exposed to glare, the iris (pupil) closes down, directing light into the eye only through the foggy cataract in the centre, which scatters light over the darker periphery. That compromises our vision beyond the brightly illuminated regions in our field of view. The elderly become somewhat blind at night. However without glare, more light enters through the clear part of the lens, and we see better.

Wildlife has similar body chemistry to humans, and some animals experience the same needs for darkness at night. There are many nocturnal animals that forage for food and mate under the safety of darkness. Although moonlight affects their routine, they have adapted their behaviour to accommodate the periodic appearance of the full Moon. However, a single unshielded outdoor light can contaminate their habitat, causing them to reduce or even abandon their foraging range, and to alter their foraging and mating behaviour. With ALAN, there is no "dark time" when they can recover.

Why do cities have fewer flying insects than rural areas? An outdoor "insecurity" light will attract insects from over 100 m away. This distracts them from their normal behaviour (feeding, mating, and migrating). As fewer insects survive, the environment supports fewer animals that depend on them for food, such as songbirds. We may not always like insects, but they are vital to the health of our environment.

Sky Glow is the third component of light pollution. Observers in rural locations see this as light domes that arch over our urban areas. Although glare and light trespass render the local night sky almost unusable for stargazing, sky glow affects the environment on a regional scale. This artificial sky glow is caused by light that scatters off particles of dust, pollen, and large molecules of air pollution in the atmosphere—primarily at altitudes below a few thousand metres. Some of these particles are raised into the air by the bustle of urban traffic. The degree of light scattering depends on wavelength, with shorter wavelengths (blue light) being scattered more than longer wavelengths (red light), a phenomenon known as Rayleigh scattering. The light that scatters back down to ground level increases the luminance of the night sky, which can overwhelm the brightness of faint stars, the Milky Way, and deep-sky objects. From just outside a city, the artificial sky glow can outshine the natural light from the full Moon. In this way, unrestricted urban lighting pollutes tens of thousands of square kilometres of countryside.

The RASC LPA Program has two aspects: public and governmental. The public program involves members of the RASC promoting the benefits of dark skies at public outreach events. Although a good event creates grassroots support, during which a dozen members may interact with up to a few thousand people, a more effective strategy is to include the local media. A single article in a newspaper or television newscast can reach 100 000 people with much less effort. Light pollution requires a change in social attitudes, which are best achieved through the media.

Governments are in a position to create change in our society. There are two instruments used by municipalities to govern lighting: by-laws and policies. As a legal document, bylaws tend to codify current standard practice and the wording of a by-law tends to be specific and binding, and therefore requires careful crafting to avoid loopholes. On the other hand, a policy is more forward-looking, to help guide a city toward a better future. Policies can be regularly reviewed and improved as support for LPA in the community increases. A lighting policy is proactive, which reduces confrontation, and will guide the development of a lighting plan for new subdivisions and encourage the renovations of older ones.

Dark-Sky Sites: The RASC attracts greater governmental support for LPA by preserving the night environment than by promoting astronomy. Dark skies cater to the growing eco-tourism industry, so it is in the best interests of towns and cities near our national and provincial parks to preserve the ecological integrity of their region.

The most effective instrument for this goal has been the RASC Dark-Sky Preserve (DSP) Program. Scotobiology is used as the basis for the lighting policy in these areas, because what is good for wildlife is also good for astronomy. It provides a rational scientific basis for reducing light pollution. Since the mandate of Parks Canada is to preserve the natural environment, it has assisted with the development of the RASC lighting protocol and Parks Canada adopted it as their internal guideline for outdoor lighting. There are three designation programs: Dark-Sky Preserves (DSPs), Urban Star Parks (USPs) and Nocturnal Preserves (NPs). Due to the simplicity of management control, they tend to be in rural federal, provincial, and commercial parks with management that agree to adhere to the RASC Lighting Protocol and outreach policies.

Although the astronomical quality of DSPs is good, they are necessarily remote. However, RASC members want to have protected observing sites closer to urban areas—even at the cost of higher levels of sky glow. The USP Program was created for this purpose. A USP may be near an urban area or even within a city. Although the sky glow in USPs is brighter than in DSPs, there is very good public access. The NP program is used for areas that, due to circumstances, cannot offer any astronomy outreach or may not always be open for full public access. It helps maintain dark areas for wildlife, and for the enjoyment of our grandchildren. The guidelines for DSPs, USPs and NPs are available at www.rasc.ca/lpa/guidelines.

As of August 2016, the RASC has recognized 17 DSPs across Canada, two USPs, and two NPs. The following list (ordered by reverse chronology) is expected to grow:

Name	Lat.	Long.	Declared*	Area† (km²)
Urban Star Parks (USPs)				
Cattle Point, Victoria, British Columbia	48.4°N	123.3°W	2013, MC	0.1
Irving Nature Park, Saint John, N.B.	45.2°N	66.1°W	2011, PO	2.4
Nocturnal Preserves (NPs)				
Ann & Sandy Cross Conservation Area, Alberta	50.9°N	114.2°W	2015, CA	19.4
Old Man on his Back Conservation Area, Saskatchewan	44.2°N	109.6°W	2015, CA	53.0
Dark-Sky Preserves (DSPs)				
North Frontenac Township, Ontario	44.9°N	76.9°W	2013, TP	1160
Wood Buffalo, Alberta/NWT	59.8°N	112.0°W	2013, NA	44 800
Bluewater, Wiarton, Ontario	44.7°N	81.2°W	2012, PO	1.3
Fundy, New Brunswick	45.6°N	65.0°W	2011, NA	208
Jasper, Alberta	52.8°N	118.0°W	2011, NA	10 900
Kejimkujik, Nova Scotia	44.4°N	65.2°W	2010, NA	404
Grasslands, Saskatchewan	49.1°N	107.4°W	2009, NA	907
Mt. Carleton, New Brunswick	47.4°N	66.9°W	2009, PR	174
Bruce Peninsula, Ontario	45.2°N	81.4°W	2009, NA	167
Kouchibouguac, New Brunswick	46.8°N	65.0°W	2008, NA	238
Gordon's Park, Ontario	45.7°N	82.0°W	2008, COM	1.1
Mont-Mégantic, Québec	45.5°N	71.2°W	2007, NA	55
Beaver Hills, Alberta	53.6°N	112.8°W	2006, NA	293
Point Pelee, Ontario	41.9°N	82.5°W	2006, NA	15
Cypress Hills, Alberta/Saskatchewan	49.7°N	110.2°W	2005, NA, PR	345
McDonald Park, British Columbia	49.1°N	122.0°W	2003, MC	4.7
Torrance Barrens, Ontario	44.9°N	79.5°W	1999, PR	19

*CA–Conservation Area COM–Commercial Park MC–Municipal Park NA–National Park
PO–Privately Owned Park PR–Provincial Park TP—Township Park †1 square kilometre = 100 hectares

Summary: The reduction of light pollution is not just a matter for astronomers. The study of scotobiology has proven that light impacts the health of humans and alters the natural environment. By speaking about the effects of ALAN on wildlife, we are able to enlist environmental groups to help reduce the impact of ALAN. We have the technology to use light effectively and to reduce light pollution. Let us encourage our municipal officials, businesses, and our neighbours to take advantage of these improvements.

More information on the RASC LPA Program is posted at www.rasc.ca/lpa, and technical information is posted at www.rasc.ca/technology. For additional information, you may also download the LPA Special Issue of the RASC *Journal* at www.rasc.ca/sites/default/files/LPA_Special_Issue.pdf.

DEEP-SKY OBSERVING HINTS

BY ALAN DYER

In the 1960s and 1970s, few observers owned telescopes larger than 200-mm aperture. Today, 250-mm to 600-mm Dobsonian-mounted reflectors are commonplace. Using computerized telescopes, observers can now find thousands of objects at the push of a button. As a result, deep-sky observing has soared in popularity.

However, owners of less-sophisticated, small-aperture instruments shouldn't think they are shut out of deep-sky viewing. In a dark sky, an 80-mm to 100-mm telescope will show all the Messier objects and reveal hundreds of brighter NGC (New General Catalogue) objects. In fact, many large objects are best seen in fast (*f*/4 to *f*/6), small-aperture telescopes or in giant 70-mm and 80-mm binoculars. Contrary to popular belief, even slow f-ratio instruments (*f*/11 to *f*/16) are useful; their only disadvantage is the difficulty of achieving a low-power wide field. No matter what telescope you use, follow these techniques to get the most out of a night's deep-sky viewing:

- Always plan each night's observing: Prepare a list of a dozen or so objects for the night. Hunt them down on star charts or with computer programs first during the day to become familiar with their location.
- Seek out dark skies; a black sky improves contrast and makes up for lack of aperture.
- To preserve night vision, always use a dim red flashlight for reading charts.
- Avoid prolonged exposure to bright sunlight earlier in the day (such as a day at the beach); it will reduce your ability to dark adapt and make for tired eyes at night.
- Use averted vision; looking to one side of an object places it on a more sensitive part of the retina.
- Another technique for picking out faint objects is to jiggle the telescope (and the image) slightly.
- Don't be afraid to use high power; it often brings out small, faint objects such as planetary nebulae and galaxies, and resolves detail in globulars, in small, rich open clusters, and in bright galaxies.
- Use a nebular filter on emission and planetary nebulae (see FILTERS on p. 64); even in a dark sky, filters can dramatically enhance the view of these kinds of objects, often making obvious an otherwise elusive nebula.
- Be comfortable; sit down while at the eyepiece and be sure to dress warmly.
- Collimate and clean your optics; a poorly maintained telescope will produce distorted star images, reduce image contrast, and make it more difficult to see faint stars and other threshold objects.
- Don't expect to use analog setting circles; in a portable telescope "dial-type" circles will rarely be accurate.
- Digital setting circles and Go To telescopes can find objects precisely. While they are wonderful observing aids, they can overwhelm observers with thousands of targets, often supplying scant information about each one. When making a list for a night's viewing, books such as the three-volume *Burnham's Celestial Handbook* and the two-volume *Night Sky Observer's Guide* by Kepple and Sanner are still the best guides.
- Don't be in a rush to check off targets; take time to examine each object, and take notes or make drawings. Both will help train your eye to see subtle detail; you'll learn to see the most through your telescope.
- Consider keeping a logbook or journal of your nightly tours of the sky; including eyepiece impressions and drawings provides a record of your improving observing skills that is fun to look back upon in future years. See the section THE OBSERVING LOGBOOK (immediately following) for suggestions on organizing a journal.

THE OBSERVING LOGBOOK

BY PAUL MARKOV

There are many good reasons for maintaining an observing logbook: A logbook is useful for recalling the details of previous observations and comparing past observations with current ones; maintaining one will make your observing organized and methodical; and having to describe an object forces you to *look* for more details, thus sharpening your observing skills. Finally, if you are planning to apply for one of the several RASC observing certificates (see note on p. 308), then a logbook with your observations may be required when submitting your application.

Logbooks can be chronological or sectional. In a chronological logbook, all observations are listed sequentially by date, regardless of object type. In a sectional logbook, observations are grouped by object type, such as open clusters and galaxies. With either format, you may want to keep a master index of objects for cross-referencing to the correct page in your logbook.

What about the book itself? Typical choices are the simple three-ring binder with standard lined paper, spiral-bound notebooks, and hardcover record/accounting books. In my opinion, the most practical is the three-ring binder because it allows you to insert auxiliary materials into your logbook with the help of a three-hole punch. With this choice, entering observations out of sequence is never an issue because you can easily rearrange the sheets. Also, should you wish to make a "soft" copy of your logbook using a scanner that generates Adobe Acrobat PDF files, it is much easier with loose sheets.

For recording observations, using a preprinted observing form offers these advantages: the fill-in-the-blank fields remind you to record the relevant data; many of these forms have a space for making a drawing of the observed object; and they give your book a neat and organized look. An example of an observing form can be found at www.rasc.ca/handbook/obsform.pdf; you may prefer to design your own observing form by using the fields suggested below. However, I prefer to use plain, lined paper as there is less repetition when writing observing session details, and I do not have to worry about using different forms for different objects or running out of forms.

There are two choices for recording your observations: using full sentences and using acronyms and abbreviations. Using full sentences is the preferred method if you enjoy re-reading your observations from past years, or if you want others to be able to easily read your logbook. But if your intent is to keep a data book for reference purposes only, then acronyms and abbreviations are the recommended choices.

It is useful to record the following information for each observing session: date; time of arrival and departure (if you have travelled somewhere to observe); location; names of other people at the observing site; sky transparency (i.e. clarity of the atmosphere, which is generally noted by faintest visible stellar magnitude; see LIMITING MAGNITUDES, p. 68); seeing (i.e. the steadiness of the atmosphere: if stars and planets appear to shimmer, that indicates poor seeing; if they appear sharp and steady, that indicates good seeing), and environmental conditions (e.g. temperature, dew, wind, sources of light pollution, snow cover, and the presence of insects). You can also number each observing session sequentially for easy referencing within your logbook.

Be sure to standardize your time/date format. For recording time, choose either the military time or a.m./p.m. format. In addition, use alpha characters to specify the month rather than numbers. For example, use 2017 Aug. 5 instead of 8/5/16; this will avoid ambiguity in reading the date.

For each object observed, record the following information as a minimum: date and time of observation, object name or designation, type of object, constellation, telescope and magnification used, type of filter (if any), and visual description. Making drawings is highly recommended and adds substantially to the value of your logbook. It is also important to record failed observations because these entries will remind you to try again in your next observing session. Remember to update the observing notes if the sky conditions change, if you have equipment trouble, if you take extended "coffee breaks," or if you see something unusual like a fireball or aurora.

If you are able to write neatly while observing, it is best to enter observations directly into your logbook. However, if this proves too difficult given the environmental circumstances, you can record your observations in a temporary notebook and transcribe them into your logbook the next day. An audio recorder can also be used if you are careful to ensure its mechanical integrity while in the field and if you are diligent enough to transcribe the recorded observations into your observing logbook regularly. Below are some suggestions on what to look for when observing deep-sky objects.

All Object Types: What is the shape of the object? What is its size (based on the field of view of your eyepiece)? Is averted vision required to see the object? Does averted vision allow you to see more detail? (If yes, describe the extra detail.) Is the object near (or in the same field of view as) other deep-sky objects or bright stars? What magnification gives the best view of the object? Does a filter improve the view? (See FILTERS, p. 64.)

Open Cluster: Is there a greater concentration of stars in a specific part of the cluster? Is it fully resolved into its component stars, or are there any unresolved stars causing the cluster to appear nebulous? How many stars can you see (only if reasonable to count them)? Are there any bright stars within the cluster? Are there any coloured stars? (If so, describe their tints and locations within the cluster.) Does the cluster stand out from the background star field?

Globular Cluster: What is the degree of star concentration (high, medium, low)? How much can be resolved to component stars (none, outer edges, middle, to the core)?

Galaxy: Is it uniform in brightness, or does it have a brighter nucleus? Is it diffuse or stellar? Can any detail or mottling be seen in the arms? Are any stars visible within the arms?

Emission or Reflection Nebula: Is the brightness even, or are there brighter/darker areas? Are the edges of the nebula well defined? Are there any stars within the nebula? Is there a hint of any colour?

Planetary Nebula: Is it stellar in appearance, or can a disk be seen? Are the edges well defined or diffuse? Are there any brighter/darker areas? Can a central star be seen? Is there a hint of any colour? Can it be "blinked" with a filter or averted vision?

Dark Nebula: Is it easy or difficult to discern the dark nebula from the background sky? Are there any stars within the nebula?

Logbooks and Databases

If you enjoy using computers, an electronic database can be a helpful complement to an observing logbook. You can obtain commercially available deep-sky databases that allow you to enter your own observations for any object. These databases are also useful for creating observing lists and planning observing sessions. A highly recommended database, which also happens to be freeware, is the Saguaro Astronomy Club (SAC) deep-sky database, available at www.saguaroastro.org. With minimal tweaking, the SAC database can be formatted to accept your own observations.

You can transcribe complete observations from your logbook into the database or simply enter four valuable pieces of information for each observed object: seen (Y/N), date, telescope used, and location. With these fields filled in, in a matter of seconds you can determine which and how many objects you have observed, and the date field for any object will direct you to the correct page in your observing logbook. You can also determine interesting facts such as from which observing location you observed the most objects or which telescope produced the most observations.

ASTRONOMICAL SKETCHING

BY KATHLEEN HOUSTON

Drawing creates a tangible connection between the observer and the sky. The visual recording of celestial wonders is part of a long-standing tradition, e.g. the Chaco Culture petroglyphs in New Mexico (c. 1000), Galileo's sketches of Jupiter's moons (1610), William Parsons' drawing of the Whirlpool Galaxy (1845), David Levy's drawings of the impact sites of Comet Shoemaker–Levy 9 on Jupiter (1994). Pencil-to-paper is an active, energy-shifting experience that allows one to see more, to go beyond the casual ten-second glance through a telescope at a public star party. Sketching is an expression of curiosity, to experience the sky on a personal, scientific, and spiritual level. For those new to sketching, you are supported by your innate skills of visual perception. Connect with other sketchers in your Centre, share images, swap stories, and learn from each other. Pose your burning questions to the RASC Astrosketchers Group (www.rasc.ca/astrosketchers-group) and sample the diverse collective of experience and ideas. Host sketching workshops at star parties and observing sessions to move this solitary activity into the realm of a group learning experience.

Drawing Toolkit: Start with a small kit of drawing supplies and build on it. The materials can be found at craft stores (e.g. *Michaels*) or art supply stores (e.g. *DeSerres*). Make up a set of wooden pencils having a range of hardness: an HB pencil makes a light grey colour, and is excellent for the mapping-out stage; for a darker black that stands out, try 2B, 4B, or 6B; some sketchers include very light pencils in the 2H range. I prefer woodless graphite pencils, because I can use the side of the pencil to create large areas of soft grey to deep black, and the coating on the pencil keeps my hands clean. A retractable eraser stick is perfect to delicately remove fine detail; a bullet pencil sharpener keeps pencil tips fine, and takes little room. Include a blending stump (rolled paper) for smudging and blending grey levels. Sure, throw in a ballpoint pen!

Experiment with your toolkit: In daylight, take your toolkit for a spin on plain paper. Draw a comet such as Hale–Bopp: create a dark dot with the side of your pencil, and extend the shape outwards. Smudge it with your finger to make the tail, and refine the shape, length, and width of the tail (work from a photograph, if you wish). Try pivoting your pencil to create stars in clusters. The hardness range of your pencils helps you to portray star magnitudes. Make a nebulous shape with the side of your pencil, smooth it with your finger, and use an adjustable eraser to carve out detail. You can modify with the blending stump to control and feather the smudge shape. Add and subtract your sketch, making marks at will. The key is to maintain a level of comfort, to be open, to learn how the hand and eye transform your experience and view to the paper surface.

Illumination: To preserve night vision, use a red-filtered book light or headlamp, with the intensity adjusted to the lowest practical setting. Cover the light while viewing at the eyepiece, to open your eyes to the darkroom of the telescope; uncover the light when drawing, enough to see the details of the pencil marks on the paper.

White paper (drawing in the negative, black stars on white background): For typical projects, use medium-weight paper with medium-tooth finish. Consider using a template on a clipboard, with pre-drawn circles and text lines to write comments and notes.

Grey paper (drawing in the positive, white & black on grey): Sketching on grey paper can be a novel experience, because on white paper one is usually focused on bright things; grey paper allows the exploration of dark dust lanes within nebulosity. Try light- to medium-grey paper, such as Canson's "Mi-Teintes" series. On this, try HB, 2B, 4B, and 6B pencils, white china marker, and white conté pencil. The white china marker is good for stars. The conté is smudgable and erasable and is excellent to build up highlights in nebulosity. (I like drawing the dark dust-lane areas with 4B–9B pencils.)

Principal Drawing Steps

- Orient yourself: select a star field from an atlas or choose a favourite subject. Frame the subject in your optics. Note guide stars in your finder, and star patterns at the eyepiece. Wander through the field, get to know the neighbourhood, and pick out details that catch your interest.
- Draw the field stars and the general shape of the subject itself. Use your natural spatial awareness to estimate separations of stars from one another. Use imaginary horizontal and vertical lines to help with angles. Draw two stars, and build up from there to form triangles, polygons, or sprays of stars.
- Either work from object to periphery, or from the outer edge in toward the object. One method may be more natural to you than the other. Experiment!
- Use averted vision, jiggle the scope. Breathe deeply, put a cover over your head to block outside light. Stay at the eyepiece to allow your eye and brain to open up.
- Vary magnification, from low to medium, to high, and back. Stack information and detail in wide, medium, and narrow fields. (Take a break at this stage, if you like.)
- Once the field becomes familiar and you have sketched out an overall map, make a second sweep. Use a clock dial to divide the field into quadrants: 12, 3, 6, and 9. Define edges, carve out highlights and texture, and capture more detail.
- Mark west (the direction of drift) and north, especially if the view is mirror-reversed.
- Finish in the warm-up shelter. Adjust tones, make field notes, tidy up.
- Share your drawings and your story. Prepare a list of subjects for your next session.

Drawing in colour: Colour is an adventure on its own, and presents a special challenge. The light level required to see colour at night closes up your dark-adapted eyes. One solution is to create a black & white drawing and to write in colour descriptors, for finishing later in the warm-up shelter, or at home. To record a lunar eclipse, create templates in advance, so you can concentrate on the shifting shadow and deepening orange colour, especially where the Earth's atmosphere bends the light.

OBSERVING SKILLS AND SKETCHING STRATEGIES

Subject	Observing Skills	Sketching Strategy
Stars and star clusters	Look for triangles and hockey sticks, stars that define a specific shape or pattern, curve, etc.	Pivot HB pencil point for small stars, 4B (softer) for larger stars.
Galaxies	Explore at high magnification to define edges and luminance details of galaxy structure.	Use the side of a 2B or 4B pencil to define the overall shape, then the fingertip to diffuse the edge and a blending stump to feather out shape and detail.
Nebulae and comets	Locate two or three field stars to orient and frame the general shape and size of the diffuse subject.	As for galaxies. Use a second sweep around the clock quadrants to detect edges and fainter stars.
Moon	Work at the the terminator for high contrast. Observe the shape of the crater, like a shadow on an inverted apple, and how the shadow defines the cavity.	Work from the crater rim, and draw the shapes of the shadow and subtle grays. Note details of surface texture. Dark adaptation of the eye is not important.

Guidelines To Facilitate Drawing

- Create a comfort zone with your binoculars or telescope. Stand or sit, as you wish, or use an adjustable chair to make yourself comfortable at the eyepiece during sustained drawing. On cool nights, take breaks to keep warm.
- Become dark adapted at the eyepiece. Take a really good long look at your subject, and let your eyes open up. Minimize exposure to your drawing light. Sketch what you see in the finder scope, to map how to get there.
- Sketching and drawing. Sketching is generally a quick observation on one sheet of paper, taking 5–10 minutes. A drawing is a sustained effort with more attention to detail and contrast, taking 30–60 minutes, or perhaps multiple sessions.

The Looking and Drawing Experience: Frederick Franck describes the experience of looking and drawing as mini-moments: **The Three Nens** (*The Awakened Eye*, Vintage, 1979). The *1st Nen* is the simple act of seeing and sketching in short, quick glances. Draw what you see using speed as a friend, and use your natural spatial awareness. The *2nd Nen* follows rapidly to build on 1st Nen ingenuity, expanding on the texture, fully mapping the field, and moving naturally from eye to hand to paper. The *3rd Nen* engages the thinking mind to redraw or improve subject distances, refine contrast, define edges, name and judge what you are looking at. You can choose to extend the sitting, or decide to look for more information. Once you notice the freedom of drawing in the 1st and 2nd Nen, you see that it is a fluid, uninterrupted, and focused energy. Use your 3rd Nen to synthesize the work, finish up, and write notes.

During the **First Sitting**, minimize eye travel between eyepiece and paper. Stay between the moments of 1st and 2nd Nen. Explore the texture variations: where is the nebula or galaxy edge? Draw everything you see, include fleeting detail. During the **Second Sitting** with the same subject/drawing, when you are familiar with the subject, the inner eye accumulates the experience, and you observe more.

Favourites, challenges, and want-to-try objects: summer and winter Milky Way, naked-eye; zodiacal light; a night landscape; a binocular field mosaic in Sagittarius; a fireball, with a collaborating observer; ashen light on Venus; objects in the Isabel Williamson Lunar Observing Program; extreme lunar libration objects; the natural bridge on the Moon; cloud belts of Jupiter; Jovian moon activities, including shadow transits; sunspots, prominences, filaments, light bridges, and transits; globular clusters (finding shapes in the complexity); meteor showers; the complete Veil Nebula; Barnard's Dark Nebulae (including B86, The Ink Spot); The Coalsack; Arp Galaxies; and (finally) anything beautiful and in colour: for the next cover of the *Observer's Handbook!*

Astronomical Sketching Publications

- Bratton, Mark, "Become a Better Observer: Sketch!" *SkyNews*, July/August 2009.
- Houston, Kathleen, "Drawing at the Eyepiece," *JRASC*, December 2010, pp. 237–240.
- French, Sue, *Celestial Sampler, 60 Small-Scope Tours for Starlit Nights* (*Sky & Telescope* Stargazing Series), Sky Publishing, 2005.
- O'Meara, Stephen James, *Deep-Sky Companions: The Messier Objects*, Cambridge University Press, 1998.
- Richard Handy et al., *Astronomical Sketching, a Step-by-Step Introduction* (Patrick Moore's Practical Astronomy Series), Springer–Verlag, 2007.

Astronomical Sketching Webpages

- Sketching techniques, tutorials, templates: tinyurl.com/27rz2ax
- Carol Lakomiak's tutorials: www.rasc.ca/lakomiak-lunar and www.rasc.ca/lakomiak-sundso
- Astronomy Sketch of the day (ASOD): www.asod.info (archive)
- *Cloudy Nights* Sketching Forums: tinyurl.com/puf2gz7

DIGITAL ASTROPHOTOGRAPHY: A PRIMER

BY TENHO TUOMI

In 1610, when Galileo turned his telescope to the heavens, he observed detail that he could not see with his eyes alone. The camera was the next step (c. 1850), capturing more detail than the eye and telescope together. Along with sketching, photography became an archiving tool for recording astronomical views and events. For many, the camera has become an artistic tool to produce beautiful pictures of astronomical objects. The recent digital camera revolution makes it possible for anyone to enjoy this endeavour. The second part of the revolution has been the rapid development of computer software for enhancing astronomical photographs. The following primer on astronomical photography is only the starting point: consult the books, websites, and user forums listed below for more information and guidance.

Field of view: The angular span of an astrophoto is determined by the focal length (f) of the image-forming optics and a linear dimension (d) of the sensor (width, height, or diagonal, accordingly). The field of view (FOV) is given by

$$\text{FOV} = 2\arctan(d/2f)\ (\approx 57.3\ d/f \text{ degrees when } f \text{ is much larger than } d).$$

For example, the 36 × 24-mm sensor of a professional "full-frame" camera on a telescope with $f = 1000$ mm has a FOV of 2.1° × 1.4°. The smaller 22.2 × 14.8-mm APS-C sensor (used in many prosumer cameras) gives a smaller 1.3° × 0.9° FOV on the same telescope, a good size to frame the Orion Nebula. At the other extreme, a 50-mm lens on a camera with an APS-C sensor gives a FOV of 25° × 17°, large enough to capture most of the constellation Orion itself.

Camera-and-tripod astrophotography: Many good astrophotos can be taken with an ordinary camera using the supplied lens, mounted on a solid tripod. Typical subjects include: aurorae, conjunctions of planets (or of the planets with the Moon), solar eclipses, lunar eclipses, and wide-field views of constellations and the Milky Way. Exposures are typically longer than for daytime photography, requiring a tripod (or some other way of holding the camera steady). For best results, turn off image stabilization (if the lens has it) and use the self-timer or a remote shutter control to reduce camera shake. Some cameras have automatic settings for nighttime photos, but manual settings are recommended. Initially set the camera sensitivity (ISO number) as high as it will go and the f/stop one or two stops higher than wide open (for sharp stars). Set the focus to infinity (which may have to be verified visually with most modern lenses). Set the shutter speed long enough to register the background sky, up to about 30 s. (For cameras with exposure histograms, the peak levels would be in the 20–30% range.) Too long an exposure time will show elongated or streaked stars. To estimate the maximum exposure time t in seconds for a lens of focal length f mm, use the formula $t = 500/f$. If the camera does not have a "full-frame" sensor, use the "35-mm equivalent focal length" (check the camera manual). Experiment with different settings to find what works best for your camera, lens, and sky conditions.

Wide-field astrophotography with cameras on equatorial mounts: If your camera has a "bulb" setting, you can capture fainter objects without stars streaking by "piggy-backing" the camera on a telescope with an equatorial (EQ) mount, or by using a specialized commercial camera mount or homemade "barn-door" tracker aligned equatorially. The EQ mount can be driven manually, mechanically, or electrically to follow the motion of the heavens. For example, a tracked exposure of several minutes with a lens focal ratio (FR) of f/3.5 and sensor sensitivity of ISO 1600 will produce acceptable photos of the Milky Way or the zodiacal light. Any EQ mount that is used for long-exposure photography with standard camera lenses should be at least approximately polar-aligned (see POLAR ALIGNMENT, p. 70).

Afocal astrophotography of Solar System objects at the telescope eyepiece: It is possible to take an astrophoto simply by placing the camera and lens at the eyepiece of a telescope. For best results, use a mechanical adapter that aligns the lens to the eyepiece and clamps them together. This afocal technique works well with older cameras and lenses, but many modern cameras with zoom lenses suffer from bad vignetting with afocal photography, showing a black border around a small image in the middle. However, one can still take very pleasing astrophotos of bright subjects such as the filtered Sun, the Moon, Saturn, and Jupiter with its moons, using simple cameras (even cell phones!), just by using the viewscreen to align the picture.

Prime-focus astrophotography: High-quality deep-sky astrophotos usually require a Digital Single-Lens Reflex (DSLR) camera at prime focus with the camera lens replaced by the telescope objective lens or mirror, which—in effect—becomes a long telephoto lens. Adapters are available for attaching the camera to the telescope. In this case, the EQ mount must be carefully polar-aligned and the drive should be guided to follow the stars exactly. Most drives have irregularities that limit unguided exposure to times as short as 15 s. Good astrophotos may result from such short exposures if the telescope optics are "fast," i.e. $f/6$ or less. Longer exposures require guiding the photographic telescope on a star using the finder or another comounted telescope, either manually or with special automatic guiding electronics. Even better astrophotos can be obtained with a camera having a modified infrared filter over the sensor (such as the Canon 60Da), and from dedicated astronomical CCD cameras. With an acceptable image (or images) as a starting point, computer software can help tease out the interesting details in images and enhance the overall appearance of the composition.

The best deep-sky astrophotos result from taking multiple short exposures, often called "subframes," and combining them in software to create a master frame. The total exposure time may range from tens of minutes to hours. The following table suggests minimum *subframe* exposure times for various objects, using an $f/5$ telescope with a camera sensitivity of ISO 1600. For other configurations, multiply the suggested times by the factor $64\ \mathrm{FR}^2/\mathrm{ISO}$ (where FR denotes the focal ratio). For example, if the FR of the telescope is 10 instead of 5, multiply the time by 4; if the ISO is 800 instead of 1600, multiply the time by 2, and so on.

Deep-Sky Object	Exposure time for $f/5$ and ISO 1600
Star clusters, bright comets	30 s
Small planetary nebulae (M57, M76)	30 s
Larger planetary nebulae (M27, M97)	120 s (2 min)
Galaxies, faint comets	120 s (2 min)
Reflection and emission nebulae	120–300 s (2–5 min)
Dim nebulae (Veil Nebula)	300 s (5 min)

Some objects have large dynamic range, like M42 (the Orion Nebula), requiring different sub-frame exposure times for different parts. The nebula centre and the Trapezium stars show best with a few seconds exposure. To show the entire nebula requires a several-minute exposure, but that overexposes the centre. Computer software can be used to combine short and long exposures to show all parts of the nebula. M45 (the Pleiades) is another example where a short exposure shows the stars sharply, but a long exposure is required to show the nebulosity around the stars.

Long-focus and eyepiece projection astrophotography: The Sun, Moon, and planets are bright and can benefit from slower telescopes (larger FR) and lower ISO settings. To increase the apparent size of the planets or details of the Sun and Moon, use a Barlow lens or eyepiece (in a special adaptor) to project a magnified image to the sensor. This increases the effective telescope focal ratio (FR). The following suggested exposure times, using an *f*/10 telescope with a camera sensitivity of ISO 400, can be adjusted for other configurations by multiplying by the factor $4\ FR^2/ISO$.

Sun, Moon, and Planets	Exposure time for *f*/10 and ISO 400
Filtered Sun	1/2000 s
Moon	1/1000 s – 1/25 s
Planets	1/800 s – 1/50 s

Webcam astrophotography: Excellent astrophotos of the lunar detail and the brighter planets have been obtained with computer webcams, such as the *Logitech QuickCam Pro*, by removing the lens and making an adaptor to attach to the telescope focuser. Capture a video of 100 to 1000 frames, and combine the best frames (those uncorrupted by atmospheric turbulence) with computer software, such as *RegiStax*. For planets, a Barlow lens can be used to increase the image size.

Postprocessing of astrophotos: Many methods can be used to reduce noise, graininess, and uneven illumination in astrophotos, most of which require specialized computer software. Steps relevant to the image data-collection stage include:

- Take multiple exposures and stack them using *RegiStax* or *DeepSkyStacker*.
- Expose "dark frames," stack them, and subtract them from the stacked "light frames." (With care, in-camera noise reduction may be used.)
- Use "flat frames" to adjust uneven exposure across the field.

Almost all astrophotos require some computer enhancement to obtain the best results. Usually the first aim is to stretch the image, that is, to darken the background and to brighten the faint detail of nebulae or galaxies without overbrightening the stars or galaxy cores. Another priority is to reduce the noise in the image without losing desirable low-level detail. No two astrophotographers enhance pictures the same way, for it is usually a matter of taste and compromise. Computer software supplied with cameras usually has some capabilities to enhance pictures. Good results can be obtained with freeware image-processing programs like *IrfanView* (www.irfanview.com) or *GIMP* (www.gimp.org), using the gamma and contrast adjustments in their menus. Best results usually require commercial image-processing software such as *Adobe PhotoShop* (www.adobe.com) or astronomy-specific software like *MaxIm DL* (www.cyanogen.com).

Suggested astrophotography resources

- Dickinson, T. and Dyer, A., "Digital Astrophotography," *The Backyard Astronomer's Guide*, Firefly Books, Ltd., 2010, Chapter 13.
- Dyer, A., *How to Photograph and Process Nightscapes and Timelapses* (interactive eBook, 2014) www.amazingsky.com/nightscapesbook.html
- RASC astrophotography online forum: tech.groups.yahoo.com/group/RASCAG
- *Cloudy Nights* (several online imaging forums): www.cloudynights.com
- *RegiStax* (image-stacking and processing freeware): www.astronomie.be/registax
- *DeepSkyStacker* (image-stacking and registration freeware): deepskystacker.free.fr
- Lodriguss, Jerry, *Catching the Light*, astrophotography page: www.astropix.com
- *Tenho Tuomi Observatory*: www.lex.sk.ca/astro/index.htm

Editor's note: The author has completely photographed the Handbook lists THE MESSIER CATALOGUE, THE FINEST NGC OBJECTS, *and* DEEP-SKY GEMS.

THE SKY MONTH BY MONTH

BY BRUCE MCCURDY (TEXT), LARRY BOGAN (JUPITER'S SATELLITES), PAT KELLY (EVENTS), DAVE LANE (TABLES), AND ALISTER LING (LUNAR IMAGES)

INTRODUCTION

In the descriptions on the left-hand monthly pages (pp. 98–120), the right ascension (**RA**), declination (**Dec**) (both for equinox J2000.0), distance from Earth's centre in astronomical units (**Dist**), visual magnitude (**Mag**), and equatorial angular diameter (**Size**) are tabulated for seven planets for 0h UT on the 1st, 11th, and 21st day of each month. The RA, Dec, distance, and diameter of the Sun are also given. **In the text below the tables, the meridian transit times at Greenwich (in UT) may be read as Standard Time at an observer's standard meridian (the error is no more than a minute or two). If the observer is west (east) of the standard meridian, the Standard Time of transit will be later (earlier) by 4 min per degree of longitude difference from the standard meridian. Remember to add one hour for Daylight Saving Time, if applicable.**

Sun

Data concerning the position, transit, orientation, rotation, and activity of the Sun plus times of sunrise and sunset appear on pp. 184–187, 189–193, and 205–207. For detailed information on this year's solar eclipses, see ECLIPSES IN 2017 on p. 126.

Moon

Conjunctions of the Moon with the naked-eye planets and the bright Messier objects that lie near the ecliptic—the Beehive Cluster (M44), M35, and the Pleiades Cluster (M45)—are given in the right-hand monthly tables (pp. 99–121). Only events for which the elongation of the Moon is at least 14° are included, and only selected such events involving the Messier objects are listed. See p. 19 for the definition of conjunction and elongation.

The Moon's phases, perigees, and apogees (computed with *Multiyear Interactive Computer Almanac 1800–2050*, Willmann-Bell, 2005) are also given in the right-hand tables. The phases new Moon, first quarter, full Moon, and last quarter correspond, respectively, to the Moon having a longitude 0°, 90°, 180°, and 270° east of the Sun. The age of the Moon is the time since the new phase; first-quarter, full, and last-quarter phases correspond approximately to 7.4, 14.8, and 22.1 days, respectively. For times of moonrise and moonset, see pp. 150–157.

The Sun's selenographic colongitude (SSC), given on the left-hand monthly pages, indicates the position of the sunrise terminator as it moves across the face of the Moon and provides a method of ascertaining the angle of illumination of features on the Moon's surface. The SSC is the angle of the sunrise terminator measured toward the observer's east (i.e. westward on the Moon) starting from the lunar meridian that passes through the mean centre of the apparent disk. Its value increases by nearly 12.2° per day, or about 0.5° per hour, and is approximately 0°, 90°, 180°, and 270° at the first-quarter, full, last-quarter, and new phases, respectively. Values of the SSC are given on pp. 98–120 for the 0th day of each month.

Selenographic longitude (λ) is measured toward the observer's west (i.e. eastward on the Moon) from the mean central lunar meridian. Thus sunrise will occur at a given point on the Moon when SSC = 360° – λ; values of 360° – λ for several lunar features are listed in the MAP OF THE MOON on p. 148. The longitude of the sunset terminator differs by 180° from that of the sunrise terminator.

Libration, also given on the left-hand pages, is the apparent rocking motion of the Moon as it orbits Earth. As a consequence, over time, about 59% of the lunar surface can be viewed from Earth (see *Sky & Telescope*, July 1987, p. 60). Libration in longitude (±8°) results from the nearly uniform axial rotation of the Moon combined with its varying orbital speed along its elliptical orbit, while libration in latitude (±7°) is caused by the tilt of the Moon's equator to its orbital plane. A smaller contribution (up to ±1°), called *diurnal libration*, is associated with the shifting of the observer due to Earth's rotation.

When the libration in longitude is positive, more of the Moon's east limb, the limb near Mare Crisium, is exposed to view (in reference to the lunar limbs, *east* and *west* are used in this lunar sense; see also the "E" and "W" labels on the MAP OF THE MOON, p. 148). When the libration in latitude is positive, more of the Moon's north limb is exposed to view. The monthly dates of the greatest positive and negative values of the libration in longitude and latitude and the dates of greatest northern and southern declination are given on the left-hand pages.

The lunar graphics on the right-hand pages give the geocentric appearance of the Moon at 0h UT on odd-numbered days of the month. They depict the Moon's phase, size, and libration. A small dot of size proportional to the amount of libration appears near the limb that is exposed. The graphics were prepared by Alister Ling with the aid of his *Lunar Calculator* software (**lunarcal.shawwebspace.ca**) jointly processed with the *JPL HORIZONS* ephemerides (**ssd.jpl.nasa.gov/?horizons**) to ensure accuracy.

The Moon's orbit is inclined 5° 09′ to the ecliptic. The gravitational influences of Earth and the Sun cause (i) the orbital plane to wobble, and (ii) the major axis of the orbit to precess: (i) The wobble shifts the line of nodes (see p. 122) westward (retrograde) along the ecliptic with a period of 18.60 years (18.61 years relative to the vernal equinox). During 2017, the ascending node regresses from longitude 156.3° to 137.7° in Leo. The Moon's declination reaches a northern extreme of +19.50° on Nov. 8 and a southern extreme of −19.59° on Dec. 19. In 2015, around the September equinox, the Moon's declination range had minimum extremes of ±18.1° (a minor standstill); from now on, the extreme range of the Moon's declination will continually increase, reaching a peak of ±29° in 2025; (ii) The precession shifts the perigee point eastward (prograde) with a period of 8.85 years, although the positions of successive perigees fluctuate considerably from the mean motion. The Moon's mean equatorial plane, its mean orbital plane, and the plane of the ecliptic intersect along a common line of nodes, the equator being inclined at 1°32′ to the ecliptic and at 1° 32′ + 5° 09′ = 6° 41′ to the orbit (i.e. the ascending node of the equator on the ecliptic coincides with the descending node of the orbit).

Jupiter's Satellites

The configurations of Jupiter's Galilean satellites, provided by Larry Bogan, are given on the right-hand monthly pages. In these diagrams the vertical double line represents the equatorial diameter of the disk of Jupiter. Time is shown on the vertical scale, successive horizontal lines indicating 0h UT on the various days of the month. The relative positions of the four satellites with respect to the disk of Jupiter are given by the four curves, where I = Io, II = Europa (dashed curve), III = Ganymede, and IV = Callisto. Note the "West–East" orientation given at the top of each diagram; these directions are those of the observer's sky, not Jupiter's limbs. Double-shadow transits of Jupiter's Galilean satellites that are not within 1.5 months of Jupiter's conjunction with the Sun are listed. Double-satellite transits that are not accompanied by a double-shadow event are generally also listed. For more information about the various transits, occultations, and eclipses of Jupiter's Galilean satellites, see PHENOMENA OF THE GALILEAN SATELLITES (p. 230).

Lunar Occultations of Bright Stars and Planetary Bodies

Occultations by the Moon of the bright stars that lie near the ecliptic (Aldebaran, Antares, Regulus, and Spica) are given in the right-hand tables along with those of the seven planets, the dwarf planet Ceres, and some bright minor planets (Pallas, Juno, and Vesta). If the elongation of the Moon is less than 14°, the event is not listed. Footnotes give areas of visibility; for more details on occultations visible in North America, including several involving members of the Pleiades (M45), see LUNAR OCCULTATIONS (p. 162) and PLANETARY OCCULTATIONS (p. 247).

Minima of Algol

Estimated predicted times of mid-eclipse are based on the formula heliocentric minimum = 2 440 953.5087+ 2.867 3075E *(courtesy of AAVSO, 2015)* and are expressed as geocentric times for comparison with observations. The first number is the Julian Date for the minimum of 1971 Jan. 2.01, and the second is the period of Algol in days; E is an integer. The presence of a third stellar component introduces variations in these times, and careful timings by observers are encouraged (see VARIABLE STARS, p. 298).

Planets

Conjunctions of the planets with each other and the bright ecliptic stars and Messier objects are listed in the right-hand tables. Only events for which the elongation of the inner planet is greater than 11° are included, and not all events involving the Messier objects are listed. Also included are oppositions, conjunctions with the Sun, greatest elongations, and stationary times. See p. 19 for definitions of these terms, and TABLE OF CONTENTS or the INDEX for the location of more information on each of the planets. The following diagrams give an overview of the circumstances of the planets in 2017.

Miscellaneous Entries

The lunation number is the number of times the Moon has circled the Earth since January 1923, based on a series described by Ernest W. Brown in *Planetary Theory*, 1933. Peaks of major meteor showers (see also p. 254), equinoxes and solstices, heliocentric phenomena of the planets, phenomena of the bright dwarf planets and minor planets, and a few other events and occasional notes are given in the right-hand tables.

MAGNITUDES OF NAKED-EYE PLANETS IN 2017

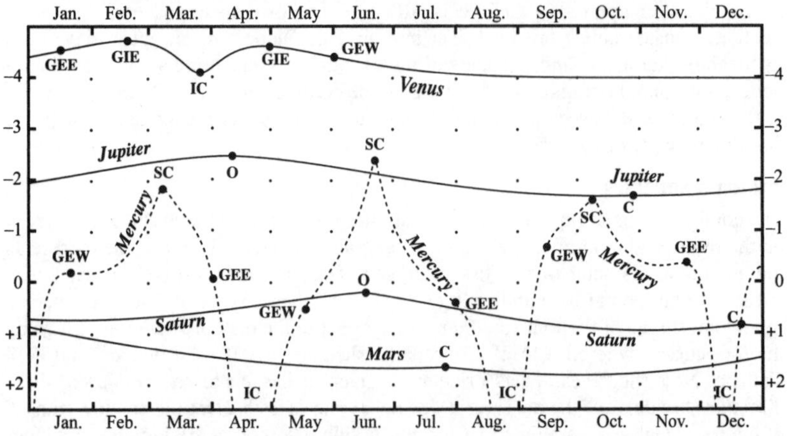

The visual magnitudes of the five classical (naked-eye) planets during 2017 are given. Oppositions (O), conjunctions (C), inferior and superior conjunctions (IC, SC), and greatest elongations east and west (GEE, GEW) are indicated. A diagram explaining these terms is on p. 20. Greatest illuminated extent (GIE, none in 2017) occurs when the illuminated area of Venus, as viewed from Earth, covers the most square degrees. (Chart provided by Patrick Kelly.)

RIGHT ASCENSIONS OF THE SUN AND PLANETS IN 2017

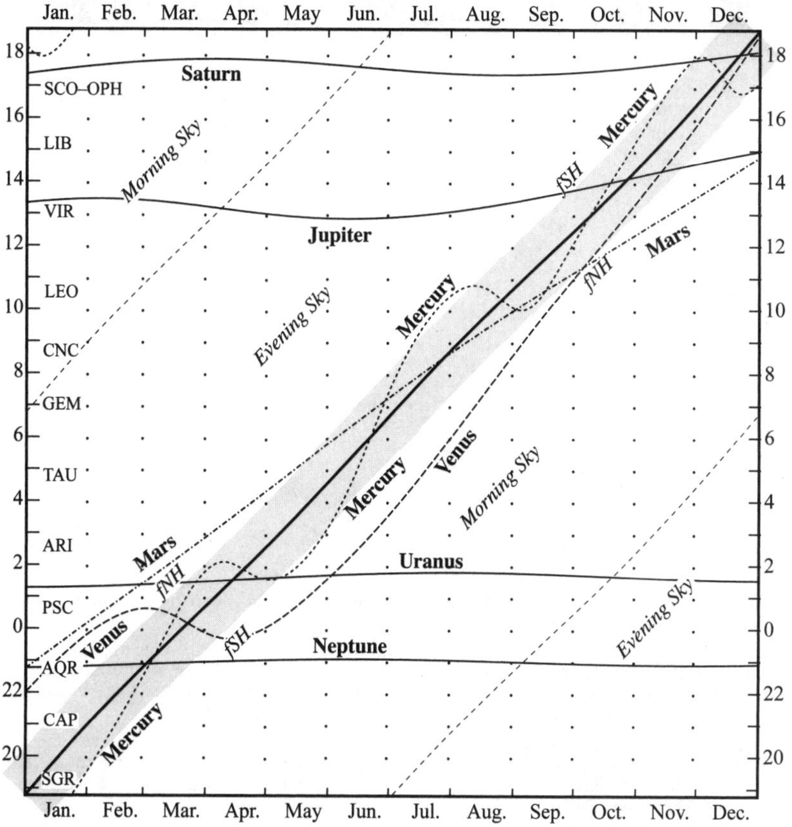

This diagram shows the variation during the year in the right ascension (vertical axis) of the Sun and planets. The slightly curved, heavy diagonal line represents the Sun; the shaded regions approximately indicate parts of the night sky affected by twilight. The two thin, dashed diagonal lines at the upper left and lower right represent the boundary between the evening sky and the morning sky.

The diagram may be used to determine in what part of the sky a planet may be found (including in which constellation—note the abbreviations along the vertical axis), when a superior planet is in conjunction with the Sun or at opposition (opposition is approximately where its curve intersects the dashed diagonal lines, and note that, due to retrograde motion, this point is also where the planet's curve has its maximum negative slope), when Mercury and Venus have their various greatest elongations and conjunctions, and when there are conjunctions of planets—that is, when the curves for planets intersect. For example, note the oppositions of Jupiter (early April) and Saturn (mid-June). In January and February, Mars and Venus are both in the evening sky. In mid-September, Mars joins Venus and Mercury in the morning. Saturn and Mercury come together at the end of November, while Jupiter and Mars meet in the morning sky at year end.

For observers in mid-latitudes, at certain times of the year the ecliptic stands steeply to the horizon in the western evening sky or the eastern morning sky, making apparitions of planets in these parts of the sky favourable from the Northern Hemisphere ("fNH" on the diagram) or favourable from the Southern Hemisphere ("fSH").

For more information on all these events, see the following 24 monthly pages and THE PLANETS FOR 2017 *(p. 211). (Chart provided by Patrick Kelly.)*

THE SKY FOR JANUARY

		Mercury	Venus	Mars	Jupiter	Saturn	Uranus	Neptune	Sun
RA	1	18h 13m	22h 00m	22h 45m	13h 19m	17h 22m	1h 16m	22h 46m	18h 46m
	11	17h 56m	22h 39m	23h 13m	13h 23m	17h 27m	1h 16m	22h 47m	19h 30m
	21	18h 30m	23h 14m	23h 40m	13h 25m	17h 31m	1h 17m	22h 48m	20h 12m
Dec	1	−20° 22′	−13° 47′	−8° 54′	−6° 58′	−21° 52′	+7° 23′	−8° 48′	−23° 01′
	11	−20° 46′	−9° 15′	−5° 51′	−7° 17′	−21° 56′	+7° 25′	−8° 42′	−21° 50′
	21	−22° 10′	−4° 30′	−2° 45′	−7° 29′	−21° 59′	+7° 28′	−8° 35′	−19° 57′
Dist	1	0.68	0.77	1.64	5.55	10.97	19.75	30.45	0.983
	11	0.84	0.70	1.71	5.39	10.90	19.92	30.59	0.983
	21	1.04	0.62	1.77	5.22	10.81	20.09	30.71	0.984
Mag	1	3.3	−4.4	0.9	−1.9	0.5	5.8	7.9	
	11	0	−4.5	1	−2	0.5	5.8	7.9	
	21	−0.2	−4.6	1	−2.1	0.6	5.8	7.9	
Size	1	9.8″	21.7″	5.7″	35.5″	15.2″	3.5″	2.2″	32′32″
	11	8.0″	24.0″	5.5″	36.6″	15.3″	3.5″	2.2″	32′32″
	21	6.5″	26.8″	5.3″	37.7″	15.4″	3.5″	2.2″	32′30″

Moon: On January 0 at 0h UT, Sun's selenographic colongitude is 294.29° and increases by 12.2° each day thereafter.

Greatest N declination on the 11th (+18.8°).

Greatest S declination on the 25th (−18.8°).

Libration in longitude: E limb most exposed on the 16th (+6.6°),
W limb most exposed on the 3rd (−5.9°) & 30th (−5.0°).

Libration in latitude: N limb most exposed on the 9th (+6.6°),
S limb most exposed on the 23rd (−6.8°).

The Moon occults both Aldebaran and Regulus somewhere in the world each lunar month in 2017. See the right-hand pages for details.

Mercury: Emerges in the morning sky early in the month and is well-placed for the duration, especially for observers at southern latitudes. Brightens throughout the month as its phase angle increases. Maximum western elongation of 24° is achieved on the Jan. 19. Makes a wide pair with the Moon on the 26th.

Venus: Begins the year in a very prominent position in the evening sky. Achieves greatest eastern elongation (47°) on the 12th, and will be in a tight conjunction with Neptune that evening. Achieves wider conjunctions with the Moon on the 2nd & 31st. In quasi-conjunction with Mars from mid-January to mid-February

Mars: Begins the year in central Aquarius, about 60° from the Sun on the evening side, around mag. +1 as it recedes from Earth. On the 1st, it has an exceedingly close conjunction with Neptune, some 400x fainter. On the 3rd, it is occulted by the waxing crescent Moon for observers in parts of Asia. Crosses the border into Pisces on the 19th. **On the 31st, Mars, Venus, and the waxing crescent Moon will fit in a 6° circle in the evening sky, roughly the field of view of standard binoculars.**

Jupiter: Begins the year in the morning sky, in central Virgo just northwest of Spica. Moon passes 3° to Jupiter's north on the morning of the 19th. Meridian transit times at Greenwich on the 1st, 11th, 21st – 06:36, 06:00, 05:23 UT*.

Saturn: Begins the year in southern Ophiucus, very near the point it will end its retrograde motion eight months hence. Emerging in the morning sky throughout January, as it begins the month just 20° west of the Sun, an elongation that will stretch near 50° by month's end. The waning crescent Moon passes 4° to the north on the 24th.

Uranus: Spends the year in eastern Pisces, nearing but never crossing the border into Aries. In January it sets in late evening.

Neptune: In central Aquarius throughout the year, it begins 2017 in extremely close conjunction with Mars, with the two separated by just 0.02° at closest point. The 7-mag. difference between them will make for a challenging observation; closest approach best seen from the longitude of Hawaii. Passes within 0.4° of Venus near its greatest elongation on the 12th–13th, although the difference of 12.5 mag. represents a factor of 100,000, the widest brightness difference possible between any two planets. Occulted by the waxing crescent Moon on the 2nd–3rd as seen from southeast Asia and the west coast of North America, then again on the 30th as seen from parts of Asia and Africa.

*See p. 94, the bold-faced sentences of the first paragraph.

Time (UT)	d	h	m	JANUARY EVENTS
Sun.	1	7		**Mars 0.02° S of Neptune**
Mon.	2	9		**Venus 1.9° S of Moon**
		10	15	Algol at minimum
Tue.	3	4		**Neptune 0.4° S of Moon, occultation†**
		7		**Mars 0.2° S of Moon, occultation‡**
		15		**Quadrantid meteors peak**
Wed.	4			Mercury at greatest heliocentric lat. N
		14		Earth at perihelion (147 100 998 km)
		15	56	**Double shadow transit on Jupiter**
Thu.	5	7	4	Algol at minimum
		19	47	**First Quarter**
Fri.	6			
Sat.	7			
Sun.	8	3	53	Algol at minimum
		10		Mercury stationary
Mon.	9	15		**Aldebaran 0.4° S of Moon, occultation††**
Tue.	10	6		Moon at perigee (363 238 km)
Wed.	11	0	42	Algol at minimum
		18	58	**Double shadow transit on Jupiter**
Thu.	12	11	34	**Full Moon**
		13		**Venus greatest elongation E (47°)**
Fri.	13	1		**Venus 0.4° N of Neptune**
		21	32	Algol at minimum
Sat.	14			
Sun.	15	5		**Regulus 0.8° N of Moon, occultation‡‡**
Mon.	16	18	21	Algol at minimum
Tue.	17			Venus at ascending node
Wed.	18	1		**Vesta at opposition**
Thu.	19	5		Jupiter 3° S of Moon
		10		**Mercury greatest elongation W (24°)**
		15	10	Algol at minimum
		22	13	**Last Quarter**
Fri.	20			
Sat.	21			
Sun.	22	0		Moon at apogee (404 914 km)
		11	59	Algol at minimum
Mon.	23			
Tue.	24	10		Saturn 4° S of Moon
Wed.	25	8	49	Algol at minimum
Thu.	26	1		Mercury 4° S of Moon
Fri.	27			
Sat.	28			Mercury at descending node
		0	7	**New Moon** (lunation 1164)
		5	38	Algol at minimum
Sun.	29			
Mon.	30	11		**Neptune 0.2° S of Moon, occultation†††**
Tue.	31	2	27	Algol at minimum
		15		**Venus 4° N of Moon**

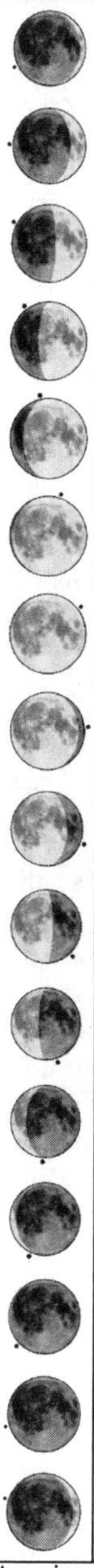

Jupiter's Satellites
West East

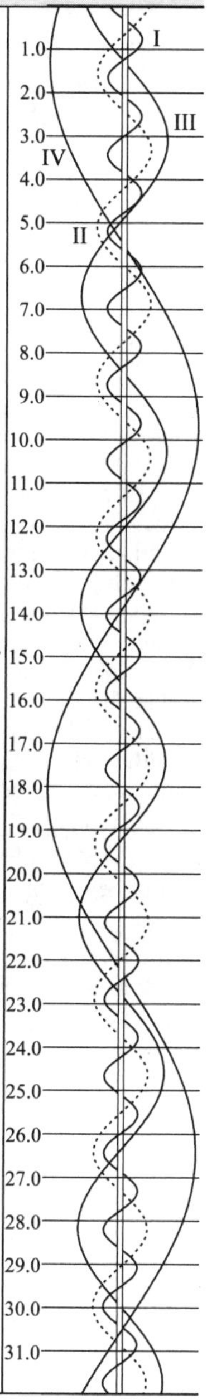

† Most of southeast Asia, Micronesia, Hawaii, west coast of N. America
‡ South tip of India, most of SE Asia, Micronesia †† NE Africa, Arabia, India, China, Japan
‡‡ South half of S. America, Antarctic Peninsula
††† Ascension Island, central Africa, Saudi Arabia, India, west China,

THE SKY FOR FEBRUARY

		Mercury	Venus	Mars	Jupiter	Saturn	Uranus	Neptune	Sun
RA	1	19h 29m	23h 48m	0h 10m	13h 27m	17h 36m	1h 18m	22h 49m	20h 58m
	11	20h 32m	0h 13m	0h 37m	13h 27m	17h 39m	1h 19m	22h 50m	21h 38m
	21	21h 37m	0h 31m	1h 04m	13h 26m	17h 43m	1h 20m	22h 52m	22h 17m
Dec	1	−22° 21′	+0° 40′	+0° 41′	−7° 35′	−22° 02′	+7° 35′	−8° 27′	−17° 10′
	11	−20° 28′	+5° 02′	+3° 45′	−7° 33′	−22° 04′	+7° 42′	−8° 19′	−14° 06′
	21	−16° 24′	+8° 44′	+6° 45′	−7° 24′	−22° 05′	+7° 51′	−8° 11′	−10° 39′
Dist	1	1.2	0.54	1.85	5.05	10.69	20.27	30.81	0.985
	11	1.31	0.47	1.92	4.90	10.55	20.43	30.88	0.987
	21	1.37	0.4	1.98	4.77	10.41	20.57	30.93	0.989
Mag	1	−0.2	−4.7	1.1	−2.1	0.6	5.9	8	
	11	−0.3	−4.8	1.2	−2.2	0.6	5.9	8	
	21	−0.7	−4.8	1.3	−2.3	0.6	5.9	8	
Size	1	5.6″	30.8″	5.1″	39.0″	15.6″	3.5″	2.2″	32′28″
	11	5.1″	35.5″	4.9″	40.2″	15.8″	3.4″	2.2″	32′25″
	21	4.9″	41.4″	4.7″	41.3″	16.0″	3.4″	2.2″	32′21″

Moon: On February 0 at 0h UT, Sun's selenographic colongitude is 311.25° and increases by 12.2° each day thereafter.
Greatest N declination on the 8th (+18.8°).
Greatest S declination on the 22nd (−18.8°).
Libration in longitude: E limb most exposed on the 12th (+5.1°),
W limb most exposed on the 25th (−5.3°).
Libration in latitude: N limb most exposed on the 5th (+6.7°),
S limb most exposed on the 19th (−6.9°).
Penumbral lunar eclipse on Feb. 10–11, visible from Asia, Europe, Africa, the Middle East, South America, North America, and the Indian Ocean, the Atlantic Ocean, and the eastern Pacific Ocean. (See p. 126).
Annular solar eclipse on Feb. 26, visible from southern South America, Antarctica, southern Africa, the south Pacific Ocean, and the south Atlantic Ocean. (See p. 126).

Mercury: Well placed in the morning sky throughout most of the month before being lost in the Sun's glare in the final few days. Excellent morning apparition for Southern Hemisphere observers.

Venus: A brilliant object in evening twilight, achieving its brightest illuminated extent on the 17th. In the eyepiece Venus is in crescent phase, thinning considerably over the course of the month as it approaches Earth.

Mars: In Pisces throughout February. Opens the month in quasi-conjunction with Venus, which pulls within about 5° of Mars for a number of days without ever overtaking it. The Moon is nearby on the 1st. Has a close conjunction with Uranus on the 27th.

Jupiter: Achieves its first stationary point on the 6th, 3.5° due north of Spica, which will make a handy guide to track Jupiter's retrograde motion over the next four months. The Moon passes 3° to Jupiter's north on the 15th. Reaches the aphelion of its 11.86-year orbit on the 17th. Meridian transit times at Greenwich on the 1st, 11th, 21st – 4:41, 4:02, 03:21 UT*.

Saturn: Low in the dawn sky, moving from Ophiucus into Sagittarius late in the month. The waning crescent Moon passes well to its north on the 20th and 21st.

Uranus: Low in the western evening sky in Pisces, and sets in mid-evening. The angle of the ecliptic favours observers in the Northern Hemisphere.

Neptune: Vanishes into the evening twilight early in the month.

*See p. 94, the bold-faced sentences of the first paragraph.

Time (UT)	d	h	m	FEBRUARY EVENTS
Wed.	1	1		Mars 2° N of Moon
Thu.	2	23	16	Algol at minimum
Fri.	3	2		**Ceres 1.0° S of Moon, occultation†**
Sat.	4	4	19	**First Quarter**
Sun.	5	20	6	Algol at minimum
		22		**Aldebaran 0.2° S of Moon, occultation‡**
Mon.	6	14		Moon at perigee (368 816 km)
		19		Jupiter stationary
Tue.	7			Mercury at aphelion
Wed.	8	16	55	Algol at minimum
Thu.	9			
Fri.	10			
Sat.	11	0	33	**Full Moon**
				Penumbral Lunar Eclipse (p. 126)
		13	44	Algol at minimum
		14		**Regulus 0.8° N of Moon, occultation††**
Sun.	12			
Mon.	13			**Zodiacal Light vis. in N lat. in W after evening twilight for next two weeks**
Tue.	14	10	33	Algol at minimum
Wed.	15	15		Jupiter 3° S of Moon
Thu.	16			
Fri.	17			Jupiter at aphelion
		7		**Venus greatest illuminated extent**
		7	23	Algol at minimum
Sat.	18	19	33	**Last Quarter**
		21		Moon at apogee (404 376 km)
Sun.	19			
Mon.	20			Venus at perihelion
		4	12	Algol at minimum
		23		Saturn 4° S of Moon
Tue.	21			
Wed.	22			
Thu.	23	1	1	Algol at minimum
Fri.	24			
Sat.	25	21	51	Algol at minimum
Sun.	26	14	58	**New Moon** (lunation 1165)
				Annular Solar Eclipse (p. 126)
Mon.	27			Mercury at greatest heliocentric lat. S
				Mars at ascending node
		8		**Mars 0.6° N of Uranus**
Tue.	28	18	40	Algol at minimum

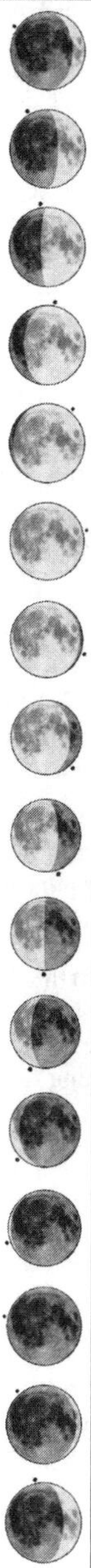

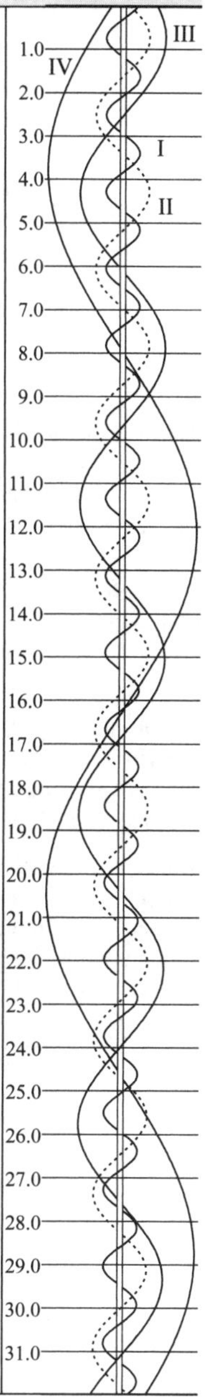

† East Siberia, Alaska, northern Canada, Greenland
‡ Central America, north S. America, Caribbean, North Africa, south Europe, west Middle East
†† Australia, Wilkes Land, New Zealand

THE SKY FOR MARCH

		Mercury	Venus	Mars	Jupiter	Saturn	Uranus	Neptune	Sun
RA	1	22h 31m	0h 37m	1h 26m	13h 24m	17h 45m	1h 22m	22h 53m	22h 47m
	11	23h 40m	0h 32m	1h 53m	13h 21m	17h 47m	1h 24m	22h 54m	23h 25m
	21	0h 49m	0h 14m	2h 21m	13h 17m	17h 49m	1h 25m	22h 56m	0h 01m
Dec	1	−11° 31′	+10° 53′	+9° 03′	−7° 12′	−22° 05′	+7° 59′	−8° 04′	−7° 41′
	11	−3° 30′	+12° 00′	+11° 47′	−6° 52′	−22° 05′	+8° 10′	−7° 55′	−3° 49′
	21	+5° 44′	+10° 45′	+14° 19′	−6° 27′	−22° 05′	+8° 22′	−7° 47′	+0° 08′
Dist	1	1.38	0.36	2.04	4.68	10.28	20.67	30.94	0.991
	11	1.33	0.31	2.10	4.58	10.12	20.77	30.93	0.993
	21	1.18	0.28	2.16	4.51	9.95	20.85	30.89	0.996
Mag	1	−1.3	−4.8	1.3	−2.3	0.5	5.9	8	
	11	−1.8	−4.6	1.4	−2.4	0.5	5.9	8	
	21	−1.2	−4.1	1.4	−2.4	0.5	5.9	8	
Size	1	4.9″	46.9″	4.6″	42.1″	16.2″	3.4″	2.2″	32′ 17″
	11	5.0″	54.0″	4.5″	43.0″	16.4″	3.4″	2.2″	32′ 12″
	21	5.7″	58.8″	4.3″	43.7″	16.7″	3.4″	2.2″	32′ 07″

Moon: On March 0 at 0h UT, Sun's selenographic colongitude is 291.87° and increases by 12.2° each day thereafter.
Greatest N declination on the 7th (+18.9°).
Greatest S declination on the 21st (–18.9°).
Libration in longitude: E limb most exposed on the 11th (+4.7°),
W limb most exposed on the 25th (–6.4°).
Libration in latitude: N limb most exposed on the 5th (+6.8°),
S limb most exposed on the 18th (–6.8°).

Mercury: Lost in Sun's glare as it passes behind the Sun early in the month, achieving superior conjunction on Mar. 7. Emerges in the evening sky in mid-month to begin **the best evening apparition of the year for observers at mid-northern latitudes.** Reaches perihelion on the 23rd, when it will be bright but relatively close to the Sun.

Venus: Stationary on the 2nd in central Pisces before undergoing its retrograde sweep through **inferior conjunction on the 25th**. Having achieved greatest heliocentric latitude north on the 14th, the brilliant planet will pass more than 8° north of the Sun at conjunction, making it possible to see in both morning and evening twilight for a few days. By month's end it will have fully emerged in the morning sky.

Mars: Opens the month in Pisces, crossing into Aries on the 8th. Makes a wide pair with the Moon on the 1st.

Jupiter: In retrograde motion in central Virgo throughout the month as it approaches its April 7 opposition. The Moon passes 2° north on the 14th. Meridian transit times at Greenwich on the 1st, 11th, 21st – 2:48, 2:06, 1:23 UT*.

Saturn: Low in the dawn sky in western Sagittarius. The third-quarter Moon passes 3° to its north in the morning of the 20th in the Americas. Meridian transit times at Greenwich on the 1st, 11th, 21st – 7:09, 6:32, 5:54 UT*.

Uranus: Vanishes into the evening twilight late in the month.

Neptune: In conjunction with the Sun on the 2nd, it is too close to the Sun to be seen all month.

*See p. 94, the bold-faced sentences of the first paragraph.

Time (UT) d	h	m	MARCH EVENTS
Wed. 1	19		Mars 4° N of Moon
Thu. 2	3		Neptune in conjunction with the Sun
	14		Venus stationary
	21		**Ceres 0.8° N of Moon, occultation†**
Fri. 3	8		Moon at perigee (369 062 km)
	15	29	Algol at minimum
Sat. 4			
Sun. 5	3		**Aldebaran 0.2° S of Moon, occultation‡**
	11	32	**First Quarter**
Mon. 6	12	18	Algol at minimum
Tue. 7	0		Mercury in superior conjunction
	3		Vesta stationary
Wed. 8			
Thu. 9	9	8	Algol at minimum
Fri. 10	23		**Regulus 0.8° N of Moon, occultation††**
Sat. 11			
Sun. 12			**DAYLIGHT SAVING TIME BEGINS**
	5	57	Algol at minimum
	14	54	**Full Moon**
Mon. 13			
Tue. 14			Venus at greatest heliocentric lat. N
			Zodiacal Light vis. in N lat. in W after evening twilight for next two weeks
	20		Jupiter 2° S of Moon
Wed. 15	2	46	Algol at minimum
	3		Pallas in conjunction with the Sun
Thu. 16			
Fri. 17	23	35	Algol at minimum
Sat. 18			Mercury at ascending node
	17		Moon at apogee (404 650 km)
Sun. 19			
Mon. 20	10		Saturn 3° S of Moon
	10	29	**Equinox**
	15	58	**Last Quarter**
	20	25	Algol at minimum
Tue. 21			
Wed. 22			
Thu. 23			Mercury at perihelion
	17	14	Algol at minimum
Fri. 24			
Sat. 25	10		Venus in inferior conjunction
Sun. 26	8		**Neptune 0.005° N of Moon, occultation‡‡**
	14	3	Algol at minimum
Mon. 27	6		Mercury 2° N of Uranus
Tue. 28	2	57	**New Moon** (lunation 1166)
Wed. 29	10	52	Algol at minimum
Thu. 30	13		Moon at perigee (363 853 km)
Fri. 31			

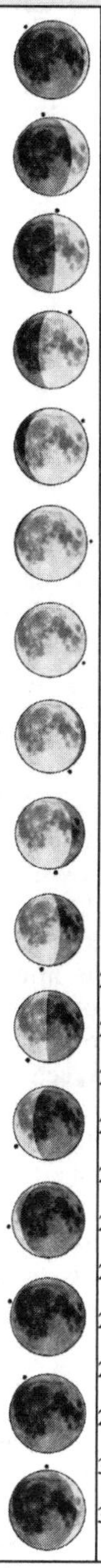

Jupiter's Satellites
West East

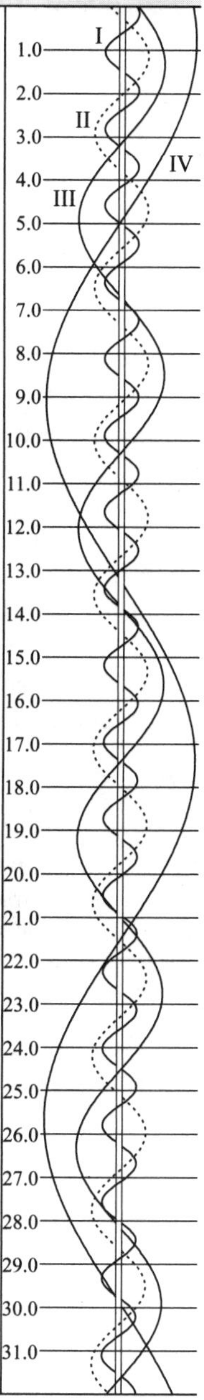

† South half of South America, Antarctic Peninsula, South Georgia
‡ Soloman Islands, Micronesia, Hawaii, North & Central America, west Caribbean
†† Southeast South America, South Georgia, Queen Maud Land, south tip of South Africa
‡‡ Ascension Island, South Africa, north Madagascar, Yemen, Oman, southwest Asia

THE SKY FOR APRIL

		Mercury	Venus	Mars	Jupiter	Saturn	Uranus	Neptune	Sun
RA	1	1h 48m	23h 51m	2h 52m	13h 12m	17h 49m	1h 28m	22h 57m	0h 41m
	11	2h 05m	23h 41m	3h 20m	13h 07m	17h 49m	1h 30m	22h 58m	1h 18m
	21	1h 48m	23h 45m	3h 49m	13h 03m	17h 49m	1h 32m	22h 59m	1h 55m
Dec	1	+13° 50′	+7° 10′	+16° 50′	−5° 56′	−22° 05′	+8° 36′	−7° 38′	+4° 26′
	11	+15° 59′	+3° 49′	+18° 52′	−5° 27′	−22° 04′	+8° 48′	−7° 31′	+8° 13′
	21	+12° 41′	+1° 51′	+20° 36′	−4° 59′	−22° 03′	+9° 01′	−7° 24′	+11° 46′
Dist	1	0.9	0.29	2.23	4.46	9.77	20.91	30.82	0.999
	11	0.67	0.32	2.29	4.46	9.61	20.93	30.73	1.002
	21	0.57	0.37	2.34	4.48	9.47	20.93	30.62	1.005
Mag	1	−0.2	−4.2	1.5	−2.5	0.4	5.9	8	
	11	2.3	−4.6	1.5	−2.5	0.4	5.9	7.9	
	21		−4.7	1.6	−2.4	0.3	5.9	7.9	
Size	1	7.5″	57.9″	4.2″	44.1″	17.0″	3.4″	2.2″	32′01″
	11	10.0″	51.9″	4.1″	44.2″	17.3″	3.3″	2.2″	31′55″
	21	11.7″	44.5″	4.0″	44.0″	17.6″	3.3″	2.2″	31′50″

Moon: On April 0 at 0 h UT, Sun's selenographic colongitude is 309.51° and increases by 12.2° each day thereafter.

Greatest N declination on the 3rd (18.9°) & 30th (+19.0°).

Greatest S declination on the 18th (–19.0°).

Libration in longitude: E limb most exposed on the 6th (+5.6°).

W limb most exposed on the 22nd (–7.4°).

Libration in latitude: N limb most exposed on the 1st (+6.7°) & 28th (+6.6°),

S limb most exposed on the 15th (–6.7°).

Large tides in the days following new Moon (Apr. 26).

Mercury: At greatest eastern elongation of 19° on the 1st and will be well placed in evening sky for a few days thereafter for Northern Hemisphere observers, even as it fades from night to night. Reaches inferior conjunction on the 20th and gradually crawls back into the morning sky by month's end.

Venus: Fresh off its inferior conjunction in late March, Venus grows ever more prominent in the morning sky throughout the month. It reaches its second stationary point in the Circlet of Pisces on the 13th and resumes prograde motion thereafter. The Moon passes 5° to its south on the 23rd. Reaches its greatest illuminated extent on the 30th, by which time it is 40° west of the Sun.

Mars: Opens the month in Aries, entering Taurus on the 12th. Passes within 4° of the Pleiades late in the month, though binoculars may be required to pull both out of the bright evening twilight. By month's end Mars is just 25° from the Sun.

Jupiter: At opposition on Apr. 7 in Virgo, mag. –2.5, 37 light minutes (4.5 au) from Earth, and 44″ in equatorial diameter. This is the first of six consecutive oppositions through 2022 that will occur south of the celestial equator. The nearly full Moon passes 2° to Jupiter's north on the 10th. Meridian transit times at Greenwich on the 1st, 11th, 21st – 0:35, 23:46, 23:02 UT*.

Saturn: Reaches its first stationary point on the 6th, beginning retrograde motion thereafter. It remains in western Sagittarius throughout the month. The waning gibbous Moon is nearby on the 16th and 17th. Meridian transit times at Greenwich on the 1st, 11th, 21st – 5:11, 4:32, 3:53 UT*.

Uranus: Too close to the Sun to be seen. In conjunction with the Sun on the 14th.

Neptune: Returns to the morning sky early in the month for observers in the Southern Hemisphere, later in the month for those in the north. It will be occulted by the waning crescent Moon on the 26th, as seen from some Southern Hemisphere locations.

*See p. 94, the bold-faced sentences of the first paragraph.

Time (UT) d	h m	APRIL EVENTS
Sat. 1	7 41	Algol at minimum
	9	**Aldebaran 0.3° S of Moon, occultation†**
	10	**Mercury greatest elongation E (19°)**
Sun. 2		Mercury at greatest heliocentric lat. N
Mon. 3	18 39	**First Quarter**
Tue. 4	4 31	Algol at minimum
Wed. 5		
Thu. 6	5	Saturn stationary
Fri. 7	1 20	Algol at minimum
	5	**Regulus 0.7° N of Moon, occultation‡**
	22	**Jupiter at opposition**
Sat. 8		
Sun. 9	22 9	Algol at minimum
Mon. 10	1	Mercury stationary
	21	Jupiter 2° S of Moon
Tue. 11	6 8	**Full Moon**
Wed. 12	18 58	Algol at minimum
Thu. 13	0	Venus stationary
Fri. 14	6	Uranus in conjunction with the Sun
Sat. 15	10	Moon at apogee (405 475 km)
	15 47	Algol at minimum
Sun. 16	18	Saturn 3° S of Moon
Mon. 17		
Tue. 18	12 36	Algol at minimum
Wed. 19	9 57	**Last Quarter**
Thu. 20	6	Mercury in inferior conjunction
Fri. 21	9 25	Algol at minimum
Sat. 22	12	Lyrid meteors peak
	20	**Neptune 0.2° N of Moon, occultation††**
Sun. 23		**Venus 5° N of Moon**
Mon. 24	6 14	Algol at minimum
	16	**Pallas 0.8° S of Moon, occultation‡‡**
Tue. 25		
Wed. 26		Mercury at descending node
	12 16	**New Moon** (lunation 1167)
Thu. 27	3 3	Algol at minimum
	16	Moon at perigee (359 327 km)
Fri. 28	18	**Aldebaran 0.5° S of Moon, occultation†††**
Sat. 29	23 52	Algol at minimum
Sun. 30	4	**Venus greatest illuminated extent**

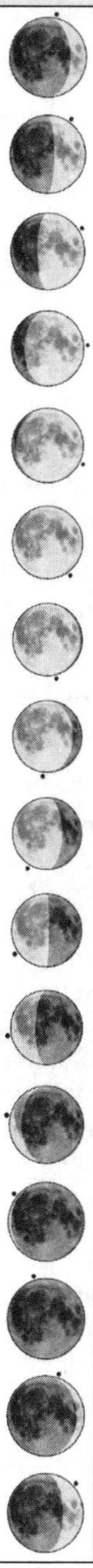

Jupiter's Satellites

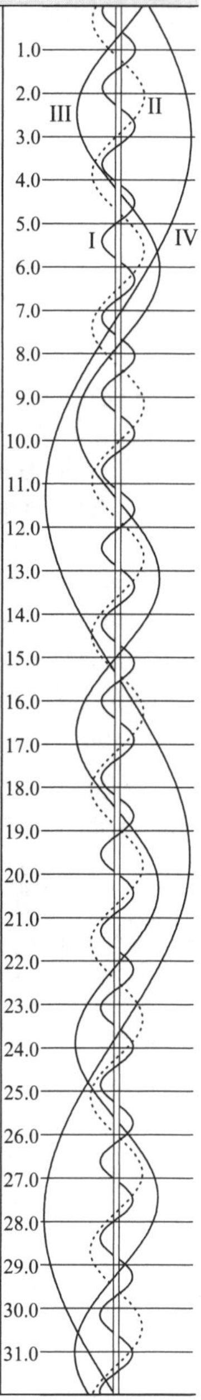

† NE Africa, Arabia, India, Mongolia, China, Japan ‡ S. Polynesia, Antarctic Peninsula, S tip of S. America
†† Most of Australia, New Zealand, SE Melanesia, C. Polynesia ‡‡ Most of N. America, Greenland, Iceland, Ireland
††† North America, Cuba, eastern Canada, south tip of Greenland, Europe, North Africa

THE SKY FOR MAY

		Mercury	Venus	Mars	Jupiter	Saturn	Uranus	Neptune	Sun
RA	1	1h 32m	0h 01m	4h 17m	12h 58m	17h 47m	1h 34m	23h 00m	2h 33m
	11	1h 41m	0h 26m	4h 47m	12h 55m	17h 45m	1h 36m	23h 01m	3h 11m
	21	2h 14m	0h 57m	5h 16m	12h 52m	17h 43m	1h 38m	23h 02m	3h 51m
Dec	1	+8° 14′	+1° 32′	+22° 01′	−4° 34′	−22° 02′	+9° 13′	−7° 19′	+15° 00′
	11	+7° 17′	+2° 35′	+23° 06′	−4° 13′	−22° 01′	+9° 25′	−7° 14′	+17° 49′
	21	+9° 55′	+4° 37′	+23° 51′	−3° 59′	−22° 00′	+9° 36′	−7° 10′	+20° 08′
Dist	1	0.6	0.44	2.4	4.53	9.34	20.90	30.48	1.008
	11	0.72	0.51	2.44	4.61	9.23	20.84	30.34	1.010
	21	0.87	0.59	2.49	4.71	9.14	20.76	30.18	1.012
Mag	1	2.5	−4.7	1.6	−2.4	0.3	5.9	7.9	
	11	0.9	−4.7	1.6	−2.4	0.2	5.9	7.9	
	21	0.2	−4.6	1.7	−2.3	0.2	5.9	7.9	
Size	1	11.2″	37.8″	3.9″	43.5″	17.8″	3.4″	2.2″	31′45″
	11	9.4″	32.4″	3.8″	42.8″	18.0″	3.4″	2.2″	31′40″
	21	7.7″	28.2″	3.8″	41.9″	18.2″	3.4″	2.2″	31′36″

Moon: On May 0 at 0 h UT, Sun's selenographic colongitude is 315.43° and increases by 12.2° each day thereafter.

Greatest N declination on the 28th (+19.4°).

Greatest S declination on the 15th (−19.3°).

Libration in longitude: E limb most exposed on the 4th (+6.8°),
W limb most exposed on the 20th (−7.9°).

Libration in latitude: N limb most exposed on the 25th (+6.5°),
S limb most exposed on the 12th (−6.6°).

Large tides in the days following new Moon (May 25).

Mercury: Well placed in the morning sky all month, especially for Southern Hemisphere observers. Reaches aphelion on the 6th, and greatest western elongation (26°) on the 17th. Will be within 2° of the thin crescent Moon on the morning of the 24th.

Venus: Prominent in the dawn sky throughout the month. Has a fine conjunction just 2° north of the waning crescent Moon on the 22nd.

Mars: Spends the entire month in Taurus, passing about 6° away from Aldebaran on the 7th. Note the similarity in colour, though on this occasion it will be the star that is roughly twice as bright as the planet.

Jupiter: Well placed for observation throughout the evening hours in central Virgo. The Moon passes 2° to Jupiter's north on the 7th. A series of double shadow transits can be seen on Jupiter throughout the month as detailed on the events calendar at right. Meridian transit times at Greenwich on the 1st, 11th, 21st – 22:19, 21:36. 20:54 UT*.

Saturn: Continues its retrograde motion in the morning sky, passing from Sagittarius westward into Ophiucus in mid-month. The waning gibbous Moon is nearby on the 13th and 14th. By mid-month Saturn is rising before midnight local daylight time. Meridian transit times at Greenwich on the 1st, 11th, 21st – 3:11, 2:30, 1:48 UT*.

Uranus: Returns to the dawn sky, early in the month for Southern Hemisphere observers, later for those in the Northern Hemisphere. Passes 2° from Mercury on the 7th when both are just 22° from the Sun.

Neptune: In the eastern morning sky, in Aquarius. Occulted by the waning crescent Moon on the 20th, as seen from parts of the Southern Hemisphere.

*See p. 94, the bold-faced sentences of the first paragraph.

Time (UT) d	h m	MAY EVENTS
Mon. 1		
Tue. 2	14	Mercury stationary
	20 41	Algol at minimum
Wed. 3	2 47	**First Quarter**
Thu. 4	10	**Regulus 0.5° N of Moon, occultation**†
Fri. 5	1	η-Aquariid meteors peak
	17 30	Algol at minimum
Sat. 6		Mercury at aphelion
Sun. 7	21	Jupiter 2° S of Moon
	23	Mercury 2° S of Uranus
Mon. 8	8	Juno stationary
	14 19	Algol at minimum
Tue. 9		Venus at descending node
Wed. 10	21 42	**Full Moon**
Thu. 11	11 8	Algol at minimum
Fri. 12	1 59	**Double shadow transit on Jupiter**
	20	Moon at apogee (406 210 km)
Sat. 13	23	Saturn 3° S of Moon
Sun. 14	7 57	Algol at minimum
Mon. 15	14 56	**Double shadow transit on Jupiter**
Tue. 16		
Wed. 17	4 46	Algol at minimum
	23	**Mercury greatest elongation W (26°)**
Thu. 18		
Fri. 19	0 33	**Last Quarter**
	3 54	**Double shadow transit on Jupiter**
Sat. 20	1 35	Algol at minimum
	6	**Neptune 0.5° N of Moon, occultation**‡
Sun. 21		
Mon. 22	13	**Venus 2° N of Moon**
	16 50	**Double shadow transit on Jupiter**
	22 24	Algol at minimum
Tue. 23		
Wed. 24	1	**Mercury 1.6° N of Moon**
Thu. 25	19 13	Algol at minimum
	19 44	**New Moon** (lunation 1168)
Fri. 26		Mercury at greatest heliocentric lat. S
	1	Moon at perigee (357 207 km) **Large tides**
	5 47	**Double shadow transit on Jupiter**
Sat. 27		
Sun. 28	0 16	**Double shadow transit on Jupiter**
	16 2	Algol at minimum
Mon. 29	18 45	**Double shadow transit on Jupiter**
Tue. 30		
Wed. 31	12 51	Algol at minimum
	17	**Regulus 0.3° N of Moon, occultation**††

Jupiter's Satellites
West East

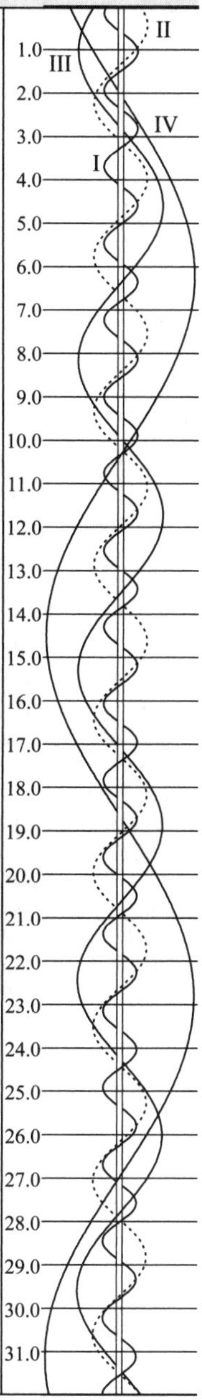

† Indonesia, Malaysia, south New Guinea, Australia, New Zealand
‡ Falkland Islands, south part of Africa, Madagascar, Maldives
†† Eastern Brazil, Cape Verde Islands, central and South Africa except south tip, Mauritius

THE SKY FOR JUNE

		Mercury	Venus	Mars	Jupiter	Saturn	Uranus	Neptune	Sun
RA	1	3h 11m	1h 35m	5h 48m	12h 50m	17h 40m	1h 40m	23h 02m	4h 35m
	11	4h 24m	2h 12m	6h 17m	12h 50m	17h 37m	1h 42m	23h 02m	5h 17m
	21	5h 55m	2h 52m	6h 46m	12h 51m	17h 33m	1h 43m	23h 03m	5h 58m
Dec	1	+15° 21′	+7° 34′	+24° 17′	−3° 50′	−21° 59′	+9° 47′	−7° 08′	+22° 01′
	11	+20° 52′	+10° 35′	+24° 18′	−3° 50′	−21° 58′	+9° 56′	−7° 07′	+23° 04′
	21	+24° 26′	+13° 39′	+23° 59′	−3° 57′	−21° 57′	+10° 04′	−7° 07′	+23° 26′
Dist	1	1.07	0.68	2.53	4.84	9.07	20.65	29.99	1.014
	11	1.24	0.76	2.57	4.98	9.05	20.52	29.82	1.015
	21	1.32	0.84	2.6	5.12	9.05	20.38	29.66	1.016
Mag	1	−0.4	−4.5	1.7	−2.2	0.1	5.9	7.9	
	11	−1.1	−4.4	1.7	−2.2	0	5.9	7.9	
	21	−2.4	−4.3	1.7	−2.1	0	5.9	7.9	
Size	1	6.3″	24.5″	3.7″	40.7″	18.3″	3.4″	2.2″	31′33″
	11	5.4″	21.9″	3.6″	39.6″	18.4″	3.4″	2.2″	31′30″
	21	5.1″	19.8″	3.6″	38.5″	18.4″	3.4″	2.3″	31′29″

Moon: On June 0 at 0h UT*., Sun's selenographic colongitude is 334.00° and increases by 12.2° each day thereafter.

Greatest N declination on the 24th (+19.3°).

Greatest S declination on the 11th (–19.4°).

Libration in longitude: E limb most exposed on the 1st (+7.5°) & 29th (+7.4°), W limb most exposed on the 17th (–7.6°).

Libration in latitude: N limb most exposed on the 22nd (+6.6°), S limb most exposed on the 8th (–6.6°).

Large tides in the days following new Moon (Jun. 24)

Mercury: Visible in the morning sky early in the month, brightening as its phase angle increases and as it approaches perihelion on the 19th, though it will no longer be visible by that date—superior conjunction is on the 21st.

Venus: Prominent in the dawn sky throughout the month. **Achieves greatest western elongation (46°) on the 3rd.** The Moon passes 2° to its south on the 20th.

Mars: Just 16° from the Sun as June begins, the tiny, faint red planet may just be seen in evening twilight very early in the month.

Jupiter: In the evening sky throughout the month, during which it continues its series of double shadow transits for telescopic observers as detailed in the events calendar at right. In conjunction with the waxing gibbous Moon in the evening hours of the 3rd and again on the 30th for observers in the Americas. Achieves its second stationary point on the 10th, when it is 11° to the northwest of Spica, thereafter resuming prograde motion. Meridian transit times at Greenwich on the 1st, 11th, 21st – 20:09, 19:30, 18:51 UT*.

Saturn: Reaches opposition on the 15th, just 6 days before the summer solstice, placing Saturn not far from the winter solstice point, very low in the southern sky for observers in the Northern Hemisphere. At opposition, Saturn is 75 light-minutes (9.04 au) from Earth, mag. 0.0, the northern side of the ring plane tilted to its maximum extent (26.7°) toward the Sun and Earth. The rings span 42 seconds of arc, the disk of the planet about 18″. The nearly full Moon passes 3° north of Saturn on the 9th. Meridian transit times at Greenwich on the 1st, 11th, 21st – 1:02, 0:20, 23:33 UT*.

Uranus: In the morning sky in Pisces. Venus near its greatest elongation is just 1.8° away on the 2nd.

Neptune: Rises after midnight among the stars of central Aquarius. Stationary on the 16th, the same day it is occulted by the waning gibbous Moon, as seen from Antarctica and southern South America. Meridian transit times at Greenwich on the 1st, 11th, 21st – 6:23, 5:44, 5:05 UT*.

*See p. 94, the bold-faced sentences of the first paragraph.

Time (UT) d	h m	JUNE EVENTS
Thu. 1	12 42	**First Quarter**
Fri. 2	7 42	**Double shadow transit on Jupiter**
	14	**Venus 1.8° S of Uranus**
Sat. 3	9 39	Algol at minimum
	13	**Venus greatest elongation W (46°)**
Sun. 4	0	Jupiter 2° S of Moon
	2 21	**Double shadow transit on Jupiter**
Mon. 5	20 49	**Double shadow transit on Jupiter**
Tue. 6	0	Ceres in conjunction with the Sun
	6 28	Algol at minimum
Wed. 7		
Thu. 8	22	Moon at apogee (406 401 km)
Fri. 9	3 17	Algol at minimum
	10 09	**Double shadow transit on Jupiter**
	13 10	**Full Moon** (smallest in 2017)
Sat. 10	1	Saturn 3° S of Moon
	5	Jupiter stationary
Sun. 11		
Mon. 12		Venus at aphelion
	0 6	Algol at minimum
	23 27	**Double shadow transit on Jupiter**
Tue. 13		
Wed. 14		Mercury at ascending node
	20 55	Algol at minimum
Thu. 15	10	**Saturn at opposition**
Fri. 16	12 46	**Double shadow transit on Jupiter**
	13	**Neptune 0.7° N of Moon, occultation†**
	23	Neptune stationary
Sat. 17	11 33	**Last Quarter**
	17 43	Algol at minimum
Sun. 18		
Mon. 19		Mercury at perihelion
Tue. 20	2 4	**Double shadow transit on Jupiter**
	14 32	Algol at minimum
	21	**Venus 2° N of Moon**
Wed. 21	4 24	**Solstice**
	14	Mercury in superior conjunction
Thu. 22	15	**Aldebaran 0.5° S of Moon, occultation‡**
Fri. 23	11	Moon at perigee (357 937 km) **Large tides**
	11 21	Algol at minimum
	15 24	**Double shadow transit on Jupiter**
Sat. 24	2 31	**New Moon** (lunation 1169)
Sun. 25		
Mon. 26	8 9	Algol at minimum
Tue. 27		
Wed. 28	1	**Regulus 0.03° N of Moon, occultation††**
Thu. 29		Mercury at greatest heliocentric lat. N
	4 58	Algol at minimum
Fri. 30		

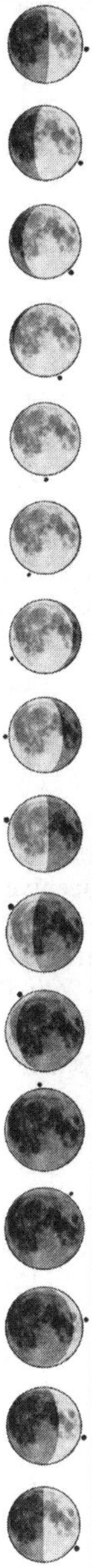

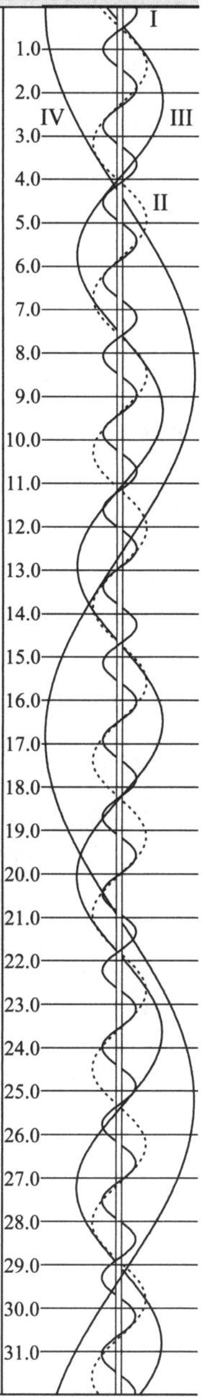

† Western Antarctica, south half of South America
‡ Most of North America, south Greenland, Azores, most of Europe, northwest Africa
†† Micronesia, Hawaii, Galapagos Islands, Peru, Ecuador

THE SKY FOR JULY

		Mercury	Venus	Mars	Jupiter	Saturn	Uranus	Neptune	Sun
RA	1	7h 28m	3h 35m	7h 15m	12h 52m	17h 30m	1h 44m	23h 02m	6h 40m
	11	8h 46m	4h 20m	7h 43m	12h 55m	17h 28m	1h 45m	23h 02m	7h 21m
	21	9h 44m	5h 07m	8h 10m	12h 59m	17h 25m	1h 46m	23h 01m	8h 01m
Dec	1	+23° 47′	+16° 31′	+23° 21′	–4° 11′	–21° 56′	+10° 10′	–7° 09′	+23° 07′
	11	+19° 38′	+18° 58′	+22° 25′	–4° 31′	–21° 55′	+10° 15′	–7° 12′	+22° 08′
	21	+13° 59′	+20° 47′	+21° 12′	–4° 56′	–21° 55′	+10° 18′	–7° 15′	+20° 31′
Dist	1	1.28	0.92	2.62	5.28	9.08	20.22	29.50	1.017
	11	1.16	1	2.64	5.43	9.14	20.06	29.36	1.017
	21	1.01	1.07	2.65	5.59	9.22	19.89	29.23	1.016
Mag	1	–1.1	–4.2	1.7	–2.1	0.1	5.8	7.9	
	11	–0.4	–4.1	1.7	–2	0.1	5.8	7.9	
	21	0	–4.1	1.7	–1.9	0.2	5.8	7.8	
Size	1	5.3″	18.2″	3.6″	37.3″	18.3″	3.5″	2.3″	31′28″
	11	5.8″	16.8″	3.5″	36.3″	18.2″	3.5″	2.3″	31′28″
	21	6.7″	15.6″	3.5″	35.3″	18.0″	3.5″	2.3″	31′29″

Moon: On July 0 at 0 h UT, Sun's selenographic colongitude is 340.62° and increases by 12.2° each day thereafter.

Greatest N declination on the 22nd (+19.4°).

Greatest S declination on the 8th (–19.3°).

Libration in longitude: E limb most exposed on the 27th (+6.7°),

W limb most exposed on the 15th (–6.6°).

Libration in latitude: N limb most exposed on the 19th (+6.7°),

S limb most exposed on the 5th (–6.7°).

Mercury: Well placed in the evening sky throughout the month, a particularly favourable apparition for observers at southern latitudes but poor for northerners. Passes in front of Beehive Cluster on the 10th at an elongation of 19°. Passes just south of the 2-day-old Moon on the 25th, and will be occulted in North Europe including British Isles, most of Greenland, and the northern half of Asia. Passes 1.1° S of Regulus on the 26th. Reaches greatest eastern elongation (27°) on the 30th.

Venus: Continues to dominate the dawn sky throughout the month, shining brilliantly in the eastern sky. Passes 3° north of the Moon on July 20, well timed for observers in the Americas.

Mars: Too close to the Sun to be seen. Reaches superior conjunction on the 27th, in Cancer.

Jupiter: Low in the evening sky throughout the month for observers at mid-northern latitudes. The Moon passes 2° to its north on the 28th. Meridian transit times at Greenwich on the 1st, 11th, 21st – 18:13, 17:37, 17:01 UT*.

Saturn: Now in the evening sky, post-opposition Saturn remains low in the sky in the constellation Ophiucus for Northern Hemisphere observers. The waxing gibbous Moon passes 3° to Saturn's north on the evening of the 6th in North America. Meridian transit times at Greenwich on the 1st, 11th, 21st – 22:50, 22:08, 21:27 UT*.

Uranus: Rises near midnight among the stars of Pisces. Meridian transit times at Greenwich on the 1st, 11th, 21st – 7:07, 6:29, 5:50 UT*.

Neptune: Rises in late evening, in retrograde motion in Aquarius. Occulted by the Moon on the 13th, as seen from parts of the Southern Hemisphere. Meridian transit times at Greenwich on the 1st, 11th, 21st – 4:26, 3:46, 3:06 UT*.

*See p. 94, the bold-faced sentences of the first paragraph.

Time (UT) d		h	m	JULY EVENTS
Sat.	1	0	51	**First Quarter**
		7		Jupiter 3° S of Moon
Sun.	2	1	47	Algol at minimum
		13		**Juno at opposition**
Mon.	3	20		Earth at aphelion (152 092 504 km)
Tue.	4	22	35	Algol at minimum
Wed.	5			Venus at greatest heliocentric lat. S
Thu.	6	4		Moon at apogee (405 934 km)
Fri.	7	3		Saturn 3° S of Moon
		19	24	Algol at minimum
Sat.	8			
Sun.	9	4	7	**Full Moon**
Mon.	10	5		Mercury 0.04° N of Beehive (M44)
		16	13	Algol at minimum
Tue.	11			
Wed.	12			
Thu.	13	13	1	Algol at minimum
		18		**Neptune 0.9° N of Moon, occultation†**
Fri.	14			
Sat.	15			
Sun.	16	9	50	Algol at minimum
		19	26	**Last Quarter**
Mon.	17			
Tue.	18			
Wed.	19	6	39	Algol at minimum
Thu.	20	0		**Aldebaran 0.4° S of Moon, occultation‡**
		11		**Venus 3° N of Moon**
Fri.	21	17		Moon at perigee (361 236 km)
Sat.	22	3	27	Algol at minimum
Sun.	23			Mercury at descending node
		9	46	**New Moon** (lunation 1170)
Mon.	24			
Tue.	25	0	16	Algol at minimum
		9		**Mercury 0.9° S of Moon, occultation††**
		11		**Regulus 0.07° S of Moon, occultation‡‡**
Wed.	26	9		**Mercury 1.1° S of Regulus**
Thu.	27	1		Mars in conjunction with the Sun
		21	4	Algol at minimum
Fri.	28	3		S. δ-Aquariid meteors peak
		20		Jupiter 3° S of Moon
Sat.	29			
Sun.	30	5		**Mercury greatest elongation E (27°)**
		15	23	**First Quarter**
		17	53	Algol at minimum
Mon.	31			

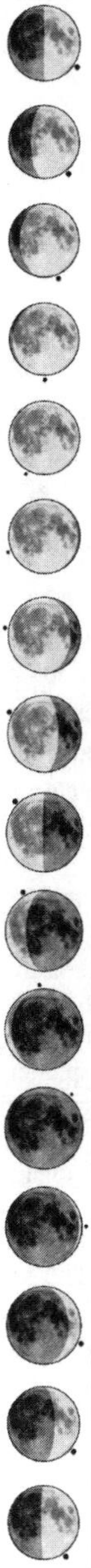

Jupiter's Satellites
West East

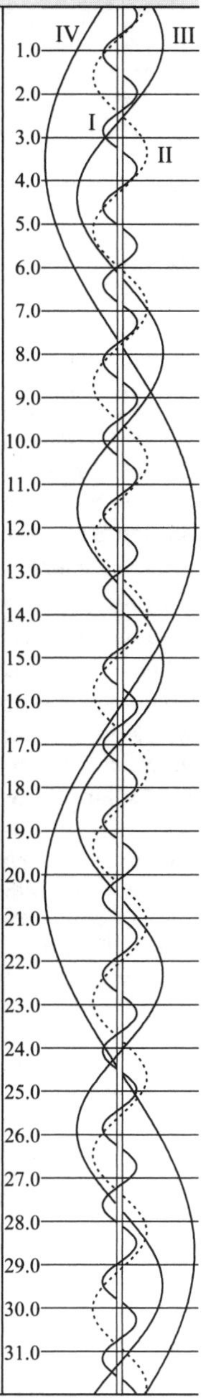

†Most of Antarctica, New Zealand, Chatham I. ‡ India, central and NE Asia, Aleutian Is., Hawaii
†† North Europe including British Isles, most of Greenland, north half of Asia
‡‡ North half of Africa, Middle East, south India, Indonesia

THE SKY FOR AUGUST

		Mercury	Venus	Mars	Jupiter	Saturn	Uranus	Neptune	Sun
RA	1	10h 28m	6h 01m	8h 39m	13h 04m	17h 23m	1h 46m	23h 01m	8h 45m
	11	10h 45m	6h 51m	9h 06m	13h 09m	17h 22m	1h 46m	23h 00m	9h 23m
	21	10h 34m	7h 41m	9h 31m	13h 15m	17h 21m	1h 45m	22h 59m	10h 00m
Dec	1	+7° 52′	+21° 52′	+19° 33′	−5° 29′	−21° 55′	+10° 19′	−7° 21′	+18° 05′
	11	+4° 02′	+21° 52′	+17° 50′	−6° 04′	−21° 55′	+10° 18′	−7° 26′	+15° 21′
	21	+4° 01′	+20° 53′	+15° 55′	−6° 42′	−21° 56′	+10° 16′	−7° 32′	+12° 12′
Dist	1	0.84	1.15	2.66	5.75	9.34	19.71	29.11	1.015
	11	0.71	1.21	2.66	5.89	9.48	19.55	29.03	1.013
	21	0.62	1.28	2.65	6.01	9.62	19.4	28.97	1.012
Mag	1	0.4	−4	1.7	−1.9	0.3	5.8	7.8	
	11	1.1	−4	1.7	−1.8	0.3	5.8	7.8	
	21	3.3	−3.9	1.8	−1.8	0.4	5.8	7.8	
Size	1	8.0″	14.5″	3.5″	34.3″	17.8″	3.6″	2.3″	31′31″
	11	9.5″	13.7″	3.5″	33.5″	17.5″	3.6″	2.3″	31′34″
	21	10.8″	13.1″	3.5″	32.8″	17.3″	3.6″	2.3″	31′37″

Moon: On August 0 at 0h UT, Sun's selenographic colongitude is 359.51° and increases by 12.2° each day thereafter.

Greatest N declination on the 18th (+19.3°).

Greatest S declination on the 5th (–19.4°).

Libration in longitude: E limb most exposed on the 24th (+5.7°),
W limb most exposed on the 11th (–5.3°).

Libration in latitude: N limb most exposed on the 15th (+6.8°),
S limb most exposed on the 1st (–6.8°) & 28th (–6.8°).

Partial lunar eclipse on Aug. 7, visible from Australia, Antarctica, Asia, Africa, the Middle East, Europe, extreme eastern South America, the Pacific Ocean, the Indian Ocean, and the south Atlantic Ocean (see p. 130).

Total solar eclipse on Aug. 21, visible across the entire continental U.S. (see p. 130).

Mercury: Well placed in the evening sky in the first half of the month, especially for observers in the Southern Hemisphere. Reaches aphelion on the 2nd. Achieves inferior conjunction on the 26th.

Venus: The second planet continues to recede from Earth but remains prominent in the dawn sky throughout the month. Passes 2° north of the Moon on the 19th.

Mars: Too close to the Sun to be seen.

Jupiter: Low in the evening sky throughout the month, although the advancing Sun pulls within 45° by month-end. The Moon passes 3° to Jupiter's north on the 25th.

Saturn: In eastern Ophiucus, where it is moderately well placed for viewing in the late evening hours. The Moon passes nearby on the 3rd and again on the 30th. Saturn achieves its second stationary point on the 25th, after which it resumes prograde motion. Meridian transit times at Greenwich on the 1st, 11th, 21st – 20:41, 20:01, 19:21 UT*.

Uranus: Rises in late evening in Pisces. Stationary on the 3rd, thereafter will be in retrograde motion for the remainder of 2017. Meridian transit times at Greenwich on the 1st, 11th, 21st – 5:07, 4:27, 3:48 UT*.

Neptune:. Rises in mid-evening, in retrograde motion in Aquarius. Occulted by the Moon on the 9th, as seen from parts of the Southern Hemisphere. Meridian transit times at Greenwich on the 1st, 11th, 21st – 2:22, 1:42, 1:02 UT*

*See p. 94, the bold-faced sentences of the first paragraph.

Time (UT)	d	h	m	AUGUST EVENTS
Tue.	1			
Wed.	2			Mercury at aphelion
		14	42	Algol at minimum
		18		Moon at apogee (405 025 km)
Thu.	3	7		Saturn 3° S of Moon
		10		Uranus stationary
Fri.	4			
Sat.	5	11	30	Algol at minimum
Sun.	6			
Mon.	7	18	11	**Full Moon**
				Partial Lunar Eclipse (p. 130)
Tue.	8	8	19	Algol at minimum
Wed.	9	23		**Neptune 0.9° N of Moon, occultation†**
Thu.	10			
Fri.	11	5	7	Algol at minimum
Sat.	12	6		Mercury stationary
		19		**Perseid meteors peak**
Sun.	13			
Mon.	14	1	56	Algol at minimum
Tue.	15	1	15	**Last Quarter**
Wed.	16	7		**Aldebaran 0.4° S of Moon, occultation‡**
		22	44	Algol at minimum
Thu.	17			
Fri.	18	13		Moon at perigee (366 121 km)
Sat.	19	5		**Venus 2° N of Moon**
		19	33	Algol at minimum
Sun.	20			
Mon.	21	18	30	**New Moon** (lunation 1171)
				Total Solar Eclipse (p. 130)
Tue.	22			Mercury at greatest heliocentric lat. S
		16	22	Algol at minimum
Wed.	23			
Thu.	24			
Fri.	25	13		Jupiter 3° S of Moon
		13	10	Algol at minimum
		15		Saturn stationary
Sat.	26	10		Juno stationary
		21		Mercury in inferior conjunction
Sun.	27			
Mon.	28	9	59	Algol at minimum
Tue.	29	8	13	**First Quarter**
Wed.	30			Venus at ascending node
				Mars at greatest heliocentric lat. N
		11		Moon at apogee (404 308 km)
		14		Saturn 4° S of Moon
Thu.	31	6	47	Algol at minimum

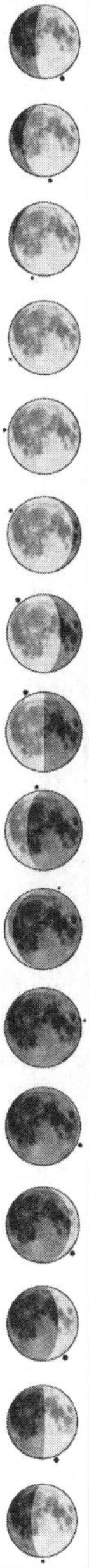

Jupiter's Satellites

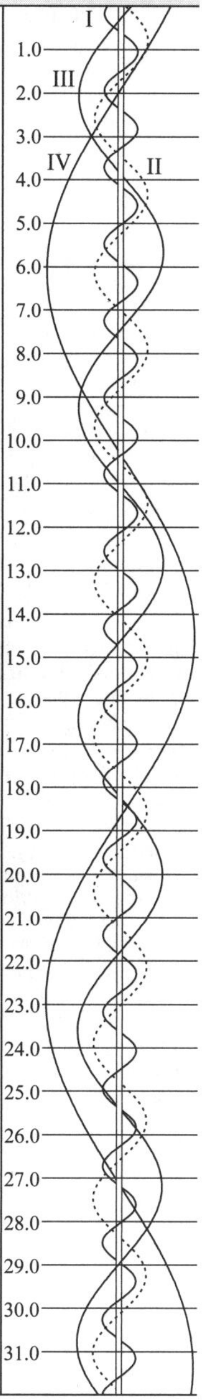

† Most of Antarctica, Kerguelen Islands, west tip of Australia
‡ North tip of South America, Caribbean, northernmost Africa, Europe, Middle East, west Asia

THE SKY FOR SEPTEMBER

		Mercury	Venus	Mars	Jupiter	Saturn	Uranus	Neptune	Sun
RA	1	10h 02m	8h 36m	9h 58m	13h 22m	17h 21m	1h 45m	22h 58m	10h 41m
	11	10h 10m	9h 25m	10h 23m	13h 29m	17h 22m	1h 44m	22h 57m	11h 17m
	21	11h 02m	10h 13m	10h 47m	13h 37m	17h 23m	1h 43m	22h 56m	11h 53m
Dec	1	+8° 50′	+18° 40′	+13° 37′	−7° 28′	−21° 58′	+10° 11′	−7° 39′	+8° 23′
	11	+11° 22′	+15° 44′	+11° 23′	−8° 11′	−22° 01′	+10° 06′	−7° 46′	+4° 40′
	21	+8° 01′	+12° 03′	+9° 02′	−8° 56′	−22° 04′	+9° 59′	−7° 52′	+0° 49′
Dist	1	0.68	1.34	2.64	6.14	9.8	19.24	28.94	1.009
	11	0.9	1.4	2.61	6.23	9.96	19.13	28.95	1.007
	21	1.17	1.45	2.59	6.31	10.13	19.03	28.98	1.004
Mag	1	3.3	−3.9	1.8	−1.7	0.4	5.7	7.8	
	11	−0.2	−3.9	1.8	−1.7	0.5	5.7	7.8	
	21	−1.1	−3.9	1.8	−1.7	0.5	5.7	7.8	
Size	1	10.0″	12.4″	3.6″	32.1″	17.0″	3.6″	2.3″	31′42″
	11	7.5″	11.9″	3.6″	31.6″	16.7″	3.7″	2.3″	31′46″
	21	5.8″	11.5″	3.6″	31.2″	16.4″	3.7″	2.3″	31′51″

Moon: On September 0 at 0h UT, Sun's selenographic colongitude is 18.18° and increases by 12.2° each day thereafter.

Greatest N declination on the 15th (+19.3°).

Greatest S declination on the 1st (19.4°) & 28th (−19.4°).

Libration in longitude: E limb most exposed on the 21st (+5.0°),
W limb most exposed on the 6th (−4.9°).

Libration in latitude: N limb most exposed on the 11th (+6.7°),
S limb most exposed on the 25th (−6.7°).

On Sep. 18 the waning crescent Moon will occult four bright objects including Venus, Regulus, Mars, and Mercury as seen from various locales around the world. The dawn sky will feature most or all of these luminaries clustered 15–25° west of the Sun, with the ecliptic favourably angled for Northern Hemisphere observers.

Mercury: Emerges in the morning sky early in the month, the **best morning apparition of the year for northern observers**. Achieves greatest western elongation (18°) on the 12th and perihelion three days later. Has an extremely close conjunction with Mars on the 16th. Occulted by the Moon on the 18th as seen from several Pacific islands and NW of South America.

Venus: Continues its extended show in the dawn sky, particularly prominent in the Northern Hemisphere due to the favourable angle of the morning ecliptic. **Will have a close conjunction with the 27-day-old Moon on the 17/18, with an occultation to occur for observers in S.E. Asia, Australia, and New Zealand.** Venus will have a close (0.5°) pass of Regulus on the 19–20, with both objects comfortably fitting within the same telescopic field of view.

Mars: Emerges into the morning sky in mid-month in Leo. Has a very close conjunction with Mercury on the 16th when both are 17° from the Sun; the steep angle of the morning ecliptic will aid observers in the Northern Hemisphere. Will be occulted by the Moon on the 18th as seen primarily from the South Pacific Ocean.

Jupiter: Has its second conjunction of the year with Spica on the 5th when the two will be separated by just over 3°. Jupiter's apparent eastward motion is accelerating even as the Sun continues to overtake it in the evening sky. By month-end, the two are separated by just 20° and the low angle of the evening ecliptic will make Jupiter difficult to see in the Northern Hemisphere.

Saturn: Low in the southwestern sky in the evening hours, setting before midnight local daylight time before month end. The waxing crescent Moon passes nearby on the 26th. Meridian transit times at Greenwich on the 1st, 11th, 21st – 18:42, 17:59, 17:21 UT*.

Uranus: Rises in mid-evening as it approaches its October opposition. Passes about 1° north of 4th-mag. Omicron Piscium in mid-month, a useful reference for observers trying to spot Uranus with the naked eye or binoculars. Meridian transit times at Greenwich on the 1st, 11th, 21st – 3:04, 2:23, 1:43 UT*.

Neptune: Visible all night in Aquarius. At opposition on the 5th, mag.+7.8, 4.0 light-hours (28.9 au), and 8° south of the celestial equator. Occulted by the full Moon on the 6th, an exceedingly difficult observation, theoretically visible from parts of the Southern Hemisphere. Meridian transit times at Greenwich on the 1st, 11th, 21st – 0:17, 23:33, 22:53 UT*.

*See p. 94, the bold-faced sentences of the first paragraph.

Time (UT) d	h	m	SEPTEMBER EVENTS
Fri. 1			
Sat. 2			
Sun. 3	3	36	Algol at minimum
Mon. 4	16		Mercury stationary
Tue. 5	5		**Neptune at opposition**
Wed. 6	0	24	Algol at minimum
	5		**Neptune 0.8° N of Moon, occultation†**
	7	3	**Full Moon**
Thu. 7			
Fri. 8			Mercury at ascending node
	21	13	Algol at minimum
Sat. 9			
Sun. 10	12		**Mercury 0.6° S of Regulus**
Mon. 11	18	2	Algol at minimum
Tue. 12	10		**Mercury greatest elongation W (18°)**
	13		**Aldebaran 0.4° S of Moon, occultation‡**
Wed. 13	6	25	**Last Quarter**
	16		Moon at perigee (369 860 km)
Thu. 14	14	50	Algol at minimum
Fri. 15			Mercury at perihelion
Sat. 16	18		**Mercury 0.06° N of Mars**
Sun. 17	11	39	Algol at minimum
Mon. 18			**Zodiacal Light vis. in N lat. in E before morning twilight for next two weeks**
	1		**Venus 0.5° N of Moon, occultation††**
	5		**Regulus 0.1° S of Moon, occultation‡‡**
	20		**Mars 0.1° S of Moon, occultation†††**
	23		**Mercury 0.03° N of Moon, occultation‡‡‡**
Tue. 19	23		**Venus 0.5° N of Regulus**
Wed. 20	5	30	**New Moon** (lunation 1172)
	8	28	Algol at minimum
Thu. 21			
Fri. 22	8		Jupiter 4° S of Moon
	20	2	**Equinox**
Sat. 23	5	16	Algol at minimum
Sun. 24			
Mon. 25			Mercury at greatest heliocentric lat. N
	11		Pallas stationary
Tue. 26	2	5	Algol at minimum
Wed. 27	0		Saturn 3° S of Moon
	7		Moon at apogee (404 348 km)
	14		Vesta in conjunction with the Sun
Thu. 28	2	54	**First Quarter**
	22	53	Algol at minimum
Fri. 29			
Sat. 30			

Jupiter's Satellites
West East

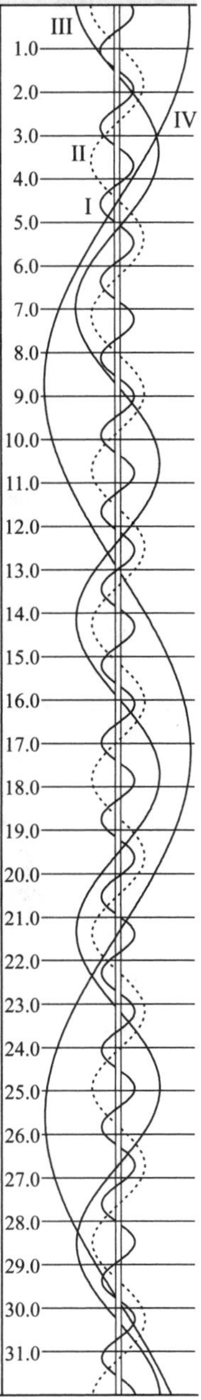

† Most of Antarctica, SE S. America, S. Georgia ‡ Hawaii, Central & North America, Azores
†† Southeast Asia, Australia, New Zealand ‡‡ NE Africa, Middle East, SE Asia, north Australia
††† NE Micronesia, Hawaii, Galapagos Is., NW S. America ‡‡‡ Easternmost Asia, Micronesia, N Polynesia

THE SKY FOR OCTOBER

		Mercury	Venus	Mars	Jupiter	Saturn	Uranus	Neptune	Sun
RA	1	12h 08m	11h 00m	11h 10m	13h 44m	17h 25m	1h 41m	22h 55m	12h 29m
	11	13h 12m	11h 46m	11h 34m	13h 53m	17h 28m	1h 40m	22h 54m	13h 05m
	21	14h 13m	12h 32m	11h 57m	14h 01m	17h 31m	1h 38m	22h 53m	13h 42m
Dec	1	+0° 58′	+7° 47′	+6° 36′	−9° 42′	−22° 08′	+9° 51′	−7° 58′	−3° 05′
	11	−6° 41′	+3° 08′	+4° 07′	−10° 27′	−22° 12′	+9° 42′	−8° 03′	−6° 55′
	21	−13° 37′	−1° 44′	+1° 36′	−11° 13′	−22° 15′	+9° 34′	−8° 07′	−10° 36′
Dist	1	1.34	1.5	2.55	6.37	10.29	18.96	29.04	1.001
	11	1.42	1.54	2.51	6.41	10.44	18.92	29.13	0.998
	21	1.42	1.57	2.47	6.43	10.59	18.92	29.25	0.996
Mag	1	−1.4	−3.9	1.8	−1.7	0.5	5.7	7.8	
	11	−1.5	−3.9	1.8	−1.7	0.6	5.7	7.8	
	21	−0.8	−3.9	1.8	−1.7	0.6	5.7	7.8	
Size	1	5.0″	11.2″	3.7″	30.9″	16.2″	3.7″	2.3″	31′57″
	11	4.7″	10.9″	3.7″	30.7″	15.9″	3.7″	2.3″	32′02″
	21	4.7″	10.6″	3.8″	30.6″	15.7″	3.7″	2.3″	32′08″

Moon: On October 0 at 0h UT, Sun's selenographic colongitude is 24.24° and increases by 12.2° each day thereafter.

Greatest N declination on the 12th (+19.6°).

Greatest S declination on the 26th (−19.7°).

Libration in longitude: E limb most exposed on the 17th (+5.2°),
W limb most exposed on the 4th (−5.5°) & 31st (−6.7°).

Libration in latitude: N limb most exposed on the 9th (+6.6°),
S limb most exposed on the 22nd (−6.6°).

The waning crescent Moon joins Venus and Mars on Oct. 17/18.

Mercury: Poorly placed for the first half of the month. Achieves superior conjunction on the 8th and gradually re-emerges in the evening sky in the late in the month. Reaches aphelion on the 29th.

Venus: Gradually becoming less prominent in the dawn sky as it heads ever closer to the Sun and its January 2017 superior conjunction. **Has a close (0.2°) conjunction with Mars on the 5th** as it passes the slower red planet pulling away from its own conjunction with the Sun. Venus shines nearly 200× brighter than its temporary companion.

Mars: Visible in the dawn sky, passing from Leo into Virgo on the 12th. **Will have a close conjunction with Venus on the 5th, when both planets are at 23° elongation from the Sun.** Reaches aphelion on the 7th, at which point its apparent diameter is just 3.7″, with apparent mag. +1.8.

Jupiter: Might be glimpsed very low in the southwestern sky early in the month, but will soon be too close to the Sun to be seen. In conjunction with the Sun on the 26th.

Saturn: Low in the southwestern sky in early evening, setting in the later evening hours. The waxing crescent Moon passes nearby on the 23rd–24th.

Uranus: Visible all night. At opposition on the 19th, 2.6 light-hours (18.9 au) from Earth, disk 3.7″. At mag. +5.7 and declination +9.6°, Uranus is accessible to the unaided eye under dark skies, <2° WNW of 4th-mag. Omicron Piscium at the time of opposition. Meridian transit times at Greenwich on the 1st, 11th, 21st – 1:02, 0:21, 23:37 UT*.

Neptune: Visible most of the night, just past opposition and retrograding in Aquarius. Occulted by the waxing gibbous Moon on the 3rd and again on the 30th, as seen from deep in the Southern Hemisphere. Meridian transit times at Greenwich on the 1st, 11th, 21st – 22:12, 21:32, 20:52 UT*.

*See p. 94, the bold-faced sentences of the first paragraph.

Time (UT) d		h	m	OCTOBER EVENTS
Sun.	1	19	42	Algol at minimum
Mon.	2			
Tue.	3			Venus at perihelion
		12		**Neptune 0.7° N of Moon, occultation†**
Wed.	4	16	31	Algol at minimum
Thu.	5	13		**Venus 0.2° N of Mars**
		18	40	**Full Moon**
Fri.	6			
Sat.	7			Mars at aphelion
		13	19	Algol at minimum
Sun.	8	9		Draconid meteors peak
		21		Mercury in superior conjunction
Mon.	9	6		Moon at perigee (366 855 km)
		19		**Aldebaran 0.6° S of Moon, occultation‡**
Tue.	10	10	8	Algol at minimum
Wed.	11			
Thu.	12	12	25	**Last Quarter**
Fri.	13	6	57	Algol at minimum
Sat.	14			
Sun.	15	11		**Regulus 0.2° S of Moon, occultation††**
Mon.	16	3	46	Algol at minimum
Tue.	17			**Zodiacal Light vis. in N lat. in E before morning twilight for next two weeks**
		10		**Mars 1.8° S of Moon**
Wed.	18	0		**Venus 2.0° S of Moon**
Thu.	19			Mercury at descending node
		0	34	Algol at minimum
		18		**Uranus at opposition**
		19	12	**New Moon** (lunation 1173)
Fri.	20			
Sat.	21	12		Orionid meteors peak
		21	23	Algol at minimum
Sun.	22			
Mon.	23			
Tue.	24			Venus at greatest heliocentric lat. N
		12		Saturn 3° S of Moon
		18	12	Algol at minimum
Wed.	25	2		Moon at apogee (405 154 km)
Thu.	26	18		Jupiter in conjunction with the Sun
Fri.	27	15	1	Algol at minimum
		22	22	First Quarter
Sat.	28			
Sun.	29			Mercury at aphelion
		0		**Pallas at opposition**
Mon.	30	11	50	Algol at minimum
		21		**Neptune 0.9° N of Moon, occultation‡‡**
Tue.	31			

Jupiter's Satellites
West East

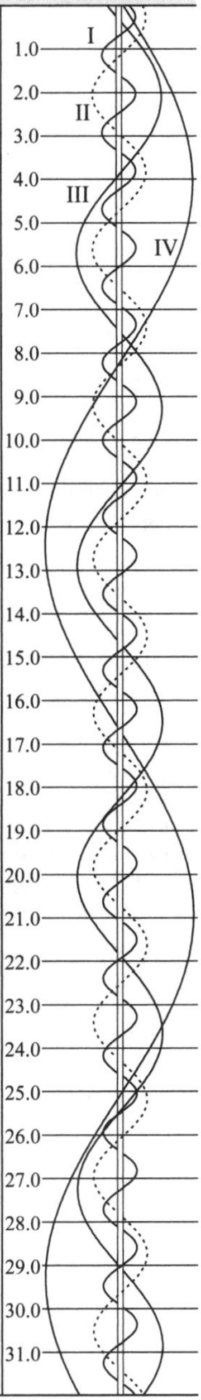

† Kerguelen Is., most of Antarctica, SE tip of Australia, New Zealand, SW Polynesia
‡ C & NE Asia, Alaska, NW Canada †† N. America except Canada, most of Caribbean, Cape Verde, W Africa
‡‡ Most of Antarctica, south tip of Africa

THE SKY FOR NOVEMBER

		Mercury	Venus	Mars	Jupiter	Saturn	Uranus	Neptune	Sun
RA	1	15h 20m	13h 22m	12h 22m	14h 10m	17h 36m	1h 36m	22h 53m	14h 25m
	11	16h 20m	14h 09m	12h 46m	14h 18m	17h 40m	1h 35m	22h 52m	15h 04m
	21	17h 17m	14h 58m	13h 09m	14h 27m	17h 44m	1h 34m	22h 52m	15h 46m
Dec	1	−19° 48′	−7° 03′	−1° 10′	−12° 02′	−22° 20′	+9° 24′	−8° 10′	−14° 20′
	11	−23° 44′	−11° 39′	−3° 41′	−12° 46′	−22° 23′	+9° 16′	−8° 12′	−17° 21′
	21	−25° 38′	−15° 48′	−6° 08′	−13° 27′	−22° 26′	+9° 09′	−8° 13′	−19° 51′
Dist	1	1.36	1.61	2.41	6.43	10.73	18.94	29.4	0.993
	11	1.25	1.64	2.35	6.4	10.84	18.99	29.55	0.99
	21	1.08	1.66	2.28	6.36	10.93	19.08	29.71	0.988
Mag	1	−0.4	−3.9	1.8	−1.7	0.6	5.7	7.9	
	11	−0.3	−3.9	1.8	−1.7	0.6	5.7	7.9	
	21	−0.4	−3.9	1.7	−1.7	0.5	5.7	7.9	
Size	1	4.9″	10.4″	3.9″	30.6″	15.5″	3.7″	2.3″	32′14″
	11	5.4″	10.2″	4.0″	30.8″	15.3″	3.7″	2.3″	32′18″
	21	6.2″	10.1″	4.1″	31.0″	15.2″	3.7″	2.3″	32′23″

Moon: On November 0 at 0h UT, Sun's selenographic colongitude is 41.95° and increases by 12.2° each day thereafter.

Greatest N declination on the 8th (+19.5°).

Greatest S declination on the 22nd (−19.6°).

Libration in longitude: E limb most exposed on the 13th (+6.7°),
W limb most exposed on the 29th (−7.6°).

Libration in latitude: N limb most exposed on the 5th (+6.5°),
S limb most exposed on the 18th (−6.6°).

Large tides in the days following full Moon (Nov. 4)

Mercury: Well placed in the evening sky throughout the month, achieving greatest eastern elongation (22°) on the 24th. Makes a wide pair with the 2-day old Moon on the 19–20. In conjunction with Saturn on the 28th.

Venus: Still prominent in the dawn sky, although its daily visibility window is shortening. Its elongation from the Sun diminishes from 16° on the 1st to 10° on the 30th. It is 4° south of the very thin crescent Moon on the 17th.

Mars: In Virgo throughout the month, it gradually pulls away from the Sun in the morning sky. The Moon passes 3° to its north on the 15th.

Jupiter: Gradually emerges from the Sun's glare to appear in morning twilight late in the month. **Will have a close conjunction with Venus on the 13th**, just 14° from the Sun but possible to be seen by telescopic observers, even during daylight hours. Crosses the border from Virgo into Libra on the 14th.

Saturn: Vanishing into evening twilight, low in SW. Passes eastward into Sagittarius in mid-month, where it will remain until early 2020.

Uranus: Well placed in the evening sky among the stars of Pisces. Meridian transit times at Greenwich on the 1st, 11th, 21st – 22:52, 22:11, 21:30 UT*.

Neptune: Well placed in the early evening sky, setting near midnight. Resumes direct eastward motion against the stars on the 22nd. Its occultation by the Moon on the 27th is the last in a series, and can only be seen from parts of Antarctica. Meridian transit times at Greenwich on the 1st, 11th, 21st – 20:08, 19:29, 18:49 UT*.

*See p. 94, the bold-faced sentences of the first paragraph.

Time (UT)	d	h	m	NOVEMBER EVENTS
Wed.	1			
Thu.	2	8	38	Algol at minimum
Fri.	3			
Sat.	4	5	23	**Full Moon**
Sun.	5	2		**DAYLIGHT SAVING TIME ENDS**
		5	27	Algol at minimum
		12		S. Taurid meteors peak
Mon.	6	0		Moon at perigee (361 438 km)
		3		**Aldebaran 0.8° S of Moon, occultation**†
Tue.	7			
Wed.	8	2	16	Algol at minimum
Thu.	9			
Fri.	10	20	36	**Last Quarter**
		23	5	Algol at minimum
Sat.	11	17		**Regulus 0.4° S of Moon, occultation**‡
Sun.	12	11		N. Taurid meteors peak
		15		Mercury 2° N of Antares
Mon.	13	6		**Venus 0.3° N of Jupiter**
		19	54	Algol at minimum
Tue.	14			
Wed.	15	1		Mars 3° S of Moon
Thu.	16	9		**Vesta 0.4° N of Moon, occultation**††
		16	43	Algol at minimum
		21		Jupiter 4° S of Moon
Fri.	17	6		**Venus 4° S of Moon**
		18		Leonid meteors peak
Sat.	18			Mercury at greatest heliocentric lat. S
		11	42	New Moon (lunation 1174)
Sun.	19	13	32	Algol at minimum
Mon.	20	9		Mercury 7° S of Moon
Tue.	21	0		Saturn 3° S of Moon
		19		Moon at apogee (406 132 km)
Wed.	22	10	21	Algol at minimum
		21		Neptune stationary
Thu.	23			
Fri.	24	0		**Mercury greatest elongation E (22°)**
Sat.	25	7	10	Algol at minimum
Sun.	26	17	3	**First Quarter**
Mon.	27	5		**Neptune 1.2° N of Moon, occultation**‡‡
Tue.	28	3	59	Algol at minimum
		9		Mercury 3° S of Saturn
Wed.	29			
Thu.	30			

Jupiter's Satellites
West East

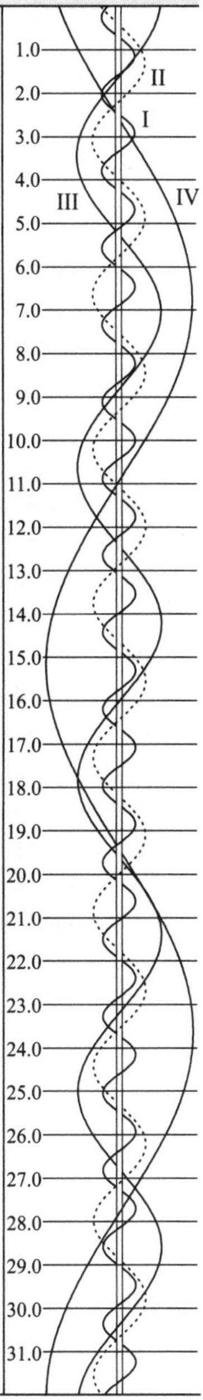

† North America except westernmost part, north Europe, northwest Asia
‡ Japan, E Asia, SW N. America, Central America †† East Brazil, southwest Africa, Kerguelen Is.
‡‡ West and Central Antarctica

THE SKY FOR DECEMBER

		Mercury	Venus	Mars	Jupiter	Saturn	Uranus	Neptune	Sun
RA	1	17h 54m	15h 49m	13h 32m	14h 35m	17h 49m	1h 33m	22h 52m	16h 28m
	11	17h 33m	16h 42m	13h 56m	14h 43m	17h 54m	1h 32m	22h 52m	17h 12m
	21	16h 48m	17h 36m	14h 20m	14h 50m	17h 59m	1h 31m	22h 53m	17h 56m
Dec	1	−25° 10′	−19° 16′	−8° 31′	−14° 06′	−22° 29′	+9° 03′	−8° 12′	−21° 45′
	11	−22° 14′	−21° 51′	−10° 48′	−14° 43′	−22° 31′	+8° 58′	−8° 10′	−22° 58′
	21	−19° 25′	−23° 22′	−12° 57′	−15° 16′	−22° 32′	+8° 55′	−8° 07′	−23° 26′
Dist	1	0.86	1.68	2.21	6.29	10.99	19.18	29.89	0.986
	11	0.69	1.69	2.13	6.2	11.03	19.31	30.06	0.985
	21	0.76	1.7	2.05	6.09	11.05	19.46	30.23	0.984
Mag	1	−0.1	−3.9	1.7	−1.7	0.5	5.7	7.9	
	11	4.3	−3.9	1.6	−1.7	0.5	5.7	7.9	
	21	0.8	−3.9	1.6	−1.8	0.4	5.8	7.9	
Size	1	7.8″	9.9″	4.2″	31.3″	15.1″	3.7″	2.2″	32′26″
	11	9.8″	9.9″	4.4″	31.8″	15.1″	3.6″	2.2″	32′29″
	21	8.8″	9.8″	4.6″	32.3″	15.1″	3.6″	2.2″	32′31″

Moon: On December 0 at 0h UT, Sun's selenographic colongitude is 47.02° and increases by 12.2° each day thereafter.

Greatest N declination on the 5th (+19.5°).

Greatest S declination on the 19th (–19.6°).

Libration in longitude: E limb most exposed on the 11th (+7.4°),
W limb most exposed on the 27th (–7.9°).

Libration in latitude: N limb most exposed on the 2nd (+6.6°) & 29th (+6.7°),
S limb most exposed on the 15th (–6.7°).

Large tides in the days following full Moon (Dec. 3)

Mercury: Visible in the evening sky very early in the month. Achieves perihelion on the 12th and inferior conjunction one day later. Returns to the morning sky late in the month.

Venus: Briefly visible in bright morning twilight early in the month, before drawing too close to the Sun to be observed.

Mars: Crosses the border from Virgo into Libra on the 21st as it continues its ascension into the morning sky. Approaching Jupiter at month-end although the official conjunction will occur very early in 2018.

Jupiter: Becomes more prominent in morning twilight throughout the month as it advances into Libra. Passes less than 1° north of Zubenelgenubi on the 20th.

Saturn: Too close to the Sun to be seen. In conjunction on the 21st just as the Sun itself reaches winter solstice, thus marking Saturn's southernmost point in its 29.5-year orbit.

Uranus: Well placed in the evening sky in Pisces, setting after midnight. Meridian transit times at Greenwich on the 1st, 11th, 21st – 20:50, 20:10, 19:30 UT*.

Neptune: In the western evening sky in Aquarius, setting in late evening. The angle of the ecliptic favours observers in northern latitudes. Meridian transit times at Greenwich on the 1st, 11th, 21st – 18:10, 17:31, 16:52 UT*.

*See p. 94, the bold-faced sentences of the first paragraph.

Time (UT) d	h m	DECEMBER EVENTS
Fri. 1	0 48	Algol at minimum
Sat. 2		
Sun. 3	8	Mercury stationary
	13	**Aldebaran 0.8° S of Moon, occultation**†
	15 47	**Full Moon** (largest in 2017)
	21 37	Algol at minimum
Mon. 4	9	Moon at perigee (357492 km) **Large tides**
Tue. 5		
Wed. 6	18 26	Algol at minimum
Thu. 7		Mercury at ascending node
Fri. 8	23	**Regulus 0.7° S of Moon, occultation**‡
Sat. 9	15 15	Algol at minimum
Sun. 10	7 51	**Last Quarter**
Mon. 11		
Tue. 12		Mercury at perihelion
	12 4	Algol at minimum
Wed. 13	2	Mercury in inferior conjunction
	16	Mars 4° S of Moon
Thu. 14	7	**Geminid meteors peak**
	14	Jupiter 4° S of Moon
	19	**Vesta 0.2° N of Moon, occultation**††
Fri. 15	8 53	Algol at minimum
Sat. 16		
Sun. 17		
Mon. 18	5 42	Algol at minimum
	6 30	**New Moon** (lunation 1175)
Tue. 19		Venus at descending node
	1	Moon at apogee (406 603 km)
Wed. 20		
Thu. 21	2 31	Algol at minimum
	16 28	**Solstice**
	21	Saturn in conjunction with the Sun
	21	Ceres stationary
Fri. 22		Mercury at greatest heliocentric lat. N
	15	Ursid meteors peak
Sat. 23	3	Mercury stationary
	23 20	Algol at minimum
Sun. 24	6	Pallas stationary
Mon. 25		
Tue. 26	9 20	**First Quarter**
	20 10	Algol at minimum
Wed. 27		
Thu. 28		
Fri. 29	16 59	Algol at minimum
Sat. 30		
Sun. 31	1	**Aldebaran 0.8° S of Moon, occultation**‡‡

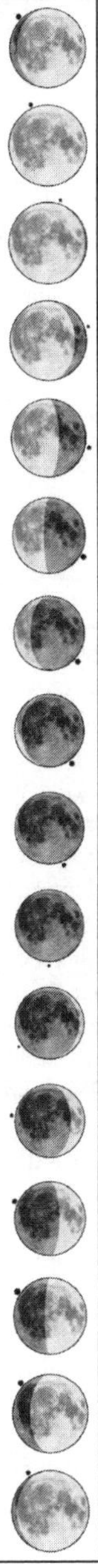

Jupiter's Satellites
West East

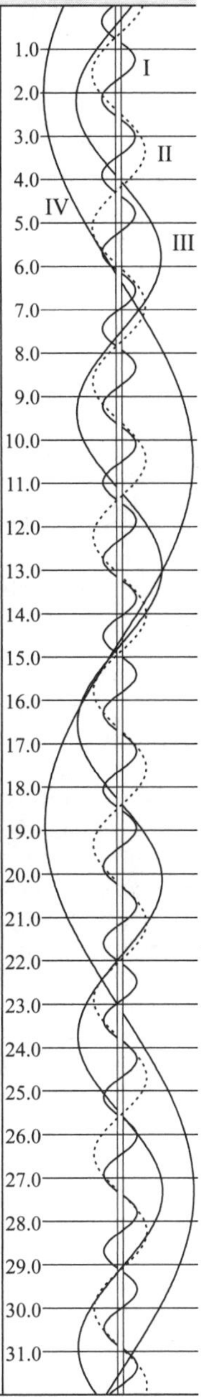

† Central and north Asia, north Greenland, northwest North America
‡Northeast and central Europe, north Greenland, north Asia, northern parts of Micronesia
†† C. Polynesia, parts of Chile & Argentina ‡‡ Most of N. America, Greenland, Europe except S, W Russia

ECLIPSES

ECLIPSE PATTERNS

BY ROY BISHOP

Eclipse Seasons

The plane of the Moon's orbit is tilted about 5° to the plane of Earth's orbit, the ecliptic. Since 5° is considerably larger than both the north–south range of lunar parallax for various localities on Earth (≈1.9°) and the angular radii of the Sun and Moon (each ≈0.25°), solar eclipses can occur only when the Sun is near (within about

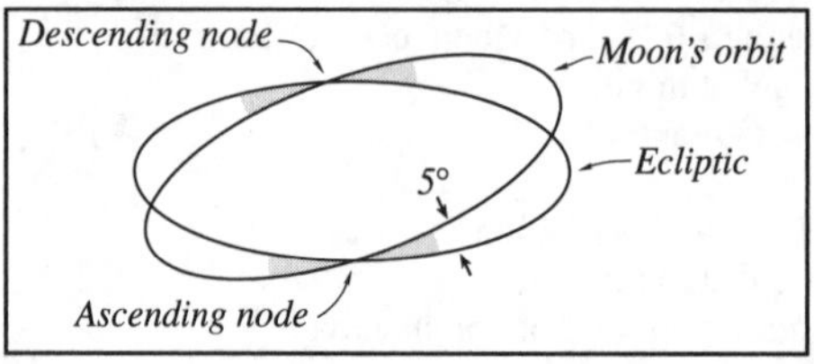

±15° to ±18°) one of the two points at which the Moon's orbit crosses the ecliptic (nodes). Lunar eclipses have a comparable restriction. The *ascending* node is the one at which the Moon crosses to the *north* side of the ecliptic.

The Sun moves eastward along the ecliptic about 1° per day; thus the interval during which an eclipse can occur is at most about (2 × 18°) ÷ 1°/d = 36 d, an *eclipse season*. The interval between new moons (29.5 days) is somewhat less, thus one or two solar eclipses will occur in each eclipse season. Six months later, when the Sun is near the other node, another eclipse season occurs. However, the plane of the Moon's orbit wobbles, making the nodes regress slowly westward along the ecliptic with a period of 18.60 years; thus the two eclipse seasons drift backward through the year, occurring about 19 days earlier each year. *The eclipse seasons of 2017 occur in February and August.*

In a calendar year,

- there can be as many as seven eclipses (solar and lunar combined, as last occurred in 1982) and as few as four (the usual number);
- there can be as many as five solar or lunar eclipses and as few as two;
- the number of total or annular solar eclipses can range from zero to two, the number of total lunar eclipses from zero to three.

In 2017, there are four eclipses: two solar (one annular and one total) and two lunar (one penumbral and one partial).

The Saros

Eclipses of the Sun and Moon recur with various periodicities that are more or less approximate. These periodicities are interesting both as numerical curiosities and because they may be used to predict eclipses. The most famous periodicity, the *Saros*, has been known since ancient times. It is a consequence of a remarkable commensurability between three lunar average periods:

Synodic month *(S)* (new to new)	= 29.530 589 d, 223*S*	= 6585.3213 d
Draconic month *(N)* (node to node)	= 27.212 221 d, 242*N*	= 6585.3575 d
Anomalistic month *(P)* (perigee to perigee)	= 27.554 550 d, 239*P*	= 6585.5375 d

Several aspects of this arithmetic are relevant to the pattern of eclipses (for brevity, the following comments are restricted primarily to the case of solar eclipses):

(1) An integer number of *S*s (223) ensures a new Moon and hence the possibility of a second solar eclipse.

(2) $242N \approx 223S$ means that the new Moon will be at almost the same position relative to a node, ensuring that an eclipse *will* occur again and that it will occur on Earth's globe about the same distance north or south of the ecliptic plane as did the first eclipse.

(3) The Saros (223*S*) = 6585.3213 d = 18 years + *only* 10.3213 d or 11.3213 d (depending on the number of intervening leap years). Thus one Saros later Earth will be at almost the same point in its elliptical orbit and hence at nearly the same distance from the Sun. Moreover, the inclination of Earth toward the Sun (season) will be nearly the same; thus the same latitude region of Earth will be exposed to the eclipse.

(text continues on next page)

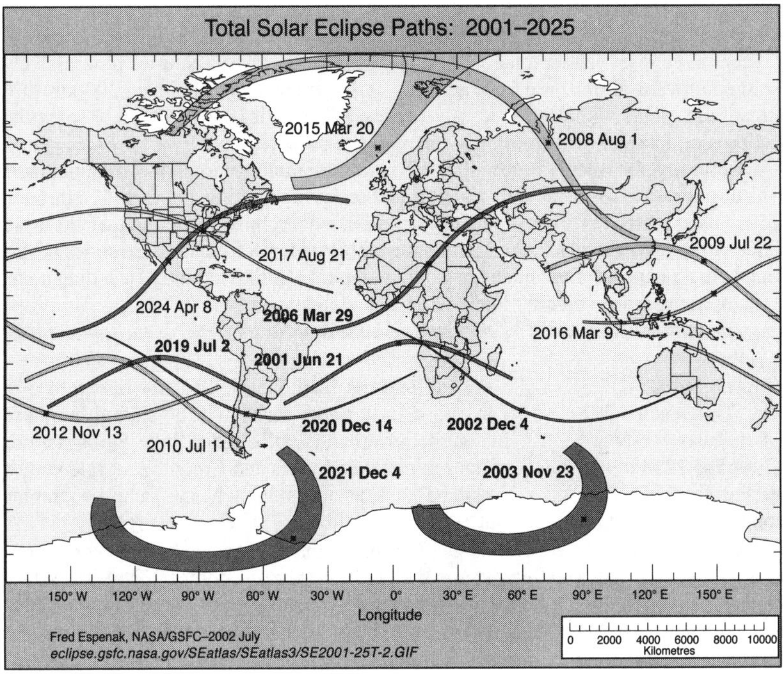

The figure shows the paths of all total solar eclipses, excluding hybrid annular/total eclipses, occurring during the years 2001–2025. There are 15 eclipses, one in each of the years 2001, 2002, 2003, 2006, 2008, 2009, 2010, 2012, 2015, 2016, 2017, 2019, 2020, 2021, and 2024. Because the 25-year period covered by the figure is somewhat longer than the 18-year Saros interval, the first four and last four eclipses, drawn with heavy shading and with labels in bold type, make up four Saros pairs, with Saros numbers 127, 142, 152, and 139, respectively. Note that the members of each pair are both total eclipses, are separated in time by one Saros, have similar path shapes, and occur at similar latitudes; note also that the later member is shifted 120° westward in longitude (see items (2) through (6) of the text explaining these features). The figure was produced by Fred Espenak and is presented here with his permission. For figures showing total solar eclipses, annular eclipses, and hybrid annular/total eclipses for the period −1999 to +3000 (2000 BC to AD 3000), see eclipse.gsfc.nasa.gov/SEatlas/SEatlas.html.

(4) $239P \approx 223S$ means that one Saros later the new Moon will be at almost the same point in its elliptical orbit and thus at the same distance from Earth. With the same lunar and solar distances, the type of eclipse (total or annular) will be the same. Since the eclipse will occur near the same geographic latitude (see **(2)** and **(3)**), the duration of totality or annularity, or the magnitude of partial eclipse if the eclipse is not central, will be almost the same as it was one Saros earlier.

(5) $242N - 223S = 0.0361$ d $= 0.87$ h. This, together with the 0.55°/h eastward speed of the Moon in its orbit, means that after one Saros the Moon will be about 0.5° west of its former position relative to its node. Thus a Saros series does not last forever; there will be about 36°/0.5° ≈ 72 eclipses in a Saros series (the number ranges from 69 to 87). Furthermore, any one Saros series will last for about 72 × 18 ≈ 1300 years (the range is 1226 to 1551 years).

A Saros series begins with about 10 partial eclipses of increasing magnitude in the north or south polar region, depending upon whether the eclipses are occurring near the ascending or descending lunar node, respectively. These are followed by about 50 central eclipses (either total or annular), which over many centuries progressively shift southward or northward across Earth (on average an approximate 300-km shift in latitude occurs with each successive eclipse). The series ends with 10 or so partial eclipses of decreasing magnitude in the opposite polar region.

Currently, for solar eclipses, 40 Saros series are running simultaneously, numbers 117 through 156 (for lunar eclipses, 41 Saros series are running, numbers 110 through 150). That is, in any 18-year 11-day interval, one eclipse from each of these 40 (and 41) series takes place, after which the whole pattern repeats. Those series occurring at the lunar ascending node are given odd numbers; those at the descending node, even numbers (vice versa for lunar eclipses).

The four eclipses of 2017 belong to the same four Saros series as the four eclipses of 1999.

(6) The Saros $= 223S = 6585.3213$ d, and the fractional 0.3213 d ≈ one-third of a day. Thus each successive solar eclipse in a Saros series will be shifted one-third of the way westward (120° in longitude) around Earth. After three Saros periods (3 × 6585.3213 d ≈ 19 756 d, or approximately 54 years and 1 month), a cycle known as the *Exeligmos*, the eclipse will be back at approximately the same geographic longitude, although shifted about 1000 km in latitude. Two examples follow:

(a) The total solar eclipse of 2017 Aug. 21 that sweeps across the contiguous United States (see the map on the previous page) is number 22 of Saros 145. Number 21 of that Saros was the total solar eclipse of 1999 Aug. 11 that began near Nova Scotia and crossed Europe and southwestern Asia.

(b) The total solar eclipse of 2024 Apr. 8 (no. 30 of Saros 139), which sweeps northeastward across eastern North America, will be geographically similar to that of 1970 Mar. 7 (no. 27 of Saros 139), which followed the eastern seaboard of North America one Exeligmos earlier. Also, one Saros earlier we had the similar total solar eclipse of 2006 Mar. 29 (no. 29 of Saros 139), which occurred about 120° to the east, across Africa and the Mediterranean (see the figure on the previous page). You, the reader, should now be able to figure out the date, the shape of the path of totality, and the geographic location of solar eclipse no. 28 of Saros 139!

The Metonic Cycle

The sequence of lunar phases and the year repeat their relative pattern at 19-year intervals, a cycle known to astronomers in ancient Babylon and that was discovered independently around 430 BC by Meton, a Greek astronomer. We have $235S = 235 \times 29.530\,589 = 6939.6884$ d;

19 years = 6939 d or 6940 d (depending on leap years).

Moreover, $255N$ is also very close to 19 years,

$255N = 255 \times 27.212\,221 = 6939.1164$ d.

Thus solar and lunar eclipses also repeat on a 19-year "Metonic" cycle. Since $255N$ is less than $235S$, the Moon does not reach the same phase (new or full for an eclipse) until it has moved eastward relative to the node by

$(235S - 255N) \times 24\text{ h} \times 0.55°/\text{h} = 7.5°$.

Thus a Metonic eclipse series will have only

eclipse season width on the ecliptic (36°) ÷ 7.5° ≈ 4 or 5 eclipses;

and the geographic latitude of successive solar eclipses in a series will change substantially (north or south, depending upon whether the Moon is at its ascending node or descending node, respectively).

What about the Moon's position in its orbit relative to its perigee? Using the anomalistic month P (the Moon returns to perigee on average every 27.554 550 d),

$235S \div P = 251.85$, which is *not* near an integer.

Thus in a Metonic series the Moon's distance is not the same from one eclipse to another. Hence the type of solar eclipse (total or annular) will vary within the series.

With only about four eclipses in a series, a mix of eclipse types, and scattered geographic occurrence, a Metonic eclipse series is not as elegant or useful as a Saros series. The main feature of a Metonic eclipse series is that, like lunar phases, the successive eclipses occur on (almost) the *same day* of the year.

Examples of the Metonic cycle for a lunar phase, lunar eclipses, and a Western Hemisphere total solar eclipse are given below. The numbers in parentheses are Saros numbers.

New Moon	Lunar Eclipses	Solar Eclipses
1979 Mar. 28	1998 Feb. 11 (no eclipse)	1960 Aug. 22 (no eclipse)
1998 Mar. 28	**2017** Feb. 11 Penumbral (114)	1979 Aug. 22 Annular (125)
2017 Mar. 28	2036 Feb. 11 Total (124)	1998 Aug. 22 Annular (135)
2036 Mar. 27	2055 Feb. 11 Total (134)	**2017** Aug. 21 Total (145)
2055 Mar. 28	2074 Feb. 11 Penumbral (144)	2036 Aug. 21 Partial (155)
2074 Mar. 27	2093 Feb. 11 (no eclipse)	2055 Aug. 21 (no eclipse)

Canons of Eclipses

Anyone with an interest in eclipses will be impressed by the *Five Millennium Canon of Solar Eclipses* (2006) and the *Five Millennium Canon of Lunar Eclipses* (2009) and their accompanying catalogues (four books in all), by Fred Espenak and Jean Meeus, and published by NASA. These monumental works give maps and tabular data for all 23 962 eclipses (11 898 solar and 12 064 lunar) occurring during the period –1999 to +3000 (2000 BC to AD 3000). The books are available from: NASA Center for AeroSpace Information, 7115 Standard Drive, Hanover MD 21076-1320, USA.

Three decades ago NASA published Fred Espenak's *Fifty Year Canon of Solar Eclipses* and *Fifty Year Canon of Lunar Eclipses*. Included are maps and data for all eclipses during the two centuries, 1901–2100, plus diagrams and maps (larger scale than in the *Five Millennium* canons) for eclipses during the 50-year period 1986–2035.

ECLIPSES IN 2017

BY FRED ESPENAK

In 2017, there are two solar eclipses and two lunar eclipses:

Feb. 11:	Penumbral Lunar Eclipse
Feb. 26:	Annular Solar Eclipse
Aug. 7:	Partial Lunar Eclipse
Aug. 21:	Total Solar Eclipse

Predictions for the solar eclipses are summarized in Figures 1 and 3 and Tables 1 through 6. World maps show the regions of visibility for each solar eclipse. For the lunar eclipses, Figure 2 illustrates the eclipse of August 7, while a URL link is provided for a diagram and map of the February 11 eclipse.

Penumbral Lunar Eclipse of February 11

The first event of the year is a penumbral lunar eclipse occurring at the lunar orbit's ascending node in Leo. The apparent diameter of the Moon is larger than average since the eclipse occurs 4.4 days after perigee.

The Moon's orbital trajectory takes it through the southern part of Earth's penumbral shadow. The times of the major eclipse phases are as follows.

Penumbral Eclipse Begins:	22:34:14 UT1
Greatest Eclipse:	00:43:54 UT1
Penumbral Eclipse Ends:	02:53:29 UT1

At the instant of greatest eclipse[1] (00:43:54 UT1[2]), the Moon lies at the zenith for a point in Mali near the capital city Bamako. The penumbral eclipse magnitude[3] is very deep and peaks at 0.9883. This is close to being a total penumbral eclipse—the southern edge of the lunar limb lies just 0.4′ outside the penumbral shadow.

Note that the beginning and end of a penumbral eclipse are not visible to the eye. In fact, no shading can be detected until about 2/3 of the Moon's disk is immersed in the penumbra. This would place the period of eclipse visibility within about ¾ hours of greatest eclipse (about 00:00 to 01:30 UT1). Keep in mind that this is only an estimate. Atmospheric conditions and the observer's visual acuity are important factors to consider. An interesting exercise is to note when penumbral shading is first and last seen.

The entire eclipse is visible from Europe, Africa, western Asia, eastern North and South America. Observers in western North and South America miss the early stages of the eclipse while eastern Asia misses the late stages. None of the eclipse is visible from Japan, Australia or New Zealand.

For more information, including an illustration and map of the worldwide visibility of this event, see www.EclipseWise.com/eclipse.html#yr2017

Annular Solar Eclipse of February 26

The first solar eclipse of 2017 occurs in Aquarius at the Moon's descending node. The central track of the annular eclipse crosses the Pacific Ocean, South America, the Atlantic Ocean, and Africa. Countries in the annular path include Chile, Argentina,

---

[1] The instant of greatest eclipse for lunar eclipses occurs when the distance between the Moon's midpoint and Earth's shadow axis reaches a minimum.

[2] *Universal Time* (UT1) is within 0.9 s of Coordinated Universal Time (UTC). See p. 44.

[3] Penumbral eclipse magnitude is defined as the fraction of the Moon's diameter occulted by Earth's penumbral shadow.

FIGURE 1—ANNULAR SOLAR ECLIPSE OF 2017 FEBRUARY 26

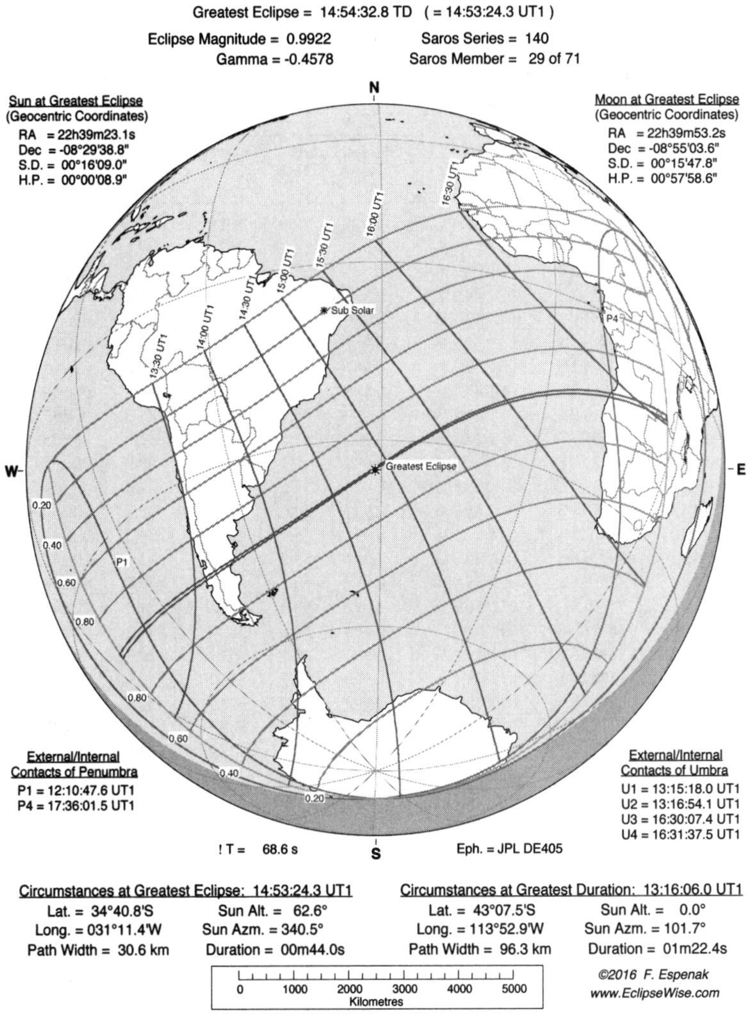

See p. 137 for an explanation of this figure.

Angola, Zambia, and Democratic Republic of the Congo. A partial eclipse is visible from a much larger region covering much of South America, Africa, and Antarctica (Figure 1, p. 127).

The width of the annular path is narrow along its entirety because the eclipse occurs only 4.7 days before perigee. As a consequence, the Sun appears only slightly

TABLE 1—CENTRAL LINE OF THE ANNULAR SOLAR ECLIPSE OF 2017 FEBRUARY 26

UT1	Central Line Latitude	Longitude	Diameter Ratio	Sun Alt. °	Sun Az. °	Path Width *km*	Central Duration
13:16.1	43°07.5′S	113°53.0′W	0.977	0.0	101.7	96.3	01m22.4s
13:20	45°17.3′S	094°55.5′W	0.981	14.4	87.6	77.5	01m15.9s
13:25	45°44.3′S	085°32.1′W	0.983	21.7	79.6	68.3	01m12.0s
13:30	45°45.1′S	078°46.2′W	0.984	27.2	73.2	61.8	01m08.8s
13:35	45°33.0′S	073°17.1′W	0.986	31.7	67.6	56.7	01m06.0s
13:40	45°12.5′S	068°36.3′W	0.987	35.6	62.5	52.6	01m03.5s
13:45	44°46.1′S	064°29.8′W	0.987	39.1	57.5	49.0	01m01.2s
13:50	44°15.2′S	060°49.1′W	0.988	42.3	52.7	46.0	00m59.0s
13:55	43°40.7′S	057°29.1′W	0.989	45.2	47.9	43.3	00m57.0s
14:00	43°03.3′S	054°25.7′W	0.989	47.8	43.1	41.0	00m55.1s
14:05	42°23.6′S	051°36.4′W	0.990	50.3	38.2	39.0	00m53.4s
14:10	41°41.7′S	048°58.8′W	0.990	52.5	33.2	37.3	00m51.8s
14:15	40°58.1′S	046°31.2′W	0.991	54.6	28.0	35.8	00m50.4s
14:20	40°12.9′S	044°12.3′W	0.991	56.4	22.6	34.5	00m49.1s
14:25	39°26.4′S	042°00.8′W	0.991	58.0	16.9	33.4	00m47.9s
14:30	38°38.6′S	039°55.8′W	0.992	59.4	11.0	32.5	00m46.8s
14:35	37°49.6′S	037°56.2′W	0.992	60.6	4.8	31.8	00m46.0s
14:40	36°59.6′S	036°01.4′W	0.992	61.5	358.4	31.2	00m45.2s
14:45	36°08.6′S	034°10.6′W	0.992	62.1	351.8	30.9	00m44.6s
14:50	35°16.7′S	032°23.1′W	0.992	62.5	345.1	30.6	00m44.2s
14:55	34°23.8′S	030°38.4′W	0.992	62.5	338.3	30.6	00m43.9s
15:00	33°30.1′S	028°55.7′W	0.992	62.3	331.7	30.7	00m43.8s
15:05	32°35.4′S	027°14.6′W	0.992	61.8	325.2	31.0	00m43.8s
15:10	31°39.9′S	025°34.5′W	0.992	61.0	319.1	31.5	00m44.0s
15:15	30°43.4′S	023°54.7′W	0.992	60.0	313.2	32.1	00m44.3s
15:20	29°46.0′S	022°14.6′W	0.992	58.7	307.8	33.0	00m44.8s
15:25	28°47.6′S	020°33.7′W	0.992	57.1	302.7	34.0	00m45.5s
15:30	27°48.2′S	018°51.1′W	0.991	55.4	298.1	35.2	00m46.3s
15:35	26°47.6′S	017°06.0′W	0.991	53.4	293.8	36.7	00m47.3s
15:40	25°45.7′S	015°17.5′W	0.991	51.3	289.9	38.3	00m48.4s
15:45	24°42.4′S	013°24.5′W	0.990	48.9	286.3	40.2	00m49.7s
15:50	23°37.5′S	011°25.6′W	0.990	46.3	283.0	42.4	00m51.2s
15:55	22°30.7′S	009°19.0′W	0.989	43.5	280.0	44.9	00m52.8s
16:00	21°21.7′S	007°02.3′W	0.989	40.4	277.2	47.8	00m54.7s
16:05	20°09.9′S	004°32.2′W	0.988	37.1	274.6	51.0	00m56.7s
16:10	18°54.6′S	001°43.7′W	0.987	33.3	272.2	54.8	00m59.0s
16:15	17°34.5′S	001°31.4′E	0.986	29.1	270.0	59.1	01m01.6s
16:20	16°07.2′S	005°28.6′E	0.985	24.1	267.8	64.4	01m04.6s
16:25	14°26.9′S	010°45.0′E	0.983	17.7	265.6	71.2	01m08.3s
16:30	12°05.1′S	020°27.9′E	0.980	6.8	262.8	82.9	01m14.1s
16:30.9	10°55.4′S	027°07.4′E	0.978	0.0	261.4	90.3	01m17.4s

larger than the Moon. The instant of greatest eclipse occurs in the South Atlantic at 14:54:32 UT1, when the eclipse magnitude[4] reaches 0.9922 (eclipse obscuration[5] is 0.9845). At that instant, the duration of annularity is 44 s, the path width is 30.6 kilometres and the Sun is 63° above the horizon.

During the course of its 3.2-hour trajectory, the antumbra's track is approximately

[4] *Eclipse magnitude for solar eclipses is defined as the fraction of the Sun's diameter occulted by the Moon.*

[5] *Eclipse obscuration is defined as the fraction of the Sun's area occulted by the Moon.*

TABLE 2—LOCAL CIRCUMSTANCES FOR THE ANNULAR SOLAR ECLIPSE OF 2017 FEBRUARY 26

Geographic Location		Eclipse Begins h:m	Max. Eclipse h:m	Eclipse Ends h:m	Sun Alt. °	Sun Azm. °	Ecl. Mag.	Ecl. Obsc.
SOUTH AMERICA								
Argentina	Buenos Aires	12:31	13:53	15:23	50	57	0.729	0.657
	Córdoba	12:26	13:42	15:07	45	69	0.603	0.506
	Rosario	12:29	13:49	15:17	48	62	0.667	0.582
	San Justo	12:31	13:53	15:23	50	58	0.730	0.658
Bolivia	La Paz	12:54	13:37	14:23	43	86	0.125	0.052
Brazil	Belford Roxo	13:10	14:40	16:10	74	25	0.529	0.423
	Belo Horizonte	13:17	14:43	16:09	77	29	0.443	0.329
	Brasília	13:25	14:37	15:51	76	59	0.273	0.164
	Curitiba	12:54	14:21	15:51	66	47	0.535	0.429
	Fortaleza	14:45	15:29	16:11	78	245	0.086	0.030
	Goiânia	13:19	14:32	15:46	74	62	0.282	0.171
	Nova Iguaçu	13:10	14:40	16:10	74	25	0.528	0.422
	Pinheirinhos	13:08	14:36	16:05	74	33	0.500	0.390
	Recife	14:19	15:31	16:37	76	267	0.261	0.154
	Rio de Janeiro	13:10	14:41	16:11	74	24	0.535	0.430
	Salvador	13:51	15:12	16:27	82	306	0.334	0.219
	São Paulo	13:03	14:30	16:00	71	40	0.511	0.402
Chile	Santiago	12:20	13:32	14:53	37	74	0.643	0.553
Paraguay	Asuncion	12:42	13:58	15:22	56	66	0.454	0.340
Uruguay	Montevideo	12:34	13:58	15:29	52	53	0.751	0.685
AFRICA								
Angola	Luanda	15:24	16:32	— s	13	263	0.862	0.820
Cameroon	Yaoundé	15:44	16:42	— s	10	261	0.496	0.384
Chad	Ndjamena	16:02	16:46	— s	5	260	0.271	0.161
Congo	Brazzaville	15:32	16:37	— s	9	262	0.751	0.682
Ghana	Accra	15:42	16:39	17:31	22	258	0.356	0.240
Ivory Coast	Abidjan	15:40	16:37	17:28	27	258	0.327	0.212
Kenya	Nairobi	15:40	15:49s	— x	0	262	0.136	0.059
Mali	Bamako	16:10	16:39	17:06	28	253	0.073	0.023
Mozambique	Maputo	15:17	16:13	— s	2	261	0.607	0.509
Nigeria	Lagos	15:46	16:42	17:32	18	259	0.361	0.245
Sierra Leone	Freetown	15:51	16:32	17:10	36	253	0.134	0.057
South Africa	Cape Town	14:58	15:59	16:55	17	271	0.515	0.406
	Durban	15:12	16:08	— s	5	263	0.531	0.423
	Johannesburg	15:14	16:13	— s	6	263	0.618	0.523
	Pretoria	15:15	16:14	— s	5	263	0.628	0.534
Tanzania	Dar-es-Salaam	15:34	15:42s	— x	0	261	0.129	0.054
Togo	Lome	15:45	16:41	17:31	21	259	0.352	0.236
Uganda	Kampala	15:42	16:05s	— x	0	262	0.351	0.234
Zambia	Lusaka	15:25	16:26	— s	1	261	0.869	0.827
Zimbabwe	Harare	15:23	16:22s	— x	0	261	0.797	0.738

All times Universal Time (UT1).
'r' indicates an eclipse in progress at sunrise.
's' indicates an eclipse in progress at sunset.

13 600 kilometres long and covers 0.15% of Earth's surface area. Path coordinates and central-line circumstances are presented in Table 1 (p. 128).

Local circumstances and eclipse times for a number of cities are listed in Table 2 (p. 129). All times are in Universal Time (UT1). The Sun's altitude and azimuth, the eclipse magnitude and eclipse obscuration are all given at the instant of maximum eclipse at each location. The 2017 Annular Solar Eclipse Circumstances Calculator (www.EclipseWise.com/solar/SEcirc/2001-2100/SE2017Feb26Acirc.html) is an interactive web page that can quickly calculate the local circumstances for the eclipse from any geographic location not included in Table 2.

This is the 29th eclipse of Saros[6] 140 (Espenak and Meeus, 2006). The series began on 1512 Apr. 16 with a string of 8 partial eclipses. The series continued with 10 consecutive total eclipses from 1674 Aug. 02 to 1836 Nov. 09. Saros 140 then changes character with 4 hybrid eclipses from 1854 Nov. 20 to 1908 Dec. 23. The first of 32 annular eclipses occurred on 1927 Jan. 03. The series reverts back to partial with the eclipse of 2503 Dec. 19. It will continue producing partial eclipses until the series ends on 2774 Jun. 01. In all, Saros 140 produces 71 solar eclipses in the sequence of 8 partial, 11 total, 4 hybrid, 32 annular and 16 partial eclipses. Complete details for the series can be found at www.EclipseWise.com/solar/SEsaros/SEsaros140.html

For additional information about this eclipse, see

www.EclipseWise.com/eclipse.html#yr2017

Partial Lunar Eclipse of August 07

The third eclipse of 2017 is a shallow partial lunar eclipse with an umbral eclipse magnitude[7] of 0.2465. The Moon's orbital trajectory takes it through the northern part of Earth's penumbral and umbral shadows. It should be easily visible to the naked eye as a dark shading in the southern quarter of the Moon (Figure 2, p. 131).

The times of the major eclipse phases are as follows.

Penumbral Eclipse Begins:	15:50:00 UT1
Partial Eclipse Begins:	17:22:56 UT1
Greatest Eclipse:	18:20:29 UT1
Partial Eclipse Ends:	19:18:12 UT1
Penumbral Eclipse Ends:	20:50:59 UT1

The eclipse occurs at the Moon's descending node in Capricornus. At the instant of greatest eclipse (18:20:29 UT1) the Moon lies near the zenith from a location in the Indian Ocean south of India. The event is well placed for observers in Africa, central Asia, and Australia. None of the eclipse will be visible from North and South America.

For more information, see www.EclipseWise.com/eclipse.html#yr2017

Total Solar Eclipse of August 21

The final eclipse of the year is one of the most anticipated astronomical events in decades. The total solar eclipse of August 21 is the first total eclipse visible from America's lower 48 states in over 38 years. The last one happened in 1979 and passed through the Pacific Northwest and central Canada in late winter.

The total eclipse is visible from within a narrow corridor that traverses the United States from the Pacific Northwest to the Southeast crossing a dozen states: Oregon, Idaho, Wyoming, Nebraska, Kansas, Missouri, Illinois, Kentucky, Tennessee,

6 The *Saros* is a period of 6585.3 days (18 y, 11 d, 8 h) in which eclipses (both solar and lunar) repeat (see ECLIPSE PATTERNS, p. 122).

7 Umbral eclipse magnitude is defined as the fraction of the Moon's diameter occulted by Earth's umbral shadow.

(text continues on p. 134)

FIGURE 2—PARTIAL LUNAR ECLIPSE OF 2017 AUGUST 7

Ecliptic Conjunction = 18:11:45.1 TD (= 18:10:36.9 UT)
Greatest Eclipse = 18:21:37.3 TD (= 18:20:29.1 UT)

Penumbral Magnitude = 1.2887 P. Radius = 1.2003° Gamma = 0.8668
Umbral Magnitude = 0.2465 U. Radius = 0.6745° Axis = 0.8024°

Saros Series = 119 Member = 62 of 83

Sun at Greatest Eclipse
(Geocentric Coordinates)

RA = 09h11m33.0s
Dec = +16°12'28.1"
S.D. = 00°15'46.4"
H.P. = 00°00'08.7"

Moon at Greatest Eclipse
(Geocentric Coordinates)

RA = 21h10m53.1s
Dec = -15°25'17.2"
S.D. = 00°15'08.1"
H.P. = 00°55'32.7"

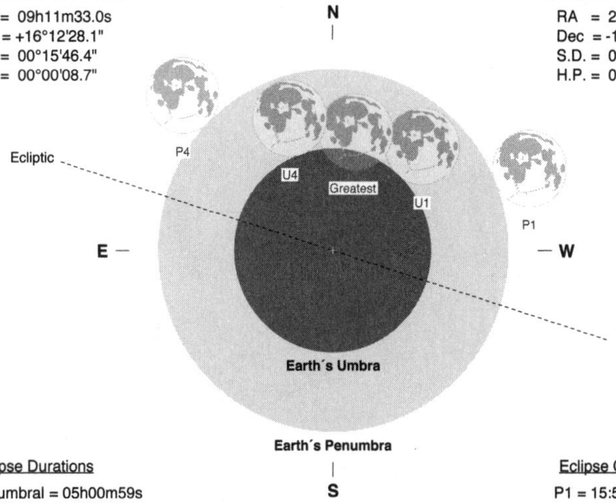

Eclipse Durations

Penumbral = 05h00m59s
Umbral = 01h55m16s

0 15 30 45 60
Arc-Minutes

Eclipse Contacts

P1 = 15:50:00 UT
U1 = 17:22:56 UT
U4 = 19:18:12 UT
P4 = 20:50:59 UT

! T = 68 s
Rule = CdT (Danjon)
Eph. = VSOP87/ELP2000-85

©2016 F. Espenak
www.EclipseWise.com

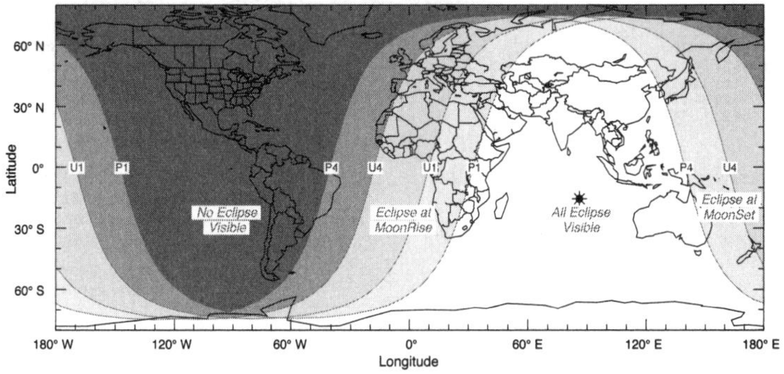

See p. 137 for an explanation of this figure

FIGURE 3—TOTAL SOLAR ECLIPSE OF 2017 AUGUST 21

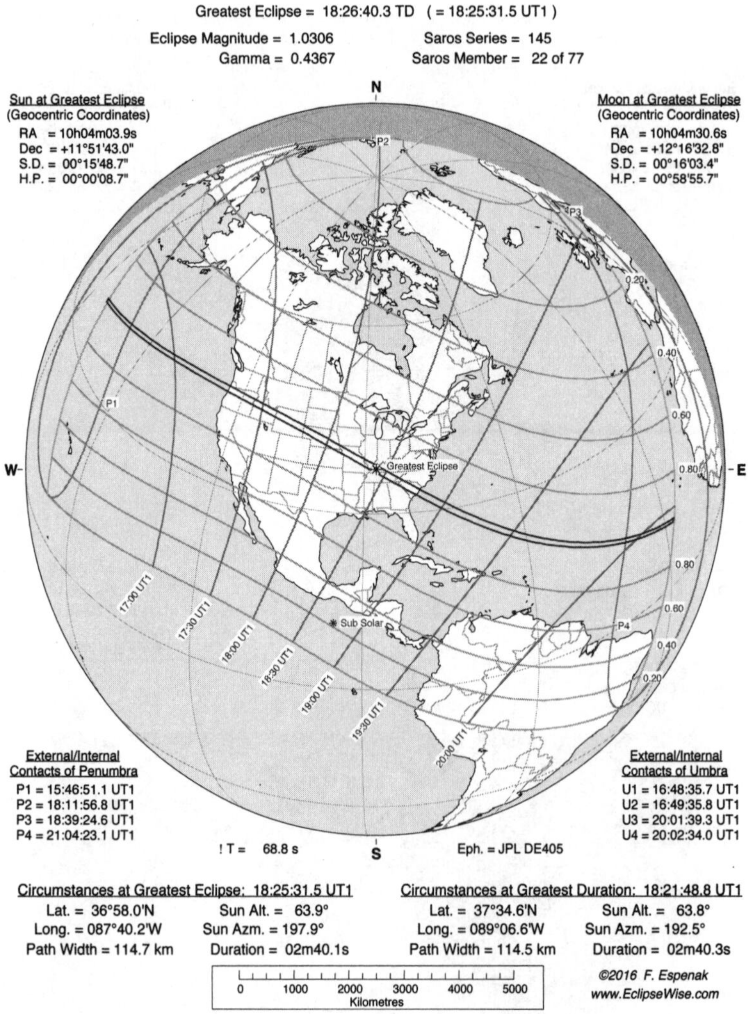

See p. 137 for an explanation of this figure.

TABLE 3—CENTRAL LINE OF THE TOTAL SOLAR ECLIPSE OF 2017 AUGUST 21

UT	Central Line Latitude	Central Line Longitude	Diameter Ratio	Sun Alt. °	Sun Az. °	Path Width *km*	Central Duration
16:49.1	39°44.2′N	171°35.4′W	1.016	0.0	74.5	62.2	00m51.6s
16:50	41°29.3′N	162°50.3′W	1.018	7.0	80.3	70.0	01m01.7s
16:55	43°35.4′N	149°21.2′W	1.021	18.0	90.6	81.4	01m19.4s
17:00	44°24.2′N	141°29.4′W	1.023	24.5	97.4	87.4	01m30.9s
17:05	44°47.3′N	135°22.0′W	1.024	29.6	103.3	91.9	01m40.4s
17:10	44°55.6′N	130°12.3′W	1.025	33.9	108.7	95.3	01m48.6s
17:15	44°53.6′N	125°41.0′W	1.026	37.7	113.8	98.2	01m55.9s
17:20	44°44.0′N	121°37.9′W	1.027	41.2	118.8	100.7	02m02.6s
17:25	44°28.2′N	117°56.7′W	1.028	44.3	123.7	102.8	02m08.6s
17:30	44°07.4′N	114°33.2′W	1.028	47.2	128.7	104.6	02m14.0s
17:35	43°42.4′N	111°24.5′W	1.029	49.8	133.8	106.2	02m18.9s
17:40	43°13.7′N	108°28.4′W	1.029	52.3	139.0	107.7	02m23.3s
17:45	42°41.8′N	105°43.0′W	1.029	54.5	144.3	108.9	02m27.1s
17:50	42°07.1′N	103°06.9′W	1.030	56.6	150.0	110.1	02m30.5s
17:55	41°29.9′N	100°39.0′W	1.030	58.4	155.9	111.1	02m33.3s
18:00	40°50.3′N	098°18.2′W	1.030	60.0	162.1	111.9	02m35.7s
18:05	40°08.6′N	096°03.6′W	1.030	61.3	168.6	112.7	02m37.5s
18:10	39°24.9′N	093°54.4′W	1.030	62.4	175.4	113.3	02m38.9s
18:15	38°39.4′N	091°49.9′W	1.031	63.2	182.5	113.9	02m39.8s
18:20	37°52.2′N	089°49.5′W	1.031	63.7	189.8	114.4	02m40.2s
18:25	37°03.2′N	087°52.5′W	1.031	63.9	197.2	114.7	02m40.2s
18:30	36°12.7′N	085°58.2′W	1.031	63.8	204.5	115.0	02m39.6s
18:35	35°20.6′N	084°06.2′W	1.030	63.4	211.6	115.1	02m38.6s
18:40	34°26.9′N	082°15.8′W	1.030	62.6	218.5	115.1	02m37.2s
18:45	33°31.7′N	080°26.5′W	1.030	61.6	224.9	115.0	02m35.2s
18:50	32°34.8′N	078°37.5′W	1.030	60.3	231.0	114.8	02m32.9s
18:55	31°36.4′N	076°48.3′W	1.030	58.8	236.6	114.4	02m30.1s
19:00	30°36.2′N	074°58.1′W	1.029	57.1	241.7	113.8	02m26.8s
19:05	29°34.2′N	073°06.2′W	1.029	55.1	246.4	113.1	02m23.2s
19:10	28°30.3′N	071°11.5′W	1.028	52.9	250.7	112.1	02m19.0s
19:15	27°24.2′N	069°13.1′W	1.028	50.5	254.6	110.8	02m14.5s
19:20	26°15.7′N	067°09.6′W	1.027	47.9	258.2	109.3	02m09.5s
19:25	25°04.6′N	064°59.3′W	1.027	45.1	261.5	107.4	02m04.0s
19:30	23°50.3′N	062°40.0′W	1.026	42.0	264.5	105.1	01m58.1s
19:35	22°32.1′N	060°08.6′W	1.025	38.6	267.3	102.3	01m51.6s
19:40	21°09.2′N	057°20.7′W	1.024	34.9	269.9	98.8	01m44.5s
19:45	19°39.9′N	054°09.0′W	1.023	30.7	272.4	94.5	01m36.6s
19:50	18°01.3′N	050°20.6′W	1.022	25.8	274.7	89.1	01m27.7s
19:55	16°07.2′N	045°26.2′W	1.020	19.8	277.1	81.9	01m17.1s
20:00	13°34.5′N	037°39.1′W	1.017	10.8	279.7	70.5	01m02.5s
20:02.1	11°01.2′N	027°26.5′W	1.014	0.0	282.1	56.7	00m47.1s

TABLE 4—LOCAL CIRCUMSTANCES FOR CITIES IN THE PATH OF TOTALITY (USA)

STATE	CITY	Partial Begins h:m	Total Eclipse h:m	Total Ends h:m	Partial Ends h:m	Sun Azm. °	Duration Totality
Idaho	Idaho Falls	10:15:11	11:33:01	11:34:50	12:58:04	50	01m49s
	Rexburg	10:15:42	11:33:15	11:35:32	12:58:22	50	02m17s
Illinois	Carbondale	11:52:25	13:20:06	13:22:43	14:47:28	64	02m37s
	Marion	11:53:01	13:20:46	13:23:13	14:47:55	64	02m27s
Kansas	Atchison	11:40:12	13:06:13	13:08:33	14:34:22	62	02m19s
	Kansas City	11:41:12	13:08:33	13:08:59	14:35:53	63	00m26s
	Kansas City	11:41:14	13:08:35	13:09:02	14:35:56	63	00m27s
	Leavenworth	11:40:37	13:07:13	13:08:47	14:35:05	62	01m34s
Kentucky	Bowling Green	11:58:40	13:27:32	13:28:27	14:53:09	63	00m55s
	Hopkinsville	11:56:32	13:24:42	13:27:22	14:51:44	64	02m40s
	Madisonville	11:56:13	13:24:32	13:26:17	14:50:54	64	01m45s
	Paducah	11:54:01	13:22:16	13:24:35	14:49:31	64	02m20s
Missouri	Cape Girardeau	11:51:59	13:20:21	13:22:08	14:47:37	64	01m47s
	Columbia	11:45:40	13:12:22	13:14:58	14:40:14	63	02m37s
	Independence	11:41:37	13:08:36	13:09:51	14:36:19	63	01m15s
	Jefferson City	11:46:07	13:13:10	13:15:38	14:41:07	63	02m28s
	Kansas City	11:41:18	13:08:39	13:09:08	14:36:01	63	00m29s
	St. Joseph	11:40:39	13:06:28	13:09:06	14:34:38	62	02m38s
Nebraska	Alliance	10:27:07	11:49:13	11:51:43	13:16:43	57	02m30s
	Beatrice	11:37:09	13:02:13	13:04:48	14:30:25	61	02m35s
	Grand Island	11:34:20	12:58:34	13:01:08	14:26:36	60	02m34s
	Kearney	11:33:03	12:57:34	12:59:28	14:25:30	60	01m54s
	Lincoln	11:37:15	13:02:35	13:03:53	14:29:47	60	01m18s
	North Platte	11:30:16	12:54:05	12:55:48	14:21:47	59	01m42s
	Scottsbluff	10:25:50	11:48:11	11:49:53	13:15:26	56	01m42s
Oregon	Albany	09:05:05	10:17:05	10:18:57	11:37:42	40	01m51s
	Baker City	09:09:51	10:24:30	10:26:05	11:46:54	44	01m35s
	Corvallis	09:04:54	10:16:55	10:18:36	11:37:24	40	01m40s
	J. Day Fossil Bed	09:07:57	10:21:33	10:23:39	11:43:42	43	02m05s
	Lincoln Beach	09:04:35	10:16:00	10:17:58	11:36:09	39	01m58s
	Madras	09:06:43	10:19:36	10:21:38	11:41:05	42	02m02s
	Ontario	10:10:07	11:25:32	11:26:59	12:48:37	45	01m28s
	Salem	09:05:25	10:17:20	10:19:15	11:37:50	40	01m55s
S. Carolina	Anderson	13:08:58	14:37:50	14:40:25	16:03:10	63	02m34s
	Charleston	13:16:59	14:46:27	14:47:56	16:10:02	62	01m29s
	Columbia	13:13:05	14:41:49	14:44:19	16:06:19	62	02m30s
	Greenville	13:09:13	14:38:02	14:40:12	16:02:55	63	02m11s
	Greenwood	13:10:22	14:39:20	14:41:48	16:04:25	63	02m28s
	North Charleston	13:16:42	14:45:56	14:47:49	16:09:44	62	01m53s
	Sumter	13:14:45	14:43:39	14:45:27	16:07:25	61	01m48s
Tennessee	Clarksville	11:57:02	13:25:35	13:27:54	14:52:30	64	02m19s
	Cleveland	13:03:25	14:33:07	14:34:13	15:58:43	64	01m06s
	Cookeville	12:01:17	13:29:44	13:32:17	14:56:02	64	02m33s
	Maryville	13:04:56	14:33:54	14:35:25	15:59:02	63	01m32s
	Nashville	11:58:30	13:27:25	13:29:21	14:54:02	64	01m56s
	Oak Ridge	13:04:05	14:33:33	14:33:51	15:58:09	63	00m18s
Wyoming	Casper	10:22:16	11:42:39	11:45:05	13:09:26	54	02m26s
	Douglas	10:23:34	11:44:24	11:46:46	13:11:17	55	02m22s
	Jackson	10:16:41	11:34:54	11:37:09	13:00:28	50	02m15s
	Riverton	10:19:33	11:39:02	11:41:17	13:05:20	53	02m14s

All Times are in Local Daylight Saving Time.

* Sun Altitude is given for mid-totality.

Georgia, North Carolina, and South Carolina*. A partial eclipse is seen within the much broader path of the Moon's penumbral shadow, which includes all of North America, the northern third of South America, and westernmost Europe and Africa (Figure 3, p. 132).

* A tiny corner of both Montana and Iowa also lie within the path of totality.

The central path begins in the North Pacific about 2400 km west of North America at 16:49 UT1. The Moon's umbral shadow travels 28 min before making first landfall along the Pacific coastline of Oregon at 17:16 UT1 (10:16 a.m. PDT). The Sun's altitude is 39° during a totality lasting 1 min 59 s. Unfortunately, the Oregon coast is often subject to heavy morning fog, making it a concern to eclipse watchers.

Rushing east, the umbra crosses the 3000-foot-high Coast Range and into the Willamette Valley. The cities of Corvallis, Albany, and Salem all lie deep in the path and have durations ranging from 1 min 40 s to 1 min 55 s. Coastal fog rarely comes this far inland and the mean cloud amount from ground records is ~50%.

The 10 000-foot-high Cascade Range tends to have a drying effect on the air as the shadow descends into the Columbia Basin. This region is notable for having the statistically lowest cloud amount (25%) along the entire eclipse track. Madras residents get just over 2 min of totality. The area will be a major draw for the eclipse and most hotels are already booked.

The elevation through eastern Oregon gradually climbs as the path reaches the Idaho border and the Snake River Plain. While Boise, Idaho's capital, lies just outside the eclipse track, it's only a short drive to get into the path of totality early on eclipse day. To the east, Idaho Falls is deep in the path where totality lasts 1 min 49 s. The duration is 2 min 18 s from the central line 34 kilometres further north. The weather prospects here are nearly as good as central Oregon.

As it crosses the Teton Range, the shadow enters Wyoming and Grand Teton National Park. With its spectacular mountain scenery, the Tetons are always a popular tourist destination. Add a total eclipse and the region will likely experience some serious congestion. The central line passes through Jackson Hole's airport bringing 2 min 20 s of totality. Teton Park lies on the dry lee side of the mountains so the weather prospects are promising. But the lack of running room and the ability to reach a better location should weather conditions deteriorate on eclipse day could be an issue.

East of the Wind River Range, the eclipse track stretches out across the high desert terrain of Wyoming. The central line passes though Casper where the duration reaches 2 min 26 s. Offering a mean cloud amount of ~40%, Casper lies at the intersection of good highways running over a 150 kilometres east and west within the eclipse path. The Astronomical League's annual convention ASTROCON 2017 will occur in Casper the week prior to the eclipse (**astrocon2017.astroleague.org**).

Gently rolling grasslands dominate much of the Nebraska landscape. Just north of the central line, Alliance enjoys 2 min 30 s of totality centred on 17:50 UT1 (11:50 a.m. MDT). About 160 kilometres to the southeast, Interstate Highway 80 (I-80) crosses into the eclipse track and follows it for ~390 kilometres. An excellent eclipse viewing strategy is to choose this section of the path, since it offers some of the best manoeuvrability to fine-tune one's location based on the weather forecast in the days leading up to the eclipse.

While North Platte is inside the path, it is just 14 kilometres from the southern limit. Nevertheless, the duration there is 1 min 46 s. The central line is 40 kilometres northeast where totality lasts 2 min 33 s. Continuing east on I-80, the interstate eventually curves deeper into the path and crosses the central line just south of Grand Island. The central duration is now 2 min 36 s with the Sun at an altitude of 60°.

From west to east Nebraska's average elevation slowly drops making the state a bit more susceptible to moist air from the Gulf of Mexico. This is reflected in the mean cloud amount that rises from ~45% to ~55% across the state.

Departing Nebraska the eclipse path crosses the northeastern corner of Kansas and enters Missouri. The southern limit bisects Kansas City, so residents there will observe either a deep partial eclipse, a grazing eclipse, or a very short total eclipse, depending on their exact location with respect to the path edge. A similar situation holds true in St. Louis, which is bisected by the northern path limit. Missouri cities deep in the path include St. Joseph, Columbia, and Jefferson City, all with totalities lasting about 2.5 min.

Crossing the Mississippi River, the track enters southern Illinois. About 10 km south of Carbondale, IL the central line duration reaches its maximum value of 2 min 40.3 s at 18:21:49 UT1 (1:21:49 p.m. CDT). Carbondale is being billed as Southern Illinois's "Eclipse Crossroads of America," since it also lies in the path of the total solar eclipse of 2024 Apr. 8.

The weather prospects from Missouri to Illinois are strongly influenced by moisture-laden air from the Gulf of Mexico. The average cloud cover from surface observations hovers around 55%. Heavier cloud cover often comes from convective clouds usually developing in the afternoon. Fortunately, the cooling effect of the partial phases before totality may help mitigate afternoon cloud formation.

After fording the Ohio River, the umbral shadow enters Kentucky and the flat landscape gradually transforms into small, rolling hills. The instant of greatest eclipse occurs at 18:25:32 UT1 (1:25:32 p.m. CDT). This is the point where the axis of the lunar shadow passes closest to the centre of Earth. The auspicious event takes place in an unassuming sorghum field about 20 kilometres northwest of Hopkinsville, Kentucky. The duration at greatest eclipse, 2 min 40.1 s, is less than 0.2 s shorter than greatest duration near Carbondale. While many may make a big fuss over a few tenths of a second, a clear sky is far more important. The weather forecast the day before the eclipse should be the ultimate guide in choosing a viewing site and not duration.

The eclipse track heads to the southeast as it enters Tennessee. Nashville is the largest city in the state lying within the path of totality. It is located ~2/3 of the way from the central line to the southern limit and receives 1 min 56 s of totality. Another 44 s can be added by traveling 40 kilometres north to the central line. The eastern Tennessee cities of Knoxville and Chattanooga both lie just outside the path where ultra deep partial eclipses will be seen.

At Tennessee's eastern border with North Carolina, the eclipse track crosses the Blue Ridge Mountains. While offering an inviting landscape of green mountains and valleys, this area has the highest mean cloud cover (~80%) along the entire track. To the south, the path clips the northeastern corner of Georgia before entering South Carolina.

Greenville and Andersonville are both deep in the path with the central line passing between them. The duration from the cities is 2 min 11 s and 2 min 34 s, respectively, centered at 19:39 UT1 (2:39 p.m. EDT) and the Sun at 63° altitude. Columbia is to the southeast and has a duration of 2 min 30 s. Just inside the southern limit is historic Charleston. The duration from downtown is 1 min 29 s, while a 50-km drive northeast to the central line offers 2 min 34 s.

While the elevation gradually drops across South Carolina as the eclipse track heads to the Atlantic coast, afternoon cloud formation is often triggered by moist air from the Atlantic. The mean cloud amount ranges from 60% to 70%. The most promising observing sites are right along the Atlantic coast, but only if a sea breeze is present on eclipse day to keep clouds formed further inland at bay.

Leaving the American coastline, the lunar shadow begins a 75-min-long journey covering 5800 km across the Atlantic before leaving Earth's surface at 20:02 UT1. Over the course of its 3.2-hour trajectory, the umbra's track is approximately 13 900 km long and covers 0.26% of Earth's surface area. Path coordinates and central line circumstances are presented in Table 3 (p. 133).

Partial phases of the eclipse are visible primarily from North America and the northern 1/3 of South America. Major American cities in the path of totality are listed in Table 4 (p. 134). Local circumstances for a number of cities in Canada and the USA are found in Tables 5 (p. 140) and 6 (p. 143). All times are in Local Time. The Sun's altitude, the eclipse magnitude and eclipse obscuration are all given at the instant of maximum eclipse at each location. The 2017 Total Solar Eclipse Circumstances Calculator (www.EclipseWise.com/solar/SEcirc/2001-2100/SE2017Aug21Tcirc.html) is an interactive web page that can quickly calculate the local circumstances for the eclipse from any geographic location not included in Tables 4, 5, and 6.

This is the 22nd eclipse of Saros 145 (Espenak and Meeus, 2006). All eclipses in the series occur at the Moon's ascending node and gamma[8] decreases with each member in the family. The series is a young one that began with a partial eclipse on 1639 Jan. 04. After 20 partial eclipses in the series, the first umbral eclipse occurred on 1891 Jun. 06. The event was a short annular eclipse and was followed by a hybrid on 1909 Jun. 17. The first total eclipse occurred on 1927 Jun. 29. Since then, Saros 145 has continued to produce total eclipses including 1963 Jul. 20 (Alaska, Canada, Maine), 1981 Jul. 31 (Russia), and 1999 Aug. 11 (Europe, Turkey, India). After 2017, the next three eclipses are 2035 Sep. 02 (China, Japan), 2053 Sep. 12 (North Africa), and 2071 Sep. 23 (Mexico, South America). The last total eclipse occurs on 2648 Sep. 09 with the series ending with a partial eclipse on 3009 Apr. 17.

Complete details for the 77 eclipses in the series (in the sequence 14 partial, 1 annular, 1 hybrid, 41 total, and 20 partial) may be found at

www.EclipseWise.com/solar/SEsaros/SEsaros145.html

Much more information and detailed maps for this event can be found in the recently published Eclipse Bulletin: The Total Solar Eclipse of 2017 August 21 (Espenak & Anderson, 2015) and Road Atlas for the Total Solar Eclipse of 2017 (Espenak 2015) as well as the EclipseWise page

www. eclipsewise.com/solar/SEnews/TSE2017/TSE2017.html

Explanation of Solar Eclipse Figures

For each solar eclipse, an orthographic projection map of Earth shows the path of the penumbral (partial) and umbral (total) or antumbral (annular) eclipse. North is to the top in all cases, and the daylight terminator is plotted for the instant of greatest eclipse. An asterisk (*) indicates the sub-solar point[9] on Earth.

The limits of the Moon's penumbra delineate the region of visibility of the partial solar eclipse. This irregular, or saddle-shaped, region often covers more than half of the daylight hemisphere of Earth and consists of several distinct zones, or limits. At the northern and/or southern boundaries lie the limits of the penumbra's path. Partial eclipses have only one of these limits, as do central eclipses when the Moon's shadow axis falls no closer than about 0.45 radii from Earth's centre. Great loops at the western and eastern extremes of the penumbra's path identify the areas where the eclipse begins at sunrise and ends at sunset. If the penumbra has both a northern and a southern limit, the rising and setting curves form two separate, closed loops. Otherwise, the curves are connected in a distorted figure eight. Bisecting the "eclipse begins/ ends at sunrise and sunset" loops is the curve of maximum eclipse at sunrise (western loop) and sunset (eastern loop). The points P1 and P4 mark the coordinates where the penumbra first contacts (partial eclipse begins) and last contacts (partial eclipse ends) Earth's surface. If the penumbral path has both a northern and a southern limit, then points P2 and P3 are also plotted. These correspond to the coordinates where the penumbral shadow cone is internally tangent to Earth's disk.

[8] Gamma is the distance of the Moon's shadow axis from Earth's centre (in Earth radii) when it reaches its minimum absolute value.

[9] The sub-solar point is the geographic location where the Sun appears directly overhead (zenith).

A curve of maximum eclipse is the locus of all points where the eclipse is at maximum at a given time. Curves of maximum eclipse are plotted at each half hour Universal Time. They generally run between the penumbral limits in the north/south direction or from the maximum eclipse at sunrise and sunset curves to one of the limits. The curves of constant eclipse magnitude delineate the loci of all points where the magnitude at maximum eclipse is constant. These curves run exclusively between the curves of maximum eclipse at sunrise and sunset. Furthermore, they are parallel to the northern/southern penumbral limits and the umbral paths of central eclipses. In fact, the northern and southern limits of the penumbra can be thought of as curves of constant magnitude of 0.0. The adjacent curves are for magnitudes of 0.2, 0.4, 0.6, and 0.8. For total eclipses, the northern and southern limits of the umbra are curves of constant magnitude of 1.0. Antumbral path limits for annular eclipses are curves of maximum eclipse magnitude.

Greatest eclipse is defined as the instant when the axis of the Moon's shadow passes closest to Earth's centre. Although greatest eclipse differs slightly from the instants of greatest magnitude and greatest duration (for total eclipses), the differences are negligible. An asterisk marks the point on Earth's surface intersected by the lunar shadow axis at greatest eclipse. For partial eclipses, the shadow axis misses Earth entirely, so the point of greatest eclipse lies on the terminator and the Sun appears on the horizon.

Data pertinent to the eclipse appear with each map. At the top is listed the instant of greatest eclipse, expressed in Terrestrial Dynamical Time and Universal Time. For central eclipses (total or annular), the magnitude listed is the geocentric ratio of diameters of the Moon and the Sun. Gamma is the minimum distance of the Moon's shadow axis from Earth's centre in Earth radii at greatest eclipse. The Saros series of the eclipse is listed, followed by the member position. The first number identifies the sequence position of the eclipse in the Saros, while the second number is the number of eclipses in the entire series.

In the upper-left and upper-right corners are the geocentric coordinates of the Sun and the Moon, respectively, at the instant of greatest eclipse. They are as follows:

RA	Right ascension
Dec	Declination
S.D.	Apparent semi-diameter
H.P.	Horizontal parallax

To the lower left are exterior/interior contact times of the Moon's penumbral shadow with Earth, which are defined as follows:

P1	Instant of first exterior tangency of penumbra with Earth's limb (partial eclipse begins)
P2	Instant of first interior tangency of penumbra with Earth's limb
P3	Instant of last interior tangency of penumbra with Earth's limb
P4	Instant of last exterior tangency of penumbra with Earth's limb (partial eclipse ends)

Not all eclipses have P2 and P3 penumbral contacts. They are only present in cases in which the penumbral shadow falls completely within Earth's disk. For central eclipses, the lower-right corner lists exterior/interior contact times of the Moon's umbral shadow with Earth's limb, which are defined as follows:

U1	Instant of first exterior tangency of umbra with Earth's limb (umbral [total/annular] eclipse begins)
U2	Instant of first interior tangency of umbra with Earth's limb
U3	Instant of last interior tangency of umbra with Earth's limb
U4	Instant of last exterior tangency of umbra with Earth's limb (umbral [total/annular] eclipse ends)

At bottom left are the geographic coordinates of the position of greatest eclipse along with the local circumstances at that location (i.e. Sun altitude, Sun azimuth, path width, and duration of totality/annularity). Similar data are also given at the bottom right for the position of greatest duration. At bottom left is a list of parameters used in the eclipse predictions, and at bottom right is the Moon's geocentric libration (optical and physical) at greatest eclipse.

The solar eclipse figures are updates of versions originally published in *Fifty Year Canon of Solar Eclipses: 1986–2035* (Espenak, 1988).

Shadow Diameters and Lunar Eclipses

To compensate for Earth's atmosphere when calculating the circumstances for lunar eclipses, Chauvenet (1891) introduced an empirical enlargement of $^1/_{50}$ to the diameters of the umbral and penumbral shadows. This rule has been used by many of the national institutes in their official eclipse predictions (including the author's work at NASA). However, Danjon (1951) pointed out a flaw in this method: it applies the same relative correction to the umbra and penumbra, instead of using the same absolute correction. From eclipse observations, Danjon proposed enlarging Earth's diameter by $^1/_{85}$ to compensate for the atmosphere. The umbral and penumbral shadow diameters are then calculated based on this modified geometry. The French almanac *Connaissance des Temps* has used the Danjon rule in its eclipse predictions since 1951. The resulting umbral and penumbral eclipse magnitudes are smaller by approximately 0.005 and 0.026, respectively, as compared to predictions using the traditional $^1/_{50}$ rule.

Beginning with *Eclipses During 2007*, we use the Danjon rule in calculating lunar eclipse circumstances and magnitudes.

Eclipse Altitudes and Azimuths

The altitude a and azimuth A of the Sun or Moon during an eclipse depends on the time and the observer's geographic coordinates. They are calculated as follows:

$$h = 15\,(\mathrm{GST} + \mathrm{UT} - \alpha) + \lambda,$$
$$a = \arcsin[\,\sin\delta\sin\varphi + \cos\delta\cos h\cos\varphi\,], \text{ and}$$
$$A = \arctan[\,-(\cos\delta\sin h)/(\sin\delta\cos\varphi - \cos\delta\cos h\sin\varphi)\,],$$

in which:

h = Hour Angle of Sun or Moon,
a = Altitude,
A = Azimuth,
GST = Greenwich Sidereal Time at 0:00 UT,
UT = Universal Time,
α = RA of Sun or Moon,
δ = Dec of Sun or Moon,
λ = Observer's Longitude (East +, West –), and
φ = Observer's Latitude (North +, South –).

During the eclipses of 2017, the values for GST and the geocentric RA and Dec of the Sun or the Moon (at greatest eclipse) are as follows:

Eclipse	Date	GST	α	δ
Penumbral Lunar	Feb. 11	9.419	9.640	13.053
Annular Solar	Feb. 26	10.443	22.656	–8.494
Partial Lunar	Aug. 7	21.097	21.181	–15.421
Total Solar	Aug. 21	22.018	10.068	11.862

Two web-based tools can also be used to calculate the local circumstances for all solar and lunar eclipses visible from any location. They are the Javascript Solar Eclipse Explorer and the JavaScript Lunar Eclipse Explorer. The URLs for these two tools are

www.eclipsewise.com/solar/JSEX/JSEX-index.html, and
www.eclipsewise.com/lunar/JLEX/JLEX-index.html

(text continues on p. 142)

TABLE 5 – LOCAL CIRCUMSTANCES FOR CITIES OUTSIDE THE PATH OF TOTALITY (CANADA)

CITY, PROVINCE	Eclipse Begins hh:mm	Maximum Eclipse hh:mm	Eclipse Ends hh:mm	Sun Alt. °	Ecl. Obsc.	Ecl. Mag.
Victoria, BC	09:08:55	10:20:14	11:37:22	38	0.891	0.908
Nanaimo, BC	09:09:26	10:20:09	11:36:30	38	0.864	0.888
Richmond, BC	09:10:00	10:21:01	11:37:37	38	0.863	0.887
Vancouver, BC	09:10:09	10:21:08	11:37:41	38	0.860	0.884
Burnaby, BC	09:10:15	10:21:19	11:37:56	38	0.860	0.884
Abbotsford, BC	09:10:30	10:21:57	11:38:56	39	0.866	0.889
Penticton, BC	09:13:14	10:25:27	11:42:53	41	0.844	0.872
Prince Rupert, BC	09:13:16	10:18:33	11:28:23	32	0.689	0.749
Kelowna, BC	09:13:48	10:25:49	11:42:55	40	0.830	0.861
Kamloops, BC	09:14:07	10:25:18	11:41:28	40	0.804	0.840
Prince George, BC	09:17:02	10:25:03	11:37:23	36	0.696	0.755
Whitehorse, YT	09:23:16	10:22:14	11:24:17	27	0.490	0.585
Fort Nelson, BC	09:25:30	10:29:11	11:35:59	34	0.540	0.627
Dawson, YT	09:29:12	10:24:06	11:21:26	24	0.398	0.504
Banff, AB	10:18:55	11:31:21	12:48:06	42	0.773	0.816
Lethbridge, AB	10:19:50	11:34:19	12:53:01	45	0.814	0.848
Calgary, AB	10:20:11	11:33:10	12:50:18	43	0.772	0.814
Red Deer, AB	10:22:03	11:34:05	12:49:55	43	0.729	0.780
Medicine Hat, AB	10:22:35	11:37:25	12:56:03	46	0.792	0.830
Edmonton, AB	10:24:08	11:35:03	12:49:28	42	0.684	0.745
Moose Jaw, SK	10:29:01	11:44:48	13:03:20	48	0.752	0.799
Saskatoon, SK	10:29:35	11:43:24	12:59:55	46	0.700	0.758
Regina, SK	10:30:10	11:46:06	13:04:34	48	0.745	0.793
Fort Simpson, NT	10:32:08	11:32:49	12:35:55	33	0.451	0.550
Yellowknife, NT	10:38:08	11:39:01	12:41:47	35	0.421	0.524
Aklavik, NT	10:39:55	11:31:20	12:24:22	24	0.301	0.414
Inuvik, NT	10:40:54	11:32:16	12:25:13	25	0.296	0.410
Brandon, MB	11:36:00	12:53:14	14:11:59	51	0.732	0.783
The Pas, MB	11:38:13	12:50:45	14:04:49	47	0.614	0.687
Winnipeg, MB	11:40:10	12:57:32	14:15:46	51	0.708	0.764
Selkirk, MB	11:40:48	12:57:53	14:15:44	51	0.697	0.755
Riverton, MB	11:41:17	12:57:24	14:14:18	50	0.672	0.735
Churchill, MB	11:53:01	12:58:47	14:04:46	43	0.432	0.534
Resolute, NU	12:14:44	12:56:52	13:39:06	27	0.134	0.237
Thunder Bay, ON	12:52:09	14:10:53	15:28:29	53	0.682	0.742
Sault Ste Marie, ON	13:00:38	14:20:33	15:37:54	54	0.684	0.744
Windsor, ON	13:03:33	14:27:40	15:47:56	57	0.793	0.831
Kapuskasing, ON	13:04:38	14:20:28	15:33:55	51	0.582	0.661
Sarnia, ON	13:04:41	14:27:56	15:47:21	57	0.765	0.809
Point Pelee N.P., ON	13:04:42	14:29:01	15:49:15	58	0.797	0.834
Chatham, ON	13:05:14	14:29:00	15:48:44	57	0.779	0.820
London, ON	13:07:01	14:29:52	15:48:38	56	0.749	0.796
Sudbury, ON	13:07:01	14:25:54	15:41:31	53	0.645	0.713
St. Thomas, ON	13:07:09	14:30:11	15:49:05	56	0.755	0.801
Woodstock, ON	13:07:58	14:30:30	15:48:51	56	0.738	0.788
Waterloo, ON	13:08:22	14:30:27	15:48:25	55	0.726	0.778
Kitchener, ON	13:08:26	14:30:32	15:48:29	55	0.726	0.778
Cambridge, ON	13:08:48	14:30:55	15:48:51	55	0.726	0.778
Guelph, ON	13:08:53	14:30:47	15:48:32	55	0.720	0.773
Brantford, ON	13:08:58	14:31:18	15:49:23	56	0.732	0.783
Hamilton, ON	13:09:47	14:31:51	15:49:35	55	0.723	0.776
Brampton, ON	13:09:51	14:31:24	15:48:46	55	0.710	0.765
Barrie, ON	13:09:53	14:30:38	15:47:21	54	0.688	0.748
Burlington, ON	13:09:55	14:31:52	15:49:31	55	0.720	0.773
North Bay, ON	13:10:01	14:28:31	15:43:26	53	0.632	0.703
Oakville, ON	13:10:05	14:31:51	15:49:21	55	0.715	0.769
Mississauga, ON	13:10:11	14:31:47	15:49:08	55	0.711	0.766
Etobicoke, ON	13:10:16	14:31:47	15:49:03	55	0.708	0.764
York, ON	13:10:25	14:31:52	15:49:04	55	0.706	0.762
North York, ON	13:10:32	14:31:52	15:48:57	55	0.703	0.759
Toronto, ON	13:10:38	14:32:05	15:49:14	55	0.706	0.762

TABLE 5 – LOCAL CIRCUMSTANCES FOR CITIES OUTSIDE THE PATH OF TOTALITY (CANADA) (continued)

CITY, PROVINCE	Eclipse Begins hh:mm	Maximum Eclipse hh:mm	Eclipse Ends hh:mm	Sun Alt. °	Ecl. Obsc.	Ecl. Mag.
East York, ON	13:10:44	14:32:07	15:49:13	55	0.704	0.760
Markham, ON	13:10:49	14:31:59	15:48:54	54	0.698	0.756
Scarborough, ON	13:10:51	14:32:10	15:49:11	55	0.702	0.759
Saint Catharines, ON	13:11:03	14:32:57	15:50:24	55	0.718	0.771
Welland, ON	13:11:06	14:33:12	15:50:47	55	0.723	0.776
Niagara Falls, ON	13:11:27	14:33:20	15:50:44	55	0.717	0.771
Oshawa, ON	13:11:40	14:32:37	15:49:15	54	0.692	0.751
Peterborough, ON	13:12:39	14:32:56	15:48:55	54	0.674	0.736
Kingston, ON	13:16:22	14:35:52	15:50:47	53	0.653	0.719
Nepean, ON	13:17:31	14:35:29	15:49:04	52	0.615	0.689
Hull, QC	13:17:37	14:35:24	15:48:49	51	0.611	0.685
Ottawa, ON	13:17:39	14:35:26	15:48:52	51	0.611	0.685
Gatineau, QC	13:17:46	14:35:27	15:48:47	51	0.609	0.683
Gloucester, ON	13:17:54	14:35:41	15:49:05	51	0.611	0.685
Cornwall, ON	13:19:42	14:37:25	15:50:33	51	0.609	0.684
Laval, QC	13:21:31	14:38:04	15:50:06	50	0.583	0.662
Saint Laurent, QC	13:21:42	14:38:19	15:50:22	50	0.584	0.663
Montréal Nord, QC	13:21:44	14:38:13	15:50:09	50	0.581	0.661
La Salle, QC	13:21:48	14:38:27	15:50:32	50	0.586	0.664
Saint Léonard, QC	13:21:51	14:38:19	15:50:14	50	0.581	0.661
Montréal, QC	13:21:54	14:38:26	15:50:24	50	0.583	0.662
Verdun, QC	13:21:55	14:38:32	15:50:33	50	0.584	0.663
Longueuil, QC	13:22:02	14:38:30	15:50:25	50	0.581	0.661
Brossard, QC	13:22:06	14:38:40	15:50:39	50	0.584	0.663
Saint Hubert, QC	13:22:12	14:38:40	15:50:33	50	0.581	0.661
Shawinigan, QC	13:23:12	14:38:06	15:48:39	49	0.547	0.632
Trois Riviäres, QC	13:23:40	14:38:40	15:49:16	49	0.550	0.635
Drummondville, QC	13:23:57	14:39:27	15:50:23	49	0.560	0.643
Grise Fiord, NU	13:25:05	14:02:22	14:39:35	25	0.094	0.185
Sherbrooke, QC	13:25:17	14:40:59	15:51:56	49	0.565	0.647
Chicoutimi, QC	13:25:59	14:37:40	15:45:25	47	0.484	0.579
Sainte Foy, QC	13:26:01	14:39:47	15:49:09	48	0.525	0.613
Charlesbourg, QC	13:26:02	14:39:42	15:49:00	48	0.523	0.612
Québec City, QC	13:26:06	14:39:48	15:49:06	48	0.523	0.612
Beauport, QC	13:26:11	14:39:48	15:49:01	48	0.522	0.611
Iqaluit, NU	13:30:46	14:20:56	15:10:00	35	0.189	0.299
Alert, NU	13:39:43	14:05:11	14:30:36	18	0.033	0.092
Edmundston, NB	14:31:32	15:42:47	16:49:39	46	0.478	0.574
Saint Stephen, NB	14:34:34	15:47:30	16:55:25	46	0.515	0.605
Saint John, NB	14:36:57	15:48:58	16:55:57	45	0.499	0.592
Chatham, NB	14:37:10	15:46:51	16:52:00	44	0.454	0.553
Yarmouth, NS	14:37:40	15:51:13	16:59:18	46	0.533	0.620
Moncton, NB	14:38:57	15:49:10	16:54:36	44	0.466	0.564
Shelburne, NS	14:39:18	15:52:20	16:59:54	45	0.525	0.614
Kentville, NS	14:40:05	15:51:10	16:57:11	44	0.485	0.580
Liverpool, NS	14:40:19	15:52:38	16:59:35	44	0.511	0.602
Bridgewater, NS	14:40:29	15:52:18	16:58:51	44	0.501	0.594
Windsor, NS	14:40:51	15:51:47	16:57:36	44	0.483	0.578
Halifax, NS	14:42:05	15:52:58	16:58:39	43	0.485	0.579
Dartmouth, NS	14:42:09	15:52:59	16:58:38	43	0.484	0.579
Truro, NS	14:42:17	15:52:11	16:57:05	43	0.465	0.563
New Glasgow, NS	14:43:19	15:52:32	16:56:49	42	0.454	0.553
Guysborough, NS	14:45:37	15:54:10	16:57:47	42	0.445	0.546
Port Hawkesbury, NS	14:45:45	15:53:57	16:57:17	41	0.439	0.540
Sydney, NS	14:47:34	15:54:20	16:56:24	40	0.416	0.519
Glace Bay, NS	14:47:57	15:54:30	16:56:22	40	0.412	0.516
Sable Island, NS	14:49:46	15:58:31	17:01:58	41	0.458	0.556
Knob Lake, NF	15:02:31	16:03:42	17:02:18	41	0.315	0.427
Gander, NF	15:25:26	16:25:02	17:20:54	36	0.311	0.423
Saint John's, NF	15:29:32	16:29:05	17:24:42	34	0.317	0.429

All Times are in Local Daylight Saving Time (except Saskatchewan).
* Sun Altitude is given for maximum eclipse.

In 2018, there are three partial solar eclipses and two total lunar eclipses:

Jan. 31:	Total Lunar Eclipse
Feb. 15:	Partial Solar Eclipse
Jul. 13:	Partial Solar Eclipse
Jul. 27:	Total Lunar Eclipse
Aug. 11:	Partial Solar Eclipse

A full report on these eclipses will be published in the *Observer's Handbook 2018*. Additional information may be found at www.EclipseWise.com/eclipse.html#yr2018

Eclipse Websites

EclipseWise.com is a website dedicated to predictions and information on eclipses of the Sun and Moon. It offers a graphically intuitive interface and contains maps, diagrams, tables, and information about every solar and lunar eclipse from 2000 BC to AD 3000. This period includes 11 898 solar eclipses and 12 064 lunar eclipses.

Much of EclipseWise is based on the newly published Thousand Year Canon of Solar Eclipses: 1501 to 2500 (Espenak 2014a) and the Thousand Year Canon of Lunar Eclipses: 1501 to 2500 (Espenak 2014b). These eclipse predictions use the Jet Propulsion Lab's DE406—a computer ephemeris used for calculating high-precision coordinates of the Sun and Moon for thousands of years into the past and future.

Although still available, the older NASA website (eclipse.gsfc.nasa.gov/eclipse.html) has been retired as an archival reference source for eclipse predictions prior to 2015. Predictions for future eclipses will be posted on the newer EclipseWise.com website.

Detailed information on solar and lunar eclipse photography, and tips on eclipse observing and eye safety may be found at www.mreclipse.com/MrEclipse.html

Acknowledgments

All eclipse predictions were generated on a Macintosh G4 PowerPC using algorithms developed from the *Explanatory Supplement...* [1974] with additional algorithms from Meeus, Grosjean, and Vanderleen [1966]. The solar and lunar coordinates used in the eclipse predictions are based on the JPL DE405. For lunar eclipses, the diameter of the umbral and penumbral shadows were calculated using Danjon's rule of enlarging Earth's radius by 1/85 to compensate for the opacity of the terrestrial atmosphere; corrections for the effects of oblateness have also been included.

All calculations, diagrams, tables, and opinions presented in this paper are those of the author, and he assumes full responsibility for their accuracy. This publication is available electronically at www.EclipseWise.com/oh/ec2017.html with additional information and updates.

References and Bibliography

Chauvenet, W., *Manual of Spherical and Practical Astronomy, Vol.1, 1891* (Dover edition 1961).

Danjon, A., "Les éclipses de Lune par la pénombre en 1951," *L'Astronomie, 65*, 51–53 (Feb. 1951).

Espenak, F. and Meeus, J., *Five Millennium Canon of Solar Eclipses: –2000 to +3000 (2000 BCE to 3000 CE)*, NASA TP–2006-214141, Goddard Space Flight Center, Greenbelt, MD (2006).

Espenak, F. and Meeus, J., *Five Millennium Canon of Lunar Eclipses: –2000 to +3000 (2000 BCE to 3000 CE)*, NASA TP-2009-214172, Goddard Space Flight Center, Greenbelt, MD (2009a).

Espenak, F., *Thousand Year Canon of Solar Eclipses: 1501 to 2500*, Astropixels Publishing, Portal, AZ (2014a).

Espenak, F., *Thousand Year Canon of Lunar Eclipses: 1501 to 2500*, Astropixels Publishing, Portal, AZ (2014b).

Espenak, F. and Anderson, J., Eclipse Bulletin: *The Total Solar Eclipse of 2017 August 21*, Astropixels Publishing, Portal, AZ (2015).

Espenak, F., *Road Atlas for the Total Solar Eclipse of 2017*, Astropixels Publishing, Portal, AZ (2015).

Explanatory Supplement to the Astronomical Ephemeris and the American Ephemeris and Nautical Almanac, Her Majesty's Nautical Almanac Office, London, 1974.

Editor's Note: For advance information on the 2017 total solar eclipse in North America, see www.greatamericaneclipse.com.

The International Astronomical Union Working Group on Solar Eclipses has a website at eclipses.info.

TABLE 6 – LOCAL CIRCUMSTANCES FOR CITIES OUTSIDE THE PATH OF TOTALITY (USA)

CITY, STATE	Eclipse Begins hh:mm	Maximum Eclipse hh:mm	Eclipse Ends hh:mm	Sun Alt. °	Ecl. Obsc.	Ecl. Mag.
Albany, NY	13:22:42	14:42:24	15:56:42	52	0.659	0.724
Albuquerque, NM	10:21:19	11:45:14	13:13:57	60	0.733	0.783
Atlanta, GA	13:05:51	14:36:45	16:01:54	65	0.971	0.971
Austin, TX	11:41:09	13:10:17	14:39:26	71	0.652	0.718
Baltimore, MD	13:18:31	14:42:56	16:01:17	56	0.793	0.831
Baton Rouge, LA	11:54:37	13:26:20	14:54:24	71	0.753	0.799
Billings, MT	10:21:07	11:39:59	13:02:59	50	0.932	0.941
Birmingham, AL	12:00:43	13:32:00	14:58:21	66	0.926	0.935
Boise, ID	10:10:34	11:27:14	12:50:06	46	0.996	0.994
Boston, MA	13:28:27	14:46:49	15:59:29	50	0.631	0.702
Charleston, WV	13:08:12	14:35:27	15:57:25	60	0.895	0.911
Charlotte, NC	13:12:21	14:41:34	16:04:22	61	0.979	0.978
Chattanooga, TN	13:02:34	14:32:57	15:58:15	64	0.995	0.993
Chicago, IL	11:54:18	13:19:48	14:42:39	59	0.866	0.889
Cleveland, OH	13:06:31	14:31:00	15:51:07	57	0.800	0.836
Columbus, OH	13:04:24	14:30:42	15:52:32	59	0.865	0.887
Dallas, TX	11:40:23	13:09:57	14:39:20	69	0.755	0.800
Denver, CO	10:23:21	11:47:07	13:14:43	57	0.923	0.933
Des Moines, IA	11:42:50	13:08:41	14:33:58	60	0.949	0.954
Detroit, MI	13:03:28	14:27:34	15:47:49	57	0.792	0.831
Dover, DE	13:20:58	14:44:55	16:02:37	55	0.781	0.821
Fairbanks, AK	08:29:39	09:21:58	10:16:33	20	0.369	0.478
Fargo, ND	11:38:45	12:59:24	14:20:48	54	0.803	0.839
Hartford, CT	13:25:25	14:45:22	15:59:33	51	0.669	0.732
Honolulu, HI	——	06:35:58	07:25:22	5	0.274	0.388
Houston, TX	11:46:39	13:16:56	14:45:44	72	0.666	0.730
Indianapolis, IN	12:57:53	14:25:03	15:48:38	61	0.915	0.927
Jackson, MS	11:54:34	13:26:07	14:53:58	69	0.832	0.862
Knoxville, TN	13:04:53	14:34:28	15:58:45	63	0.999	0.997
Las Vegas, NV	09:09:08	10:27:23	11:52:59	51	0.717	0.771
Little Rock, AR	11:47:56	13:18:19	14:46:31	67	0.887	0.905
Los Angeles, CA	09:05:43	10:21:12	11:44:49	48	0.622	0.694
Manchester, NH	13:27:16	14:45:15	15:57:45	50	0.620	0.693
Miami, FL	13:26:56	14:58:25	16:20:48	64	0.783	0.823
Milwaukee, WI	11:53:38	13:18:03	14:40:09	58	0.833	0.862
Montpelier, VT	13:24:21	14:41:42	15:54:01	50	0.602	0.678
New Orleans, LA	11:57:42	13:29:40	14:57:20	71	0.754	0.800
New York, NY	13:23:15	14:44:59	16:00:44	53	0.715	0.769
Newark, NJ	13:22:53	14:44:42	16:00:33	53	0.717	0.771
Oklahoma City, OK	11:37:07	13:05:44	14:34:53	66	0.845	0.872
Omaha, NE	11:38:27	13:04:13	14:30:19	60	0.985	0.983
Pierre, SD	11:31:54	12:54:19	14:18:39	56	0.922	0.932
Philadelphia, PA	13:21:14	14:44:18	16:01:19	54	0.753	0.799
Phoenix, AZ	09:13:53	10:33:44	12:00:26	56	0.629	0.700
Portland, ME	13:29:23	14:45:57	15:57:08	49	0.589	0.667
Portland, OR	09:06:20	10:19:12	11:38:34	40	0.993	0.991
Providence, RI	13:28:05	14:47:12	16:00:28	50	0.650	0.717
Richmond, VA	13:17:57	14:44:11	16:03:57	57	0.857	0.881
St. Louis, MO	11:49:55	13:18:16	14:44:16	63	1.000	1.000
St. Paul, MN	11:44:11	13:06:59	14:29:20	57	0.831	0.861
Salt Lake City, UT	10:13:58	11:33:50	12:59:36	51	0.912	0.925
San Francisco, CA	09:01:31	10:15:16	11:37:08	43	0.755	0.802
Seattle, WA	09:08:44	10:20:54	11:39:00	39	0.919	0.931
Springfield, IL	11:50:44	13:18:11	14:43:18	62	0.960	0.963
Topeka, KS	11:39:16	13:06:41	14:34:05	62	0.991	0.989
Washington, DC	13:17:58	14:42:53	16:01:40	56	0.809	0.844

All Times are in Local Daylight Saving Time (Except Honolulu & Phoenix).
* Sun Altitude is given for maximum eclipse.

ECLIPSE MAP FOR NORTH AMERICA 2017 AUGUST 21

2017 Eclipse Map courtesy of Michael Zeilor, GreatAmericanEclipse.com
(See also eclipsewise.com/solar/SEnews/TSE2017/TSE2017fig/TSE2017-usa.jpg.)

VIEWING A SOLAR ECLIPSE—A WARNING

Solar eclipses are among the most widely publicized and observed celestial events. It is essential to be aware of the visual danger associated with a solar eclipse. The safety rule is simple but not widely appreciated: **Never look at the surface of the Sun, either directly with the unaided eyes or through binoculars or a telescope.** To do so one risks permanent partial blindness, and this can occur almost instantly in the case of telescopic viewing. Viewing our Sun is just as dangerous on any clear day, but at the time of an eclipse people have a reason to want to look at it—and often resort to dangerous methods.

A direct view of the Sun is safe only if a suitable filter is used in a proper manner. In the case of binoculars or a telescope, the filter must be one that attaches *securely* to the *front* end of the instrument, never one that attaches to the eyepiece end (the heat developed near the eyepiece can shatter such a filter).

Filters specifically designed for solar viewing include aluminized Mylar and glass filters plated with a slightly transparent, metallic film. Such filters may be purchased at telescope supply stores. Shade #14 (no other shade) rectangular welder's glass may be used; however, since these filters are of low optical quality, they are useful only for views not involving binoculars or a telescope. All of these are commercial items and cannot be replaced with ordinary household items. For example, layers of photographic colour film, coloured glass, stacked sunglasses, crossed polarizers, smoked glass, or photographic neutral-density filters must never be used. Although one may devise a combination that dims the *visible* sunlight to a comfortable level, the makeshift filter may be quite transparent in the infrared part of the solar spectrum, and this invisible radiation will damage the retina of the observer's eye. For the same reason, one must never rely on clouds or heavy atmospheric haze to dim the solar image when using a telescope. Two layers of fully exposed and developed, silver-based, black and white photographic film provides adequate protection, but many modern films, including all colour films, are based on dyes that do not provide protection in the infrared. Thus it is best to avoid using filters made of photographic film.

One of the simplest, safest, and least known ways to observe the partial phases of a solar eclipse is *pinhole mirror projection*. Take a small pocket mirror and, with masking tape, cover all but a small section of the mirror's surface. The shape and size of the small opening are not critical, but a square about 6 mm on a side works well. Prop the mirror up on a sunny windowsill and orient the mirror so the reflected sunlight shines on the ceiling or a wall of the room—but not directly into anyone's eyes! The spot of light on the viewing surface will be a *pinhole image* of the solar disk. The mirror has a great advantage over the usual "pinhole-in-a-box arrangement" in that the image can be aimed across a substantial distance to a convenient viewing screen. The greater the projection distance, the larger, but dimmer, the Sun's image. The size of the mirror aperture should be adjusted for the best compromise between image brightness and image sharpness. With this simple device the progress of a solar eclipse can be viewed in complete safety by a group of children in a darkened room.

A sharper and brighter image of the solar disk may be projected onto a white viewing screen placed 30 or 40 cm behind the eyepiece of binoculars or a small telescope (the telescope aperture should be stopped down to about 50 mm in order to limit the intensity of sunlight passing through the instrument, and the viewing screen should be shielded from direct sunlight). However, one must *not* look through the instrument when aiming it, and, especially if children are present, a physical barrier should be used to prevent anyone from attempting to look into the eyepiece. If the telescope has a finderscope, it should be either covered or removed.

WEATHER PROSPECTS: 2017 TOTAL SOLAR ECLIPSE

BY JAY ANDERSON

America's 2017 eclipse comes at a favourable time of year. August weather typically brings generous amounts of sunshine; the thunderstorm season is winding down; temperatures are pleasant; and the storms of winter are still a month or two away. Nevertheless, even a casual glance at the graph of centreline cloud climatology shows that there is a considerable difference in the average monthly cloudiness between east and west, with sunnier weather west of the Missouri River and gloomier conditions to the east. Within this broad trend there is substantial regional variation, so that a cautious eclipse seeker can maximize his or her chances of good weather by careful site selection.

Daytime cloudiness responds dramatically to solar heating and terrain, with afternoon convective clouds forming over dark forests on the higher slopes and peaks. In contrast, valleys and low plateaus enjoy a sunny disposition. This is especially true among the various mountain chains of the western USA—the Cascade, Teton, Wind River, and Sawtooth Ranges—where topography is a mixture of high peaks and deep valleys. The relationship between slope and valley is less distinct east of the Missouri River as the later parts of the eclipse track move away from dry western plains and mountains into the sub-tropical moisture of the American Southeast. Higher elevations, especially over the Appalachians, are still a potent cloud manufacturer, but intermountain valleys are less inclined to produce sunny skies. The eclipse also comes at a later time of day over the southeastern United States, allowing convective clouds time to build deeply and spread more extensively in the afternoon sunshine.

The centreline cloud graph illustrates five prime valley locations for setting up to view the eclipse. All are in the lee of a prominent mountain ridge. These are the Columbia Basin in Oregon, the two parts of the Snake River Plain in Oregon, a region near Riverton, Wyoming, and a site in western Nebraska near Alliance. At each of these locations, the prevailing westerlies are blocked by the terrain, forcing the air to first rise upward before descending into the valley on the lee side. Air cools during the ascent, typically converting its moisture into cloud and precipitation. On descending the lee side, the air column is warmed and dried, arriving at the valley bottom with a lower humidity and cloud-free skies. The effect is very dramatic and quite reliable, especially in the lee of the highest mountain peaks.

Eclipse sites along the Oregon coast, while the first to see the eclipse shadow, do not have any protection from the prevailing marine winds and so have a large and persistent cloud and fog climatology. But this eclipse is in August, so that even unfavourable locations still enjoy summer weather with abundant sunshine. If you want to gaze out across

TOTAL SOLAR ECLIPSE OF 2017 AUGUST 21—CLOUD GRAPH

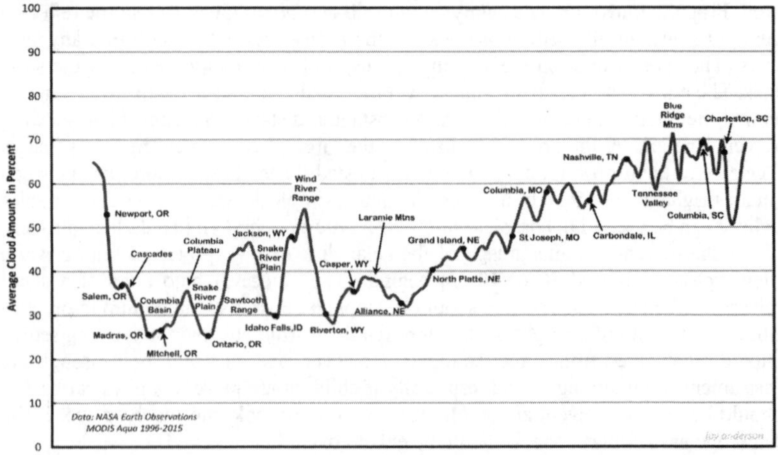

the Pacific to the oncoming shadow, pay close attention to the weather forecast and be prepared to move. That move will likely be inland, across the 1000-m Coast Range into the protected Willamette Valley where the city of Salem lies just north of the central axis. The Coast Range is relatively low as mountains go and provides only modest shelter from the ocean moisture. Better is the Columbia Basin, which offers additional protection from the 1700-m Cascade Mountains. The Basin has one of the lowest cloud amounts along the whole of the track, making Madras, Oregon, a very popular site for viewing this eclipse. It's not a very scenic location, but it does have very sunny weather—likely more than 80% of the maximum amount possible.

East from the Columbia Basin, cloud cover climbs as the terrain rises to the Columbia Highlands toward the Idaho border. At the border, the track drops abruptly into the Snake River Plain at Ontario, Oregon. This region, north of Boise, Idaho, ties Madras for the best eclipse-viewing location. East of Ontario, the track (and cloud) rises across the very cloudy Sawtooth Range and then drops once again into the Snake River Plain near Idaho Falls. This large river plain provides a broad and flat valley for ease of movement with the added appeal of the scenic Teton Mountains to the east.

Jackson, Wyoming, is a popular spot because of its mountain beauty and extensive tourist facilities, but the Basin in which it lies is very small and has a limited effect on cloud cover. The graph of centreline cloud does not do it justice, as the resolution of the satellite observations does not reveal Jackson Hole's true impact on cloudiness. If you chose to fence with Mother Nature here, use the road across the Teton Range to get into Idaho as your cloud-escape route. Better yet, try Riverton, Wyoming, which lies 320 km farther along the track from Jackson and provides a climatology that is much more friendly, thanks to the 4000-m Wind River Range that separates the two communities. At Riverton, the terrain begins to open toward the Great Plains, making short-notice, long-distance travel a much more viable option than the occasionally tortuous roads of the Mountain states.

From Casper, Wyoming, onward, moisture spreading northward from the Gulf of Mexico becomes a factor in the climatology of August cloudiness, but the impact is very small in western Nebraska and eastern Wyoming. Alliance, Nebraska, is a very attractive home base, as average cloud cover is only 7% higher than in the Columbia Basin. From Alliance, good highways lead all the way to the Missouri River to the east, and to Riverton in the west, a span of 1200 km that should be able to defeat the largest weather system for the travelling eclipsophile.

Beyond Alliance, average August cloud cover increases almost monotonically, with little ups and downs to reflect the various types of terrain along the way. There are small minimums near St. Joseph, Missouri, and Carbondale, Illinois, but the impact of tropical moisture and the rising terrain toward the Appalachians, along with a mid-afternoon eclipse, increases the odds of a cloudy day. Even so, eclipse chasers shouldn't be too pessimistic, as the percent of maximum possible sunshine measured along the eastern half of the eclipse track never sinks below 60% and ranges up to 70% along the Mississippi River. The eastern half of the eclipse track is cloudier than the west, but the satellite record makes it seem more dismal than reality.

From Tennessee to South Carolina, eclipse seekers will have to pay close attention to the weather forecast in the days ahead of Aug. 21. The heights of the Appalachians from eastern Tennessee and beyond are well known for their extensive cloudiness. Valleys tend to be narrow, limiting their impact on cloud clearing, except for the wide Tennessee Valley, which has a substantial local impact. The eastern slopes of the Appalachians, where the air would be expected to dry on heading downslope, are not rewarded by smaller cloud amounts, thanks to the warm and humid atmosphere that typically lies over the region.

The best location along the eastern slopes is probably on the coast of South Carolina, where afternoon sea breezes push cloud inland, often leaving a several-kilometre-wide band of clear skies along the ocean front. Most August afternoon cloud is convective and should weaken or dissipate as temperatures fall with the oncoming lunar shadow.

American weather forecasting competes with the best in the world, so no mobile eclipse expedition should miss this eclipse given a day or two of advance notice of adverse weather. Plan ahead with climatology, but move to your eventual site with the forecast.

THE MOON

MAP OF THE MOON

BY ROY BISHOP

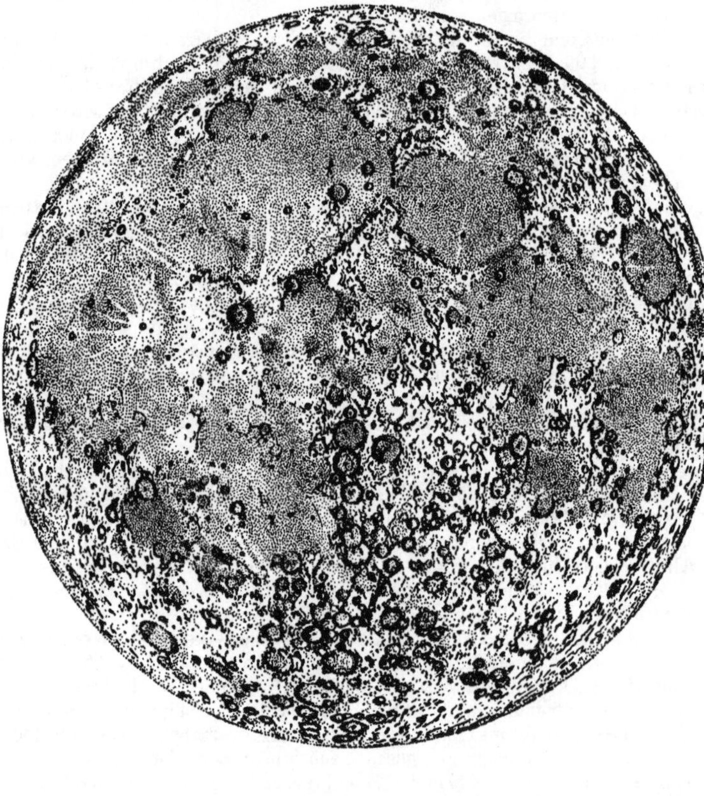

Maria	Lunar Probes
LS Lacus Somniorum (Lake of Dreams) (330°)	2 *Luna 2*, First to reach Moon (1959-9-13) (0°)
MC Mare Crisium (Sea of Crises) (300°)	7 *Ranger 7*, First close pictures (1964-7-31) (21°)
MFe Mare Fecunditatis (Sea of Fertility) (310°)	9 *Luna 9*, First soft landing (1966-2-3) (64°)
MFr Mare Frigoris (Sea of Cold) (0°)	11 *Apollo 11*, First men on Moon (1969-7-20) (337°)
MH Mare Humorum (Sea of Moisture) (40°)	12 *Apollo 12* (1969-11-19) (23°)
MI Mare Imbrium (Sea of Rains) (20°)	14 *Apollo 14* (1971-2-5) (17°)
MNe Mare Nectaris (Sea of Nectar) (325°)	15 *Apollo 15* (1971-7-30) (356°)
MNu Mare Nubium (Sea of Clouds) (15°)	16 *Apollo 16* (1972-4-21) (344°)
MS Mare Serenitatis (Sea of Serenity) (340°)	17 *Apollo 17* (1972-12-11) (329°)
MT Mare Tranquillitatis (Sea of Tranquillity) (330°)	
MV Mare Vaporum (Sea of Vapours) (355°)	
OP Oceanus Procellarum (Ocean of Storms) (50°)	
SA Sinus Aestuum (Seething Bay) (8°)	
SI Sinus Iridum (Bay of Rainbows) (32°)	
SM Sinus Medii (Central Bay) (0°)	
SR Sinus Roris (Bay of Dew) (60°)	

Angles in parentheses equal 360°– λ, where λ is the selenographic longitude of the centre of the feature. 0° marks the mean centre of the lunar disk and the angles increase toward the observer's east (i.e. westward on the Moon). These angles facilitate locating the feature on the accompanying map, and may be correlated with the Sun's selenographic colongitude (see THE SKY MONTH BY MONTH (p. 98) to determine the optimum times for viewing the feature.

Mountains

- A Alpine Valley (356°)
- B Alps Mountains (359°)
- E Altai Scarp (336°)
- F Apennine Mountains (2°)
- G Carpathian Mountains (24°)
- H Caucasus Mountains (352°)
- K Haemus Mountains (349°)
- M Jura Mountains (34°)
- N Pyrenees Mountains (319°)
- R Rheita Valley (312°)
- S Riphaeus Mountains (27°)
- V Spitzbergen (5°)
- W Straight Range (20°)
- X Straight Wall (8°)
- Y Taurus Mountains (319°)
- Z Teneriffe Mountains (13°)

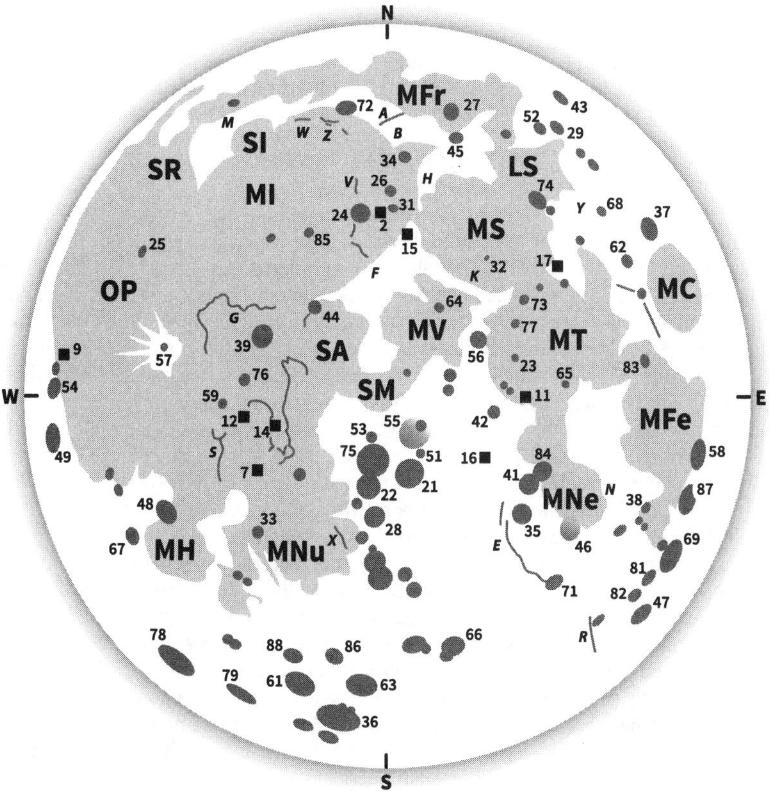

chart by Roy Bishop and Michael Gatto

Craters

- 21 Albategnius (356°)
- 22 Alphonsus (3°)
- 23 Arago (338°)
- 24 Archimedes (4°)
- 25 Aristarchus (47°)
- 26 Aristillus (358°)
- 27 Aristoteles (342°)
- 28 Arzachel (2°)
- 29 Atlas (315°)
- 31 Autolycus (358°)
- 32 Bessel (342°)
- 33 Bullialdus (22°)
- 34 Cassini (355°)
- 35 Catharina (336°)
- 36 Clavius (15°)
- 37 Cleomedes (304°)
- 38 Cook (311°)
- 39 Copernicus (20°)
- 41 Cyrillus (336°)
- 42 Delambre (342°)
- 43 Endymion (305°)
- 44 Eratosthenes (11°)
- 45 Eudoxus (343°)
- 46 Fracastorius (326°)
- 47 Furnerius (299°)
- 48 Gassendi (40°)
- 49 Grimaldi (68°)
- 51 Halley (354°)
- 52 Hercules (321°)
- 53 Herschel (2°)
- 54 Hevelius (66°)
- 55 Hipparchus (354°)
- 56 Julius Caesar (345°)
- 57 Kepler (38°)
- 58 Langrenus (299°)
- 59 Lansberg (27°)
- 61 Longomontanus (21°)
- 62 Macrobius (314°)
- 63 Maginus (6°)
- 64 Manilius (351°)
- 65 Maskelyne (330°)
- 66 Maurolycus (345°)
- 67 Mersenius (49°)
- 68 Newcomb (316°)
- 69 Petavius (298°)
- 71 Piccolomini (327°)
- 72 Plato (10°)
- 73 Plinius (336°)
- 74 Posidonius (330°)
- 75 Ptolemaeus (2°)
- 76 Reinhold (23°)
- 77 Ross (338°)
- 78 Schickard (55°)
- 79 Schiller (40°)
- 81 Snellius (304°)
- 82 Stevinus (305°)
- 83 Taruntius (313°)
- 84 Theophilus (333°)
- 85 Timocharis (13°)
- 86 Tycho (11°)
- 87 Vendelinus (298°)
- 88 Wilhelm (20°)

For expanded photographic views of the lunar surface see the-moon.wikispaces.com/Rükl+Index+Map (based on the Rükl zones) and wms.LROC.asu.edu/LROC (a *Lunar Reconnaissance Orbiter* Camera mosaic).

UNIVERSAL TIME OF NEW-MOON DATES

2017			2018		
Jan. 28.0	May 25.8	Sep. 20.2	Jan. 19.9	May 19.0	Sep. 13.3
Feb. 26.6	Jun. 24.1	Oct. 19.8	Feb. 18.8	Jun. 17.5	Oct. 12.5
Mar. 28.1	Jul. 23.4	Nov. 18.5	Mar. 20.7	Jul. 16.8	Nov. 10.9
Apr. 26.5	Aug. 21.8	Dec. 18.3	Apr. 19.4	Aug. 15.1	Dec. 10.3

These dates will be useful for planning observing sessions, determining favourable dates for observing very thin lunar crescents, and setting Moon dials on clocks. The dates are indicated to lower precision in the 2017 calendar on the inside back cover.

TIMES OF MOONRISE AND MOONSET

The table on pp. 152–157 gives the times of moonrise and moonset for locations ranging from 20°N to 60°N latitude. Dates of new Moon and full Moon are given in **bold** and *italic* respectively. The table may be interpolated linearly for nontabular latitudes and can be extrapolated beyond the 20° and 60° limits a few degrees without significant loss of accuracy. "Rise" and "Set" correspond to the upper limb of the Moon appearing at the horizon for an observer at sea level. The times are local mean time (LMT) for the Greenwich meridian (i.e. UT at 0° longitude). Because of the relatively rapid eastward motion of the Moon, unlike the sunrise and sunset table, for observers not near 0° longitude, the times cannot be read directly as LMT; the table must be interpolated according to the observer's longitude. Also, to convert from the observer's LMT to standard time, the observer's longitude correction relative to his or her standard meridian must be applied. After it is prepared for a given location, the chart at the right enables the sum of these two corrections to be determined in one step.

To prepare the **Moonrise/Moonset Correction Diagram**, first mark your longitude on the *West or East Longitude* scale. Draw a diagonal line from this mark to the (0,0) point. Next, the *Correction in minutes* axis (which is subdivided at two-minute intervals) must be labelled. As a guide, the first three divisions have been tentatively labelled 0, ±2, ±4 *(use + if you are west of the prime meridian in Greenwich, England, – if east)*; but, to these numbers must be added your longitude correction relative to your standard meridian (see the third paragraph on p. 205). As an aid both for labelling and for reading the chart, the vertical lines at 10-min intervals are wider. **Examples:** For Edmonton, which is 8.5° W of its standard meridian of 105°W, the longitude correction is +34 min, so an observer in Edmonton would label the Correction axis 34, 36, 38,…; an observer in Boston (longitude correction –16) would label the axis –16, –14, –12,…; an observer in Hong Kong (east longitude, longitude correction +24) would label the axis 24, 22, 20,…; an observer in Vienna (longitude correction –6) would label the axis –6, –8, –10,….

The chart is now ready for use on any day from your position. Interpolating for nontabular latitudes, from the table obtain today's time for the event (moonrise, or moonset) and tomorrow's time if you are west of Greenwich, yesterday's time if east, enter the difference on the *Tabular Delay* axis, and run horizontally across to meet the diagonal line. The correction, to the nearest minute, can then be read directly below off the Correction axis. This correction is applied to the tabular "today's time" and results in the standard time of the event for your position. **Example:** The latitude of Saskatoon is 52°N. Interpolating the 50°N and 55°N entries, the table gives for 52°N a moonrise time of 2:05 on Jul. 21 and 3:04 on Jul. 22. The Correction corresponding to a 59-min Tabular Delay, when the chart is prepared for Saskatoon as described above, is +84 min; hence the time of moonrise is 2:05 + 84 min = 3:29 CST Jul. 21.

MOONRISE/MOONSET CORRECTION DIAGRAM

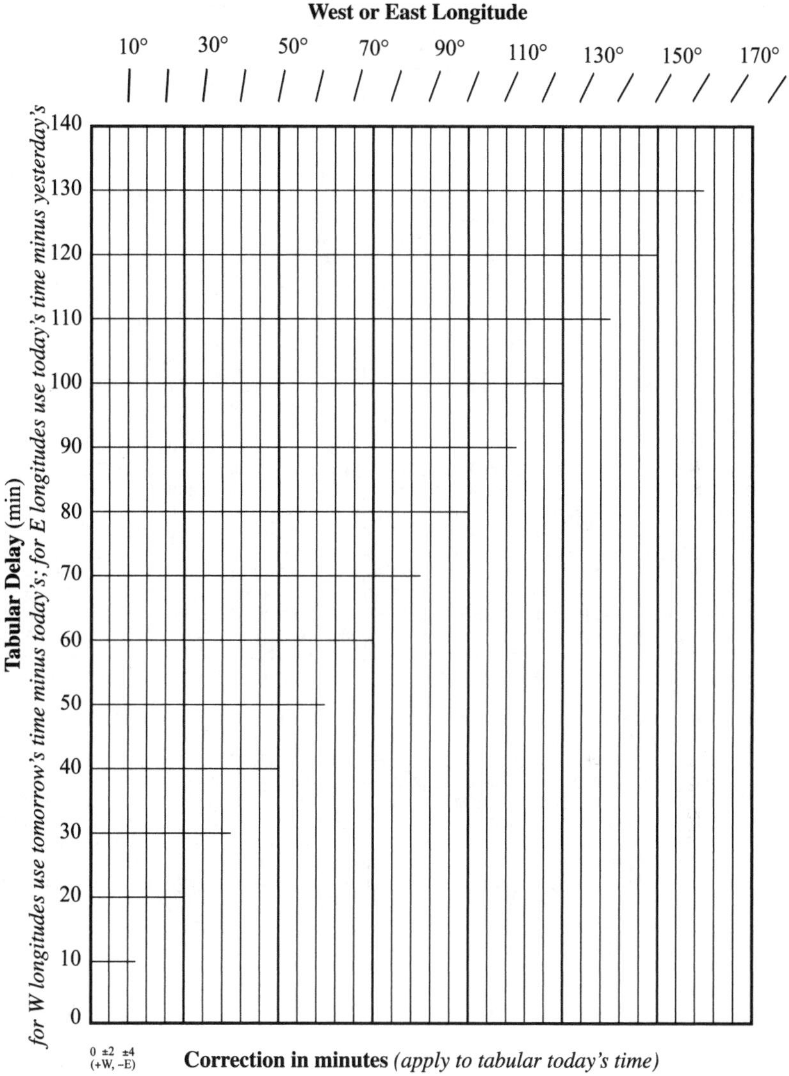

Note: Due to a difference in elevation between the observer and the actual horizon, the observed time may differ by several minutes from the predicted time.

The correction in minutes can also be calculated from the formula:

$$(L/360) \times (\text{Tabular Delay}) + 4(L - Ls)$$

in which L = longitude of the observer from Greenwich, and Ls = longitude of the observer's time-zone standard meridian (L and Ls are in degrees, and are negative if east of Greenwich). The term 4(L − Ls) is tabulated for several North American cities on p. 205.

Alternatively, see p. 10 for computer-based planetarium programs or applications for mobile devices. A browser-based online rise/set calculator can be found at aa.usno.navy.mil/data/docs/RS_OneYear.php (United States Naval Observatory).

MOONRISE AND MOONSET, JANUARY AND FEBRUARY 2017
UNIVERSAL TIME AT GREENWICH MERIDIAN

Latitude:	**+20°**		**+30°**		**+35°**		**+40°**		**+45°**		**+50°**		**+55°**		**+60°**	
Event:	**RISE**	**SET**	**RISE**	**SET**	**RISE**	**SET**	**RISE**	**SET**	**RISE**	**SET**	**RISE**	**SET**	**RISE**	**SET**	**RISE**	**SET**
Jan. 1	08:51	20:33	09:04	20:21	09:12	20:14	09:20	20:06	09:30	19:57	09:42	19:46	09:57	19:32	10:17	19:14
2	09:35	21:27	09:45	21:19	09:51	21:14	09:57	21:08		21:02	00:00	20:54	10:25	20:44	10:40	20:31
3	10:18	22:22	10:24	22:17	10:28	22:15	10:32	22:12	10:37	22:08	10:43	22:04	10:50	21:58	10:59	21:51
4	11:00	23:18	11:03	23:17	11:04	23:17	11:06	23:16	11:08	23:16	11:10	23:15	11:13	23:14	11:17	23:13
5	11:43		11:41		11:41		11:40		11:39		11:38		11:36		11:35	
6	12:27	00:15	12:21	00:18	12:18	00:20	12:15	00:22	12:11	00:25	12:06	00:28	12:00	00:32	11:53	00:37
7	13:13	01:13	13:04	01:21	12:58	01:25	12:52	01:30	12:45	01:36	12:37	01:43	12:27	01:51	12:14	02:02
8	14:02	02:14	13:50	02:25	13:42	02:32	13:34	02:39	13:24	02:48	13:13	02:58	12:58	03:11	12:39	03:29
9	14:56	03:16	14:40	03:30	14:31	03:39	14:21	03:49	14:09	04:00	13:55	04:13	13:37	04:31	13:12	04:54
10	15:53	04:19	15:36	04:36	15:26	04:45	15:15	04:57	15:01	05:10	14:45	05:26	14:24	05:46	13:56	06:14
11	16:53	05:21	16:36	05:39	16:26	05:49	16:14	06:01	16:00	06:15	15:43	06:31	15:22	06:53	14:53	07:22
12	*17:55*	*06:21*	*17:38*	*06:38*	*17:29*	*06:48*	*17:18*	*06:59*	*17:05*	*07:12*	*16:49*	*07:29*	*16:29*	*07:49*	*16:02*	*08:17*
13	18:56	07:16	18:41	07:32	18:33	07:40	18:24	07:51	18:13	08:02	17:59	08:16	17:42	08:34	17:20	08:58
14	19:55	08:07	19:43	08:20	19:37	08:27	19:30	08:35	19:21	08:45	19:11	08:56	18:58	09:10	18:41	09:29
15	20:51	08:54	20:43	09:03	20:39	09:08	20:34	09:14	20:28	09:21	20:21	09:29	20:12	09:39	20:01	09:53
16	21:45	09:36	21:41	09:42	21:38	09:45	21:36	09:49	21:33	09:53	21:29	09:58	21:25	10:04	21:20	10:12
17	22:36	10:16	22:36	10:18	22:36	10:19	22:36	10:21	22:36	10:22	22:36	10:24	22:35	10:26	22:35	10:29
18	23:26	10:55	23:30	10:53	23:32	10:52	23:34	10:51	23:37	10:50	23:40	10:48	23:44	10:46	23:49	10:44
19		11:32		11:27		11:24		11:21		11:17		11:12		11:07		11:00
20	00:15	12:10	00:22	12:02	00:26	11:57	00:31	11:51	00:36	11:45	00:42	11:38	00:50	11:28	01:01	11:16
21	01:04	12:49	01:14	12:38	01:20	12:31	01:27	12:24	01:35	12:15	01:44	12:05	01:56	11:52	02:11	11:35
22	01:53	13:30	02:06	13:16	02:14	13:08	02:22	12:59	02:32	12:48	02:44	12:35	03:00	12:19	03:20	11:57
23	02:43	14:13	02:58	13:57	03:07	13:48	03:17	13:37	03:29	13:25	03:43	13:10	04:02	12:51	04:26	12:25
24	03:33	14:59	03:49	14:41	03:59	14:31	04:10	14:20	04:24	14:06	04:40	13:50	05:00	13:29	05:28	13:01
25	04:22	15:47	04:40	15:30	04:50	15:19	05:02	15:08	05:16	14:54	05:33	14:37	05:54	14:15	06:24	13:46
26	05:12	16:38	05:29	16:21	05:39	16:11	05:51	16:00	06:05	15:47	06:21	15:30	06:42	15:10	07:11	14:41
27	06:00	17:32	06:17	17:16	06:26	17:07	06:37	16:57	06:49	16:45	07:04	16:30	07:24	16:12	07:50	15:47
28	**06:48**	**18:26**	**07:02**	**18:13**	**07:10**	**18:06**	**07:19**	**17:57**	**07:30**	**17:47**	**07:43**	**17:35**	**07:59**	**17:20**	**08:21**	**16:59**
29	07:33	19:22	07:44	19:12	07:51	19:06	07:58	19:00	08:06	18:52	08:17	18:43	08:29	18:32	08:46	18:17
30	08:17	20:17	08:25	20:11	08:29	20:08	08:34	20:04	08:40	19:59	08:47	19:54	08:56	19:47	09:07	19:38
31	09:00	21:14	09:04	21:12	09:06	21:10	09:09	21:09	09:12	21:07	09:16	21:05	09:20	21:03	09:26	21:00
Feb. 1	09:43	22:10	09:43	22:12	09:43	22:14	09:43	22:15	09:43	22:16	09:43	22:18	09:43	22:20	09:43	22:23
2	10:26	23:08	10:22	23:14	10:20	23:18	10:17	23:22	10:14	23:26	10:11	23:32	10:07	23:39	10:01	23:48
3	11:11		11:03		10:59		10:54		10:48		10:41		10:32		10:21	
4	11:58	00:07	11:47	00:17	11:40	00:22	11:33	00:29	11:24	00:37	11:14	00:46	11:01	00:57	10:44	01:13
5	12:49	01:07	12:34	01:20	12:26	01:28	12:16	01:37	12:05	01:47	11:52	01:59	11:35	02:15	11:13	02:36
6	13:43	02:07	13:26	02:23	13:16	02:33	13:05	02:43	12:53	02:56	12:37	03:11	12:17	03:30	11:50	03:56
7	14:40	03:08	14:22	03:25	14:12	03:35	14:00	03:47	13:47	04:00	13:30	04:17	13:09	04:38	12:40	05:07
8	15:39	04:07	15:22	04:24	15:12	04:34	15:00	04:46	14:47	05:00	14:31	05:16	14:10	05:37	13:41	06:06
9	16:39	05:03	16:23	05:19	16:14	05:28	16:04	05:39	15:52	05:52	15:37	06:07	15:19	06:26	14:54	06:52
10	17:38	05:55	17:25	06:09	17:18	06:17	17:09	06:26	17:00	06:37	16:48	06:50	16:33	07:06	16:13	07:27
11	*18:35*	*06:43*	*18:26*	*06:54*	*18:21*	*07:01*	*18:14*	*07:08*	*18:07*	*07:16*	*17:59*	*07:26*	*17:48*	*07:38*	*17:34*	*07:54*
12	19:31	07:28	19:25	07:35	19:22	07:40	19:18	07:45	19:14	07:50	19:08	07:57	19:02	08:05	18:54	08:15
13	20:24	08:10	20:22	08:14	20:21	08:16	20:20	08:18	20:18	08:21	20:17	08:24	20:14	08:28	20:12	08:33
14	21:16	08:50	21:18	08:50	21:19	08:50	21:20	08:50	21:21	08:50	21:23	08:50	21:25	08:50	21:28	08:50
15	22:06	09:28	22:11	09:24	22:15	09:22	22:18	09:20	22:22	09:17	22:27	09:14	22:33	09:10	22:41	09:05
16	22:56	10:06	23:04	09:59	23:09	09:55	23:15	09:51	23:22	09:46	23:30	09:39	23:40	09:32	23:53	09:22
17	23:45	10:45	23:57	10:35		10:29		10:23		10:15		10:06		09:54		09:40
18		11:25		11:12	00:04	11:05	00:11	10:56	00:20	10:46	00:31	10:35	00:45	10:20	01:03	10:00
19	00:34	12:07	00:49	11:52	00:57	11:43	01:06	11:33	01:17	11:21	01:31	11:07	01:48	10:49	02:11	10:26
20	01:24	12:51	01:40	12:35	01:49	12:25	02:00	12:14	02:13	12:01	02:28	11:45	02:48	11:25	03:15	10:57
21	02:13	13:38	02:31	13:21	02:41	13:11	02:52	12:59	03:06	12:45	03:22	12:29	03:44	12:07	04:13	11:38
22	03:03	14:28	03:20	14:11	03:30	14:01	03:42	13:49	03:56	13:35	04:13	13:19	04:34	12:58	05:03	12:28
23	03:52	15:20	04:08	15:04	04:18	14:55	04:29	14:44	04:42	14:31	04:58	14:16	05:18	13:56	05:46	13:29
24	04:39	16:15	04:54	16:00	05:03	15:52	05:13	15:43	05:25	15:32	05:39	15:19	05:56	15:02	06:20	14:39
25	05:26	17:10	05:38	16:59	05:46	16:53	05:54	16:45	06:03	16:37	06:15	16:26	06:29	16:13	06:48	15:56
26	**06:11**	**18:07**	**06:21**	**17:59**	**06:26**	**17:55**	**06:32**	**17:50**	**06:39**	**17:44**	**06:47**	**17:37**	**06:58**	**17:28**	**07:11**	**17:17**
27	06:56	19:04	07:01	19:01	07:04	18:59	07:08	18:56	07:12	18:54	07:17	18:50	07:23	18:46	07:31	18:41
28	07:40	20:03	07:41	20:03	07:42	20:03	07:43	20:04	07:44	20:04	07:46	20:05	07:47	20:05	07:49	20:06

Bold = new Moon, *italic* = full Moon. A gap in a column indicates the event will take place early the next day.

MOONRISE AND MOONSET, MARCH AND APRIL 2017
UNIVERSAL TIME AT GREENWICH MERIDIAN

Latitude:	+20°	+30°	+35°	+40°	+45°	+50°	+55°	+60°
Event:	RISE SET	RISE SET	RISE SET	RISE SET	RISE SET	RISE SET	RISE SET	RISE SET
Mar. 1	08:24 21:01	08:21 21:06	08:20 21:09	08:18 21:12	08:16 21:16	08:14 21:20	08:11 21:25	08:08 21:32
2	09:09 22:01	09:03 22:10	08:59 22:15	08:55 22:21	08:50 22:27	08:44 22:36	08:36 22:46	08:27 22:59
3	09:57 23:01	09:46 23:14	09:40 23:21	09:33 23:29	09:25 23:39	09:16 23:50	09:04	08:49
4	10:46	10:32	10:25	10:16	10:05	09:53	09:37 00:05	09:16 00:24
5	11:39 00:02	11:23 00:17	11:13 00:26	11:03 00:36	10:50 00:48	10:35 01:02	10:16 01:20	09:51 01:45
6	12:34 01:02	12:16 01:19	12:06 01:29	11:55 01:40	11:41 01:53	11:25 02:10	11:04 02:30	10:35 02:58
7	13:31 02:00	13:14 02:18	13:03 02:28	12:52 02:40	12:38 02:53	12:22 03:10	12:00 03:31	11:32 04:00
8	14:29 02:56	14:13 03:13	14:04 03:22	13:53 03:33	13:40 03:47	13:25 04:02	13:05 04:22	12:39 04:50
9	15:27 03:48	15:13 04:03	15:05 04:12	14:56 04:21	14:45 04:33	14:32 04:47	14:16 05:04	13:54 05:27
10	16:24 04:37	16:13 04:49	16:07 04:56	16:00 05:04	15:51 05:13	15:41 05:24	15:29 05:38	15:12 05:56
11	17:19 05:22	17:12 05:31	17:08 05:36	17:03 05:42	16:57 05:48	16:51 05:56	16:42 06:06	16:32 06:19
12	*18:13 06:04*	*18:10 06:09*	*18:07 06:12*	*18:05 06:16*	*18:02 06:20*	*17:59 06:25*	*17:55 06:30*	*17:50 06:38*
13	19:05 06:44	19:06 06:46	19:06 06:47	19:06 06:48	19:06 06:49	19:06 06:51	19:06 06:52	19:07 06:55
14	19:56 07:23	20:00 07:21	20:03 07:20	20:05 07:19	20:08 07:17	20:12 07:16	20:16 07:13	20:22 07:10
15	20:47 08:02	20:54 07:56	20:58 07:53	21:03 07:50	21:09 07:45	21:16 07:40	21:24 07:34	21:35 07:26
16	21:37 08:41	21:47 08:32	21:53 08:27	22:00 08:21	22:08 08:14	22:18 08:06	22:31 07:56	22:47 07:44
17	22:26 09:20	22:39 09:08	22:47 09:02	22:56 08:54	23:06 08:45	23:19 08:34	23:35 08:21	23:56 08:03
18	23:16 10:01	23:31 09:47	23:40 09:39	23:50 09:29	09:18	09:05	08:48	08:26
19	10:45	10:28	10:19	10:08	00:03 09:56	00:17 09:40	00:36 09:21	01:02 08:55
20	00:05 11:30	00:22 11:13	00:32 11:03	00:43 10:51	00:56 10:38	01:13 10:21	01:34 10:00	02:02 09:31
21	00:54 12:18	01:11 12:01	01:22 11:50	01:33 11:39	01:47 11:25	02:04 11:08	02:26 10:46	02:55 10:17
22	01:42 13:09	02:00 12:52	02:10 12:42	02:21 12:31	02:35 12:17	02:51 12:01	03:12 11:41	03:41 11:12
23	02:30 14:01	02:46 13:46	02:55 13:37	03:06 13:27	03:18 13:15	03:33 13:01	03:52 12:42	04:18 12:17
24	03:16 14:56	03:30 14:43	03:38 14:36	03:47 14:27	03:58 14:17	04:11 14:05	04:27 13:50	04:48 13:30
25	04:02 15:52	04:13 15:42	04:19 15:37	04:26 15:31	04:34 15:23	04:44 15:15	04:57 15:04	05:13 14:49
26	04:47 16:49	04:54 16:44	04:58 16:40	05:03 16:37	05:08 16:32	05:15 16:27	05:23 16:21	05:34 16:12
27	05:31 17:48	05:35 17:46	05:36 17:46	05:39 17:45	05:41 17:44	05:44 17:42	05:48 17:41	05:53 17:39
28	**06:16 18:48**	**06:15 18:51**	**06:15 18:52**	**06:14 18:54**	**06:14 18:57**	**06:13 18:59**	**06:12 19:03**	**06:11 19:07**
29	07:02 19:49	06:57 19:56	06:54 20:00	06:51 20:05	06:47 20:11	06:43 20:17	06:37 20:26	06:30 20:36
30	07:50 20:51	07:41 21:02	07:36 21:09	07:30 21:16	07:23 21:25	07:15 21:35	07:05 21:48	06:52 22:06
31	08:40 21:54	08:28 22:08	08:20 22:17	08:12 22:26	08:02 22:37	07:51 22:51	07:36 23:08	07:17 23:31
Apr. 1	09:33 22:56	09:18 23:12	09:09 23:22	08:59 23:33	08:47 23:46	08:32	08:14	07:50
2	10:29 23:56	10:12	10:02	09:50	09:37	09:21 00:02	09:00 00:22	08:32 00:50
3	11:26	11:09 00:13	10:58 00:24	10:47 00:35	10:33 00:49	10:16 01:06	09:54 01:27	09:25 01:57
4	12:24 00:52	12:07 01:10	11:58 01:20	11:47 01:31	11:33 01:45	11:17 02:01	10:57 02:22	10:29 02:50
5	13:22 01:45	13:07 02:01	12:59 02:10	12:49 02:21	12:37 02:33	12:23 02:47	12:06 03:06	11:42 03:31
6	14:18 02:34	14:06 02:48	13:59 02:55	13:52 03:04	13:42 03:14	13:31 03:26	13:17 03:41	12:59 04:01
7	15:13 03:20	15:05 03:30	15:00 03:36	14:54 03:42	14:47 03:50	14:39 03:59	14:30 04:10	14:17 04:25
8	16:06 04:02	16:02 04:09	15:59 04:13	15:55 04:17	15:52 04:22	15:47 04:28	15:42 04:35	15:34 04:45
9	16:58 04:42	16:57 04:45	16:56 04:47	16:56 04:49	16:55 04:51	16:54 04:54	16:52 04:57	16:51 05:01
10	17:49 05:21	17:52 05:20	17:53 05:20	17:55 05:20	17:57 05:19	17:59 05:18	18:02 05:18	18:06 05:17
11	*18:40 05:59*	*18:46 05:55*	*18:49 05:53*	*18:53 05:50*	*18:58 05:47*	*19:04 05:43*	*19:11 05:38*	*19:20 05:32*
12	19:30 06:38	19:39 06:30	19:44 06:26	19:51 06:21	19:58 06:15	20:07 06:08	20:18 05:59	20:32 05:48
13	20:19 07:17	20:32 07:06	20:39 07:00	20:47 06:53	20:57 06:45	21:09 06:35	21:23 06:22	21:43 06:06
14	21:09 07:57	21:24 07:44	21:33 07:36	21:43 07:27	21:54 07:17	22:08 07:04	22:26 06:49	22:50 06:28
15	21:59 08:40	22:15 08:24	22:25 08:15	22:36 08:05	22:49 07:52	23:05 07:38	23:25 07:19	23:53 06:54
16	22:47 09:24	23:05 09:07	23:15 08:57	23:27 08:46	23:41 08:32	23:58 08:16	07:55	07:27
17	23:36 10:11	23:53 09:53	09:43	09:31	09:17	09:00	00:20 08:38	00:49 08:08
18	11:00	10:42	00:04 10:32	00:15 10:21	00:29 10:07	00:46 09:50	01:08 09:29	01:38 08:59
19	00:23 11:51	00:40 11:34	00:49 11:25	01:00 11:14	01:14 11:01	01:29 10:46	01:50 10:26	02:17 09:59
20	01:09 12:43	01:24 12:29	01:32 12:21	01:42 12:12	01:54 12:01	02:08 11:47	02:26 11:31	02:49 11:08
21	01:53 13:37	02:06 13:26	02:13 13:20	02:21 13:12	02:31 13:04	02:42 12:53	02:56 12:40	03:15 12:23
22	02:37 14:33	02:47 14:25	02:52 14:21	02:58 14:16	03:05 14:10	03:13 14:03	03:24 13:54	03:37 13:43
23	03:21 15:30	03:27 15:26	03:30 15:24	03:33 15:22	03:37 15:19	03:42 15:16	03:48 15:12	03:56 15:06
24	04:05 16:29	04:07 16:30	04:07 16:30	04:08 16:30	04:09 16:31	04:11 16:32	04:12 16:32	04:14 16:33
25	04:50 17:30	04:48 17:35	04:46 17:38	04:44 17:41	04:42 17:45	04:40 17:50	04:36 17:56	04:33 18:03
26	**05:38 18:33**	**05:31 18:42**	**05:27 18:48**	**05:22 18:54**	**05:17 19:01**	**05:10 19:10**	**05:02 19:21**	**04:53 19:35**
27	06:28 19:37	06:17 19:50	06:10 19:58	06:03 20:07	05:55 20:17	05:45 20:29	05:32 20:45	05:16 21:06
28	07:21 20:42	07:07 20:58	06:58 21:07	06:49 21:18	06:38 21:31	06:24 21:46	06:08 22:05	05:45 22:32
29	08:18 21:45	08:01 22:03	07:51 22:13	07:40 22:25	07:27 22:39	07:11 22:56	06:51 23:17	06:24 23:47
30	09:17 22:46	08:59 23:03	08:49 23:14	08:37 23:26	08:23 23:39	08:06 23:56	07:44	07:14

MOONRISE AND MOONSET, MAY AND JUNE 2017

UNIVERSAL TIME AT GREENWICH MERIDIAN

Latitude:	+20°		+30°		+35°		+40°		+45°		+50°		+55°		+60°	
Event:	RISE	SET	RISE	SET	RISE	SET	RISE	SET	RISE	SET	RISE	SET	RISE	SET	RISE	SET
May 1	10:17	23:42	09:59	23:58	09:49		09:38		09:24		09:07		08:46	00:18	08:17	00:48
2	11:16		11:00		10:51	00:08	10:41	00:19	10:28	00:32	10:14	00:47	09:55	01:07	09:29	01:33
3	12:14	00:33	12:01	00:47	11:53	00:55	11:45	01:05	11:34	01:16	11:22	01:29	11:07	01:45	10:46	02:07
4	13:10	01:20	13:00	01:31	12:54	01:37	12:48	01:45	12:40	01:53	12:31	02:04	12:20	02:16	12:05	02:33
5	14:03	02:03	13:57	02:11	13:53	02:15	13:49	02:20	13:44	02:26	13:39	02:33	13:32	02:42	13:22	02:53
6	14:55	02:43	14:52	02:47	14:51	02:50	14:49	02:53	14:47	02:56	14:45	03:00	14:42	03:04	14:39	03:10
7	15:46	03:22	15:47	03:22	15:47	03:23	15:48	03:23	15:49	03:23	15:50	03:24	15:52	03:25	15:54	03:25
8	16:35	03:59	16:40	03:56	16:43	03:55	16:46	03:53	16:50	03:50	16:55	03:48	17:00	03:44	17:07	03:40
9	17:25	04:37	17:33	04:31	17:38	04:27	17:44	04:23	17:50	04:18	17:58	04:12	18:07	04:05	18:20	03:55
10	*18:15*	*05:16*	*18:26*	*05:06*	*18:33*	*05:00*	*18:40*	*04:54*	*18:49*	*04:46*	*19:00*	*04:38*	*19:14*	*04:27*	*19:31*	*04:12*
11	19:04	05:55	19:19	05:43	19:27	05:35	19:36	05:27	19:47	05:17	20:01	05:06	20:18	04:51	20:41	04:32
12	19:54	06:37	20:10	06:22	20:20	06:13	20:31	06:03	20:43	05:51	20:59	05:37	21:19	05:19	21:46	04:56
13	20:43	07:21	21:01	07:04	21:11	06:54	21:23	06:43	21:37	06:30	21:54	06:14	22:15	05:53	22:45	05:26
14	21:32	08:07	21:50	07:49	22:00	07:38	22:12	07:27	22:26	07:12	22:44	06:55	23:06	06:33	23:36	06:03
15	22:19	08:55	22:37	08:37	22:47	08:26	22:58	08:14	23:12	08:00	23:29	07:43	23:50	07:21		06:51
16	23:05	09:44	23:21	09:27	23:30	09:17	23:41	09:06	23:53	08:53		08:36		08:16	00:19	07:47
17	23:49	10:35		10:20		10:11		10:01		09:49	00:08	09:35	00:27	09:17	00:53	08:52
18		11:28	00:03	11:15	00:11	11:08	00:20	11:00	00:31	10:50	00:43	10:38	00:59	10:23	01:20	10:03
19	00:32	12:21	00:43	12:12	00:49	12:06	00:56	12:00	01:05	11:53	01:15	11:44	01:27	11:34	01:43	11:19
20	01:15	13:16	01:22	13:10	01:26	13:07	01:31	13:03	01:37	12:59	01:43	12:54	01:51	12:47	02:02	12:39
21	01:57	14:12	02:01	14:11	02:03	14:10	02:05	14:09	02:08	14:08	02:11	14:06	02:15	14:05	02:19	14:02
22	02:40	15:11	02:40	15:14	02:39	15:15	02:39	15:17	02:39	15:19	02:38	15:22	02:37	15:25	02:37	15:29
23	03:25	16:12	03:20	16:19	03:18	16:23	03:15	16:28	03:11	16:33	03:07	16:40	03:01	16:48	02:55	16:59
24	04:13	17:15	04:04	17:26	03:59	17:33	03:53	17:40	03:46	17:49	03:38	18:00	03:28	18:13	03:15	18:30
25	**05:05**	**18:21**	**04:52**	**18:35**	**04:45**	**18:44**	**04:36**	**18:54**	**04:26**	**19:05**	**04:15**	**19:19**	**04:00**	**19:37**	**03:41**	**20:01**
26	06:01	19:26	05:45	19:44	05:36	19:54	05:25	20:05	05:13	20:18	04:58	20:35	04:39	20:56	04:14	21:24
27	07:00	20:30	06:42	20:49	06:32	20:59	06:20	21:11	06:06	21:25	05:50	21:43	05:28	22:05	04:59	22:35
28	08:02	21:31	07:44	21:48	07:33	21:58	07:21	22:10	07:07	22:24	06:50	22:40	06:28	23:01	05:57	23:30
29	09:04	22:26	08:47	22:42	08:37	22:51	08:26	23:01	08:13	23:13	07:57	23:27	07:36	23:45	07:08	
30	10:05	23:16	09:50	23:29	09:42	23:36	09:32	23:45	09:21	23:54	09:07		08:50		08:27	00:10
31	11:03		10:52		10:45		10:38		10:29		10:18	00:06	10:05	00:20	09:48	00:39
Jun. 1	11:58	00:02	11:51	00:11	11:46	00:16	11:41	00:22	11:35	00:29	11:28	00:38	11:20	00:48	11:08	01:01
2	12:51	00:44	12:47	00:49	12:45	00:53	12:43	00:56	12:40	01:00	12:36	01:05	12:32	01:12	12:26	01:19
3	13:43	01:23	13:42	01:25	13:42	01:26	13:42	01:27	13:42	01:29	13:42	01:30	13:42	01:32	13:42	01:35
4	14:33	02:01	14:36	01:59	14:38	01:58	14:41	01:57	14:43	01:56	14:47	01:54	14:51	01:52	14:56	01:50
5	15:22	02:38	15:29	02:33	15:33	02:30	15:38	02:27	15:44	02:23	15:50	02:18	15:58	02:12	16:09	02:04
6	16:11	03:16	16:22	03:07	16:28	03:02	16:35	02:57	16:43	02:50	16:53	02:42	17:05	02:33	17:21	02:20
7	17:01	03:55	17:14	03:43	17:22	03:37	17:31	03:29	17:41	03:20	17:54	03:09	18:10	02:56	18:31	02:38
8	17:50	04:36	18:06	04:21	18:15	04:13	18:26	04:04	18:38	03:53	18:53	03:39	19:12	03:22	19:38	03:00
9	*18:40*	*05:19*	*18:57*	*05:02*	*19:07*	*04:53*	*19:19*	*04:42*	*19:33*	*04:29*	*19:49*	*04:14*	*20:11*	*03:54*	*20:40*	*03:27*
10	19:29	06:04	19:47	05:46	19:58	05:36	20:10	05:24	20:24	05:10	20:41	04:53	21:04	04:32	21:35	04:02
11	20:17	06:51	20:35	06:33	20:45	06:23	20:57	06:11	21:11	05:56	21:28	05:39	21:50	05:16	22:20	04:46
12	21:03	07:41	21:20	07:23	21:30	07:13	21:41	07:01	21:54	06:47	22:10	06:30	22:30	06:09	22:57	05:39
13	21:48	08:31	22:03	08:15	22:11	08:06	22:21	07:55	22:33	07:43	22:46	07:27	23:04	07:08	23:27	06:41
14	22:31	09:23	22:43	09:09	22:50	09:01	22:58	08:52	23:07	08:41	23:18	08:28	23:32	08:12	23:50	07:50
15	23:13	10:15	23:22	10:05	23:27	09:58	23:33	09:51	23:39	09:43	23:47	09:33	23:57	09:20		09:04
16	23:54	11:08	23:59	11:01		10:57		10:52		10:47		10:40		10:32	00:10	10:21
17		12:03		11:59	00:02	11:57	00:06	11:55	00:10	11:53	00:14	11:49	00:20	11:46	00:27	11:41
18	00:35	12:58	00:37	12:59	00:37	12:59	00:38	13:00	00:39	13:00	00:40	13:01	00:42	13:02	00:44	13:03
19	01:18	13:56	01:15	14:01	01:14	14:04	01:12	14:07	01:10	14:11	01:07	14:15	01:04	14:21	01:00	14:29
20	02:03	14:56	01:56	15:05	01:52	15:11	01:47	15:17	01:42	15:24	01:36	15:32	01:28	15:43	01:19	15:57
21	02:51	15:59	02:40	16:12	02:34	16:20	02:27	16:28	02:18	16:38	02:09	16:51	01:56	17:06	01:40	17:27
22	03:43	17:04	03:29	17:20	03:21	17:29	03:11	17:40	03:00	17:53	02:47	18:08	02:30	18:27	02:08	18:54
23	04:40	18:09	04:23	18:27	04:14	18:37	04:02	18:49	03:49	19:03	03:33	19:20	03:13	19:42	02:46	20:12
24	**05:41**	**19:13**	**05:23**	**19:31**	**05:13**	**19:41**	**05:01**	**19:53**	**04:46**	**20:07**	**04:29**	**20:25**	**04:07**	**20:47**	**03:37**	**21:17**
25	06:45	20:12	06:27	20:29	06:16	20:38	06:05	20:50	05:51	21:03	05:34	21:18	05:12	21:38	04:42	22:05
26	07:48	21:06	07:32	21:21	07:23	21:29	07:12	21:38	07:00	21:49	06:45	22:02	06:25	22:19	05:59	22:40
27	08:49	21:55	08:36	22:06	08:29	22:13	08:20	22:20	08:10	22:28	07:58	22:38	07:43	22:50	07:22	23:06
28	09:48	22:40	09:39	22:48	09:33	22:52	09:27	22:56	09:20	23:02	09:11	23:08	09:00	23:16	08:46	23:27
29	10:44	23:22	10:38	23:25	10:35	23:27	10:31	23:29	10:27	23:32	10:22	23:35	10:16	23:39	10:08	23:44
30	11:37		11:35		11:34		11:33		11:32	00:00	11:30	00:00	11:29	23:59	11:26	23:59

Bold = new Moon, *italic* = full Moon. A gap in a column indicates the event will take place early the next day.

MOONRISE AND MOONSET, JULY AND AUGUST 2017
UNIVERSAL TIME AT GREENWICH MERIDIAN

Latitude:	+20°		+30°		+35°		+40°		+45°		+50°		+55°		+60°	
Event:	**RISE**	**SET**	**RISE**	**SET**	**RISE**	**SET**	**RISE**	**SET**	**RISE**	**SET**	**RISE**	**SET**	**RISE**	**SET**	**RISE**	**SET**
Jul. 1	12:28	00:01	12:30		12:31		12:33		12:35		12:37		12:39		12:42	
2	13:18	00:39	13:24	00:35	13:27	00:32	13:31	00:30	13:36	00:27	13:41	00:23	13:48	00:19	13:56	00:13
3	14:08	01:17	14:17	01:09	14:22	01:05	14:28	01:00	14:35	00:54	14:44	00:48	14:55	00:39	15:09	00:29
4	14:57	01:55	15:09	01:44	15:16	01:38	15:25	01:31	15:34	01:23	15:46	01:14	16:00	01:02	16:20	00:46
5	15:46	02:35	16:01	02:22	16:10	02:14	16:20	02:05	16:32	01:55	16:46	01:42	17:04	01:27	17:28	01:06
6	16:36	03:17	16:53	03:01	17:03	02:52	17:14	02:42	17:27	02:29	17:43	02:15	18:04	01:56	18:32	01:31
7	17:25	04:01	17:43	03:44	17:54	03:34	18:06	03:22	18:20	03:09	18:37	02:52	18:59	02:31	19:30	02:02
8	18:14	04:48	18:32	04:30	18:43	04:19	18:55	04:07	19:09	03:53	19:26	03:36	19:49	03:13	20:19	02:43
9	*19:01*	*05:37*	*19:19*	*05:19*	*19:29*	*05:09*	*19:40*	*04:57*	*19:54*	*04:43*	*20:10*	*04:25*	*20:31*	*04:03*	*21:00*	*03:33*
10	19:47	06:28	20:03	06:11	20:12	06:01	20:22	05:50	20:34	05:37	20:49	05:21	21:07	05:00	21:32	04:32
11	20:31	07:19	20:44	07:05	20:52	06:56	21:00	06:47	21:10	06:35	21:22	06:21	21:37	06:04	21:57	05:40
12	21:13	08:12	21:23	08:00	21:29	07:53	21:36	07:45	21:43	07:36	21:52	07:25	22:04	07:11	22:18	06:53
13	21:55	09:05	22:01	08:56	22:05	08:51	22:09	08:46	22:14	08:39	22:20	08:31	22:27	08:21	22:36	08:09
14	22:35	09:58	22:38	09:53	22:39	09:51	22:41	09:47	22:43	09:44	22:46	09:39	22:49	09:34	22:52	09:27
15	23:16	10:52	23:15	10:51	23:14	10:51	23:13	10:51	23:13	10:50	23:11	10:49	23:10	10:48	23:08	10:47
16	23:59	11:48	23:54	11:51	23:50	11:53	23:47	11:55	23:43	11:58	23:38	12:01	23:33	12:05	23:25	12:10
17		12:45		12:53		12:57		13:02		13:07		13:14	23:58	13:23	23:45	13:34
18	00:44	13:45	00:35	13:56	00:29	14:03	00:23	14:10	00:16	14:19	00:08	14:29		14:43		15:00
19	01:33	14:47	01:20	15:01	01:12	15:10	01:04	15:20	00:54	15:31	00:42	15:45	00:28	16:03	00:08	16:26
20	02:26	15:50	02:10	16:07	02:01	16:17	01:50	16:28	01:38	16:42	01:23	16:58	01:05	17:19	00:40	17:47
21	03:23	16:53	03:05	17:11	02:55	17:22	02:43	17:34	02:30	17:48	02:13	18:05	01:52	18:28	01:22	18:58
22	04:24	17:54	04:06	18:12	03:56	18:22	03:44	18:34	03:29	18:47	03:12	19:04	02:50	19:25	02:19	19:54
23	**05:27**	**18:51**	**05:10**	**19:07**	**05:00**	**19:16**	**04:49**	**19:26**	**04:36**	**19:39**	**04:20**	**19:53**	**03:59**	**20:12**	**03:30**	**20:36**
24	06:30	19:44	06:16	19:57	06:07	20:04	05:58	20:12	05:46	20:22	05:33	20:34	05:15	20:48	04:52	21:07
25	07:32	20:32	07:20	20:41	07:14	20:46	07:06	20:52	06:58	20:59	06:47	21:07	06:34	21:17	06:17	21:30
26	08:30	21:16	08:23	21:21	08:18	21:24	08:13	21:27	08:08	21:31	08:01	21:36	07:52	21:42	07:41	21:49
27	09:26	21:57	09:22	21:58	09:20	21:59	09:18	22:00	09:16	22:01	09:12	22:02	09:09	22:04	09:03	22:06
28	10:19	22:36	10:20	22:34	10:20	22:32	10:20	22:31	10:21	22:29	10:21	22:27	10:22	22:24	10:23	22:21
29	11:11	23:15	11:15	23:09	11:18	23:05	11:20	23:01	11:24	22:57	11:28	22:51	11:33	22:45	11:39	22:36
30	12:01	23:53	12:09	23:44	12:14	23:39	12:19	23:32	12:25	23:25	12:32	23:17	12:41	23:06	12:53	22:53
31	12:51		13:02		13:09		13:16		13:25	23:56	13:35	23:44	13:48	23:30	14:05	23:12
Aug. 1	13:41	00:33	13:55	00:21	14:03	00:13	14:12	00:05	14:23		14:36		14:53	23:58	15:15	23:35
2	14:31	01:14	14:47	00:59	14:56	00:51	15:07	00:41	15:19	00:29	15:35	00:15	15:54		16:21	
3	15:20	01:58	15:38	01:41	15:48	01:31	15:59	01:20	16:13	01:07	16:30	00:51	16:52	00:31	17:22	00:03
4	16:09	02:43	16:27	02:26	16:38	02:15	16:50	02:03	17:04	01:49	17:21	01:32	17:44	01:10	18:14	00:40
5	16:57	03:32	17:15	03:14	17:25	03:03	17:37	02:51	17:51	02:37	18:07	02:19	18:29	01:57	18:58	01:26
6	17:44	04:22	18:00	04:05	18:09	03:55	18:20	03:43	18:33	03:30	18:48	03:13	19:08	02:52	19:34	02:23
7	*18:29*	*05:14*	*18:43*	*04:58*	*18:51*	*04:49*	*19:00*	*04:39*	*19:11*	*04:27*	*19:24*	*04:12*	*19:40*	*03:53*	*20:02*	*03:28*
8	19:12	06:07	19:23	05:54	19:30	05:46	19:37	05:38	19:46	05:28	19:56	05:16	20:08	05:00	20:25	04:40
9	19:54	07:00	20:02	06:50	20:06	06:45	20:11	06:38	20:17	06:31	20:24	06:22	20:33	06:11	20:44	05:56
10	20:36	07:54	20:39	07:48	20:42	07:45	20:44	07:41	20:47	07:36	20:51	07:30	20:55	07:24	21:01	07:15
11	21:17	08:48	21:17	08:46	21:17	08:45	21:17	08:44	21:17	08:42	21:17	08:40	21:17	08:38	21:17	08:35
12	21:59	09:43	21:55	09:46	21:52	09:47	21:50	09:48	21:47	09:50	21:43	09:52	21:39	09:54	21:33	09:57
13	22:42	10:40	22:34	10:46	22:30	10:50	22:24	10:54	22:18	10:58	22:11	11:04	22:03	11:11	21:51	11:20
14	23:29	11:38	23:17	11:48	23:10	11:54	23:03	12:00	22:54	12:08	22:43	12:17	22:30	12:29	22:13	12:44
15		12:37		12:51	23:55	12:59	23:45	13:08	23:34	13:18	23:20	13:31	23:03	13:47	22:40	14:09
16	00:18	13:38	00:04	13:55		14:04		14:15		14:28		14:43	23:45	15:03	23:17	15:30
17	01:12	14:40	00:55	14:57	00:46	15:08	00:34	15:20	00:21	15:34	00:05	15:51		16:13		16:43
18	02:10	15:40	01:52	15:58	01:42	16:08	01:30	16:20	01:15	16:34	00:58	16:51	00:36	17:13	00:06	17:43
19	03:11	16:37	02:53	16:54	02:43	17:04	02:31	17:15	02:17	17:28	02:00	17:44	01:39	18:03	01:09	18:30
20	04:13	17:31	03:57	17:45	03:48	17:54	03:37	18:03	03:25	18:14	03:10	18:27	02:50	18:44	02:24	19:05
21	**05:14**	**18:21**	**05:01**	**18:32**	**04:54**	**18:38**	**04:45**	**18:45**	**04:35**	**18:54**	**04:23**	**19:03**	**04:08**	**19:16**	**03:47**	**19:32**
22	06:14	19:07	06:05	19:14	05:59	19:18	05:53	19:23	05:46	19:28	05:37	19:35	05:26	19:43	05:12	19:53
23	07:11	19:50	07:06	19:53	07:03	19:55	06:59	19:57	06:55	19:59	06:50	20:02	06:44	20:06	06:36	20:10
24	08:07	20:30	08:05	20:30	08:05	20:29	08:04	20:29	08:03	20:28	08:02	20:28	08:00	20:27	07:58	20:26
25	09:00	21:10	09:03	21:06	09:04	21:03	09:06	21:00	09:08	20:57	09:10	20:53	09:13	20:48	09:17	20:42
26	09:52	21:49	09:58	21:41	10:02	21:37	10:06	21:31	10:11	21:25	10:17	21:18	10:24	21:09	10:34	20:58
27	10:43	22:29	10:53	22:18	10:58	22:11	11:05	22:04	11:13	21:55	11:22	21:45	11:33	21:32	11:48	21:16
28	11:33	23:10	11:46	22:56	11:54	22:48	12:02	22:39	12:12	22:28	12:24	22:15	12:39	21:59	13:00	21:37
29	12:23	23:53	12:39	23:36	12:47	23:27	12:58	23:16	13:10	23:04	13:24	22:49	13:43	22:29	14:08	22:04
30	13:13		13:30		13:40		13:51	23:58	14:05	23:44	14:21	23:27	14:42	23:06	15:11	22:37
31	14:02	00:37	14:20	00:20	14:30	00:10	14:42		14:57		15:14		15:36	23:50	16:07	23:19

MOONRISE AND MOONSET, SEPTEMBER AND OCTOBER 2017

UNIVERSAL TIME AT GREENWICH MERIDIAN

Latitude:	+20°		+30°		+35°		+40°		+45°		+50°		+55°		+60°	
Event:	RISE	SET	RISE	SET	RISE	SET	RISE	SET	RISE	SET	RISE	SET	RISE	SET	RISE	SET
Sep. 1	14:50	01:24	15:08	01:06	15:19	00:56	15:31	00:44	15:45	00:30	16:02	00:12	16:24		16:54	
2	15:37	02:14	15:54	01:56	16:04	01:46	16:15	01:34	16:29	01:20	16:45	01:03	17:05	00:41	17:33	00:11
3	16:23	03:05	16:38	02:49	16:47	02:39	16:57	02:28	17:08	02:16	17:22	02:00	17:40	01:40	18:04	01:13
4	17:08	03:58	17:20	03:44	17:27	03:36	17:35	03:26	17:45	03:15	17:56	03:02	18:10	02:45	18:29	02:23
5	17:51	04:52	18:00	04:41	18:05	04:34	18:11	04:27	18:18	04:18	18:26	04:08	18:36	03:55	18:49	03:38
6	*18:33*	*05:46*	*18:38*	*05:39*	*18:41*	*05:34*	*18:45*	*05:30*	*18:49*	*05:24*	*18:54*	*05:17*	*18:59*	*05:08*	*19:07*	*04:57*
7	19:15	06:41	19:16	06:38	19:17	06:36	19:18	06:34	19:19	06:31	19:20	06:28	19:22	06:24	19:23	06:19
8	19:57	07:37	19:54	07:38	19:53	07:38	19:51	07:39	19:49	07:39	19:47	07:40	19:44	07:41	19:40	07:42
9	20:41	08:34	20:34	08:39	20:30	08:42	20:26	08:45	20:21	08:49	20:15	08:54	20:07	08:59	19:58	09:06
10	21:27	09:33	21:16	09:42	21:10	09:47	21:03	09:53	20:55	10:00	20:46	10:08	20:34	10:18	20:18	10:32
11	22:16	10:32	22:02	10:45	21:54	10:52	21:44	11:00	21:34	11:10	21:21	11:22	21:05	11:37	20:44	11:57
12	23:08	11:32	22:51	11:48	22:42	11:57	22:31	12:07	22:18	12:20	22:03	12:34	21:43	12:53	21:17	13:19
13		12:33	23:46	12:50	23:35	13:01	23:23	13:12	23:09	13:26	22:52	13:43	22:30	14:04	22:00	14:34
14	00:03	13:32		13:50		14:01		14:13		14:27	23:50	14:45	23:28	15:07	22:57	15:37
15	01:02	14:29	00:44	14:47	00:33	14:57	00:21	15:08	00:07	15:22		15:38		15:59		16:28
16	02:02	15:23	01:45	15:38	01:35	15:47	01:24	15:57	01:11	16:09	00:55	16:23	00:35	16:42	00:07	17:05
17	03:02	16:13	02:47	16:25	02:39	16:33	02:30	16:41	02:19	16:50	02:05	17:01	01:48	17:16	01:25	17:34
18	04:01	16:59	03:50	17:08	03:44	17:13	03:36	17:19	03:28	17:26	03:18	17:34	03:05	17:44	02:48	17:56
19	04:58	17:43	04:51	17:48	04:47	17:51	04:42	17:54	04:37	17:58	04:30	18:02	04:22	18:08	04:12	18:15
20	**05:54**	**18:24**	**05:51**	**18:25**	**05:49**	**18:26**	**05:47**	**18:27**	**05:45**	**18:27**	**05:42**	**18:28**	**05:38**	**18:29**	**05:34**	**18:31**
21	06:48	19:04	06:49	19:01	06:50	19:00	06:50	18:58	06:51	18:56	06:52	18:53	06:53	18:50	06:54	18:46
22	07:41	19:44	07:46	19:37	07:49	19:34	07:52	19:29	07:56	19:24	08:00	19:18	08:06	19:11	08:13	19:02
23	08:33	20:24	08:41	20:14	08:46	20:08	08:52	20:01	08:58	19:54	09:06	19:45	09:16	19:34	09:29	19:19
24	09:24	21:04	09:36	20:51	09:43	20:44	09:50	20:35	10:00	20:25	10:11	20:14	10:24	19:59	10:43	19:39
25	10:15	21:47	10:29	21:31	10:38	21:22	10:47	21:12	10:59	21:00	11:12	20:46	11:30	20:27	11:53	20:03
26	11:05	22:31	11:21	22:13	11:31	22:03	11:42	21:52	11:55	21:39	12:11	21:22	12:31	21:01	12:59	20:33
27	11:54	23:17	12:12	22:59	12:22	22:48	12:34	22:36	12:48	22:22	13:06	22:04	13:28	21:42	13:58	21:11
28	12:43		13:01	23:47	13:11	23:36	13:24	23:24	13:38	23:10	13:56	22:52	14:18	22:30	14:49	21:59
29	13:30	00:05	13:48		13:58		14:09		14:23		14:40	23:47	15:02	23:26	15:31	22:57
30	14:16	00:55	14:32	00:38	14:41	00:28	14:52	00:16	15:04	00:03	15:19		15:39		16:04	
Oct. 1	15:00	01:46	15:14	01:31	15:22	01:22	15:31	01:12	15:42	01:01	15:54	00:46	16:10	00:28	16:31	00:03
2	15:44	02:39	15:54	02:27	16:01	02:20	16:07	02:11	16:16	02:02	16:25	01:50	16:37	01:35	16:53	01:16
3	16:26	03:34	16:33	03:24	16:37	03:19	16:42	03:13	16:47	03:06	16:54	02:58	17:01	02:47	17:12	02:33
4	17:09	04:29	17:12	04:24	17:14	04:21	17:16	04:17	17:18	04:13	17:21	04:08	17:24	04:02	17:28	03:54
5	*17:51*	*05:25*	*17:50*	*05:24*	*17:50*	*05:24*	*17:49*	*05:23*	*17:48*	*05:22*	*17:47*	*05:21*	*17:46*	*05:20*	*17:45*	*05:18*
6	18:36	06:23	18:30	06:26	18:27	06:28	18:24	06:30	18:20	06:33	18:15	06:36	18:09	06:39	18:02	06:44
7	19:22	07:23	19:12	07:30	19:07	07:34	19:01	07:39	18:54	07:45	18:46	07:52	18:35	08:01	18:22	08:12
8	20:11	08:23	19:58	08:35	19:50	08:42	19:42	08:49	19:32	08:58	19:20	09:09	19:05	09:22	18:46	09:40
9	21:03	09:25	20:47	09:40	20:38	09:49	20:27	09:59	20:15	10:10	20:00	10:24	19:41	10:42	19:16	11:06
10	21:59	10:27	21:41	10:44	21:30	10:54	21:19	11:06	21:05	11:19	20:48	11:36	20:26	11:57	19:57	12:26
11	22:57	11:28	22:38	11:46	22:28	11:57	22:15	12:09	22:01	12:23	21:44	12:41	21:21	13:03	20:50	13:34
12	23:56	12:26	23:39	12:44	23:28	12:54	23:17	13:06	23:03	13:20	22:46	13:37	22:25	13:59	21:56	14:28
13		13:20		13:36		13:46		13:56		14:09	23:55	14:24	23:36	14:43	23:11	15:09
14	00:55	14:10	00:40	14:24	00:31	14:31	00:21	14:40	00:09	14:51		15:03		15:19		15:39
15	01:54	14:56	01:41	15:07	01:34	15:13	01:26	15:19	01:17	15:27	01:05	15:36	00:51	15:48	00:32	16:03
16	02:50	15:40	02:42	15:46	02:37	15:50	02:31	15:54	02:25	15:59	02:17	16:05	02:07	16:12	01:54	16:21
17	03:46	16:21	03:41	16:24	03:38	16:25	03:35	16:27	03:32	16:29	03:27	16:31	03:22	16:34	03:15	16:37
18	04:39	17:01	04:39	16:59	04:38	16:59	04:38	16:58	04:37	16:57	04:37	16:56	04:36	16:54	04:35	16:52
19	**05:32**	**17:40**	**05:35**	**17:35**	**05:37**	**17:32**	**05:39**	**17:28**	**05:42**	**17:25**	**05:45**	**17:20**	**05:49**	**17:14**	**05:54**	**17:07**
20	06:24	18:19	06:31	18:11	06:35	18:06	06:40	18:00	06:45	17:53	06:52	17:46	07:00	17:36	07:11	17:23
21	07:16	19:00	07:26	18:48	07:32	18:41	07:39	18:33	07:47	18:24	07:57	18:13	08:10	17:59	08:26	17:42
22	08:07	19:41	08:20	19:27	08:28	19:18	08:37	19:08	08:48	18:57	09:01	18:43	09:17	18:26	09:39	18:03
23	08:57	20:25	09:13	20:08	09:23	19:58	09:33	19:47	09:46	19:34	10:01	19:18	10:21	18:58	10:47	18:31
24	09:47	21:10	10:05	20:52	10:15	20:41	10:27	20:29	10:41	20:15	10:58	19:58	11:20	19:36	11:50	19:05
25	10:36	21:57	10:54	21:39	11:05	21:28	11:17	21:16	11:32	21:01	11:50	20:43	12:13	20:20	12:44	19:49
26	11:24	22:46	11:42	22:28	11:52	22:18	12:04	22:06	12:19	21:52	12:36	21:35	12:59	21:12	13:29	20:42
27	12:09	23:36	12:27	23:20	12:36	23:10	12:48	23:00	13:01	22:47	13:17	22:31	13:38	22:11	14:06	21:44
28	12:54		13:09		13:18		13:27	23:56	13:39	23:46	13:53	23:32	14:11	23:16	14:34	22:53
29	13:37	00:28	13:49	00:14	13:56	00:06	14:04		14:13		14:25		14:39		14:57	
30	14:19	01:20	14:28	01:09	14:33	01:03	14:39	00:56	14:45	00:47	14:53	00:37	15:03	00:25	15:16	00:08
31	15:00	02:14	15:05	02:07	15:08	02:03	15:12	01:58	15:16	01:52	15:20	01:45	15:26	01:37	15:33	01:26

Bold = new Moon, *italic* = full Moon. A gap in a column indicates the event will take place early the next day.

MOONRISE AND MOONSET, NOVEMBER AND DECEMBER 2017
UNIVERSAL TIME AT GREENWICH MERIDIAN

Latitude:	+20°		+30°		+35°		+40°		+45°		+50°		+55°		+60°	
Event:	RISE	SET	RISE	SET	RISE	SET	RISE	SET	RISE	SET	RISE	SET	RISE	SET	RISE	SET
Nov. 1	15:42	03:09	15:43	03:06	15:44	03:04	15:45	03:02	15:46	02:59	15:47	02:56	15:48	02:53	15:49	02:48
2	16:26	04:06	16:22	04:07	16:21	04:08	16:19	04:09	16:16	04:09	16:13	04:10	16:10	04:11	16:06	04:13
3	17:11	05:05	17:04	05:11	16:59	05:14	16:55	05:17	16:49	05:22	16:42	05:27	16:34	05:33	16:24	05:41
4	*18:00*	*06:07*	*17:48*	*06:16*	*17:42*	*06:22*	*17:34*	*06:29*	*17:26*	*06:36*	*17:15*	*06:45*	*17:02*	*06:56*	*16:45*	*07:11*
5	18:52	07:10	18:37	07:24	18:29	07:32	18:19	07:41	18:07	07:51	17:53	08:04	17:36	08:20	17:13	08:42
6	19:49	08:14	19:31	08:31	19:21	08:41	19:09	08:52	18:56	09:05	18:39	09:21	18:18	09:41	17:50	10:08
7	20:48	09:18	20:29	09:36	20:18	09:47	20:06	09:59	19:52	10:14	19:34	10:31	19:11	10:54	18:40	11:25
8	21:49	10:19	21:31	10:38	21:20	10:48	21:08	11:01	20:54	11:15	20:36	11:33	20:14	11:56	19:43	12:27
9	22:50	11:16	22:33	11:33	22:24	11:43	22:13	11:55	22:00	12:08	21:45	12:24	21:25	12:45	20:58	13:13
10	23:49	12:09	23:36	12:23	23:28	12:32	23:19	12:42	23:08	12:53	22:56	13:06	22:40	13:24	22:18	13:46
11		12:56		13:08		13:14		13:22		13:31		13:41	23:56	13:54	23:41	14:11
12	00:46	13:40	00:36	13:48	00:31	13:53	00:24	13:58	00:16	14:04	00:07	14:11		14:19		14:30
13	01:42	14:21	01:35	14:25	01:32	14:28	01:28	14:30	01:23	14:33	01:18	14:37	01:11	14:41	01:02	14:47
14	02:35	15:01	02:33	15:01	02:32	15:01	02:30	15:01	02:29	15:01	02:27	15:01	02:24	15:01	02:21	15:01
15	03:27	15:39	03:29	15:35	03:30	15:33	03:31	15:31	03:33	15:28	03:34	15:25	03:37	15:21	03:39	15:15
16	04:18	16:18	04:24	16:10	04:28	16:06	04:31	16:01	04:36	15:56	04:41	15:49	04:48	15:41	04:56	15:30
17	05:09	16:57	05:19	16:46	05:24	16:40	05:30	16:33	05:38	16:25	05:46	16:15	05:57	16:03	06:11	15:47
18	**06:00**	**17:38**	**06:13**	**17:24**	**06:20**	**17:16**	**06:29**	**17:07**	**06:38**	**16:56**	**06:50**	**16:44**	**07:05**	**16:28**	**07:25**	**16:06**
19	06:51	18:21	07:06	18:04	07:15	17:55	07:26	17:44	07:38	17:32	07:52	17:16	08:11	16:57	08:36	16:31
20	07:41	19:05	07:59	18:47	08:09	18:37	08:20	18:25	08:34	18:11	08:51	17:54	09:12	17:32	09:41	17:02
21	08:31	19:52	08:49	19:33	09:00	19:22	09:12	19:10	09:27	18:55	09:45	18:37	10:08	18:14	10:40	17:42
22	09:19	20:40	09:38	20:21	09:49	20:11	10:01	19:58	10:16	19:44	10:34	19:26	10:57	19:03	11:29	18:31
23	10:05	21:29	10:23	21:12	10:34	21:02	10:46	20:51	11:00	20:37	11:17	20:20	11:38	19:59	12:08	19:30
24	10:50	22:20	11:06	22:04	11:15	21:56	11:26	21:45	11:39	21:34	11:54	21:19	12:13	21:01	12:39	20:36
25	11:33	23:11	11:46	22:58	11:54	22:51	12:03	22:43	12:14	22:33	12:26	22:21	12:42	22:07	13:03	21:47
26	12:14		12:25	23:53	12:31	23:48	12:38	23:42	12:46	23:35	12:55	23:27	13:07	23:16	13:23	23:02
27	12:54	00:03	13:01		13:06		13:10		13:16		13:22		13:30		13:40	
28	13:35	00:55	13:38	00:50	13:40	00:47	13:42	00:43	13:44	00:39	13:47	00:34	13:51	00:28	13:55	00:20
29	14:16	01:50	14:15	01:49	14:15	01:48	14:14	01:47	14:13	01:46	14:13	01:45	14:12	01:43	14:11	01:42
30	14:59	02:46	14:54	02:49	14:51	02:51	14:48	02:53	14:44	02:55	14:39	02:58	14:34	03:02	14:27	03:06
Dec. 1	15:45	03:46	15:36	03:53	15:31	03:57	15:25	04:02	15:18	04:08	15:09	04:15	14:59	04:23	14:46	04:34
2	16:36	04:48	16:22	04:59	16:15	05:06	16:06	05:14	15:56	05:23	15:44	05:33	15:29	05:47	15:09	06:05
3	*17:31*	*05:52*	*17:14*	*06:08*	*17:05*	*06:16*	*16:54*	*06:27*	*16:41*	*06:38*	*16:26*	*06:53*	*16:07*	*07:11*	*15:41*	*07:36*
4	18:30	06:58	18:12	07:16	18:01	07:26	17:49	07:38	17:35	07:52	17:17	08:09	16:55	08:31	16:24	09:01
5	19:33	08:03	19:14	08:22	19:03	08:33	18:51	08:45	18:36	09:00	18:18	09:18	17:55	09:42	17:23	10:14
6	20:37	09:05	20:19	09:23	20:09	09:34	19:57	09:46	19:44	10:00	19:27	10:17	19:05	10:39	18:36	11:09
7	21:39	10:02	21:24	10:18	21:16	10:27	21:06	10:37	20:54	10:50	20:40	11:05	20:22	11:24	19:58	11:49
8	22:39	10:53	22:28	11:06	22:21	11:13	22:14	11:22	22:05	11:32	21:54	11:44	21:41	11:58	21:23	12:18
9	23:37	11:39	23:29	11:49	23:25	11:54	23:20	12:00	23:14	12:07	23:07	12:15	22:58	12:26	22:47	12:39
10		12:22		12:28		12:31		12:34		12:38		12:43		12:49		12:56
11	00:31	13:02	00:28	13:04	00:26	13:04	00:23	13:05	00:21	13:06	00:18	13:08	00:14	13:09	00:08	13:11
12	01:24	13:41	01:25	13:38	01:25	13:37	01:25	13:35	01:26	13:33	01:26	13:31	01:27	13:29	01:27	13:25
13	02:15	14:19	02:20	14:13	02:22	14:09	02:25	14:05	02:29	14:00	02:33	13:55	02:38	13:48	02:44	13:39
14	03:06	14:57	03:14	14:48	03:19	14:42	03:24	14:36	03:30	14:29	03:38	14:20	03:47	14:09	04:00	13:55
15	03:56	15:37	04:08	15:24	04:15	15:17	04:22	15:08	04:31	14:59	04:42	14:47	04:55	14:32	05:13	14:13
16	04:47	16:19	05:01	16:03	05:10	15:54	05:19	15:44	05:31	15:32	05:44	15:18	06:02	14:59	06:25	14:35
17	05:37	17:02	05:54	16:45	06:04	16:35	06:15	16:23	06:28	16:10	06:44	15:53	07:05	15:32	07:33	15:03
18	**06:27**	**17:48**	**06:45**	**17:30**	**06:56**	**17:19**	**07:08**	**17:06**	**07:22**	**16:52**	**07:40**	**16:34**	**08:03**	**16:11**	**08:34**	**15:39**
19	07:16	18:36	07:35	18:17	07:45	18:06	07:58	17:54	08:13	17:39	08:31	17:21	08:54	16:57	09:27	16:25
20	08:03	19:25	08:21	19:07	08:32	18:57	08:44	18:45	08:59	18:31	09:16	18:13	09:39	17:51	10:10	17:20
21	08:48	20:15	09:05	19:59	09:15	19:50	09:26	19:39	09:40	19:26	09:56	19:11	10:16	18:51	10:44	18:24
22	09:31	21:06	09:46	20:52	09:55	20:44	10:05	20:35	10:16	20:24	10:30	20:11	10:47	19:55	11:10	19:33
23	10:13	21:57	10:25	21:46	10:32	21:40	10:39	21:33	10:49	21:25	11:00	21:15	11:13	21:02	11:31	20:46
24	10:53	22:48	11:01	22:41	11:06	22:37	11:12	22:32	11:18	22:27	11:26	22:20	11:36	22:12	11:48	22:02
25	11:32	23:40	11:37	23:37	11:40	23:35	11:43	23:33	11:47	23:31	11:51	23:28	11:57	23:24	12:04	23:19
26	12:11		12:12		12:13		12:14		12:14		12:15		12:17		12:18	
27	12:52	00:33	12:49	00:34	12:47	00:35	12:45	00:36	12:43	00:36	12:40	00:37	12:37	00:38	12:33	00:40
28	13:35	01:29	13:27	01:34	13:23	01:37	13:19	01:41	13:13	01:45	13:07	01:49	12:59	01:55	12:49	02:03
29	14:21	02:28	14:10	02:37	14:03	02:42	13:56	02:49	13:48	02:56	13:38	03:04	13:25	03:15	13:09	03:30
30	15:12	03:29	14:57	03:42	14:49	03:50	14:39	03:59	14:28	04:09	14:14	04:22	13:57	04:37	13:35	04:58
31	16:08	04:33	15:51	04:50	15:41	04:59	15:29	05:10	15:16	05:23	14:59	05:39	14:38	05:59	14:10	06:26

LUNAR OBSERVING

BY BRUCE MCCURDY

I feel quite sure that I first viewed the moon in my small scope with just as much incredible delight as Galileo did in his. It is true that I had seen photographs of the moon and therefore had some vague idea of what its appearance would be like, but I was still wholly unprepared for all the wonders which I found on that first night as I explored the lunar surface. No photograph has yet been made which is not cold and flat and dead when compared with the scenes that meet one's eyes when the moon is viewed through even a small telescope.

Leslie Peltier, *Starlight Nights*

The Moon is the first astronomical object to grab anyone's eye in the night sky, and has provided "first light" for countless telescopes in the four centuries from Galileo's time to the present. Galileo himself was beaten to the punch by the underappreciated Englishman, Thomas Harriot, who was likely the first telescopic visual observer of Earth's satellite, and certainly the first to sketch an eyepiece view, on 1609 Jul. 26. This was some four months before Galileo did the same.

While the invention of the telescope may be considered the birth of modern astronomy, the Moon has been an object of fascination and mystique since the earliest annals of history, and presumably long before that. Early scientists in ancient observatories carefully tracked lunar cycles and recorded the extremes of its rising and setting points along the horizon. Some 23 centuries ago, the enterprising Aristarchus of Samos carefully observed a total lunar eclipse and derived impressively accurate measurements of the Moon's diameter ($^{1}/_{3}$ that of Earth; the actual percentage is 27.2) and distance (30 Earth diameters, similar to the modern accepted mean value).

One hardly needs a telescope to enjoy the Moon. If observed even briefly on a regular basis, Earth's only natural satellite has much to offer the modern-day naked-eye observer. Noteworthy phenomena include its wandering path through the constellations of the zodiac, the inexorable progression of phases, frequent conjunctions with planets and bright stars, occasional eclipses, libration, earthshine, and atmospheric effects.

Many of the cycles that fascinated the ancients can be observed directly. Understanding these cycles is interesting in its own right. It is also of value to telescopic lunar observers who can benefit when the Moon is favourably placed in the sky, as well as to dark-sky enthusiasts who may be more interested in knowing when it is below the horizon.

Every child learns that the Moon, like the Sun, rises in the east and sets in the west. Relative to a terrestrial landmark (or when viewed through an unpowered telescope!) the Moon appears to move its own diameter (~0.5°) westward in about 2 min. When measured against the background stars, however, it moves about its own diameter *eastward* in an hour, the same direction that Earth rotates. The 30:1 ratio between these rates nicely squares with the time periods involved: one day for Earth to rotate, one sidereal month (about 27.3 d) for the Moon to complete an orbit.

If one observes the Moon at about the same time from night to night, its eastward motion against the background stars becomes apparent. The Moon transits the meridian about 50 min later from one day to the next, a period that rules the tides (see TIDES AND THE EARTH–MOON SYSTEM, p. 179). However, rise and set times vary much more as the Moon's eastward motion also contains a significant northward or southward component, causing moonrise times to bunch together for part of each month, and moonset times to similarly cluster two weeks later. This is famously manifest in the Harvest Moon, an observation of interest to almost everyone. Every two weeks, a rise or set event occurs just after midnight, explaining why one day has no moonrise and another no moonset; over the course of a synodic month (new Moon to new Moon), Luna transits the meridian one fewer time than does the Sun (see TIMES OF MOONRISE AND MOONSET, p. 150).

2017 passages of the Moon through 6 h RA (highest declination, in northern Orion)

Date	Age (d)	Phase
Jan. 10	13	waxing gibbous
Feb. 07	11	waxing gibbous
Mar. 06	9	just past first quarter
Apr. 02	6	thick waxing crescent
Apr. 29	4	waxing crescent
May 27	2	thin waxing crescent
Jun. 23	0	new Moon
Jul. 20/21	27	thin waning crescent
Aug. 17	25	waning crescent
Sep. 13	23	last quarter
Oct. 10	21	waning gibbous
Nov. 07	18	waning gibbous
Dec. 04	16	just past full Moon
Dec. 31–Jan. 01	14	nearly full Moon

Note the Moon's phase during a conjunction with a bright star, and again the following month when it returns: the phase is 2 d less (see the table). The extra couple of days it needs to get back to the same phase means travelling almost an additional 30°. This is due to the Sun's own apparent motion across the sky, also about 30° per month. If one tracks its position among the stars from, for example, one full Moon to the next, it is easy to see that the full Moon appears to be shifted eastward by about one zodiacal constellation each lunar month.

No two months are the same: the lunar orbit is significantly out of round ($e = 0.0549$) and its path ever-changing. While mean distances and periods are known to high accuracy, the Moon's distance from Earth is not constant, rather it is constrained between 356 000 and 407 000 km. Each month, the Moon's perigee (closest approach to Earth) ranges from 35 000 to 50 000 km closer than its apogee, depending on the orientation of these orbital positions relative to the Sun. Thus the Moon varies in size from about 30′ to 34′. Nor is its speed constant; the Moon near perigee and apogee can be travelling as much as 5% faster and slower, respectively, than its mean orbital speed of 1.023 km/s. Our perception of the Moon's ever-changing path is further enhanced through the effects of parallax.

Among the major satellites of the Solar System, only the Moon and Neptune's Triton do not orbit in the plane of the equator of its planet. The Moon roughly orbits in the plane of the ecliptic, causing it to ride high or low at different points in the month, and at different phases throughout the calendar year. For example, a first-quarter Moon always cruises high in the sky around the time of the spring equinox but low around the autumn equinox; a full Moon is high around the time of the winter solstice but low around the summer solstice. The same statements apply to both Northern and Southern Hemispheres; however, the seasons themselves are six months out of phase.

Moreover, the Moon's orbit is tilted some 5°09′ to the ecliptic, with the nodes (crossing points) of its orbit regressing rapidly, completing a full cycle (the regression of the nodes) in just 18.61 years. The combination of these two tilts can be constructive or destructive, exaggerating or muting the seasonal effects noted above. The extremes of azimuth for rise and set points, and of altitude for meridian transits, are likewise modulated. In 2017, this effect is mostly destructive, with the Moon having a declination range of ~19.0° in January, increasing to ~20° in December (see THE SKY MONTH BY MONTH, p. 98 and p. 120). Occultation series for stars near the ecliptic, the brightest of which are listed in the Zodiacal Catalog, also follow the 18.61-year cycle (see LUNAR OCCULTATIONS p. 162).

A period quite similar to the 18.61 year period of "lunar nodes regression" is the $6585\,^{1}/_{3}$ day (or 18.03 year) period of the Saros. Used for many centuries to explain and predict solar and lunar eclipses, the Saros also explains near-repetitions of the lunar librations and such phenomena as extreme perigees and apogees. Remarkably, the major lunar and solar cycles (draconic, sidereal, anomalistic, and synodic month, eclipse year, and calendar year) all have near-integer values during this important cycle, with the result that all three bodies return to very nearly their starting positions (see ECLIPSE PATTERNS, p. 122 and SOME ASTRONOMICAL AND PHYSICAL DATA, p. 29).

At the eyepiece, the closest astronomical target offers the greatest wealth of detail available to any given telescope, binocular, or camera, regardless of its size or quality. Of the countless recognizable features on the lunar nearside, over 1000—virtually all of them within reach of a moderate amateur telescope—have been formally named by the International Astronomical Union. Many of the greatest names in astronomy, exploration, and discovery are so commemorated. Observation of the Moon can be a lesson in the history of science. Seven Canadians have been immortalized by having observable lunar craters named after them: Ostwald Avery (1877–1955), Frederick Banting (1891–1941), Carlyle Beals (1899–1979), Reginald Daly (1871–1957), Simon Newcomb (1835–1909), John S. Plaskett (1865–1941), and Joshua Slocum (1844–1909). Remarkably, four of the seven—Avery, Beals, Newcomb, and Slocum—were born in Nova Scotia. Both Newcomb and Plaskett have been commemorated with RASC awards.

The face of the Moon is itself a history lesson of the early bombardment period of the inner Solar System. On a world devoid of erosion processes like wind, water, weather, glaciation, volcanism, plate tectonics, sedimentation, and life itself that have modified Earth, most of the Moon's features were sculpted billions of years ago. The largest of the ancient impact basins were subsequently filled with lava flows from its then-molten interior that hardened into basaltic rock and formed the distinctively dark, primarily circular regions wrongly but permanently identified as lunar maria, or seas. The brighter white areas, highlands that surround the maria and dominate the southern portion of the Earth-facing hemisphere, feature innumerable smaller but similarly ancient impact craters. With bombardment slowed to a relative trickle and the Moon remaining geologically inert since those ancient lava flows, Luna's appearance has changed but little over the past three billion years. Today, only the cosmic sandblasting of micrometeorites serves to gradually soften her features.

Observation of the Moon is nonetheless a very dynamic activity, due to the ever-changing angles of illumination. The terminator (the sunrise/sunset line) shifts westward across lunar features at ~0.5° per hour, a consequence of its 360° rotation in one month, about 12° per 24 hours. (Note that lunar east and west are reversed to celestial east and west, having been changed to the terrestrial standard during the early days of lunar exploration so as not to confuse the astronauts.) This slow but inexorable progression is particularly dramatic near the lunar terminator, where oblique sunlight reveals "in-depth" details of lunar features.

During the Moon's waxing phases (from new Moon to full), the sunrise terminator advances across new ground, exposing the most elevated features first. It can be a fascinating experience to look a little beyond the terminator for little points of light that might be mountain peaks or raised crater rims, and over the course of a single observing session, watch these features gradually expand under the oblique illumination of the rising Sun. It may take a few hours or even days before all the features on the crater floors are completely lighted. It is well worth revisiting an area of interest night after night to observe its changing appearance, even as the advancing Sun is revealing new wonders by the hour. Or, as the eloquent Peltier put it, "the geography of a whole new world…turning page by nightly page."

Under magnification, the darker areas, including the maria and the floors of large craters called "walled plains," are primarily flat and smooth. Occasional shift features such as scarps, wrinkle ridges, rilles, and rounded domes catch the eye, especially under low angles of illumination. Relatively few craters dot the landscape, proof positive of the greatly reduced rate of bombardment since those lava plains were formed. Frequently, they are surrounded by circular mountain ranges that represent the vestiges of the outer rings of the ancient impact structures. At low Sun angles, these cast long and impressive shadows whose jagged forms give a false impression of the rounded mountain tops. Long shadows yield interesting information about the topography under careful measurement, yet they often obscure features of interest in the lower terrain beyond. Hadley Rille of *Apollo 15* fame, is theoretically well placed near the terminator at first quarter, but is lost in the shadows of towering Mount Hadley and the Apennine Mountains, which take days to recede. A return to this area just before last quarter will reveal the same scene lit from the opposite direction, the western faces of the mountains bathed in sunlight and the rille nicely illuminated.

At times of high angles of illumination around full Moon, a different aspect of the Moon is revealed. The three-dimensional context created in the brain from the pattern of light and dark is lost when the shadows are cast directly behind the features. Depth perception is problematic except right along the terminator, which now effectively encircles the Moon. Although the surface looks flat, a huge range of tonality is gained. Relatively young craters and their splash effects, such as ray systems and ejecta blankets, appear especially bright. Many small and otherwise unremarkable features stand out as brilliant points of light.

Full Moon is also the best time to observe the lunar libration zones. For line-of-sight reasons, explained on p. 95, the Moon displays a gentle rocking motion, revealing, over time, about 59% of its total surface area to the Earth-bound observer. Librations of longitude are zero when the Moon is at perigee or apogee; librations of latitude are zero when the Moon crosses the ecliptic at its ascending or descending node. Therefore, these librations follow the anomalistic month and draconic month, respectively, and thus gradually change with respect to each other, to bring different quadrants into favourable position. Libration has a more general effect on every lunar observing session, as even accessible nearside features can become more or less favourably situated to the line of sight, offering a more vertical or horizontal aspect from one viewing to the next. Details on current librations can be found in THE SKY MONTH BY MONTH, p. 98 and following.

The RASC's Isabel Williamson Lunar Observing Program is a detailed guide containing key information about the lunar surface and how to observe it. The program booklet lists 135 specific observing objectives (with sub-objectives) and optional activities such as Libration Challenge Features, lunar surface drawings, imaging, Observable Craters with Canadian Connections, and more. It also provides a detailed overview of the history of the Moon and the various geological eras that have shaped its surface, explaining each type of lunar feature and providing tips for observing each of them. See www.rasc.ca/observing/williamson-lunar-observing-certificate (open to all to download, but RASC membership is required to earn the pin and certificate).

From Aristarchus to Galileo, from Peltier to the 21st-century amateur astronomer, the Moon has remained among the most reliable and rewarding celestial targets for observers of all experience levels.

Recommended Reading:

- Brunier, S. and Legault, T., *New Atlas of the Moon*, Firefly Books Ltd., 2006.
- Peltier, L., *Starlight Nights: The Adventures of a Sky-Gazer*, Sky Publishing, 2007.
- Rükl, A., *Atlas of the Moon*, Sky Publishing, 2004.
- Sheehan, W. and Dobbins, T., *Epic Moon: A History of Lunar Exploration in the Age of the Telescope*, Willmann–Bell Inc., 2001.
- Westfall, J., *Atlas of the Lunar Terminator*, Cambridge University Press, 2000.
- Wood, C., *The Modern Moon: A Personal View*, Sky Publishing, 2003.
- Lunar Picture of the Day: lpod.wikispaces.com

LUNAR OCCULTATIONS

BY DAVID W. DUNHAM

The Moon often passes between Earth and a star, an event called an *occultation*. During an occultation, a star suddenly disappears as the advancing limb of the Moon crosses the line between the star and the observer. The star reappears from behind the following limb some time later. Because the Moon moves through an angle about equal to its own diameter every hour, the longest time for an occultation is about an hour. The time is shorter if the occultation is not central. Solar eclipses are actually occultations: the star being occulted by the Moon is the Sun.

Since observing occultations is rather easy, amateur astronomers should try this activity. The slow, majestic drift of the Moon in its orbit is interesting, with the disappearance or reappearance of a star at the Moon's limb a remarkable sight, particularly when it occurs as a graze near the Moon's northern or southern limb. During a graze, a star may disappear and reappear several times in succession as mountains and valleys in the Moon's polar regions drift by it. On rarer occasions, the Moon occults a planet.

In 2017, the only occultation of a major planet visible from North America will occur on Jan. 3 (UT; evening of Jan. 2 local time) when 7.9-mag. Neptune will be occulted by the 22% sunlit waxing crescent Moon, only visible at low altitude from the West Coast. The UT, Moon altitude, and angle measured around the Moon's disk on the dark side from the northern (N) or southern (S) cusp are given for selected cities in descending order of altitude: Eureka, California, 5:04:37, 7°, 87N; San Francisco, California, 5:07:11, 6°, 82S; Portland, Oregon, 5:03:14, 4°, 72N; Vancouver, B.C., 5:02:56, 4°, 59N; and Los Angeles, California, 5:12:07, 2°, 66S. For all locations, the times are for the disappearance of the centre of Neptune's 2.2″ disk; the Moon's limb will take 5 s to cover Neptune.

The series of occultations of 0.9-mag. α Tauri (Aldebaran) continue in 2017, with eight of them visible from different parts of our continent. Also, there will be two occultations of 1.4-mag. α Leonis (Regulus) late in the year. Other bright stars occulted during 2017, ranging from mag. 2.5 to 3.9, are the Hyades stars γ, θ^1, and θ^2 Tauri; ρ Leonis, γ Virginis (Porrima), and γ Librae (Zuben-el-Akrab).

Lunar-occultation and graze observations refine our knowledge of the shape of the lunar profile and the fundamental star-coordinate system. These observations complement those made by other techniques, such as *Kaguya* and *Lunar Reconnaissance Orbiter* laser ranging and photographs. Improved knowledge of the lunar profile is useful in determinations of the Sun's diameter from solar-eclipse records. Occultation observations are also useful for detecting double stars and measuring their separations. Binaries with separations as small as 0.02″ have been discovered visually during grazes. Doubles with separations in this range are useful for filling the gap between doubles that can be directly resolved and those whose duplicity has been discovered spectroscopically. Now that the *Kepler* spacecraft is observing stars for exoplanet transits in the zodiac, that project is interested in occultation of close double stars since stellar duplicity complicates their analysis.

Observations

The **International Occultation Timing Association (IOTA)** analyzes lunar-occultation observations and is the world clearinghouse for such observations. Anyone interested in pursuing a systematic program of lunar-occultation observations should consult the lunar- and grazing-occultation sections of *Chasing the Shadow: The IOTA Occultation Observer's Manual*, available as a free Adobe PDF download at www.poyntsource.com/IOTAmanual/Preview.htm. Readers without access to the Internet may download the file at any public library, or write to IOTA's North American coordinator of lunar-occultation observations: Derek Breit, 17370 B Hawkins Lane, Morgan Hill, CA 95037 (e-mail breit_ideas@poyntsource.com). For general information, write to IOTA at PO Box 7152, Kent, WA 98042, USA (email business@occultations.org). IOTA provides predictions and coordination services for occultation observers—detailed graze predictions are available ($1.50

USD each; free by email); observing instructions are also available ($5 USD or see the IOTA manual). Annual IOTA membership is $40 USD in North America ($45 overseas). Online electronic-only membership is just $15 U.S. for all and is strongly encouraged. Membership includes free graze predictions, descriptive materials, and a subscription to *Journal for Occultation Astronomy*. IOTA's administrative website is www.occultations.org; www.lunar-occultations.com/iota is the site for predictions, updates, observations, and other technical information, including more predictions than can be given here. For observers in the southwestern Pacific (New Zealand, Australia, Papua New Guinea, and nearby areas), the Royal Astronomical Society of New Zealand (RASNZ) provides occultation data (total lunar, lunar grazing, planetary, and Jupiter's satellites), plus comprehensive instructions for new observers, at www.occultations.org.nz.

The main information required in a lunar-occultation observation is the time of the event and the observer's location. Supplementary data include the seeing conditions, telescope size, timing method, estimate of the observer's reaction time and the accuracy of the timing, and whether or not the reaction-time correction has been applied. The timing should be accurate to 0.5 s or better (a short-wave radio time signal and audio recorder provide a simple, permanent time record, but a video record provides higher accuracy). The observer's longitude, latitude, and altitude should be reported to the nearest tenth of an arcsecond and 10 m, respectively, and should be accurate to at least 0.5″ or 16 m. These can be determined from either GPS measurements (10 min of position averaging and an unobstructed view of the sky above about 15° altitude are needed) or a suitable topographical map. For Canada, the maps are available from Regional Distributors, who are listed at www.nrcan.gc.ca/earth-sciences/geography/topographic-information/maps/9783 (email geoginfo@NRCan.gc.ca or call 800-465-6277 for more information). For the United States (except Alaska), write to US Geological Survey, Map Sales, PO Box 25286, Denver CO 80225, asking for an index to topographical maps in the desired state, or call 800-USA-MAPS. For Alaska, write to US Geological Survey, Map Sales, 4230 University Dr, Room 101, Anchorage AK 99508-4664, or phone 907-786-7011. Parts of USGS maps can be viewed and printed at nationalmap.gov/ustopo—enter a location or click on the USA map to zoom in and click on the "Topo map" tab. Detailed imagery is also available from Google Earth and other websites. IOTA is using these resources for predictions; they are usually (especially for North America) accurate enough for reporting lunar-occultation observations.

Observers are encouraged to learn how to video-record occultations in order to obtain reliable and accurate timings. Inexpensive yet sensitive video cameras are available. Visual timings must be accurate to ±0.2 s to be good enough for further improvement of the lunar profile and other parameters, except for grazes, where ±0.5 s is adequate. Information about video-recording occultations is on IOTA's technical website and in the IOTA manual mentioned previously. Check IOTA's technical website for report forms and reporting procedures. If you have questions, correspond with the North American coordinator specified on the previous page.

Tables of total-occultation predictions start on p. 165 and a table and maps of northern or southern limits for grazing occultations start on p. 174.

1. TOTAL LUNAR-OCCULTATION PREDICTIONS

BY DAVID HERALD AND DAVID W. DUNHAM

The total lunar-occultation predictions listed in the tables on pp. 165–170 are for the 18 standard stations identified on the map on the next page; the longitudes and latitudes of these stations are given in the table headings. The predictions were computed for IOTA by David Herald in Murrumbateman, Australia.

The predictions include all stars brighter than mag. 6.0. The first five columns give for each occultation the **Date**, the Zodiacal Catalog (**ZC**) number of the star, its magnitude (**mag.**), the phenomenon (**PH**), and the elongation (**El**) of the Moon from the Sun, in degrees (see p. 171 for equivalent Bayer/Flamsteed names for some stars). Under each station are the event time (**UT**), time factors **A** and **B** (see below), and the position angle (**PA**) of the point of occurrence, measured in degrees from celestial north through celestial east around the Moon's disk. If no data appear for a given station, it is because there is no occultation, the star is below the horizon, or it is daytime there. If A or B have values larger than 5 min/degree, as can happen in the case of near-grazes, they will not give a reliable prediction for other places.

The terms A and B are for determining corrections to the times of the events for stations within 300 km of the standard stations. If Lo* and La* represent the longitude and latitude of the standard station, and Lo and La those of the observer, then for the observer,

$$\text{UT of event} = \text{UT of event at the standard station} + A(\text{Lo} - \text{Lo}^*) + B(\text{La} - \text{La}^*),$$

where Lo, etc. are expressed in degrees, and A and B are in minutes of time per degree. Longitude measured west of Greenwich is assumed to be *negative* (which is now the IAU convention and that used by IOTA's *Occult* software). Due regard must be paid to the algebraic signs of the terms. To convert UT to the standard time of the observer, see the section STANDARD TIME ZONES on p. 45.

As an example, consider the occultation of 5.1-mag. ZC 192 (89 Piscium) on 2017 Jan. 6 as seen from Boulder, Colorado. For Boulder, Lo = –105.3° and La = 40.0°. The nearest standard station is Denver, for which Lo* = –105.0° and La* = 39.8°. Therefore, the UT of the disappearance at the dark limb (DD) is 3:06.2 + 2.3 × (–105.3° +105.0°) min – 2.3 × (40.0° – 39.8°) min = 3:05.0. The solar elongation is 93°, showing the Moon is very close to first quarter. The position angle of disappearance is 114°, actually about halfway from the southern cusp to the centre of the Moon's dark limb. At Boulder, northwest of Denver, the position angle should be about the same; an accurate calculation shows that it will be 113°. The local time is 8:05.0 p.m. MST of Jan. 5, since Mountain Standard Time is 7h behind UT (that is, MST = UT –7 hours). Data are not given for the reappearance since the sunlit edge of the Moon will be too bright.

The number of events observable from any location increases *rapidly* as predictions are extended to fainter stars. Observers who wish to pursue such work should email (preferred) webmaster@lunar-occultations.com to request software or more extensive lists, or write to Walter Robinson, 515 W Kump, Bonner Springs KS 66012-1439, USA—please provide accurate geographical coordinates, your largest telescope aperture, and a long, self-addressed envelope (with postage). Alternatively, you can generate your own predictions with IOTA's free *Occult 4* software available at www.lunar-occultations.com/iota/occult4.htm.

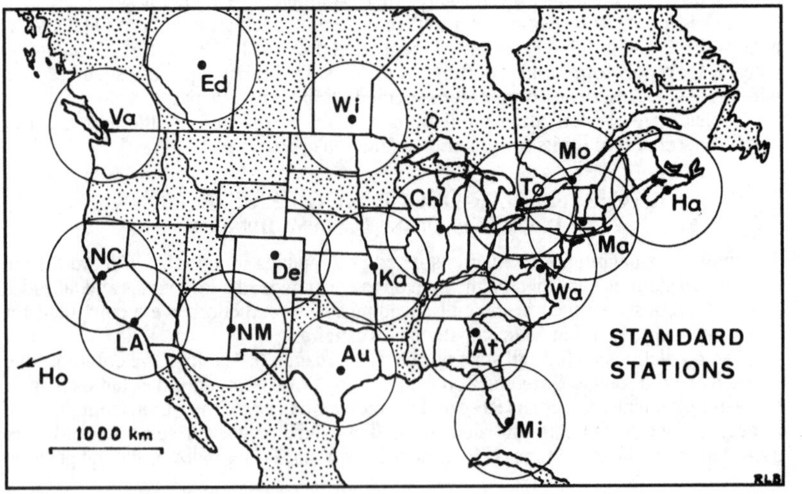

TOTAL LUNAR OCCULTATIONS FOR 2017

					HALIFAX 63.6°W, 44.6°N				MONTRÉAL 73.6°W, 45.5°N				TORONTO 79.4°W, 43.7°N			
Date	ZC	mag.	PH	El °	UT	A m/deg	B m/deg	PA °	UT	A m/deg	B m/deg	PA °	UT	A m/deg	B m/deg	PA °
Jan. 6	192	5.1	DD	93					03:36.5	+0.7	−2.4	113	03:36.8	+0.9	−2.9	120
18	1821	2.8	RD	108	06:24.6	+0.7	−1.3	333	06:16.9	+0.6	−0.8	327	06:14.2	+0.6	−0.3	316
19	1941	4.7	RD	96	09:19.9	+4.6	+4.7	225								
23	2399	4.9	RD	52	09:14.7	+1.2	+1.8	258	09:05.6	+0.9	+2.2	249				
Feb. 3	405	4.3	DD	87	22:44.7	+2.2	−1.4	111	22:23.1	+2.0	−0.1	96				
18	2223	3.9	RD	94	09:25.4	+2.4	+0.8	255	09:02.4	+2.4	+2.0	243	08:40.8	+3.5	+4.9	222
Mar. 2	249	4.5	DD	44					01:37.0	+0.1	−1.2	85	01:38.2	+0.3	−1.4	92
5	669	3.8	DD	83	00:16.3	+1.4	−1.1	92	00:00.4	+1.6	−0.6	89	23:51.5	+1.8	−0.6	93
5	671	3.4	DD	83	00:22.2	+1.3	−2.0	113	00:05.7	+1.6	−1.6	110	23:58.3	+1.9	−1.7	115
5	677	4.8	DD	84	01:25.2	+1.1		56	01:13.0	+1.3	+0.2	56	01:04.4	+1.5	+0.2	63
6	814	5.4	DD	97	00:01.3	+1.7	+1.4	48	23:45.8	+1.6	+2.1	43	23:32.6	+1.6	+2.0	48
24	3108	5.3	RD	47									10:05.1	+0.7	+1.4	270
Apr. 1	635	3.7	DD	54					03:26.7	−0.2	−0.8	74	03:29.1	−0.1	−1.0	83
28	692*	0.9	DD	32	16:47.7	+1.4	+1.3	72	16:37.4	+1.0	+1.8	60	16:28.9	+0.8	+1.9	58
28	692*	0.9	RB	32	18:01.5	+1.7	+0.5	260	17:45.6	+1.6	+0.6	270	17:35.3	+1.5	+0.8	270
May 2	1207	5.6	DD	77					02:59.4	+0.8	−0.6	60	02:55.9	+0.9	−0.8	72
21	3526	4.9	RD	62	07:05.9	+0.4	−0.7	321								
29	1158	5	DD	46					02:38.3	−0.4	−1.9	134	02:44.5	−0.5	−2.2	144
Jun. 1	1547	3.8	DD	86					04:40.2	+0.2	−0.8	61	04:40.2	+0.3	−0.9	69
22	692*	0.9	DB	22	14:05.7	+1.7	+0.4	88	13:50.9	+1.4	+1.1	77	13:41.1	+1.3	+1.3	76
22	692*	0.9	RD	22	15:19.2	+1.6	+0.7	245	15:03.8	+1.6	+0.8	254	14:53.1	+1.6	+1.0	253
Jul. 1	1821	2.8	DD	91	02:50.2	+0.5	−1.9	119	02:41.8	+0.8	−2.0	122	02:40.5	+0.9	−2.1	128
18	444	5.9	RD	70					08:17.7	+0.6	+1.8	244	08:11.6	+0.4	+1.7	246
20	741	5.5	RD	43	07:40.1	+0.4	+0.7	298	07:37.6	+0.2	+0.3	311				
Aug. 1	2223	3.9	DD	106	02:58.7	+1.0	−2.0	120	02:45.1	+1.3	−1.8	117	02:39.9	+1.6	−1.8	120
10	3421	4.9	RD	150	07:31.2	+1.2	+0.8	223	07:18.3	+1.5	+0.7	237	07:07.5	+1.7	+0.9	241
14	405	4.3	RD	99	07:47.3	+3.1	−2.0	312								
16	699	5.8	RD	73	06:56.6	−0.7	+4.2	187								
Sep. 10	364	4.3	RD	130	05:47.0	+0.8	+2.5	208	05:40.7	+0.8	+2.1	223	05:32.2	+0.8	+2.1	226
11	508	4.1	RD	115	09:55.7	+1.0	+3.6	194	09:47.1	+1.2	+2.3	208	09:35.8	+1.2	+2.6	207
12	635	3.7	RD	103	05:21.0	+0.8	+1.3	269	05:14.8	+0.6	+1.1	282	05:09.7	+0.5	+1.0	284
12	667	5	RD	101					09:48.0	+2.3	−2.2	308	09:37.7	+2.5	−1.8	307
12	669	3.8	RD	101	09:54.9	+1.3	+3.3	203	09:44.5	+1.3	+2.4	215	09:32.7	+1.2	+2.6	214
12	671	3.4	RD	102					09:22.4	−0.7	+9.6	177	09:10.6	−1.2	+9.6	176
12	677	4.8	RD	101									10:56.2	+1.7	+1.0	239
12	692*	0.9	DB	100	13:06.8	+0.9	−0.9	79	12:55.3	+1.2	−0.7	80	12:49.1	+1.4	−0.8	86
12	692*	0.9	RD	100	14:10.9	+0.4	−1.3	269	14:03.6	+0.8	−1.2	266	14:00.3	+1.0	−0.8	258
13	814	5.4	RD	88	09:29.3	+1.4	+2.6	218	09:18.5	+1.2	+2.1	230	09:07.9	+1.1	+2.3	229
Oct. 13	1236	5.1	RD	78	09:10.7	+1.6	+0.6	275	08:56.9	+1.3	+0.7	280	08:48.3	+1.1	+1.0	276
15	1487	1.4	DB	52	10:07.1	+1.6	+3.7	51	09:57.6	+1.0	+3.9	48	09:46.6	+0.7	+2.9	57
15	1487	1.4	RD	52	10:48.2	+1.0	−3.2	345	10:35.3	+1.0	−2.8	344	10:33.1	+1.1	−1.6	333
26	2734	5.2	DD	69					01:05.2	+0.6	−0.6	58	01:01.9	+0.8	−0.4	56
27	2981	5.1	DD	90	23:33.4	−0.3	+3.9	3								
Nov. 5	508	4.1	RD	167	00:06.8	+0.1	+2.0	226	00:07.6		+1.8	236	00:04.7	−0.1	+1.7	237
6	692*	0.9	DB	154	01:09.5	+0.5	+1.3	88	01:07.9	+0.1	+1.5	78	01:05.0		+1.4	76
6	692*	0.9	RD	153	02:07.9	+0.5	+1.9	239	02:04.8	+0.4	+1.6	251	02:00.0	+0.3	+1.6	253
9	1175	4.9	RD	111	03:44.2	+0.3	+1.3	271	03:42.7	+0.2	+1.0	282	00:00.0			
Dec. 5	947	5.2	RD	159	01:52.3	+0.3	+2.6	222	01:51.3	+0.3	+2.0	236	10:29.0	+1.8	−0.2	273
29	405	4.3	DD	124	03:54.5	+1.0	−0.4	67	03:43.2	+1.2		61	03:35.6	+1.4	+0.1	64
29	508	4.1	DD	135	21:18.7	+0.8	+1.4	86	00:39.3	+1.2	−9.1	153				
30	677	4.8	DD	149	21:08.8	+0.4	+1.2	94								
30	692*	0.9	DD	150	23:41.1	+1.6	+0.1	114	23:28.5	+1.0	+1.0	99	23:21.1	+0.8	+1.1	97
31	692*	0.9	RB	150	00:33.7	+0.8	+2.7	212	00:27.7	+0.8	+2.1	227	00:19.5	+0.7	+2.1	229

DB/DD = Disappearance at Bright/Dark limb; RB/RD = Reappearance at Bright/Dark limb

See p. 163 for additional explanation of these tables.

*ZC 692 = Aldebaran

"Since observing occultations is rather easy, amateur astronomers should try this activity. The slow, majestic drift of the Moon in its orbit is interesting, with the disappearance or reappearance of a star at the Moon's limb a remarkable sight, particularly when it occurs as a graze near the Moon's northern or southern limb."

TOTAL LUNAR OCCULTATIONS FOR 2017 (continued)

					WINNIPEG 97.2°W, 49.9°N				EDMONTON 113.4°W, 53.6°N				VANCOUVER 123.1°W, 49.2°N			
Date	ZC	mag.	PH	El °	UT	A m/deg	B m/deg	PA °	UT	A m/deg	B m/deg	PA °	UT	A m/deg	B m/deg	PA °
Jan. 1	3064	5.9	DD	31									02:13.0	+1.1	−2.1	111
6	192	5.1	DD	93	03:05.5	+1.3	−0.9	85	02:44.0	+1.2	+0.3	62	02:29.0	+1.4	+0.8	63
9	635	3.7	DD	136	08:43.4	+0.3	−1.2	83	08:31.1	+0.7	−1.1	81	08:29.1	+0.9	−1.4	97
18	1821	2.8	RD	108	06:06.0	+0.1	−0.5	331								
Feb. 6	741	5.5	DD	117									06:47.2	+1.3	+1.1	38
7	878	5.5	DD	128					01:29.9	+1.5	−1.0	140				
18	2223	3.9	RD	94	08:21.4	+3.2	+8.3	212								
Mar. 2	249	4.5	DD	44	01:22.3	+0.7	−0.8	71								
5	677	4.8	DD	84	00:44.1	+1.3	+1.9	36								
5	699	5.8	DD	86					04:19.0	+0.8	−2.9	130				
8	1158	5	DD	126					06:18.9	+2.1	+2.6	32	05:55.9	+1.8	+0.6	63
Apr. 1	635	3.7	DD	54	03:20.7	+0.3	−1.1	78	03:08.4	+0.7	−1.0	76	03:05.5	+1.0	−1.3	92
1	661	4.5	DD	56					05:56.7	−0.3	−1.9	116	06:09.9	−0.4	−2.8	139
1	669	3.8	DD	56									06:54.5	−0.1	−0.8	69
1	671	3.4	DD	56									06:54.8	−0.2	−1.2	89
2	806	5	DD	69	05:24.8	−0.5	−2.7	142	05:19.8	−0.2	−3.3	147				
15	2399	4.9	RD	134	09:41.6	+0.8	−2.9	351	09:23.3	+0.6	−1.1	341	09:18.3	+0.9	−0.2	319
28	692*	0.9	DD	32	16:37.4	−0.1	+3.1	20								
28	692*	0.9	RB	32	17:12.7	+1.4	−0.1	310								
May 2	1207	5.6	DD	77	02:31.6	+1.3	−0.7	75								
Jun. 1	1547	3.8	DD	86	04:22.3	+0.9	−1.1	72	04:00.4	+1.2	−1.0	81	03:52.2	+1.4	−1.1	100
13	2981	5.1	RD	137	00:00.0								10:06.8	+1.6	+1.1	242
22	692*	0.9	DB	22	13:37.8	+0.4	+2.3	42	13:47.2	−0.4	+3.4	11	13:37.5	−0.6	+3.3	11
22	692*	0.9	RD	22	14:32.3	+1.3	+0.5	287	14:12.6	+1.4	−0.4	320	14:01.6	+1.2	−0.3	320
Jul. 1	1821	2.8	DD	91	02:09.5	+1.1	−1.7	133	01:46.1	+1.0	−1.3	143	01:45.6	+0.5	−2.4	168
1	1821	2.8	RB	91	03:22.2	+1.2	−1.5	278								
Aug. 10	3421	4.9	RD	150	06:43.7	+1.5	+0.9	268								
16	704	4.7	RD	73	07:20.0	−1.3	+4.6	179	07:40.5	−0.5	+2.0	210				
Sep. 3	2981	5.1	DD	144					0				05:38.3	+1.7	+0.3	81
10	364	4.3	RD	129	05:32.0	+0.5	+1.7	252	05:32.1	+0.2	+1.6	266	10:28.5	−0.2	+1.8	231
11	508	4.1	RD	115	09:24.5	+1.3	+1.3	244	09:10.3	+1.0	+1.2	267	08:55.2	+0.9	+1.4	268
12	635	3.7	RD	103	05:07.4	+0.3	+0.3	317								
12	661	4.5	RD	102	07:57.4	+0.2	+2.8	208	08:02.8	+0.2	+2.0	232	07:53.3		+1.9	232
12	669	3.8	RD	101	09:23.5	+1.1	+1.5	250	09:13.0	+0.8	+1.3	272	09:00.2	+0.6	+1.3	272
12	671	3.4	RD	101	09:19.8	+0.9	+2.1	230	09:14.1	+0.7	+1.7	252	09:01.2	+0.4	+1.7	252
12	677	4.8	RD	101	10:31.8	+1.5	+0.5	270	10:10.2	+1.4	+0.3	295	09:55.5	+1.2	+0.6	294
12	692*	0.9	DB	100	12:21.4	+1.5	+0.6	64	12:05.1	+1.1	+1.9	43	11:46.3	+1.0	+2.0	48
12	692*	0.9	RD	100	13:33.3	+1.3	−1.0	275	13:05.9	+1.5	−1.0	291	12:52.6	+1.7	−0.2	282
13	814	5.4	RD	88	09:02.2	+0.8	+1.5	262	08:56.4	+0.5	+1.2	284	08:47.2	+0.3	+1.1	283
Oct. 9	635	3.7	RD	130	12:53.9	+1.3	+3.7	192	12:43.5	+1.1	+1.5	211	12:20.6	+0.9	+4.8	190
11	947	5.2	RD	104	09:56.3	+1.6	−0.5	299	09:27.2	+1.8	−2.1	331	09:17.6	+1.5	−0.9	323
13	1236	5.1	RD	78	08:37.0	+0.7	+0.4	306	08:27.0	+0.7	−0.7	335				
14	1375	5.4	RD	64	11:36.6	+1.2	+0.3	294	11:22.1	+0.8	+0.3	309	11:13.6	+0.6	+0.6	298
16	1609	4.6	RD	38					12:54.1	+0.6	+1.3	278	12:42.4	+0.4	+1.7	263
26	2734	5.2	DD	69	00:49.4	+0.6	+1.4	21								
27	2886	4.9	DD	81					03:46.7	+1.1	−1.3	92	03:39.4	+1.5	−1.0	91
Nov. 6	692*	0.9	DB	153	01:18.3	−0.4	+1.6	54								
6	692*	0.9	RD	153	02:05.7	+0.1	+1.2	278	02:10.5	−0.1	+1.0	294				
11	1466	5.3	RD	81	12:12.6	+1.7	+0.7	264	11:52.6	+1.2	+1.2	268	11:34.3	+1.0	+2.1	250
11	1487	1.4	DB	80									16:39.5	+2.5	+1.2	52
11	1487	1.4	RD	79									17:14.3	−0.1	−3.9	354
24	2963	5.3	DD	61					02:54.5	+1.2	−2.0	112	02:49.1	+1.7	−1.8	111
25	3079	4.1	DD	71	01:25.1	+2.4	−2.9	130	00:47.8	+1.7	−0.5	102	00:30.7	+1.9	+0.1	101
Dec. 3	692*	0.9	DB	174					13:55.9	−0.2	−1.6	104	14:06.0	−0.3	−2.1	124
4	832	4.3	RD	168	12:06.1	+0.3	−1.2	264	11:53.0	+0.7	−1.1	264	11:47.8	+1.1	−0.4	246
6	1175	4.9	RD	139					14:03.8	+0.7	−1.2	262	13:57.7	+1.3	−0.2	241
8	1434	5.4	RD	113									11:56.4	+0.4	−5.7	358
15	2223	3.9	RD	29					15:26.7	+1.0	+0.3	303	15:14.3	+1.0	+0.9	283
22	3058	5.8	DD	41									02:37.8	+3.3	−7.1	148
29	405	4.3	DD	124	03:18.8	+1.0	+1.8	29	05:02.6	+0.2	−1.4	88	05:07.4	+0.3	−1.9	104
30	692*	0.9	DD	150	23:22.0	+0.1	+1.7	68	23:29.3	−0.2	+1.8	51				
31	692*	0.9	RB	150	00:19.3	+0.5	+1.5	260	00:18.1	+0.3	+1.3	280	00:10.9	+0.1	+1.2	280

DB/DD = Disappearance at Bright/Dark limb; RB/RD = Reappearance at Bright/Dark limb

See p. 163 for additional explanation of these tables.

*ZC 692 = Aldebaran

TOTAL LUNAR OCCULTATIONS FOR 2017 (continued)

					MASSACHUSETTS 72.5°W, 42.5°N				WASHINGTON, D.C. 77.0°W, 38.9°N				CHICAGO 87.7°W, 41.9°N			
Date	ZC	mag.	PH	El °	UT	A m/deg	B m/deg	PA °	UT	A m/deg	B m/deg	PA °	UT	A m/deg	B m/deg	PA °
Jan. 6	192	5.1	DD	93	03:46.0	+0.6	−3.7	129					03:32.8	+1.4	−3.4	124
18	1821	2.8	RD	108	06:19.4	+0.8	−0.5	317	06:16.3	+0.9	+0.1	301	06:09.7	+0.5	+0.2	305
23	2399	4.9	RD	52	08:59.5	+1.2	+2.7	239								
Feb. 3	405	4.3	DD	87	22:26.6	+2.4	−0.8	108								
12	1547	3.8	RD	167					00:26.0	+0.4	−1.3	335				
18	2223	3.9	RD	94	08:58.5	+3.0	+2.8	234								
Mar. 2	249	4.5	DD	44	01:40.9	+0.1	−1.4	95	01:46.5	+0.1	−1.9	110	01:37.8	+0.5	−1.6	99
5	667	5	DD	84					00:24.9	+1.6	+5.3	13				
5	669	3.8	DD	83	00:04.8	+1.7	−1.1	99	00:01.2	+2.0	−1.6	112	23:36.2	+2.0	−0.3	95
5	671	3.4	DD	83	00:13.3	+1.7	−2.4	122	00:16.7	+2.1	−4.7	141	23:44.1	+2.2	−1.6	118
5	677	4.8	DD	84	01:14.5	+1.4	−0.2	67	01:09.0	+1.6	−0.5	80	00:50.5	+1.8	+0.3	69
5	814	5.4	DD	97	23:42.6	+1.8	+1.4	55	23:29.6	+2.0	+1.1	66				
24	3108	5.3	RD	47					10:00.1	+0.8	+1.4	262				
Apr. 1	635	3.7	DD	54					03:33.8	−0.3	−1.1	95	03:31.8		−1.3	94
15	2399	4.9	RD	134									10:17.0	+1.9	−2.7	333
28	692*	0.9	DD	32	16:33.5	+1.1	+1.5	69	16:23.1	+1.1	+1.4	73	16:19.9	+0.5	+2.0	54
28	692*	0.9	RB	32	17:45.2	+1.6	+0.9	260	17:34.4	+1.5	+1.2	254	17:21.8	+1.4	+0.8	274
29	741	5.5	DD	36									02:45.9	−0.1	−1.0	87
May 2	1207	5.6	DD	77	03:02.1	+0.7	−0.7	67	03:02.1	+0.7	−1.0	82	02:49.9	+1.0	−1.1	86
29	1158	5	DD	46	02:43.5	−0.5	−2.0	141	02:54.4	−0.8	−2.6	157	02:53.6	−0.7	−3.1	161
Jun. 1	1547	3.8	DD	86	04:42.8	+0.1	−0.8	67	04:45.3	+0.2	−1.0	78	04:38.4	+0.5	−1.1	79
22	692*	0.9	DB	22	13:49.7	+1.6	+0.8	86	13:39.7	+1.6	+0.7	92	13:29.1	+1.0	+1.5	72
22	692*	0.9	RD	22	15:02.8	+1.6	+1.1	244	14:50.6	+1.6	+1.6	236	14:38.6	+1.4	+1.2	255
Jul. 1	1821	2.8	DD	91	02:48.7	+0.7	−2.1	126	02:52.9	+0.8	−2.3	135	02:36.0	+1.1	−2.2	138
1	1821	2.8	RB	91									03:44.4	+1.0	−1.4	271
12	3206	5.1	RD	144									09:37.8	+2.4	−1.3	288
18	444	5.9	RD	70	08:12.8	+0.5	+1.9	237	08:03.9	+0.4	+1.9	235	08:05.7	+0.2	+1.6	249
20	741	5.5	RD	43	07:36.6	+0.1	+0.5	302								
Aug. 1	2223	3.9	DD	106	02:52.2	+1.4	−2.0	122	02:52.9	+1.6	−2.1	129	02:29.1	+1.8	−1.7	126
10	3421	4.9	RD	150	07:17.5	+1.5	+1.0	230	07:06.4	+1.6	+1.3	227	06:51.4	+1.8	+1.1	246
14	405	4.3	RD	99					07:15.8	+4.1	−4.1	323				
Sep. 10	364	4.3	RD	130	05:34.9	+0.8	+2.4	215	05:23.0	+0.6	+2.5	212	05:22.9	+0.6	+2.0	231
11	508	4.1	RD	115	09:39.1	+0.9	+4.1	192	09:16.5	−1.1	+9.7	173	09:21.6	+1.1	+2.6	211
12	635	3.7	RD	103	05:12.0	+0.6	+1.2	274	05:05.5	+0.4	+1.2	271	05:05.0	+0.3	+0.9	288
12	667	5	RD	101	09:55.3	+2.2	−1.2	294	09:48.2	+2.3	−0.5	284	09:19.5	+2.7	−1.8	311
12	669	3.8	RD	101	09:37.0	+1.1	+3.7	201	09:16.9	+0.2	+6.0	186	09:18.7	+1.1	+2.6	218
12	671	3.4	RD	101									09:02.1	−0.1	+5.4	187
12	677	4.8	RD	101									10:40.1	+1.7	+1.4	238
12	692*	0.9	DB	100	12:59.4	+1.2	−1.1	89	12:58.1	+1.4	−1.5	103	12:37.4	+1.7	−0.8	92
12	692*	0.9	RD	100	14:07.6	+0.8	−0.9	258	14:05.5	+1.1	−0.2	243	13:51.7	+1.3	−0.3	249
13	814	5.4	RD	88	09:12.5	+1.1	+2.8	218	08:56.8	+0.7	+3.5	208	08:56.0	+0.8	+2.2	233
13	832	4.3	RD	87									11:30.0	+9.9	+9.9	339
Oct. 11	947	5.2	RD	104	10:42.1	+1.8	−0.4	269	10:33.4	+2.1	+0.4	256	10:13.2	+1.9	+0.3	268
13	1236	5.1	RD	78	08:55.7	+1.4	+1.0	270	08:45.3	+1.2	+1.5	259	08:38.3	+0.8	+1.1	275
14	1375	5.4	RD	64									11:46.1	+1.7	+0.8	269
15	1487	1.4	DB	52	09:49.4	+1.0	+2.5	64	09:37.7	+0.8	+1.7	78	09:37.3	+0.4	+2.4	63
15	1487	1.4	RD	52	10:42.8	+1.2	−1.6	329	10:41.1	+1.3	−0.7	313	10:27.0	+0.9	−0.9	325
26	2734	5.2	DD	69	01:07.8	+0.7	−0.7	66	01:06.5	+1.0	−0.6	70	00:54.2	+1.1		52
27	2981	5.1	DD	90					23:07.1	+0.3	+6.1	1				
Nov. 6	692*	0.9	DB	154	01:03.9	+0.2	+1.3	84	00:58.8	+0.1	+1.1	88	01:03.5	−0.2	+1.3	74
6	692*	0.9	RD	153	02:00.1	+0.4	+1.7	244	01:52.6	+0.2	+1.7	240	01:55.9	+0.1	+1.4	256
9	1175	4.9	RD	111	03:39.6	+0.1	+1.1	273								
11	1466	5.3	RD	82									12:24.6	+2.6	+1.5	244
Dec. 4	832	4.3	RD	168									12:16.7	+0.2	−0.7	251
5	947	5.2	RD	159	01:45.1	+0.1	+2.3	226								
29	405	4.3	DD	124	03:45.1	+1.3	−0.4	72	03:40.3	+1.6	−0.6	82	03:22.5	+1.6	+0.4	64
30	692*	0.9	DD	150	23:27.3	+1.3	+0.6	108	23:19.7	+1.2	+0.4	113	23:13.3	+0.5	+1.2	92
31	692*	0.9	RB	150	00:21.5	+0.7	+2.5	217	00:09.3	+0.5	+2.8	211	00:10.8	+0.5	+2.0	234

DB/DD = Disappearance at Bright/Dark limb; RB/RD = Reappearance at Bright/Dark limb

See p. 163 for additional explanation of these tables.

*ZC 692 = Aldebaran

"Lunar occultation and graze observations refine our knowledge of the shape of the lunar profile and the fundamental star coordinate system. These observations complement those made by other techniques, such as Kaguya *and* Lunar Reconnaissance Orbiter *laser ranging and photographs."*

TOTAL LUNAR OCCULTATIONS FOR 2017 (continued)

					MIAMI 80.3°W, 25.8°N				ATLANTA 84.3°W, 33.8°N				AUSTIN 97.8°W, 30.2°N			
Date	ZC	mag.	PH	El °	UT	A m/deg	B m/deg	PA °	UT	A m/deg	B m/deg	PA °	UT	A m/deg	B m/deg	PA °
Jan. 7	322	5.6	DD	106	03:33.5	+1.3	+1.6	37								
18	1821	2.8	RD	108	06:00.8	+1.3	+2.2	249	06:07.9	+0.8	+0.8	279	05:56.1	+0.3	+1.5	259
Feb. 5	692*	0.9	DD	113	19:59.4	–0.3	+2.9	24								
5	692*	0.9	RB	113	20:40.3	+1.5	–0.5	302								
Mar. 2	249	4.5	DD	44					02:00.1	+0.1	–5.0	141				
4	667	5	DD	83	23:53.1	+2.4	+0.6	72	23:55.6	+1.9	+2.4	39				
4	669	3.8	DD	83					23:55.8	+2.8	–3.4	133				
5	677	4.8	DD	84	01:23.4	+1.8	–3.5	133	00:59.6	+2.0	–1.0	98	00:31.7	+2.6	–1.0	106
5	692*	0.9	DD	85	04:03.2	+0.5	–0.7	85	03:57.2	+0.8	–0.1	61	03:44.7	+1.3	–0.7	83
5	692*	0.9	RB	86	05:01.9		–0.8	270	04:52.2		–1.7	292	04:52.6	+0.6	–0.9	269
8	1158	5	DD	126	07:02.8	+0.4	–0.8	88	06:55.4	+0.8	–0.4	69	06:45.6	+1.1	–1.1	96
24	3108	5.3	RD	47	09:34.0	+0.9	+2.4	224	09:46.9	+0.6	+1.7	245				
25	3253	5.4	RD	34	10:39.8	+0.6	+0.1	294	10:34.4	–0.1	–1.7	325				
Apr. 1	635	3.7	DD	54					03:42.9	–0.4	–1.7	117	03:58.0	–0.8	–4.3	152
15	2399	4.9	RD	134					10:44.1	+2.2	–2.2	311	10:18.1	+2.6	–1.4	299
28	692*	0.9	DD	32	16:07.3	+1.6	+0.1	107	16:08.8	+0.9	+1.3	78	15:55.5	+0.4	+1.4	72
28	692*	0.9	RB	32	17:05.2	+0.9	+2.7	217	17:16.9	+1.3	+1.5	248	16:57.2	+0.9	+1.3	254
29	741	5.5	DD	36									03:05.3	–0.4	–2.2	133
May 2	1207	5.6	DD	77	03:17.3	+0.3	–1.7	120	03:03.0	+0.7	–1.4	103	02:58.4	+0.9	–2.2	130
3	1336	5.2	DD	90	02:57.2	+1.7	–0.3	77	02:50.6	+2.4	+0.9	54	02:20.1	+2.3	–0.6	91
Jun. 1	1547	3.8	DD	85	04:59.7		–1.3	110	04:49.1	+0.3	–1.2	94	04:48.2	+0.6	–1.6	113
22	669	3.8	RD	23									10:51.7	–0.3	+1.6	233
22	671	3.4	RD	23									10:45.5	–0.5	+2.2	209
22	692*	0.9	DB	22	13:39.5	+4.1	–4.4	142	13:24.6	+1.6	+0.6	98	13:04.9	+0.9	+0.9	90
22	692*	0.9	RD	22	14:05.3	–0.8	+7.3	181	14:30.2	+1.3	+2.2	227	14:07.6	+0.9	+1.9	234
Jul. 1	1821	2.8	DD	91	03:28.9	+0.3	–4.5	175	02:59.4	+0.8	–2.8	152	03:05.7	–0.5	–6.1	187
1	1821	2.8	RB	91					03:57.0	+1.0	–0.8	256	03:33.8	+3.2	+2.3	227
6	2399	4.9	DD	147	04:29.2	+2.9	+0.6	66	04:29.0	+3.0	+2.7	39	03:36.9	+3.3	+1.4	67
12	3206	5.1	RD	144	09:57.0	+1.5	+0.9	231	09:52.0	+2.0	–0.3	260	09:19.6	+2.8	–0.1	271
18	444	5.9	RD	70					07:52.4	+0.1	+1.9	230				
Aug. 1	2223	3.9	DD	106	03:29.8	+2.0	–6.9	173	02:52.1	+1.8	–2.6	142	02:38.0	+1.6	–3.8	162
9	3307	4.8	RD	161	10:31.9	+1.2	–1.0	272								
10	3421	4.9	RD	150	06:32.7	+1.1	+3.4	197	06:46.1	+1.7	+1.8	226	06:15.9	+1.7	+1.9	233
14	405	4.3	RD	99	07:13.6	+1.5	+0.6	276	07:05.9	+2.3	–1.5	314				
16	692*	0.9	RD	73	05:54.4	+0.2	–0.5	309								
Sep. 3	2987	4.9	DD	144									07:38.9	+1.3	–0.8	86
9	249	4.5	RD	141	10:42.2	+1.7	–0.6	265	10:19.3	+2.8	–4.2	308	09:42.4	+9.9	+9.9	322
7	3526	4.9	RD	166									11:22.4	+1.0	–0.9	268
10	364	4.3	RD	130					05:06.2	+0.4	+2.6	209	04:54.0	+0.1	+2.3	214
11	508	4.1	RD	115									08:31.1	–0.9	+6.2	178
12	635	3.7	RD	103	04:47.9		+1.4	243	04:57.6	+0.1	+1.1	266				
12	667	5	RD	101	09:33.9	+2.1	+1.5	243	09:31.8	+2.3	+0.3	274	09:01.8	+2.0	+0.3	281
12	669	3.8	RD	101									08:32.5	–0.6	+5.2	186
12	677	4.8	RD	101					10:26.7	+1.3	+3.8	203	09:58.0	+1.0	+3.4	208
13	814	5.4	RD	88					08:33.7	–0.1	+4.6	196	08:20.8	–0.1	+3.2	206
13	832	4.3	RD	87									11:30.5	+2.5	–0.3	285
Oct. 11	947	5.2	RD	104					10:12.5	+2.1	+1.7	238	09:39.2	+1.6	+2.3	233
13	1236	5.1	RD	78					08:29.1	+0.8	+2.0	246	08:15.8	+0.2	+1.8	245
14	1375	5.4	RD	64									10:59.2	+1.0	+7.4	210
15	1487	1.4	DB	52	09:26.4	+0.9	–0.5	125	09:25.7	+0.6	+0.9	95	09:18.0	+0.2	+0.6	101
15	1487	1.4	RD	52	10:33.9	+1.5	+1.1	265	10:33.3	+1.2	+0.1	294	10:19.6	+0.7	+0.5	284
26	2734	5.2	DD	69	01:14.5	+1.7	–1.4	102	01:00.8	+1.5	–0.5	75	00:36.9	+2.2	+0.1	71
Nov. 1	3526	4.9	DD	139	04:56.0	+0.7	+2.7	17								
6	692*	0.9	DB	153	00:50.2	+0.3	–0.1	120	00:53.7	–0.1	+0.9	93	12:39.3	+3.0	–5.6	143
6	692*	0.9	RD	153	01:26.8	–0.4	+2.5	207	01:43.5	–0.1	+1.7	236	01:40.9	–0.3	+1.4	239
11	1487	1.4	DB	80									17:26.6	+1.2	–0.4	72
11	1487	1.4	RD	79									18:14.2	–0.1	–2.6	334
Dec. 25	3421	4.9	DD	74	01:24.7	+0.9	+1.4	36	01:47.0	–2.4	+9.1	345				
29	405	4.3	DD	124	04:06.3	+9.9	+9.9	152	03:30.4	+2.2	–0.9	95	02:59.1	+2.6	–0.1	90
30	692*	0.9	DD	150					23:09.8	+1.1	+0.1	118	22:58.9	+0.4	+0.4	110
30	692*	0.9	RB	150					23:52.8	+0.1	+2.9	206	23:43.4	–0.1	+2.3	215

DB/DD = Disappearance at Bright/Dark limb; RB/RD = Reappearance at Bright/Dark limb

See p. 163 for additional explanation of these tables.

*ZC 692 = Aldebaran

TOTAL LUNAR OCCULTATIONS FOR 2017 (continued)

					KANSAS CITY 94.5°W, 39.0°N				DENVER 105.0°W, 39.8°N				NEW MEX., ARIZ. 109.0°W, 34.0°N			
Date	ZC	mag.	PH	El °	UT	A m/deg	B m/deg	PA °	UT	A m/deg	B m/deg	PA °	UT	A m/deg	B m/deg	PA °
Jan. 6	192	5.1	DD	93	03:33.0	+2.3	−5.8	136	03:06.2	+2.3	−2.3	114				
9	635	3.7	DD	136	09:00.0		−1.8	114	08:57.4	+0.2	−2.2	120	09:15.5	−0.6	−5.6	155
18	1821	2.8	RD	108	06:05.8	+0.3	+0.5	293								
Feb. 17	2128	5.8	RD	104									12:33.5	+1.7	−2.2	327
Mar. 2	249	4.5	DD	44	01:39.0	+0.8	−2.1	110	01:27.0	+1.2	−1.8	103	01:36.3	+1.8	−4.2	130
4	671	3.4	DD	83	23:32.6	+2.6	−1.9	125								
5	677	4.8	DD	84	00:36.9	+2.0	+0.3	76								
5	692*	0.9	DD	85	03:47.3	+1.2	+0.4	50	03:33.5	+1.5	+0.6	52	03:26.0	+1.7	−0.2	74
5	692*	0.9	RB	85	04:40.4	+0.3	−2.3	301	04:33.2	+0.7	−2.2	297	04:39.1	+1.1	−1.2	274
8	1158	5	DD	126	06:42.6	+1.2	−0.4	66	06:27.7	+1.5	−0.6	76	06:26.6	+1.5	−1.2	98
Apr. 1	635	3.7	DD	54	03:36.0		−1.6	109	03:33.0	+0.3	−2.0	114	03:47.5	−0.1	−3.8	144
15	2399	4.9	RD	134	10:10.7	+2.0	−2.0	322	09:49.2	+1.8	−1.3	317	09:46.9	+2.2	−0.7	299
28	692*	0.9	DD	32	16:11.3	+0.3	+2.0	53	16:11.7	−0.1	+2.2	39	16:00.3	−0.1	+1.8	50
28	692*	0.9	RB	32	17:10.5	+1.2	+0.9	274	17:00.1	+1.0	+0.6	289	16:52.5	+0.7	+0.8	278
29	741	5.5	DD	36	02:50.0	−0.1	−1.3	100	02:48.7	+0.1	−1.6	107	02:59.6	−0.1	−2.4	131
May 2	1207	5.6	DD	77	02:46.3	+1.1	−1.4	101	02:32.0	+1.4	−1.5	110	02:37.6	+1.3	−2.4	132
3	1336	5.2	DD	90	02:29.8	+2.8	+1.4	52	02:03.1	+2.5	+0.8	67				
Jun. 1	1547	3.8	DD	85	04:37.7	+0.7	−1.3	91	04:27.6	+1.0	−1.5	99	04:33.0	+1.0	−1.8	116
13	2981	5.1	RD	138	10:38.0	+0.6	+2.5	196	10:27.3	+1.5	+1.5	214	10:08.3	+1.6	+3.1	201
13	2987	4.9	RD	137									11:50.2	+2.3	−0.7	271
20	364	4.3	RD	52	10:03.3	−0.2	+3.1	192	10:07.0	−0.1	+2.4	205	09:52.4	−0.4	+3.2	189
22	692*	0.9	DB	22	13:18.6	+0.8	+1.5	72	13:14.1	+0.3	+1.8	58	13:03.1	+0.3	+1.5	68
22	692*	0.9	RD	22	14:25.7	+1.3	+1.3	255	14:14.3	+1.1	+1.1	269	14:03.4	+0.8	+1.3	259
Jul. 1	1821	2.8	DD	91	02:35.7	+1.0	−2.6	151	02:23.7	+0.8	−3.1	165				
1	1821	2.8	RB	91	03:39.8	+1.4	−1.0	261	03:20.1	+2.2	−0.3	251				
1	1825	5.9	DD	91									03:41.8	+1.1	−2.8	151
6	2399	4.9	DD	147					03:34.0	+3.5	+3.2	45	03:09.1	+2.6	+1.6	73
12	3206	5.1	RD	144	09:23.4	+2.8	−1.1	290	08:49.6	+3.3	−1.9	312	08:44.3	+3.0	−0.8	297
Aug. 1	2223	3.9	DD	106	02:21.6	+1.9	−1.8	135					02:09.5	+1.0	−3.4	167
10	3421	4.9	RD	150	06:35.9	+1.7	+1.4	248	06:20.0	+1.5	+1.4	257	06:05.6	+1.3	+1.6	248
Sep. 3	2981	5.1	DD	144					06:20.5	+2.4	−1.8	115	06:21.8	+3.4	−2.8	129
3	2987	4.9	DD	144					07:28.0	+0.9	+0.2	49	07:22.9	+1.3	+0.1	60
7	3526	4.9	RD	166	11:08.9	+1.4	−3.6	305					10:58.5	+2.3	−3.0	299
10	364	4.3	RD	129	05:13.6	+0.4	+2.0	232	05:11.6	+0.2	+1.7	241	05:00.8		+1.8	232
11	508	4.1	RD	115	09:06.6	+1.0	+2.8	210	08:57.7	+1.0	+2.1	228	08:40.6	+0.7	+2.5	217
12	635	3.7	RD	103	05:01.6		+0.8	287								
12	661	4.5	RD	102					07:24.9	−1.1	+4.9	182				
12	667	5	RD	101	09:06.1	+2.6	−1.4	311					08:36.5	+2.7	−2.4	321
12	669	3.8	RD	101	09:04.6	+0.8	+2.7	217	08:57.9	+0.8	+2.1	233	08:42.4	+0.5	+2.4	222
12	671	3.4	RD	101	08:48.5	−0.4	+5.2	186	08:49.8	+0.4	+2.9	210	08:30.7	−0.3	+3.7	195
12	677	4.8	RD	101	10:24.3	+1.6	+1.8	235	10:09.7	+1.4	+1.5	249	09:54.5	+1.2	+1.9	237
12	692*	0.9	DB	100	12:27.0	+2.1	−0.9	101	12:04.4	+2.1		92	11:57.2	+2.6	−0.8	109
12	692*	0.9	RD	100	13:41.2	+1.7	+0.5	238	13:23.3	+1.8	+0.7	242	13:07.8	+1.9	+2.2	221
13	814	5.4	RD	88	08:44.7	+0.6	+2.2	232	08:40.8	+0.4	+1.8	246	08:28.9	+0.2	+1.9	235
13	832	4.3	RD	87	11:25.8	+2.9	−3.7	323					10:58.2	+2.8	−2.3	317
13	836	5.7	RD	87					12:02.2	+2.3	−1.2	302	11:56.4	+2.2	−0.1	283
26	2399	4.9	DD	68									03:59.8	+0.3	+0.3	48
Oct. 2	3206	5.1	DD	136									08:08.7	+1.0	−0.7	79
11	947	5.2	RD	104	09:58.7	+1.8	+0.9	261	09:41.4	+1.6	+0.8	271	09:29.2	+1.4	+1.4	257
13	1236	5.1	RD	78	08:30.1	+0.6	+1.2	271	08:26.0	+0.3	+0.9	282	08:19.4	+0.1	+1.1	268
14	1375	5.4	RD	64	11:31.2	+1.6	+1.5	257	11:18.5	+1.1	+1.5	261	11:03.2	+0.8	+2.5	240
15	1487	1.4	DB	52	09:29.3	+0.2	+1.9	71	09:31.1	−0.2	+2.2	62				
15	1487	1.4	RD	52	10:22.9	+0.8	−0.4	315	10:15.7	+0.5	−0.6	322	10:15.2	+0.3	+0.1	302
16	1609	4.6	RD	39					12:26.7	+1.2	+7.4	216				
26	2734	5.2	DD	69	00:44.9	+1.5	+0.3	52	00:27.7	+1.9	+1.1	42				
Nov. 6	692*	0.9	RD	153	01:52.0	−0.1	+1.3	256	01:54.7	−0.2	+1.1	265				
11	1487	1.4	DB	80					17:14.9	+2.1	+0.7	51	17:08.4	+1.7	−0.6	78
11	1487	1.4	RD	79					17:45.6	−0.5	−3.9	356	18:04.1	+0.2	−2.6	330
Dec. 8	1434	5.4	RD	113	12:51.0	−0.5	−5.3	359	12:44.9	+0.8	−3.3	339	12:55.3	+1.5	−2.1	313
23	3181	6	DD	52					03:04.4	+0.3		50	03:03.5	+0.6	−0.3	64
29	405	4.3	DD	124	03:09.2	+1.8	+0.7	66	02:52.2	+1.5	+1.5	51	02:37.0	+1.8	+1.4	62
30	692	0.9	DD	150	23:07.0	+0.3	+1.1	91	23:06.4		+1.3	80				
31	692	0.9	RB	150	00:02.2	+0.3	+1.9	235	00:00.7	+0.2	+1.6	247	23:51.0		+1.6	238

DB/DD = Disappearance at Bright/Dark limb; RB/RD = Reappearance at Bright/Dark limb

See p. 163 for additional explanation of these tables.

*ZC 692 = Aldebaran

TOTAL LUNAR OCCULTATIONS FOR 2017 (continued)

					LOS ANGELES 118.3°W, 34.1°N				N. CALIFORNIA 122.0°W, 38.0°N				HONOLULU 157.9°W, 21.3°N			
Date	ZC	mag.	PH	El °	UT	A m/deg	B m/deg	PA °	UT	A m/deg	B m/deg	PA °	UT	A m/deg	B m/deg	PA °
Jan. 3	Mars	0.9	DD	58									08:02.9	+0.4	–1.6	108
6	192	5.1	DD	93	02:40.9	+3.3	–2.1	116	02:26.8	+2.4	–0.2	94				
9	667	5	DD	138									12:35.6	+0.4	–1.1	101
Feb. 6	741	5.5	DD	117	06:55.1	+1.3	–1.0	90	06:47.0	+1.4	–0.5	79	05:50.4	+4.2	–5.2	142
15	1924	5.8	RD	125									14:44.6	+3.3	–0.2	271
17	2128	5.8	RD	104	12:17.0	+1.8	–1.3	313	12:06.2	+1.5	–1.2	318				
Mar. 5	692*	0.9	DD	85	03:08.5	+2.0	+0.1	74	03:03.2	+1.9	+0.9	59	01:33.5	+1.6	+1.0	80
5	692*	0.9	RB	86	04:27.2	+1.5	–0.9	270	04:16.9	+1.6	–1.4	283	02:54.3	+2.1	+1.6	243
8	1158	5	DD	126	06:11.1	+1.8	–1.4	108	05:59.9	+1.9	–0.9	99				
Apr. 1	635	3.7	DD	55	03:48.3	–0.4	–7.6	158	03:29.2	+0.7	–3.3	134				
1	667	5	DD	56									07:15.3	+0.5	–0.9	97
1	677	4.8	DD	57									08:23.2	–0.8	–3.5	149
2	814	5.4	DD	70	06:40.2	+0.2	–0.5	69	06:37.7	+0.3	–0.3	61				
10	1821	2.8	DD	169	08:02.0	+4.0	+1.9	60					06:53.5	+0.1	–4.5	176
15	2399	4.9	RD	134	09:27.2	+2.0		290	09:20.6	+1.6	+0.1	295				
28	692*	0.9	DD	32	16:02.7	–0.4	+2.0	40	16:13.0	–0.6	+2.5	24				
28	692*	0.9	RB	32	16:47.0	+0.5	+0.5	290	16:46.3	+0.6	+0.1	306				
May 18	3173	5.2	RD	94									15:21.8	+2.4	+2.0	229
19	3307	4.8	RD	83									14:00.8	+1.6	+1.4	252
22	170	6	RD	44									14:52.9	–0.3	+5.4	177
Jun. 1	1547	3.8	DD	85	04:22.7	+1.2	–2.1	127	04:10.4	+1.3	–1.9	123	09:24.8	+2.8	–0.5	103
13	2981	5.1	RD	137	09:50.8	+2.1	+2.8	209	09:52.4	+2.0	+2.1	222				
13	2987	4.9	RD	137	11:26.1	+2.8	–0.7	283	11:12.3	+2.8	–1.0	297	09:48.5	+1.5	+1.3	254
17	3526	4.9	RD	88									15:28.1	+2.9	+0.4	271
21	508	4.1	RD	37	12:10.8		+1.9	228	12:17.5		+1.7	240				
22	692*	0.9	DB	22	13:02.1		+1.6	58	13:09.5	–0.2	+2.0	45				
22	692*	0.9	RD	22	13:56.8	+0.6	+1.0	270	13:58.0	+0.7	+0.8	284				
27	1487	1.4	DD	53									23:09.1	+1.7	+0.6	92
28	1487	1.4	RB	54									00:28.1	+2.1	–1.3	306
29	1609	4.6	DD	67	03:13.0	+3.0	+1.3	53								
Jul. 12	3206	5.1	RD	144	08:18.7	+2.4	–0.9	307								
15	76	5.9	RD	105									15:21.7	+2.5	+1.2	244
Aug. 10	3421	4.9	RD	150	05:55.3	+1.0	+1.6	251								
Sep. 3	2981	5.1	DD	144	05:52.3	+3.0	–1.1	114	05:39.9	+2.5	–0.3	101				
3	2987	4.9	DD	144	07:09.8	+1.5	+0.8	47	07:09.2	+1.2	+1.5	31	05:20.2	+2.1	+1.9	60
10	405	4.3	RD	125									13:21.9	+1.0	+3.7	198
11	508	4.1	RD	115	08:34.1	+0.7	+2.1	230	08:38.8	+0.7	+1.8	244				
12	661	4.5	RD	102	07:13.4	–1.3	+4.9	181	07:28.6	–0.4	+2.6	205				
12	669	3.8	RD	101	08:38.7	+0.4	+1.9	234	08:44.2	+0.4	+1.6	248				
12	671	3.4	RD	101	08:31.8		+2.6	212	08:40.5	+0.2	+2.1	227				
12	677	4.8	RD	101	09:44.3	+1.0	+1.6	250	09:46.0	+1.0	+1.3	264				
12	692*	0.9	DB	100	11:34.7	+2.2	+0.3	97	11:30.2	+1.7	+1.1	81	10:34.1	+0.3	+0.9	82
12	692*	0.9	RD	100	12:50.5	+1.9	+1.9	229	12:49.5	+1.9	+1.2	246	11:34.8	+0.6	+1.6	241
13	814	5.4	RD	88	08:28.2		+1.6	246								
13	836	5.7	RD	87	11:36.3	+2.1	–0.3	295	11:24.7	+2.5	–1.9	318				
26	2399	4.9	DD	68	03:55.7	+0.6	+1.3	37								
Oct. 2	3206	5.1	DD	137	07:58.5	+1.2	–0.2	67	07:54.5	+1.0	+0.3	51	06:31.6	+2.3	+2.2	45
11	947	5.2	RD	104	09:17.8	+1.1	+1.1	267	09:17.3	+1.1	+0.7	282				
14	1375	5.4	RD	64	10:57.7	+0.4	+2.0	246	11:02.7	+0.5	+1.4	262				
15	1487	1.4	RD	52	10:13.0	+0.1	–0.1	309	10:10.8	+0.2	–0.8	328				
22	2223	3.9	RB	27									04:37.8	+0.8	–0.7	269
27	2886	4.9	DD	81	04:20.8	+3.8	–5.8	145	03:57.8	+2.3	–2.2	119				
Nov. 7	913	5.1	RD	134									12:31.6	+2.7	–0.6	286
11	1487	1.4	DB	80	16:51.8	+1.9	–0.9	92	16:41.5	+2.0	–0.7	87				
11	1487	1.4	RD	79	18:00.0	+0.6	–2.3	318	17:48.3	+0.7	–2.5	323				
24	2981	5.1	DD	63									07:32.0	+0.5	–0.3	76
Dec. 8	1434	5.4	RD	113	12:39.0	+1.9	–1.4	301	12:26.6	+1.7	–1.5	309	11:07.3	+0.8	+3.5	227
15	2223	3.9	DB	29	14:12.4	–0.2	–2.3	167	14:06.3		–1.2	155				
15	2223	3.9	RD	29					15:00.4	+1.9	+2.1	251				
23	3181	6	DD	52	02:57.3	+0.7	+0.2	52	02:57.0	+0.5	+0.8	34				
29	405	4.3	DD	124	02:22.7	+1.3	+2.0	48	02:27.5	+0.9	+2.5	32				

DB/DD = Disappearance at Bright/Dark limb; RB/RD = Reappearance at Bright/Dark limb

See p. 163 for additional explanation of these tables.

*ZC 692 = Aldebaran

NAMES OF STARS OCCULTED IN 2017

ZC	Name	ZC	Name	ZC	Name
12	4 (Cet)/Psc	806	111 Tau	1941	74 Vir
13	5 (Cet)/Psc	814	15 Tau	1978	88 Vir
55	10 Cet	832	119 Tau	2020	94 Vir
76	14 Cet	836	120 Tau	2128	ξ^1 Lib
150	26 Cet	878	30 Tau	2223	γ Lib (Zuben-el-Akrab)
170	33 Cet	895	57 Ori	2399	24 (Sco)/Oph
178	35 Cet	947	71 Ori	2448	29 Oph
192	89 Psc	995	ν Gem	2639	16 Sgr
249	ν Psc	1158	74 Gem	2642	17 Sgr
327	ξ^1 Cet	1207	3 Cnc	2666	21 Sgr
364	ξ^2 Cet	1236	ζ^1 Cnc (Tegmine)	2729	V356 Sgr
401	85 (Cet)/Ari	1262	25 Cnc	2734	29 Sgr
405	μ Cet	1275	θ Cnc	2886	56 Sgr
508	5 Tau	1336	o^1 Cnc	2963	σ Cap
626	48 Tau	1337	o^2 Cnc	2981	π Cap
635	γ Tau (Hyadum I)	1371	81 Cnc	2993	o^1 Cap
636	55 Tau	1420	11 Leo	2994	o^2 Cap
659	70 Tau	1434	ψ Leo	3017	υ Cap (Loo Sieu)
661	71 Tau	1466	ν Leo	3071	21 Cap 3079
667	75 Tau	1487	α Leo (Regulus)	3079	θ Cap (Tsin)
669	θ^1 Tau	1547	ρ Leo	3206	μ Cap (Kuh)
671	θ^2 Tau	1550	49 Leo	3262	40 Aqr
678	81 Tau	1609	χ Leo	3268	42 Aqr
682	85 Tau	1644	σ Leo (Shang Tseang)	3347	70 Aqr
692	α Tau (Aldebaran)	1749	10 Vir	X12393	ζ^2 Cnc*
699	89 Tau	1821	γ Vir (Porrima)	X25958	BB Sgr
704	σ^2 Tau				* = (Tegmine Companion)

Names of occulted stars

The stars that are occulted by the Moon are stars that lie along the zodiac; hence they are known by their number in the ZC compiled by James Robertson and published in the *Astronomical Papers Prepared for the Use of the American Ephemeris and Nautical Almanac, Vol. 10*, Part 2 (U.S. Government Printing Office, Washington, 1940). Robertson's ZC has been out of print for several years. In 1986, Isao Sato, a member of the Lunar Occultation Observers Group in Japan, republished the ZC. This new edition is based on the epoch J2000 and includes much new data, particularly on double stars. Since stars are not usually recognized by their ZC numbers, the equivalent Bayer designations or Flamsteed numbers of the stars occulted during the year are given in the table above. The ZC and XZ (now version XZ80Q) catalogues, updated in 2005 by D. Herald using *HIPPARCOS*, Tycho–2, and UCAC–2 data, are available through IOTA's website.

2. GRAZING OCCULTATIONS: PREDICTIONS AND STAR DATA

BY EBERHARD RIEDEL AND DAVID W. DUNHAM

Grazing occultation predictions

The table on pp. 174–175 lists grazing lunar-occultation predictions for much of North America for 2017. The events are limited to stars of mag. 7.0 or brighter that will graze the limb of the Moon when it is at a favourable elongation from the Sun and at least as high above the horizon in degrees as the star's magnitude (e.g. a 3rd-mag. star is included only if its altitude is at least 3°). The star's USNO reference number is the ZC number, unless the number is prefixed with an X, which are not in the ZC; their numbers are from the XZ catalogue, a more extensive zodiacal catalogue first prepared at the U.S. Naval Observatory but now updated by D. Herald of Australia.

The maps on pp. 176–178 show the predicted graze tracks. The maps are "false" projections, since the lat/long scales are both linear. This makes it much easier for measuring coordinates or plotting locations with known coordinates than is possible with any other type of projection. The longitude scale is compressed by a factor of cos 50°. The maps are not detailed enough for locating oneself in the zone 2–3 km wide where multiple disappearances of a star may occur. To obtain detailed predictions of any observable graze the GRAZPREP software can be downloaded via www.grazprep.com (password "IOTA/ES"). The software gives complete worldwide information needed for a successful observation for any location in relation to the projected lunar profile and corrected for elevation. For many grazes, IOTA overlays the predicted limit line on the very detailed maps and imagery of maps.google.com, available at www.iota.timerson.net, but further corrections are needed based on the predicted lunar profile and the observer's elevation above sea level.

Each track is keyed to the sequential number in the table. The computer-drawn number appears at the east and west ends of the track and is aligned parallel to it. Some overlapping numbers have been omitted for legibility; in these cases, check the other end of the track for the number. Conditions are represented by three different types of lines:

solid line = dark limb (night)
dashed line = bright limb (night)
dotted line = dark or bright limb (day)

Thicker lines are drawn for 1st-mag. stars and planets. Many tracks begin and/or end with the letter A, B, or S: A denotes that the Moon is at a low altitude, B that the bright limb interferes, and S that sunlight or twilight interferes. The tick marks along the tracks indicate multiples of 10 min of every hour. For example, if the time for the west end of the track is 3:16.2, the tick marks proceeding eastward correspond to 3:20, 3:30, etc. Time always increases from west to east along the path. *The time ticks, track numbers, and the A, B, and S letters are on the side of the limit with an occultation*, that is, north of southern limits and south of northern limits. Asterisks on the graze maps indicate the locations of the North American standard stations for lunar total-occultation predictions (see p. 164).

Occulted stars known to be double

In the table on the next page are data on double stars for which graze predictions are given. This information is from DSFILE, a comprehensive file of zodiacal double-star data compiled by Don Stockbauer, Henk Bulder, Mitsuru Sôma, David Herald, and David Dunham; most of the data for the ZC stars are in the Sato ZC catalogue. The successive columns give the **USNO** reference number of the star, the **Graze#**, the double star code (**d**), the **magnitude** of the brighter (**A**) and dimmer (**B**) components, the separation (**Sep.**) in arcseconds, and the position angle (**PA**) of B from A measured eastward from north. If the star is triple, the third component's magnitude is given under **C**, and its separation and PA from A are given in the last columns. XZ numbers are given for the last seven non-ZC stars. The bright double star Porrima (ZC 1821) has no graze index number; it only appears in the Honolulu total occultation list.

The parameters are given for the epoch of the occultation, computed from orbital elements when available or from extrapolations from a long series of observations. If there is little change in the available observations, the last-observed separation and PA are used. The motion for ZC 2798 is so large between the two occultations listed that separate entries are given for it. Most components fainter than magnitude 11.5 are not listed, and some very close doubles whose parameters are not known, generally with separations less than 0.2″, are also not listed. The latter include spectroscopic binaries (code J, U, or sometimes V) and visual occultation doubles (most codes K and X, and many Vs).

STARS OCCULTED IN 2017 AND KNOWN TO BE DOUBLE

USNO	Graze #	d	magnitude A	B	Sep. ″	PA °	C	Sep. ″	PA °
55	3	M	6.5	8.9	0.4	267			
150	206	A	6.2	8.6	16.0	253			
398	34	V	6.9	8.5	0.006	298			
401	35	V	6.9	7.2	0.01	21			
405	36, 128	V	4.5	8.5	0.1	133			
508	38, 105	V	4.5	6.5	0.01				
608	122	$	6.1	8.8	3.8	222	9.6	0.1	30
636	161	O	7.4	8.0	0.6	9			
659	141	O	7.0	7.3	0.1	331			
667	44, 108, 143, 178	V	5.4	7.9	0.02	238			
669	41	V	4.0	7.8	0.1	212			
671	42, 107, 142	V	4.0	5.0	0.02				
672	144	O	7.0	7.7	0.2	264			
672	47	O	7.0	7.7	0.2	265			
741	22, 86, 123	V	6.5	6.5	0.08	240			
806	56, 71	C	5.1	8.9	108.7	271			
814	8, 57, 72	T	5.7	6.6	0.1	98	10.1	10.1	306
823	58, 146	T	6.8	7.5	0.02	232	10.4	3.3	131
947	75, 162	A	5.2	11.2	7.9	202	10.5	64.3	279
995	195	B	4.3	6.0	0.2	139	8.6	112.5	329
1124	80	A	6.9	11.7	12.8	58			
1236	112, 163	Z	5.6	6.0	6.0	64	6.2	5.9	52
1241	165	A	6.4	12.3	1.6	320	9.1	57.3	297
1371	113	O	7.2	7.2	0.1	236			
1547	89	M	4.3	5.4	0.01				
1550	99	H	6.0	8.0	0.001		7.7	2.2	157
1609	114	C	4.7	11.0	5.0	274	9.0	51.3	310
1821	10, 115	O	3.5	3.5	2.3	5			
1923	183	M	7.0	10.8	0.4	239			
2223	29, 125, 202	T	4.7	4.9	0.1	132	11.2	41.7	153
2352	30, 203	M	7.6	7.8	0.2	75			
2629	32	H	7.2	8.5	0.02	321	7.2	1.3	193
2642	157	V	7.2	8.9	0.2	132			
2666	184	M	5.0	7.5	1.7	284			
2798	82	O	7.0	7.2	0.10	35			
2798	158	O	7.0	7.2	0.07	206			
2963	187	A	5.5	9.0	55.9	182			
2981	134, 173	M	5.2	8.5	3.4	147			
2994	175	A	5.9	6.7	21.9	239			
3071	188	V	6.8	8.2	0.4	77			
X11708	131	A	7.9	9.6	6.3	273			

The double-star codes (**d**) have the following meanings:

A or C..........visual double
B or V..........close double, usually discovered by occultation
D..................primary of wide pair; secondary has separate catalogue entry
H..................triple, with close occultation pair and third visual component; prediction uses a mean position
J...................single-line spectroscopic binary (2nd star at least two magnitudes fainter than the primary star)
K..................possible double from occultation
M.................mean position (centre of light) of a close pair is used by the ZC and/or XZ catalogue
O..................orbital elements available and used to calculate the separation and PA
P..................prediction is for the preceding component of a visual double
T..................visual triple star
X..................probable double from occultation
Z..................triple, O (A/B components) and V (C component)
$..................M with 2nd star either M, J, U, or V (3rd star's data referred to 2nd star)

Some close pairs have rapid orbital motion so the current PA is unknown.

GRAZING LUNAR OCCULTATIONS FOR 2017

This table lists lunar grazing occultation predictions for much of North America (p. 171). Graze tracks are shown in the 6 maps on pp. 176–178. For each graze, the table provides:

No............ a chronological sequential number used on the maps
Date......... the date
USNO d... the star's USNO (U.S. Naval Observatory) reference number and its double-star code (in the "**d**" column)—(see the bottom of the facing page)
m.............. its visual magnitude
%sl.......... the percent of the Moon sunlit (+ for waxing, − for waning, E for lunar eclipses)
L.............. whether the track is a northern (N) or southern (S) limit
W.U.T...... the Universal Time at the west end of the track
Lo., La..... the longitude and latitude of the west end of the track

No.	Date	USNO	d	*m*	%sl	L	W.U.T.	Lo.	La.	No.	Date	USNO	d	*m*	%sl	L	W.U.T.	Lo.	La.
1	Jan. 3	3325	U	6.9	21+	S	2:16.8	−122	20	47	Mar. 5	672	O	6.7	44+	N	0:55.1	−67	54
2	4	X31608	0	7	30+	S	1:32.6	−84	20	48	5	680	V	6.5	44+	S	1:02.4	−102	24
3	5	55	M	6.4	42+	N	5:01.6	−111	31	49	5	677	X	4.8	44+	N	1:43.3	−62	55
4	6	192	0	5.1	53+	S	2:28.6	−130	24	50	5	682*	V	6	44+	S	1:22.5	−110	44
5	6	202	0	6.9	54+	N	6:32.7	−130	30	51	5	692*	A	0.9	45+	N	3:25.3	−130	49
6	7	327	K	4.4	64+	N	4:20.7	−111	21	52	5	685	0	6.6	45+	S	2:12.9	−119	21
7	9	627	0	6.6	86+	N	7:46.6	−130	29	53	5	685	0	6.6	45+	N	2:53.8	−88	55
8	10	814	T	5.4	94+	N	11:28.2	−130	53	54	5	699	0	5.8	46+	S	4:26.8	−130	49
9	17	1732	0	6.8	74−	S	9:06.7	−100	35	55	5	704	0	4.7	46+	S	5:21.0	−90	55
10	18	1821	O	2.8	66−	N	5:51.9	−81	55	56	5	806	C	5	55+	S	22:36.6	−71	48
11	19	1941	0	4.7	56−	S	8:31.9	−92	55	57	6	814	T	5.4	55+	N	0:01.7	−82	51
12	22	2280	0	6.5	27−	S	11:00.2	−106	51	58	6	823	T	6.7	56+	N	1:23.8	−82	29
13	Feb. 1	12	0	6.4	17+	S	0:37.4	−104	35	59	6	829	0	6.8	56+	N	2:18.1	−94	39
14	1	13	J	6.2	17+	S	0:53.8	−107	32	60	6	836	0	5.7	56+	N	3:05.3	−108	24
15	1	15	K	7	17+	S	1:17.3	−109	22	61	8	1158	K	5	79+	N	6:31.1	−112	55
16	1	X00144	0	6.8	17+	S	1:22.7	−122	47	62	20	2571	0	6.8	52−	S	10:56.8	−130	35
17	1	128	0	7	25+	S	23:25.0	−84	31	63	23	2989	0	6.7	24−	S	11:51.0	−125	28
18	3	303	X	6.4	39+	N	6:41.9	−130	44	64	25	3262	K	6.9	9−	S	11:30.5	−96	36
19	5	692*	A	0.9	69+	N	20:11.6	−104	22	65	30	X03132	0	6.8	5+	S	1:57.9	−110	48
20	5	695	D	6.6	69+	S	21:12.7	−59	50	66	30	462	K	6	11+	S	23:35.9	−76	41
21	5	704	0	4.7	69+	S	22:13.8	−80	53	67	Apr. 1	626	0	6.3	20+	S	1:56.5	−111	39
22	6	741	V	5.5	73+	N	6:58.4	−130	55	68	1	627	0	6.6	20+	N	2:52.9	−109	25
23	7	878	K	5.5	81+	S	1:29.8	−123	47	69	1	635	K	3.6	21+	S	3:44.2	−130	35
24	7	886	X	6.8	81+	N	4:31.0	−88	39	70	1	661	V	4.5	22+	S	6:28.9	−130	47
25	7	X07736	0	7	81+	N	4:39.4	−87	46	71	2	806	C	5	32+	S	5:28.1	−130	54
26	9	1207	X	5.6	96+	N	7:59.4	−130	44	72	2	814	T	5.4	33+	N	6:43.7	−130	52
27	16	2008	V	6.6	73−	S	7:07.9	−110	40	73	2	934	0	6.4	40+	S	23:38.2	−73	51
28	16	2020	K	6.5	72−	S	11:05.3	−130	49	74	3	943	0	6.6	41+	N	0:53.7	−76	50
29	18	2223	T	3.9	55−	S	8:12.3	−103	51	75	3	947	A	5.2	41+	N	1:08.9	−102	23
30	19	2352	M	7	45−	S	7:40.7	−83	42	76	3	951	V	6.6	41+	S	1:30.9	−103	42
31	21	2611	0	7	27−	S	9:17.5	−74	48	77	3	X08716	0	7	41+	N	2:15.9	−106	37
32	21	2629	H	6.4	26−	S	12:05.1	−110	53	78	3	985	A	6.8	44+	N	6:25.0	−130	42
33	Mar. 2	249	0	4.5	14+	S	1:43.6	−116	31	79	4	1114	0	6.8	54+	N	5:02.0	−130	47
34	3	398	V	6.5	24+	N	4:37.0	−124	37	80	4	1124	A	6.9	55+	N	6:31.9	−130	47
35	3	401	V	6.3	24+	N	4:56.6	−130	27	81	15	2396	V	6.7	85−	S	8:39.6	−130	46
36	3	405	V	4.3	25+	S	5:39.6	−130	40	82	18	2798	O	6.1	61−	S	7:33.4	−95	42
37	3	498	V	6.3	32+	S	22:48.3	−72	43	83	21	3206	0	5.1	30−	S	12:13.0	−126	55
38	4	508	V	4.1	32+	S	0:14.7	−95	43	84	28	692*	A	0.9	7+	S	16:34.4	−75	20
39	4	516	K	6.9	33+	N	2:14.2	−90	36	85	28	692*	A	0.9	7+	N	16:34.1	−130	41
40	4	526	0	6.7	35+	N	4:32.1	−121	49	86	29	741	V	5.5	10+	S	3:13.3	−126	33
41	4	669	V	3.8	44+	S	22:50.7	−118	20	87	May 3	1337	0	5.7	49+	N	2:23.9	−114	31
42	4	671	V	3.4	44+	S	22:36.3	−130	21	88	3	1336	0	5.2	49+	N	2:24.0	−106	47
43	4	661	V	4.5	43+	S	23:04.5	−78	45	89	4	1547	M	3.8	68+	S	20:17.4	−86	27
44	5	667	V	5	44+	N	0:27.9	−84	40	90	15	2729	U	6.9	84−	S	3:58.7	−66	48
45	5	678	0	5.5	44+	S	0:50.5	−104	52	91	15	2734	0	5.2	84−	S	5:01.4	−75	54
46	5	677	X	4.8	44+	S	0:54.5	−102	21	92	15	X25958	V	6.8	84−	S	5:34.9	−84	51

*ZC 692 = Aldebaran

No.	Date	USNO	d	*m*	%sl	L	W.U.T.	Lo.	La.
93	May 17	3022	0	7	67–	S	9:17.6	–130	27
94	27	832	0	4.3	3+	N	2:40.5	–115	34
95	29	1158	K	5	15+	S	2:57.3	–108	47
96	31	1425	X	7	35+	N	4:08.8	–130	37
97	31	1427	0	7	36+	N	4:45.1	–128	49
98	Jun. 1	1522	0	6.8	44+	N	0:06.0	–79	22
99	1	1550	H	5.6	47+	S	6:01.1	–112	55
100	2	1644	0	4	56+	N	2:23.7	–130	37
101	3	1749	0	6	66+	N	2:49.2	–116	29
102	5	1985	0	6.9	84+	S	8:58.1	–119	41
103	18	76	0	5.9	41–	N	8:06.1	–70	45
104	20	364	0	4.3	19–	S	9:36.0	–107	31
105	21	508	V	4.1	10–	S	11:28.7	–118	20
106	22	661	V	4.5	4–	S	9:38.0	–86	36
107	22	671	V	3.4	4–	S	10:21.5	–94	25
108	22	667	V	5	4–	N	10:34.1	–97	30
109	22	682	V	6	4–	S	11:46.6	–115	37
110	22	692*	A	0.9	4–	S	13:29.6	–90	20
111	22	692*	A	0.9	4–	N	13:48.4	–130	49
112	26	1236	Z	5.1	5+	N	1:56.7	–103	26
113	27	1371	O	6.5	12+	N	2:00.6	–100	31
114	29	1609	C	4.6	30+	N	3:22.5	–119	38
115	Jul. 1	1821	O	2.8	50+	S	2:02.6	–130	47
116	3	2043	K	6.5	70+	N	2:42.9	–111	31
117	3	2047	0	6.6	70+	N	3:09.0	–113	38
118	5	2280	0	6.5	86+	S	7:47.7	–106	20
119	16	170	0	6	56–	N	6:13.4	–87	34
120	16	178	0	6.5	56–	N	7:32.6	–99	52
121	17	306	0	6.8	44–	N	7:38.8	–104	40
122	19	608	$	6	21–	N	11:42.1	–130	45
123	20	741	V	5.5	13–	N	7:30.0	–80	50
124	30	2008	V	6.6	44+	S	3:07.5	–88	37
125	Aug. 1	2223	T	3.9	63+	S	3:11.6	–98	26
126	1	2231	0	6.8	64+	N	3:42.9	–126	36
127	3	2497	X	6.5	82+	S	7:10.2	–122	30
128	14	405	V	4.3	59–	N	6:33.6	–111	27
129	16	692*	A	0.9	36–	N	5:43.9	–81	30
130	17	871	0	6.7	24–	N	9:23.3	–113	26
131	19	X11708	A	7	7–	N	9:39.6	–91	35
132	19	X11721	0	6.9	7–	N	10:01.6	–100	44
133	30	2448	K	6.3	58+	S	5:40.9	–130	40
134	Sep. 3	2981	M	5.1	90+	S	6:09.8	–124	23
135	9	249	0	4.5	89–	N	8:45.3	–116	20
136	10	X03361	0	7	82–	N	5:19.6	–120	28
137	11	491	0	6	73–	N	5:24.4	–116	46
138	11	516	K	6.9	71–	N	9:39.1	–117	20
139	11	526	0	6.7	70–	N	13:07.1	–130	47
140	12	635	K	3.6	62–	N	4:59.5	–107	51
141	12	659	O	6.6	61–	N	7:19.1	–130	49
142	12	671	V	3.4	61–	S	7:51.9	–130	22
143	12	667	V	5	61–	N	8:06.0	–130	26
144	12	672	O	6.7	61–	N	8:45.6	–130	49
145	12	692*	A	0.9	60–	S	11:36.1	–127	20
146	13	823	T	6.7	49–	N	8:59.4	–130	33
147	13	832	0	4.3	49–	N	10:11.6	–130	28
148	13	836	0	5.7	48–	N	10:58.9	–130	37
149	14	X08716	0	7	39–	N	4:23.8	–66	46
150	15	1151	0	6.8	26–	N	12:16.4	–130	24
151	Sep. 16	1262	K	6.1	17–	N	8:15.5	–96	51
152	17	1396	0	6.8	9–	N	9:45.3	–98	49
153	23	2128	0	5.8	14+	N	22:55.1	–73	44
154	24	2245	0	6.3	21+	N	23:03.8	–75	47
155	26	2399	0	4.9	31+	N	3:58.4	–130	35
156	28	2639	A	6	48+	S	0:41.9	–83	31
157	28	2642	V	7	49+	S	1:23.1	–84	51
158	29	2798	O	6.1	59+	N	1:52.0	–119	31
159	30	2935	0	7	70+	S	6:41.6	–128	20
160	Oct. 9	627	0	6.6	83–	N	10:26.2	–130	31
161	9	636	O	7	83–	N	12:23.1	–130	28
162	11	947	A	5.2	64–	N	8:59.8	–130	50
163	13	1236	Z	5.1	41–	N	8:13.9	–128	52
164	13	X12393	X	6.2	41–	N	8:14.1	–127	52
165	13	1241	A	6.5	41–	N	8:54.0	–130	47
166	15	1487	A	1.4	20–	N	9:56.6	–119	44
167	17	1728	0	6.7	5–	N	13:04.0	–128	33
168	25	2591	K	6.2	24+	S	1:31.2	–116	22
169	25	2729	U	6.9	31+	N	23:54.6	–99	41
170	26	2734	0	5.2	32+	N	0:37.6	–114	49
171	26	X25958	V	6.8	32+	N	1:19.7	–122	45
172	27	2886	0	4.9	42+	S	4:18.8	–130	27
173	27	2981	M	5.1	50+	N	22:57.1	–85	37
174	28	2993	P	6.7	50+	S	0:08.3	–95	35
175	28	2994	A	5.9	50+	S	0:08.5	–95	34
176	28	3017	0	5.2	53+	S	5:59.8	–130	48
177	30	3268	0	5.3	71+	S	3:09.3	–130	46
178	Nov. 5	667	V	5	95–	N	22:47.6	–62	47
179	7	836	0	5.7	89–	N	0:05.3	–71	52
180	7	895	U	5.9	87–	N	8:39.4	–112	20
181	11	1466	V	5.3	44–	S	11:19.0	–108	41
182	11	1487	A	1.4	41–	N	16:43.9	–128	55
183	15	1923	M	7	8–	N	14:11.8	–130	44
184	21	2666	M	4.9	9+	N	20:19.1	–65	53
185	22	2697	0	6.5	11+	S	1:35.3	–126	29
186	22	2829	0	6.7	17+	S	23:44.2	–103	40
187	24	2963	A	5.3	26+	S	3:19.1	–130	36
188	24	3071	V	6.1	32+	S	22:34.3	–86	38
189	25	3079	0	4.1	33+	S	1:00.8	–122	33
190	25	3091	0	6.7	34+	S	4:12.3	–108	20
191	27	3347	0	6.2	54+	S	3:25.7	–130	36
192	27	3355	0	6.7	55+	S	6:31.1	–130	40
193	29	49	0	6.1	73+	S	1:04.1	–103	22
194	Dec. 3	692*	A	0.9	100+	S	14:33.6	–130	43
195	5	995	B	4.1	96–	N	6:55.1	–118	20
196	7	1275	X	5.3	82–	N	5:02.6	–92	20
197	8	1420	0	6.6	71–	N	8:40.9	–130	53
198	8	1434	0	5.4	70–	N	11:34.8	–130	51
199	9	1529	0	6.6	62–	N	5:37.7	–96	36
200	11	1758	0	6.9	39–	N	8:11.1	–103	49
201	13	1978	V	6.6	21–	S	8:21.3	–63	51
202	15	2223	T	3.9	7–	S	14:25.5	–130	35
203	16	2352	M	7	3–	N	13:39.6	–109	42
204	22	3041	0	6.2	11+	S	0:03.7	–101	29
205	26	20	0	6.7	47+	S	4:13.7	–122	20
206	27	150	A	6.1	58+	S	5:55.3	–130	31
207	30	692*	A	0.9	93+	S	23:08.6	–102	20

*ZC 692 = Aldebaran

GRAZING OCCULTATION MAPS

JANUARY 1 – FEBRUARY 28

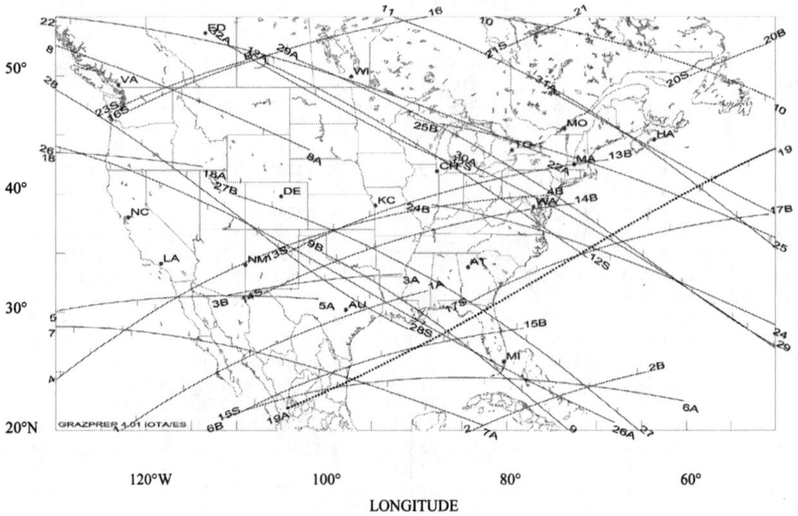

MARCH 1 – MARCH 31

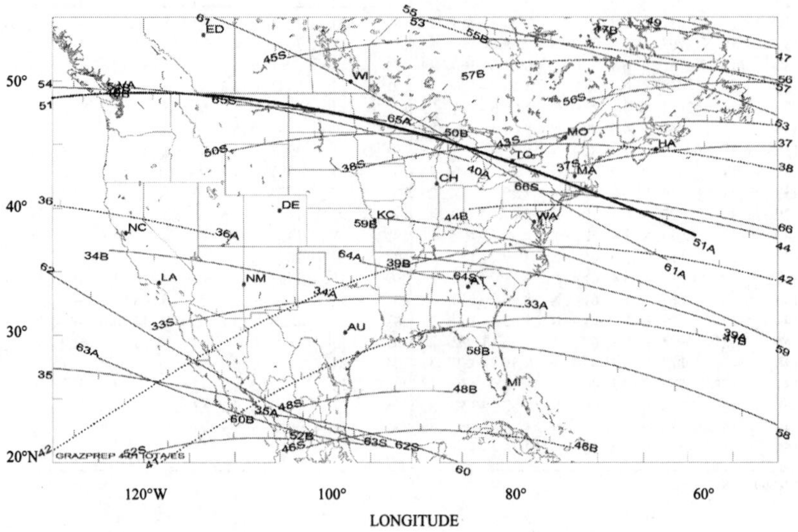

GRAZING OCCULTATION MAPS (continued)

APRIL 1 – JUNE 15

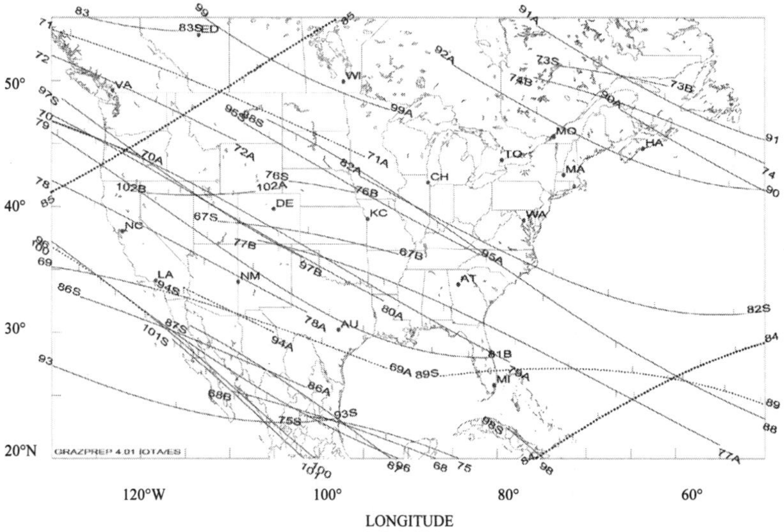

JUNE 16 – SEPTEMBER 10

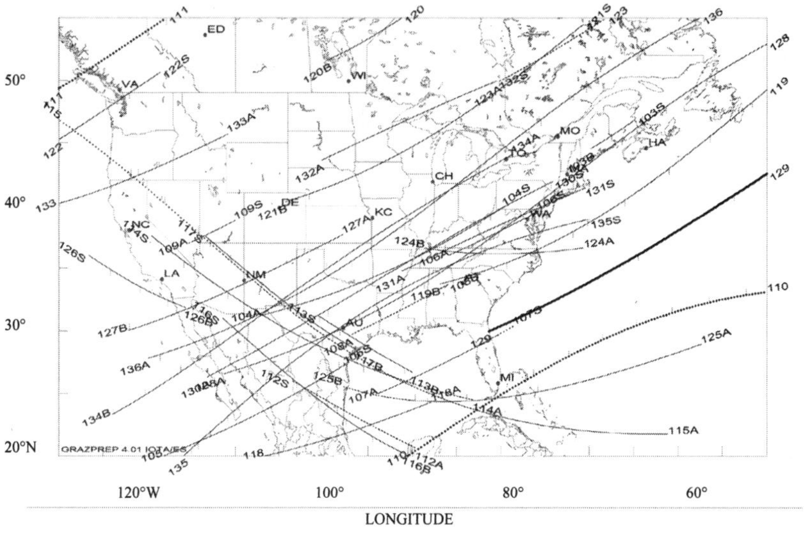

GRAZING OCCULTATION MAPS (continued)

SEPTEMBER 11 – OCTOBER 26

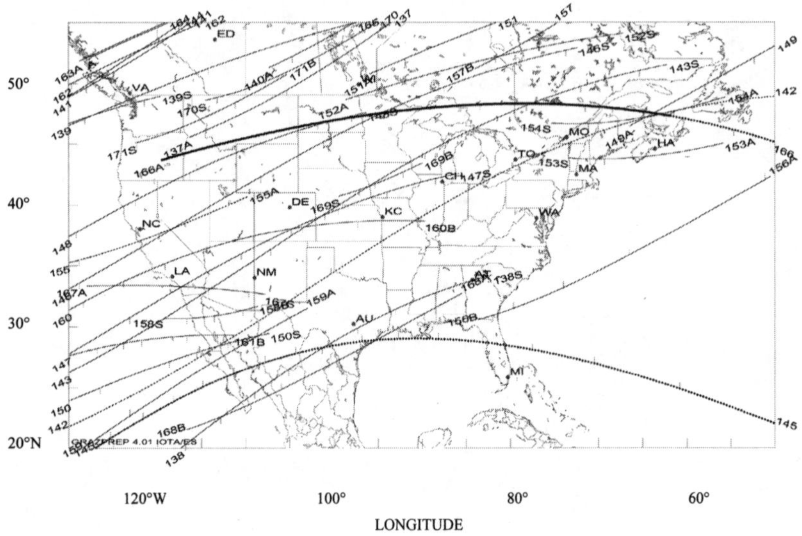

OCTOBER 27 – DECEMBER 31

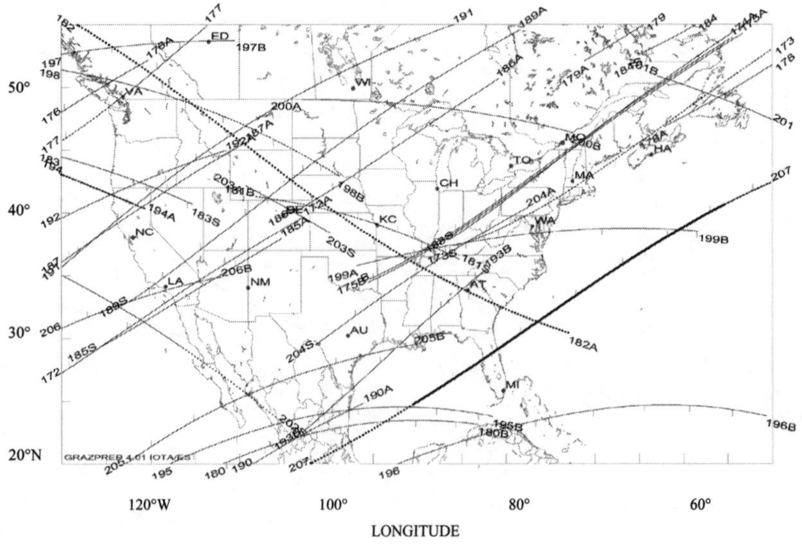

TIDES AND THE EARTH–MOON SYSTEM

BY ROY BISHOP

The tidal aspect of gravitation produces some of the most interesting phenomena in the Universe, from the structure of interacting galaxies, such as M51, to the volcanoes of Io, the fragmentation of Comet Shoemaker–Levy 9 by Jupiter in 1992, the synchronous rotation of our Moon, and the pulse of the seas on our planet. Because they occur at our feet, the tides of the oceans are often overlooked when considering the heavens; yet the pulse of the tides is the heartbeat of a greater Universe beyond Earth.

Newtonian Tides

Tides have been known for millennia, but an understanding of their origin came just over three centuries ago with the publication of Newton's *Principia* (1687). In the Newtonian context, the decrease of the force of gravity with distance causes the tides. The Moon exerts a force on Earth, and Earth responds by accelerating toward the Moon; however, the waters on the hemisphere facing the Moon, being closer to the Moon, accelerate more and fall ahead of Earth. Similarly, Earth itself accelerates more than the waters on the other hemisphere and falls ahead of those waters; the Moon is yanking Earth out from under the waters on the more distant hemisphere, leaving those waters behind. Thus two tidal bulges are produced, one on the side of Earth facing the Moon and one on the side facing away from the Moon. Because the Moon is quite far from Earth (about 60 Earth radii), the two tidal bulges are essentially equal in size.

Note that the waters directly under the Moon and the waters farthest from the Moon do not rise up because of the slightly larger and smaller, respectively, lunar gravity at these two locations; all that results from the Moon's action on the waters at these two points is a slight decrease in the pressure on the floor of the sea. The two tidal bulges form because the variation in the Moon's gravity causes the *surrounding* waters on each hemisphere to flow horizontally across Earth's surface into these regions:

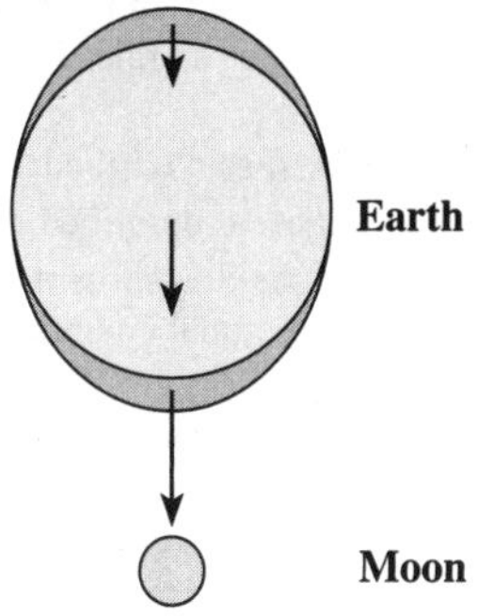

In order of decreasing length, the arrows indicate the force per unit mass (acceleration) produced by the Moon's gravity on the near side, centre, and far side of Earth. It is the resulting horizontal flow of the water across Earth's surface toward the two points nearest and farthest from the Moon that produces the two tidal bulges (indicated by heavy shading).

As Earth rotates on its axis, the orientation of the two bulges relative to the Moon remains fixed; hence the rise and fall of the oceans on Earth. The solid Earth is not perfectly rigid. It too responds to the tidal influences of Moon and Sun, resulting in an elastic *body tide* (vertical range ~0.4 m). Lesser, more-localized deformations of the solid Earth are caused indirectly by *ocean tide loading*.

Because of the Moon's orbital motion, it transits on average 50.47 min later each day. Thus on successive days, high tides recur about 50 min later; or for the many regions experiencing two high tides daily, these tides recur at intervals of 12 h 25 min.

The Sun exerts a gravitational force 180 times stronger than that exerted by the Moon on Earth; however, because the Moon is so much closer, the *variation* in the Moon's force across Earth's diameter is about 2.2 times larger than the variation in the Sun's force. As described above, it is this variation that produces tides; thus the pair of bulges raised by the Moon is considerably larger than the pair raised by the Sun. As the Moon goes through its monthly cycle of phases, the two pairs of tidal bulges get in and out of step, combining in step to produce *spring tides* (no connection with the season) when the Moon is new or full (syzygy) and out of step to produce *neap tides* when the Moon is at first or last quarter (quadrature).

Another factor having a substantial influence on tidal ranges is the elliptical shape of the Moon's orbit. The Moon is only 9% to 12% closer at perigee than at apogee; however, because the *variation* in its gravitational force varies inversely as the cube of its distance (the force itself varies inversely as the square of the distance), the Moon's tidal influence is 31% to 49% greater at perigee than at apogee. Because the Sun tidally influences the shape of the Moon's orbit, exceptionally close perigees coincide with full or new Moon, and the resulting extreme tides are known as *perigean spring tides*. If the lunar orbit were fixed in orientation, such tides would recur at half-year intervals, alternately with new and full Moon; however, the major axis of the lunar orbit rotates prograde with a period of 8.85 years, making the average interval between perigean spring tides about 23 days longer than half a year (205.9 days).

The extreme range of a spring tide, or of a perigean spring tide, occurs a day or two after the astronomical influences peak. The variation in the range of the tides at a given locality is determined both by the energy being put into the tides and by the energy being lost through friction with the seabed. As long as the input is greater than the loss, the tide range will increase even though the input may have peaked and already be decreasing. Hence the tide range is greatest not when the astronomical factors are greatest, but a day or two later when the decreasing input equals the increasing loss. At that point the energy in the tides is at a maximum.

Influences on the Tides

Five, basic, astronomical periods impact the tides. In increasing length these are: Earth's mean rotation day, the draconic, sidereal, and anomalistic months, and the sidereal year (see p. 29). The resulting periods that show up in the tides include (in ascending order):

(1) semidiurnal, 12 h 00 min (two solar-induced tidal bulges, as described above);

(2) semidiurnal, 12 h 25 min (two lunar-induced tidal bulges, as described above);

(3) diurnal, 24 h 00 min (the usual nonzero declination of the Sun shifts the pair of solar tidal bulges out of Earth's equatorial plane, resulting in a tidal component with a one-day period);

(4) diurnal, 24 h 50 min (the usual nonzero declination of the Moon shifts the pair of lunar tidal bulges out of Earth's equatorial plane, resulting in a tidal component with a one-day period; that is the dominant tide in some areas, such as parts of the southern coast of Canada's Gulf of St. Lawrence);

(5) semimonthly, 13.66 days (variation in the Moon's declination);

(6) semimonthly, 14.77 days (spring–neap cycle, described above);

(7) monthly, 27.55 days (perigee–apogee cycle, described above);

(8) semiannual, 182.63 days (variation in the Sun's declination);

(9) semiannual, 205.9 days (perigean spring cycle, described above);

(10) annual, 365.26 days (perihelion–aphelion cycle);

(11) 4.43 years (perigean-spring tides near an equinox recur at half the prograde precession period of the major axis of the lunar orbit); and

(12) 18.61 years (retrograde precession of the nodes of the lunar orbit).

In addition to astronomical factors, the tides on Earth are strongly influenced by the sizes, boundaries, and depths of ocean basins and inlets and by Earth's rotation, winds, and barometric pressure fluctuations. Using Newton's gravitation and laws of motion, the French physicist Pierre-Simon Laplace (1749–1827) developed the dynamical theory of the tides on the rotating Earth (*Mécanique Céleste*, 1799), but because of the complexity of the tides the full application of his theory was not possible until the advent of the digital computer in the last third of the 20th century.

Tides typically have ranges (vertical high to low) of a metre or two, but there are regions in the oceans where the various influences conspire to produce virtually no tides at all (called amphidromic points) and others where the tides are greatly amplified. Among the latter regions are the Sea of Okhotsk, the Gulf of Alaska, the northwest coast of Australia, the English Channel, and in Canada, Ungava Bay in northern Québec, and the Bay of Fundy between New Brunswick and Nova Scotia. The tidal ranges in these regions are of the order of 10 m.

Fundy Tides

Only two localities on Earth sometimes have a vertical tide range exceeding 16 m (52 ft.), and both are in Canada: Minas Basin, the eastern extremity of the Bay of Fundy in Nova Scotia, and Leaf Basin, a remote inlet on the southwestern side of Ungava Bay in northern Québec. The current best data give Minas Basin a slight edge; however, several years of tide gauge data continuing through a peak in the 18.61-year tide cycle are needed to determine which site, if either (to the precision that measurements can be made), has the greater tide range.

The primary cause of the immense tides of Fundy is a resonance of the Bay of Fundy/Gulf of Maine system. The system is effectively bounded at its outer end by the edge of the continental shelf with its approximately 40:1 increase in depth. The system has a natural period of approximately 13 hours, a Q-value* of about 5, and is driven near resonance, not directly by the Moon, but by the dominant semidiurnal tides of the Atlantic Ocean. Like a father pushing his daughter on a swing, the gentle Atlantic tidal pulse pushes the waters of the Bay of Fundy/Gulf of Maine basin at nearly the optimum frequency to cause a large oscillation. The seventh Astronomer Royal, Sir G.B. Airy (1801–1892), first developed the theory of the behaviour of tides in restricted arms of the ocean such as the Fundy system.

Fundy tides are unique in that they respond more to the perigee–apogee influence than they do to the spring–neap influence. That is because the lunar tidal period (12.42 hours) is closer to the system's resonant period than is the solar tidal period (12.00 hours). Although the variation in the Moon's distance is not obvious when viewing the Moon directly, near the head of the Bay of Fundy the 3-m to 6-m *increase* in the vertical tidal range makes it obvious when the Moon is near perigee, clear skies or cloudy!

The most dramatic view of the vertical range of Fundy tides is at the Minas Basin Pulp & Power Company wharf in the town of Hantsport, Nova Scotia. That site is practically unknown and, unfortunately, it is not open to the public.

Perhaps the most awesome display of the tides on our planet occurs at Cape Split, Nova Scotia, on the southern side of the entrance to Minas Basin. (Cape Split may be reached by a pleasant two-hour walk along a popular hiking trail from the village of Scots Bay.) Here, at the time of the midpoint of an incoming tide, for a considerable distance the forest on the towering cliffs is filled with a hollow roar produced by

* The Q-value, or quality-value, of an oscillator indicates its efficiency. A large Q means low energy loss per cycle and a well-defined resonant frequency. A Q of 5 is relatively small, indicative of considerable damping in the Fundy system, yet it is large enough to make these tides among the highest on Earth.

the turbulence of the waters surging over the submarine ridges below. The currents exceed 8 knots (4 m/s), and the flow in the deep, 5-km-wide channel on the north side of Cape Split equals the combined flow of all the streams and rivers of Earth (approximately 1 million tonnes per second, or 4 cubic kilometres per hour). Three hours later the spectacle pauses and then begins flowing in the opposite direction.

The highest of the high tides in the Bay of Fundy occur when a perigean spring high tide coincides with a low-barometric-pressure storm system sweeping northward across New Brunswick, accompanied by hurricane-force southerly winds over the Gulf of Maine and the Bay of Fundy. The close Moon, the in-phase solar tide, the reduced air pressure above the water, and the wind drag pushing more water into the Bay of Fundy (the last two effects are called a storm surge) all contribute to an especially high tide. An additional favourable influence is if all this occurs near an equinox, for then the axis of the tidal bulges of the spring tide is at a right angle to Earth's rotation axis, optimizing the semidiurnal tidal range at all latitudes (see item (11), above). This right-angle-axes enhancement of the tides is strengthened in those years when the declination range of the Moon (±18° to ±29°) is near a minimum, a situation that recurs with the 18.61-year period of the retrograde motion of the nodes of its orbit relative to the equinoxes. (The declination range was at its ±18° minimum in 1959, 1978, 1997, and 2015, and will be again in 2034 and 2052. See p. 95 for the shift in the longitude of the ascending node of the Moon's orbit during 2017.) Furthermore, since perihelion occurs in January, the highest tides of all tend to occur just prior to the March equinox or after the September equinox. The infamous Bay of Fundy "Saxby gale" of 1869 Oct. 5 was a time when all seven of these factors approximately coincided (perigee, spring tide, low pressure, south wind, equinox, minimum declination range, and perihelion enhancement). Weather is unpredictable. Thus, so too is the next major tidal flood in the Bay of Fundy.

Paradoxically, the large tides of Fundy protect its shores from flooding associated with most storm surges, since the normal variation in its high tide levels is already several metres. Only those rare storm surges that happen to coincide with a perigean spring high tide will be a problem. In contrast, shorelines with small tides are much more susceptible to storm surges.

Sea level is slowly increasing in the Bay of Fundy region. That is bringing the resonant period of the Fundy/Gulf of Maine system closer to the lunar tidal period which, in turn, is causing Fundy tides to gradually become even larger (by a few centimetres per decade).

Tidal Friction

Tidal friction, which occurs primarily in shallow seas around the margins of the oceans, transforms Earth's rotational kinetic energy into heat at a rate of about 3.7 TW, comparable to humankind's total rate of energy use. Approximately 1% of this energy transformation occurs in the Bay of Fundy, and, since 1984, a tiny portion of this (20 MW peak) is being turned into commercial electric power at the Annapolis Basin tidal power plant in Nova Scotia. Two larger tidal power plants exist: the Rance in France (240 MW) and the Sihwa Lake in South Korea (254 MW peak), and a third one is nearing completion at Incheon Bay, South Korea (1320 MW).

The aforementioned tidal power plants use turbines located in dams (also called barrages). At a few sites, including the Bay of Fundy, studies presently are underway for using isolated turbines located in tidal currents—effectively underwater windmills. The problem with this approach is that the power available in currents of 8 knots or less is dilute. To generate significant electrical power (100 MW or more), large turbine cross-sections are required, with attendant high capital and maintenance costs.

Tidal friction also transfers angular momentum from Earth to the Moon, lengthening the day and increasing the size of the orbit of the Moon. The day is lengthening by about 1 s every 40 000 years—imperceptible on a human time scale but of profound significance to Earth's rotation over a few billion years. (For example, 900 million years ago, when Earth was already 80% of its present age, there were about 480 18-hour days in a year.) The Moon is receding about 3.8 cm per year, with the result that about one billion years from now total solar eclipses will cease. Presently we are well into the transitional phase: Annular eclipses already outnumber total solar eclipses.

General Relativity and Tides

Einstein's theory of gravitation, general relativity, superseded Newton's theory a century ago, yet descriptions of the tides almost invariably ignore Einstein (as has this article to this point). There are three reasons for using the older, wrong theory: (1) Newton's theory describes the gentle tides on Earth to high accuracy; (2) the mathematics involved is much simpler than that of general relativity; (3) the Newtonian description of the tides is compatible with cultivated common sense. Because of #3, Newton's concepts regarding motion and gravitation form the essential foundation for anyone attempting to understand the tides. One must climb up on Newton's towering shoulders before it is possible to focus clearly on Einstein.

As mentioned in the section ORBITAL MOTION (see p. 27), Newton's Euclidean universe with its force of gravity never did exist. Although Newton's ideas are more than adequate for describing the tides on Earth, for some purposes, such as the Global Positioning System (GPS), Newton's concepts of space, time, and gravitation are inadequate. We inhabit an Einsteinian universe, a universe in which gravitation is a manifestation of the structure of spacetime, the four-dimensional stage of our existence in which space and time are interwoven. The geometry of spacetime is curved by the mass–energy of matter, and the curvature instructs matter how to move. That instruction has an astounding grip. If spacetime were not curved, a mind-boggling 300-km diameter steel cable, stressed to its breaking point, would be required to connect Earth and Moon in order to maintain their mutual orbit.

The Moon's mass alters the structure of spacetime at its location, and this distortion propagates outward, becoming more dilute with the volume encompassed according to the inverse cube of the distance. At Earth, the distortion results in the waters of the oceans following slightly different paths through spacetime than does the rigid planet beneath, producing the characteristic egglike shape of the tidal effect. The tidal heartbeat is that of the very fabric of spacetime. The tides at our feet carry a profound message.

References

For more information, see the superb introduction *The Tides* by E.P. Clancy, Anchor Books, Doubleday and Co., 1969 (now, unfortunately, out of print). For a detailed account of the evolution of our understanding of the tides see *Tides, A Scientific History*, by D.E. Cartwright, Cambridge University Press, 1999. An excellent book covering tides, storm surges, tsunamis, and sea level in general is *Sea-Level Science* by D. Pugh and P. Woodworth, Cambridge University Press, 2014. (Note, however, that none of these four authors mentions general relativity.) For a popular account of general relativity, see *A Journey into Gravity and Spacetime*, by J.A. Wheeler, Scientific American Library, 1990. The major astronomical factors influencing the tides (the phases, perigees, and apogees of the Moon) are tabulated in THE SKY MONTH BY MONTH section (see p. 94) of this Handbook. For information on tides in Canadian waters see www.tides.gc.ca/eng/data/predictions/2017. For tide predictions at many sites world-wide, see tbone.biol.sc.edu/tide/tideshow.cgi.

THE SUN

EPHEMERIS FOR THE SUN

BY PAT KELLY

Sundial Correction

The **Greenwich Transit** time in the table opposite may be used to calculate the sundial correction at the observer's position. For example, to find the correction at Halifax on 2017 Apr. 5, determine the following: At Greenwich the Sun transits at 12:03:21 on Apr. 3 and at 12:02:12 on Apr. 7. Thus, to the nearest min, on Apr. 5 at both Greenwich and Halifax, the Sun will transit at 12:03 local mean solar time (LMT), or 12:17 Atlantic Standard Time (AST) since Halifax has a longitude correction of +14 min (see the 3rd paragraph on p. 205). Thus a 3-min correction must be added to the reading of a simple sundial to obtain LMT (compare with the horizontal position of the light dot marking Apr. 5 on the analemma, on the bottom right of the facing page), an additional 14 min must be added to obtain AST, and a further 1 hour for Atlantic Daylight Time (ADT). Thus solar noon will occur at 1:17 p.m. ADT.

Even with these corrections, a sundial may still read incorrectly. For the horizontal sundial, the *gnomon* (vertical part) must be aligned to true north with the *dial* (horizontal part) level. The angle of the gnoman and the hour angles on the dial mush be appropriate for the latitude. Beware of "consumer" sundials with poorly marked hour angles and crooked styles. (The *style* is the edge of the gnomon that casts the shadow.) Thick gnomons should taper to an edge, otherwise they have two styles, neither casting a shadow in the right place. The 6 a.m. and 6 p.m. hour angles should form a straight line perpendicular to the gnomon, meeting where the style meets the dial.

Orientation of the Sun

The table on the next page gives three angles that specify the orientation of the Sun.

P is the position angle of the axis of rotation, measured eastward in the observer's sky from the north point on the disk (i.e. counterclockwise). Note that P varies between +26° (solar north pole tilted eastward) and −26° (tilted westward) during the year. This tilt is associated mainly with the inclination of the ecliptic in the observer's sky, with a smaller contribution from the Sun's 7.2° inclination to the ecliptic (the longitude of the ascending node of the solar equator on the ecliptic is 76°).

$\boldsymbol{B_0}$ is the heliographic latitude of the centre of the disk, and is the result of the Sun's 7.2° inclination to the ecliptic. Note that positive values of B_0 correspond to the solar equator passing south of the centre of the disk, with the solar north pole being tipped toward the observer.

$\boldsymbol{L_0}$ is the heliographic longitude of the centre of the disk measured from Carrington's solar prime meridian in the direction of rotation. L_0 decreases about 13° per day. The dates during the year when L_0 = 0° are given in the table below. The rotation period of the Sun depends upon heliographic latitude. The synodic and sidereal periods of rotation at the solar equator are 27.2753 days and 25.38 days, respectively.

Commencement (UT) of Numbered Synodic Solar Rotations

No.*	Commences	No.	Commences	No.	Commences	No.	Commences
2185	'16 Dec. 14.05	2189	Apr. 2.36	2193	Jul. 20.25	2197	Nov. 6.30
2186	'17 Jan. 10.38	2190	Apr. 29.63	2194	Aug. 16.47	2198	Dec. 3.61
2187	Feb. 6.72	2191	May 26.85	2195	Sep. 12.73	2199	'17 Dec. 30.94
2188	Mar. 6.06	2192	Jun. 23.05	2196	Oct. 10.00	2220	'18 Jan. 27.27

*Based on R.C. Carrington's Greenwich photoheliocentric series in which rotation No. 1 commenced 1853 Nov. 9.

EPHEMERIS FOR THE SUN, 2017

Date 0h UT	Apparent RA (2017) h m	Apparent Dec ° ′	Greenwich Transit UT	Orientation *P*	Orientation B_0	Orientation L_0
Jan. 1	18 46.8	−23 00	12:03:26	2.0	−3.0	123.5
5	19 04.4	−22 37	12:05:17	0.0	−3.5	70.9
9	19 21.9	−22 06	12:07:00	−1.9	−3.9	18.2
13	19 39.2	−21 29	12:08:35	−3.8	−4.4	325.5
17	19 56.4	−20 45	12:09:59	−5.7	−4.8	272.8
21	20 13.4	−19 54	12:11:13	−7.5	−5.1	220.2
25	20 30.2	−18 58	12:12:14	−9.9	−5.5	167.5
29	20 46.8	−17 56	12:13:03	−11.0	−5.8	114.8
Feb. 2	21 03.2	−16 49	12:13:39	−12.6	−6.1	62.2
6	21 19.3	−15 37	12:14:02	−14.2	−6.4	9.5
10	21 35.3	−14 21	12:14:12	−15.7	−6.6	316.8
14	21 51.0	−13 02	12:14:09	−17.1	−6.8	264.2
18	22 06.5	−11 38	12:13:54	−18.4	−7.0	211.5
22	22 21.9	−10 12	12:13:29	−19.6	−7.1	158.8
26	22 37.0	−8 44	12:12:54	−20.8	−7.2	106.1
Mar. 2	22 52.1	−7 12	12:12:11	−21.8	−7.2	53.4
6	23 07.0	−5 41	12:11:19	−22.7	−7.3	0.8
10	23 21.8	−4 07	12:10:20	−23.6	−7.2	308.0
14	23 36.5	−2 33	12:09:16	−24.3	−7.2	255.3
18	23 51.1	−0 58	12:08:07	−24.9	−7.1	202.6
22	0 05.7	+0 37	12:06:56	−25.4	−7.0	149.9
26	0 20.3	+2 12	12:05:44	−25.8	−6.8	97.1
30	0 34.8	+3 45	12:04:32	−26.0	−6.6	44.4
Apr. 3	0 49.4	+5 18	12:03:21	−26.2	−6.4	351.6
7	1 04.0	+6 49	12:02:12	−26.3	−6.2	298.8
11	1 18.7	+8 18	12:01:06	−26.2	−5.9	246.0
15	1 33.5	+9 45	12:00:05	−26.0	−5.6	193.2
19	1 48.3	+11 10	11:59:10	−25.7	−5.3	140.4
23	2 03.3	+12 31	11:58:21	−25.3	−4.9	87.6
27	2 18.4	+13 49	11:57:40	−24.8	−4.6	34.7
May 1	2 33.6	+15 04	11:57:07	−24.1	−4.2	341.9
5	2 48.9	+16 15	11:56:42	−23.3	−3.8	289.0
9	3 04.4	+17 21	11:56:26	−22.4	−3.3	236.1
13	3 20.1	+18 22	11:56:19	−21.5	−2.9	183.2
17	3 35.9	+19 19	11:56:22	−20.4	−2.4	130.3
21	3 51.9	+20 11	11:56:33	−19.2	−2.0	77.4
25	4 08.0	+20 56	11:56:53	−17.9	−1.5	24.5
29	4 24.2	+21 37	11:57:21	−16.5	−1.0	331.6
Jun. 2	4 40.6	+22 11	11:57:56	−15.0	−0.5	278.6
6	4 57.0	+22 39	11:58:37	−13.4	−0.1	225.7
10	5 13.5	+23 00	11:59:22	−11.8	0.4	172.7
14	5 30.1	+23 15	12:00:11	−10.2	0.9	119.8
18	5 46.8	+23 24	12:01:03	−8.4	1.4	66.8
22	6 03.4	+23 26	12:01:55	−6.7	1.8	13.9
26	6 20.0	+23 21	12:02:47	−4.9	2.3	321.0
30	6 36.6	+23 10	12:03:36	−3.1	2.8	268.0
Jul. 4	6 53.2	+22 52	12:04:22	−1.3	3.2	215.1
8	7 09.6	+22 28	12:05:02	0.6	3.6	162.1
12	7 25.9	+21 58	12:05:35	2.3	4.0	109.2
16	7 42.1	+21 22	12:06:02	4.1	4.4	56.3
20	7 58.2	+20 40	12:06:20	5.9	4.8	3.3
24	8 14.1	+19 52	12:06:30	7.6	5.2	310.4
28	8 29.9	+18 59	12:06:30	9.2	5.5	257.5
Aug. 1	8 45.5	+18 01	12:06:21	10.9	5.8	204.6
5	9 01.0	+16 58	12:06:01	12.4	6.1	151.7
9	9 16.3	+15 51	12:05:32	13.9	6.3	98.8
13	9 31.4	+14 40	12:04:54	15.3	6.5	45.9
17	9 46.4	+13 25	12:04:07	16.7	6.7	353.0
21	10 01.2	+12 07	12:03:12	18.0	6.9	300.2
25	10 16.0	+10 46	12:02:10	19.2	7.0	247.3
29	10 30.6	+9 22	12:01:01	20.3	7.1	194.5
Sep. 2	10 45.1	+7 55	11:59:46	21.3	7.2	141.6
6	10 59.6	+6 27	11:58:26	22.3	7.2	88.8
10	11 13.9	+4 57	11:57:04	23.1	7.2	36.0
14	11 28.3	+3 25	11:55:39	23.9	7.2	343.2
18	11 42.6	+1 53	11:54:13	24.5	7.2	290.4
22	11 57.0	+0 20	11:52:48	25.1	7.1	237.6
26	12 11.4	−1 14	11:51:25	25.6	6.9	184.8
30	12 25.8	−2 47	11:50:04	25.9	6.8	132.0
Oct. 4	12 40.3	−4 20	11:48:48	26.1	6.6	79.2
8	12 54.9	−5 52	11:47:37	26.2	6.3	26.4
12	13 09.6	−7 23	11:46:32	26.2	6.1	333.6
16	13 24.4	−8 52	11:45:37	26.1	5.8	280.9
20	13 39.4	−10 20	11:44:50	25.9	5.5	228.1
24	13 54.6	−11 44	11:44:14	25.6	5.1	175.4
28	14 09.9	−13 06	11:43:49	25.1	4.8	122.6
Nov. 1	14 25.5	−14 25	11:43:36	24.5	4.4	69.9
5	14 41.2	−15 40	11:43:35	23.7	4.0	17.1
9	14 57.2	−16 51	11:43:47	22.9	3.5	324.4
13	15 13.4	−17 57	11:44:14	21.9	3.1	271.6
17	15 29.9	−18 58	11:44:54	20.8	2.6	218.9
21	15 46.5	−19 54	11:45:47	19.6	2.1	166.2
25	16 03.4	−20 44	11:46:54	18.2	1.6	113.5
29	16 20.5	−21 28	11:48:12	16.8	1.1	60.8
Dec. 3	16 37.7	−22 05	11:49:40	15.2	0.6	8.0
7	16 55.1	−22 36	11:51:19	13.6	0.1	315.3
11	17 12.7	−22 59	11:53:05	11.9	−0.4	262.6
15	17 30.3	−23 16	11:54:58	10.1	−0.9	209.9
19	17 48.1	−23 24	11:56:56	8.3	−1.4	157.2
23	18 05.8	−23 26	11:58:55	6.4	−1.9	104.5
27	18 23.6	−23 19	12:00:54	4.5	−2.4	51.8
31	18 41.3	−23 06	12:02:51	2.6	−2.9	359.2

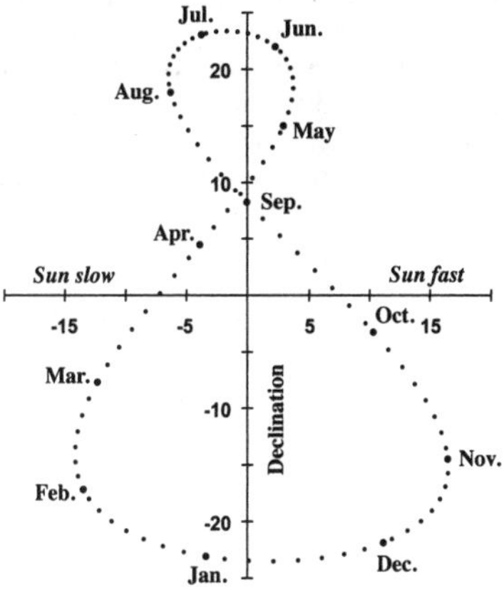

The bowling-pin-shaped ***analemma*** *depicts the drift of apparent solar time or sundial time relative to LMT (horizontal axis) and the changing declination of the Sun (vertical axis) during 2017. For points to the left of the vertical axis ("Sun slow") the Sun transits after 12:00 LMT. To the right ("Sun fast"), the Sun transits before 12:00 LMT. For each month, a heavy dot marks day 1 with small dots for days 5, 9, 13, 17, 21, 25, and 29.* *See p. 40 for further details.*

SOLAR OBSERVING

BY KIM HAY

The Sun, our closest star, is a wonderful Solar System object to observe with any type of telescope, if used **SAFELY**. Never look directly at the Sun, and always use a **full-aperture solar filter**. The solar filters that screw into the base of an eyepiece should be **thrown out** and **never used**. The telescope objective concentrates sunlight on such an eyepiece filter, making it very hot, leading to possible breakage, with a high risk of vision loss. The only safe filter is the kind that covers the full aperture of the telescope, at the front, allowing only 1/100 000th of the sunlight through the telescope, thus lowering the heating effect and allowing you to view the Sun safely. Ensure that the filter material is specifically certified as suitable for solar observing.

The preferred solar filters are made of Thousand Oaks glass or Baader film. The Thousand Oaks glass gives the Sun a golden-orange colour. The Baader film gives the Sun a natural, white look, which can provide good contrast if there is any plage on the Sun (see below). Other options include lightweight Mylar film (which gives a blue-white tint) and eyepiece projection. Projecting the image from the eyepiece onto white card-stock paper or a wall produces an image that can be safely shared with others.

For safety, the finder must be kept covered. Since your telescope and finder are aligned, look at the shadow of the telescope on the ground and move the telescope until you have the smallest shadow on the ground. The Sun should be in the eyepiece, or close to it. Alternatively, make a small filter for your finder, if you want to use it.

For the amateur, there are alternatives for observing the Sun in various wavelength bands—the simplest method involves a wide spectrum of sunlight, using the solar filters described above. For the enthusiast, narrowband filters, such as the hydrogen-alpha (Hα) red filter (656.3 nm) or the calcium K-line (CaK) violet filter (393.4 nm), can be fitted to existing telescopes (but they also need a broadband pre-filter). Recently, dedicated solar telescopes with built-in narrowband filters have become affordable. An Hα filter shows solar prominences at the solar limb and possibly granulation on the disk. The CaK filter (especially in photographs) enhances granularity and flares.

A Herschel wedge (a type of prism used for white-light observing and photography) can be used, but **with caution**. Only 5% of the light is reflected to the eyepiece. The remaining 95% that is directed out the end of the diagonal is very intense and can burn. Herschel wedges should only be used with refractors or a telescope with an aperture stop to avoid the buildup of heat, which could damage internal components. The cover should only be taken off after the telescope has been set up. You will also need a neutral-density filter (optical density 3.0–4.0, 0.01%–0.001% transmittance). For enhanced viewing comfort, a filter (either green or polarizing) may help, depending on the sky conditions. **A Herschel wedge should only be used by an experienced observer.**

The Sun is best observed at high angular altitude, minimizing the optical effects of the unstable lower 100 m of atmosphere. Try to observe when the Sun is at least 25° above the horizon. Keep in mind that daytime atmospheric seeing conditions are usually very poor, so even a small telescope can be used without loss of detail. Another observing tip is to use a dark hood to cover your head and the eyepiece to block stray light, improving views of fine details.

Observing the morphology of prominences, filaments, flares, sunspots, and other solar phenomena is a great way to witness the dynamics of the Sun. These phenomena result from the strong magnetism within the Sun, which erupts to the surface. An active area can start with plage (white area) and faculae, turn into a pore, and then blossom into a small dark spot. As a pore grows into a sunspot (umbra), a grey area (penumbra) surrounds the sunspot. The umbra is cooler than the surrounding penumbra. Prominences are solar plasma ejections, some of which fall back to the Sun in the form of teardrops or loops; against the Sun's disk, prominences appear as

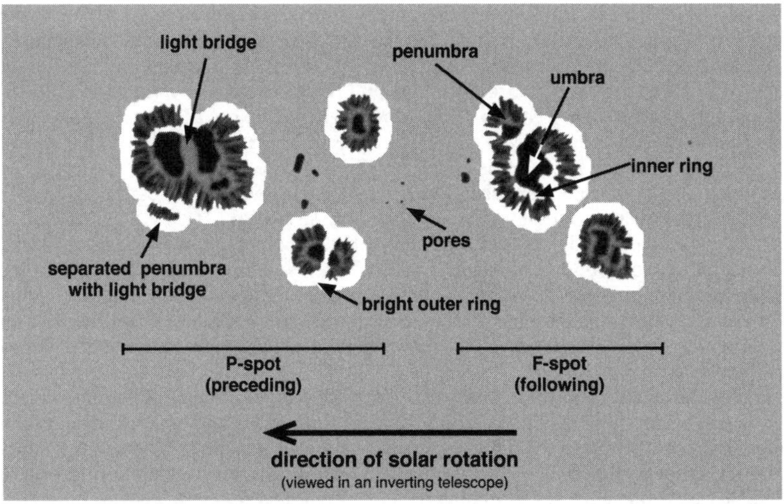

Nomenclature of phenomena related to sunspots. As the morphology of a sunspot changes, growing into a larger group, it eventually starts to dissipate and show trailing sunspots. Light bridges are formed early and stay with a sunspot over its lifetime. The formation of a light bridge is a slow process taking several days. The light-bridge material generally appears first on the outside of the umbra-penumbra boundary then extends across the umbra. When the light bridge is seen, it can signify the division or final dissolution of the spot. Light bridges have three general features: classic light bridges, islands, and streamers. (Image used with permission from the Solar Astronomy Handbook *and adapted for publication.)*

dark filaments. In a turbulence-free atmosphere, look for white-light flares, which are flash-points produced from sudden discharges of energy. Flares can last from a few moments to several hours, but they are generally measured in minutes. There are also limb flares, flare kernels/hot cores, two-ribbon/two-strand flares, Hyder/impact flares, homologous flares, and Moreton waves, which are shock waves emanating from a white-light flare. An intense solar flare can eject charged particles, which may reach Earth, possibly exciting the upper atmosphere to create aurorae.

Counting sunspots and groups is another interesting activity. For consistency, observing should be done at the same time each day. Start at the limb of the Sun, because this is where you will notice plage and faculae. Then sweep across the disk in a grid pattern to look for disturbances or sunspots. These can be in either hemisphere and at any latitude, depending on the progression of the sunspot cycle. The relative sunspot number (also Wolf number or Zurich number) is $R = 10g + s$, where g is the number of groups (including groups of one) and s is the number of individual spots (including those in groups). Individuals may submit their observations to the Solar Section of the American Association of Variable Star Observers (AAVSO, see below), which compiles monthly averages from all observers. To help locate the latitude and longitude of a sunspot, and to find instructions and a template (called the Stonyhurst disk) to place over your sketch or image, see the weblinks below. See also the EPHEMERIS FOR THE SUN on p. 187, which lists the orientation of the Sun (P, B_0, and L_0) in four-day increments. Solar activity can be mapped as an exercise, using disk templates (Stonyhurst, Porter, or grid) and solar orientation elements (see BAA Solar Section and Atmospheric Optics websites, below).

The Sun takes 25 to 29 days to make a full rotation, with an average of 27 days. The Carrington rotation number, invented by Richard Carrington, counts the number of rotations of the Sun since 1895 Nov. 3. The Solar Section of the Association of Lunar & Planetary Observers (ALPO) uses Carrington rotation numbers for the study and archiving of solar morphology and prominence activity. For an updated Carrington list, visit www.alpo-astronomy.org/solarblog. ALPO accepts sketches and photographs (at all wavelengths) on the Sun Forms that are available on the solar blog webpage All submissions are stored on the online Solar Gallery. (For instruction on astronomical sketching see ASTRONOMICAL SKETCHING, p. 88; for a primer on astrophotography, see DIGITAL ASTROPHOTOGRAPHY, p. 91.)

A wide range of digital cameras and webcams, combined with various filters, can produce phenomenal images of the Sun. Numerous computer programs allow the combination of multiple images to create an enhanced image or video. Libraries, online chat rooms, and email lists provide a wealth of information on solar photography. The best way to learn is to read and ask questions of experienced solar imagers.

A solar cycle takes 9–14 years (11 years on average) to complete, and we are now on the downward side of Solar Cycle 24. Sunspot counts were waning in the first half of 2016 with 10 days reported having no sunspots. Though the spots are not evident, the Sun is still very active, and is in a very unstable time where activity can spring up at any moment.

Solar Cycle 24 has been very weak with two mini-peaks; perhaps the weakest (see science.nasa.gov/science-news/science-at-nasa/2014/10jun_solarminimax). We will have a few years of unpredictable solar activity, which then will plateau for a few years before starting Solar Cycle 25.

If you do not have the proper equipment to observe the Sun, you can always visit the *Solar and Heliospheric Observatory* (SOHO) Internet site (see below) and see daily images of the Sun. The following Handbook sections contain related information: FILTERS (p. 64), SOLAR ACTIVITY (p. 189), and VIEWING A SOLAR ECLIPSE—A WARNING (p. 145).

References

ALPO Solar Astronomy Handbook, ALPO Solar Section

Beck, R., Hilbrecht, H., Reinsch, K., and Völker, P., *Solar Astronomy Handbook*, Willmann–Bell, Inc., Richmond, Virginia, 1995.

Bray, R.J. and Loughhead, R.E., *Sunspots*, Dover Publications, 1964.

Broxton, T., *Solar Observer's Handbook*, Authorhouse, 2009.

Jenkins, J.L., *The Sun and How to Observe It*, Springer, 2009.

Rix E., Hay, K., Russell, S., and Handy, R., *Solar Sketching: A Comprehensive Guide to Drawing the Sun*, Springer, 2015.

Websites for Solar Observing and Astrophysics

www.aavso.org/solar (AAVSO)
www.alpo-astronomy.org/solar (ALPO)
www.alpineastro.com/Solar_Observation/Solar_Observation.htm (Alpine Astronomical)
www.atoptics.co.uk/tiltsun.htm (Atmospheric Optics Tilting Sun)
www.oneminuteastronomer.com/999/choose-solar-filter (choosing solar filters)
www.petermeadows.com/html/stonyhurst.html (Stonyhurst disks and instructions)
www.britastro.org/section_front/21 (BAA: Stonyhurst, Porter, and Grid disks)
sdo.gsfc.nasa.gov (NASA *Solar Dynamics Observatory*)
sohowww.nascom.nasa.gov (*Solar and Heliospheric Observatory*)
www.stce.be (STCE: Solar-Terrestrial Centre of Excellence—Belgium)
www.swpc.noaa.gov (NOAA Space Weather Prediction Center)
radiojove.gsfc.nasa.gov (NASA Solar and Planetary Radio Astronomy for Schools)
www.solarham.net (solar page by amateur radio station VE3EN)
www.spaceweatherwoman.com (Dr. Tamitha Skov—Heliosphere Physicist)

SOLAR ACTIVITY
BY KEN TAPPING

Cycle 24 is now definitely in decline, as is clearly visible in the plot. Unless there is a surge in activity, which is highly unlikely this late in the cycle, it will be lowest since the beginning of the F10.7 record. However, these is more to Cycle 24 than is evident in the plot. Various indices of solar activity, such as sunspot number and F10.7, which have traditionally marched in lock-step, showed during late Cycle 23 a excess of activity in the corona compared with the level at the photosphere. Since the Maunder and Dalton Minima seemed to show this, in a more extreme form, we are monitoring Cycle 24 very carefully.

Solar activity is fundamentally a magnetic phenomenon. Deep below the photosphere, differential rotation and convection cause the solar material to move in a complex manner. The density of this material is high enough for its movement to drag the magnetic fields along with it. This generates electric currents, which in turn produce magnetic fields. The result is a complex system of subphotospheric "magnetic flux ropes." The penetration of sections of these flux ropes through the photosphere and into the chromosphere and corona gives rise to the many observed forms of solar activity. Above the photosphere the situation is strikingly different: the density is much lower, and the magnetic fields trap and confine the ionized gas of the solar atmosphere, supporting loops and filaments, and forming the diverse menagerie of photospheric, chromospheric, and coronal structures with which we are familiar, such as sunspots, active regions, complexes of activity, and systems of loops. Changing emissions in the X-ray and ultraviolet wavelengths, and at radio wavelengths, are due to the changing amount of trapped plasma and the strengths of the magnetic fields containing them. The Sun's total energy output is also affected by magnetic activity, fortunately only slightly.

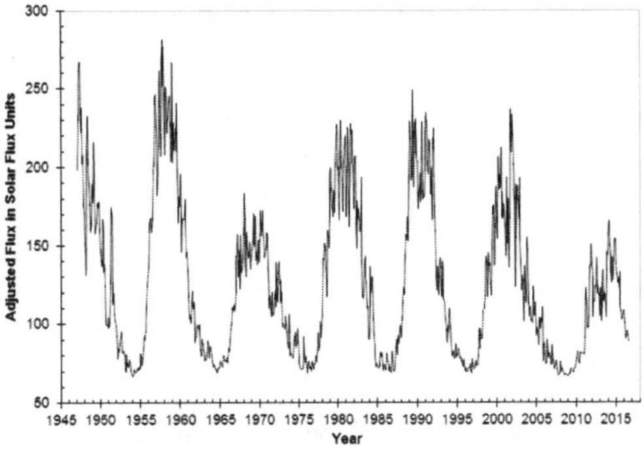

The 10.7-cm solar radio flux, averaged monthly (see p. 193). This index, which originates in the low solar corona overlying active regions, is a more global index of magnetic activity than sunspot number. The 10–13 year solar activity cycle is clearly visible. The shorter-term spikes are shorter episodes of activity as active regions and clusters of regions form, evolve, and decay. There is some level of activity even during solar minima.

The organization of the subphotospheric magnetic fields gives rise to a consistent pattern in the magnetic configuration of active regions. Each region is magnetically bipolar, with the bipoles arranged east–west on the disk. All bipoles lying in the same hemisphere are arranged with the same magnetic polarity leading (facing in the direction in which the region appears to move as it is carried across the disk by solar rotation—westward in the observer's sky). In the other hemisphere, the leading and following magnetic polarities are reversed.

Exceptions do occur. Regions are sometimes formed that have a magnetic orientation perpendicular to or even the reverse of the norm for that hemisphere. Such

*The numbering system for solar activity cycles was started by Rudolph Wolf, who arbitrarily designated the activity maximum of 1750 as that of Cycle 1.

regions usually try to move into the conventional orientation but are impeded by the magnetic linkages formed with their surroundings. These regions tend to produce flares as potential energy builds up in their magnetic structures and is subsequently released catastrophically.

The "conventional" magnetic configurations for active regions reverse on alternate activity cycles. For example, during Cycle 22, active regions in the northern solar hemisphere were oriented with their "negative" (i.e. south-seeking) magnetic polarity ends leading and "positive" (north-seeking) ends following, with the reverse situation in the southern hemisphere. In Cycle 23, this arrangement was reversed. Cycle 24 re-establishes the pattern of Cycle 22. A *magnetic* activity cycle, which is probably a more realistic description of the rhythms of solar activity, is equal to two of Wolf's activity cycles and takes about 22 years to complete.

Active regions are not isolated phenomena; they occur in complexes, comprising several active regions at various stages of development, together with the network of elements remaining from decayed regions. This localization of activity gives rise to a rotational modulation of the 10.7-cm flux as active-region clusters are carried across the disk and disappear around the east limb. To smooth out this modulation in long-term studies of solar activity, the data are averaged over solar rotations rather than by month. Active regions can persist for one or more solar rotations and the complexes for a dozen or so.

The large-scale organization of solar magnetic activity is also apparent in the spatial distribution of active regions during the solar cycle. The first activity of the new cycle is marked by the formation of active regions at high latitudes. As activity builds toward the maximum of the cycle, the number of active regions increases, and they tend to form at lower latitudes. As the activity wanes toward the next minimum, the number of regions decreases, but the average latitude continues to decrease until the last activity of the cycle is located near the equator. Then, as the new cycle starts, new active regions form at high latitudes.

The formation of a new active region begins with the emergence of magnetic loops through the photosphere and into the overlying chromosphere and corona. This is heralded by the appearance of small pores, about 1000 km across, which coalesce and spread into a patch of magnetic flux that may exceed 50000 km in length. The average magnetic-field strength in such patches is of the order of 0.01 T (100 gauss). The emergence of these magnetic fields modifies the spatial and density structure of the chromosphere, giving rise to enhanced emission in the calcium and magnesium II K spectral lines. These bright patches (called plage), which stand out prominently in filtergrams, are the most conspicuous aspect of active regions. In some areas of the new active region, magnetic field strengths reach or exceed 0.1 T. These magnetic fields are strong enough to impede the transfer of energy from within the Sun, leading to these patches being cooler (3000 K) compared with the surrounding photosphere, which has a temperature of about 6000 K. Although actually quite hot and shining quite brightly, in contrast with their hotter surroundings, these flux concentrations appear as dark spots: sunspots. As a region grows, one or more large spots form at the leading end, and a scattering of smaller ones form at the trailing end. Sunspots are a prominent feature of active regions and are the aspect of solar activity that has been longest known.

The growth of the new active region continues through repeated episodes of magnetic flux emergence. In general, the size is directly proportional to the total magnetic flux in the region. Growth stops when the emergence of new magnetic flux ceases. Soon after, the region starts to decay. This proceeds partly by the resubmergence of magnetic flux and partly by fragmentation. The spots disappear, and eventually, all that remains is a large area of magnetic flux arranged in a network pattern, blending in slowly with the remains of other decayed active regions.

Repeated episodes of magnetic-flux emergence, together with motions of the footpoints, which are the photospheric anchors of magnetic loops, lead to the magnetic field overactive regions becoming complex and tangled and storing enormous amounts of energy. The relaxation of these fields is an important aspect of the evolution and dissipation of active regions. In some cases, this can occur noncatastrophically; otherwise, stresses increase until various plasma instabilities allow rapid relaxation and reconnection of the magnetic fields and a rapid release of the stored energy. These energy releases are known as flares.

The Solar Wind and Aurorae

The solar atmosphere is not stable. It is constantly flowing outward as a stream of particles and magnetic fields—the *solar wind*. The flow is strongest where the magnetic loops are very large and impose the least drag on the outwardly flowing particles. Because of their lower coronal densities, these regions produce a lower flux of X-rays and appear in X-ray images as dark patches, known as "coronal holes." The solar wind is not homogeneous or steady; its speed, density, and direction can change according to the positions of coronal holes and the nature of current solar activity.

The solar wind profoundly changes Earth's magnetic field. The wind pressure pushes the field out of its dipole shape into a long teardrop. The magnetic geometry in the tail of the drop makes it the site of many plasma instabilities. The flow of the solar wind over the boundary of Earth's magnetic field (the magnetopause) excites many types of waves, which move along Earth's magnetic field lines and which can be detected on the ground at high magnetic latitudes. Increases in the density or velocity of the solar wind change the pressure equilibrium between the solar wind and the magnetosphere, producing fluctuations in the strength and direction of the magnetic field lines at ground level. If the fluctuations are strong enough, the events are referred to as magnetic storms and substorms. These can disrupt any human activity that involves connected metal networks covering large geographical areas, especially at high magnetic latitudes.

Complex interactions between the solar wind and Earth's magnetic field lead to an accumulation of trapped particles in the magnetosphere. During magnetic storms, instabilities and waves excited in the magnetosphere by the solar wind accelerate some of the trapped particles downward along Earth's magnetic field into increasingly dense atmosphere, where they collide with the atmospheric constituents, exciting them with sufficient energy to produce light. These displays are called aurorae, or the northern and southern lights: *aurora borealis* and *aurora australis*, respectively. Views from space show that aurorae fall in a rough circle (the auroral oval), centred around the magnetic pole, that is, in a definite band of magnetic latitudes. As activity increases, the auroral oval expands, covering lower and lower magnetic latitudes. It also becomes increasingly distorted. During the period of very high activity in March 1989, auroral displays were seen as far south as the Caribbean.

Aurorae occur in many forms and can be steady, moving, or rapidly pulsating, depending upon the nature of the particle streams causing them. Aurorae can appear green or red, although if they are faint, the eye cannot respond in colour and they appear grey. The greenish colour is due to spectral lines from oxygen (558 nm) and a range of lines from nitrogen covering the band 391 nm to 470 nm. Under highly disturbed conditions, red spectral-line emissions at 630 nm and 636 nm and in a series of bands between 650 nm and 680 nm can also be seen. The green emissions are produced at a height of about 110 km; the red, 630-nm and 636-nm emissions, due to atomic oxygen, originate at heights between 200 km and 400 km; the 650-nm to 680-nm emissions are produced at about 90 km.

AURORAL FORMS

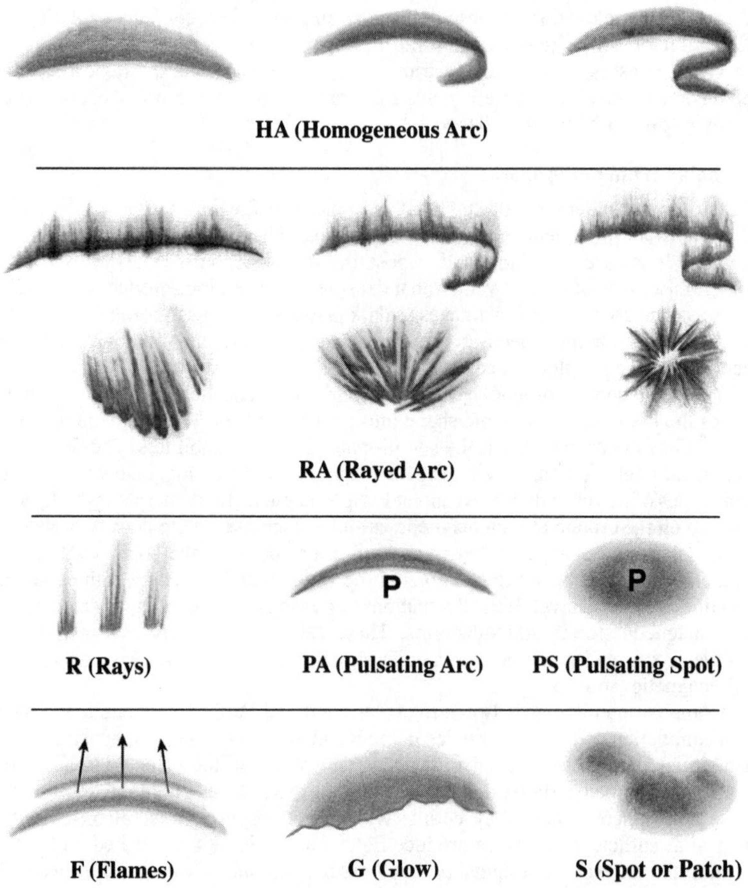

The above sketches illustrate standard auroral forms. This simplified classification was devised for visual observers during the International Geophysical Year six decades ago (1957–58). Although there is great variety in auroral patterns, the sketches emphasize fundamental features and minimize variations that depend on the location of the observer. The light of the aurora is emitted by the upper fringes of Earth's atmosphere (heights of 100 to 400 km) as it is bombarded by electrons of the solar wind (solar-wind protons contribute a smaller amount of energy). The modification of the trajectories of these particles by Earth's magnetic field restricts activity to high latitudes, producing the "aurora borealis" in the Northern Hemisphere and the "aurora australis" in the Southern Hemisphere. The wavelengths of four atmospheric molecular and atomic emission lines that can contribute strongly to auroral light are included in the list on p. 32. Whether aurorae appear coloured depends on their luminance—light that is too faint will not activate colour vision and appears grey. When the luminance is sufficiently great, the relative contributions of blue, green, and red emission lines can result in a variety of auroral hues.

The Impact and Measurement of Solar Activity

We find evidence of the profound effects of solar activity upon Earth extending as far back in time as we have been able to look. The rhythm of the solar activity cycle is reflected in cores from ocean beds, ice cores, and sediments from lakes that dry up in summer. It is also apparent in the growth rates of trees (determined from the study of tree rings) in recently living timber, wood from medieval buildings, and fossilized trees.

Solar activity can dramatically affect our lives. Magnetic storms due to solar activity induce currents in communications and power-transmission systems having long-distance wires, disrupting their operation for hours. The power blackouts in Québec and Scandinavia produced by a large flare on 1989 Mar. 10 are a particularly outstanding example. Railway signalling systems might also be affected. Increased X-ray emissions from flares cause enhanced ionization of Earth's atmosphere at D-region heights (about 90 km), producing blackouts of shortwave communications.

Solar activity heats the upper atmosphere, causing it to expand further into space, increasing the drag experienced by artificial satellites in low orbits. It is ironic that the lifetime of the *Solar Max* satellite was dramatically shortened in this way. Above the atmosphere, satellites have no protection from high-energy particle fluxes produced by the Sun. Their electronic systems can be damaged, leading to catastrophic failures in some cases, as occurred with two *Anik* communications satellites in January 1994.

The oldest index of solar activity is the sunspot number. A number of techniques, many empirical, have been developed to combine observations from various observatories and observers to form the International Sunspot Number. This is a rather poor index; however, it has given us a database extending back to at least the 17th century.

Probably the best available index of solar activity, at least covering the last six decades or so, is the *10.7-cm flux*, or $F_{10.7}$. This index is an objective measurement of the integrated emission at the 10.7-cm wavelength (a frequency of 2.8 GHz) from all sources present on the solar disk. It has been measured daily by the National Research Council of Canada for over 65 years and is now used worldwide as a primary index of solar activity. In 2003, the program became a joint one with the Canadian Space Agency. $F_{10.7}$ is expressed in solar-flux units (1 sfu = 10^{-22} W·m^{-2}Hz^{-1}). The 10.7-cm flux has the great advantage that it can be measured in all weather conditions and requires no human involvement or "interpretation." When quiet, the Sun produces a $F_{10.7}$ value of 64 sfu, due to free-free thermal emission from the quiet solar corona. Also, $F_{10.7}$ can be used as an objective proxy for other activity-related quantities. The strength of the radio emission constituting $F_{10.7}$ is modulated by the annual variation in the distance between Earth and Sun. When considering solar-driven phenomena at the Earth and in near-Earth space, this is not important, so the "Observed" value of the flux may be applicable. On the other hand, when considering solar activity, this modulation has to be removed from the data. In such instances, the "Adjusted" flux, which is scaled to an Earth–Sun distance of 1 au, should be used.

We are a long way from understanding the nature and the extent of the effects solar activity has upon Earth. Some correlations, like that between the length of miniskirts and solar activity, are probably spurious; others might not be. As we exploit our environment more fully, we become increasingly sensitive to things that might affect it, even slightly.

(See pp. 16, 64, 145, and 186 for safe methods of observing the Sun.)

RAINBOWS AND SOME OTHER SKY PHENOMENA

BY ROY BISHOP

Sunlight, and more rarely moonlight, interacting with water drops or ice crystals in the sky can result in aerial patterns displaying striking symmetry. This brief account is restricted to the more common sky phenomena. For more extensive treatments, including a dozen relatively rare patterns involving ice crystals, see the book by Greenler in the references and the websites listed there. For comprehensive accounts of the history and physics of the rainbow, see the books by Boyer, and Lee and Fraser.

In order of increasing angular distance from the Sun, ice crystals produce coronae, pillars, halos, sundogs, and circumhorizontal (or circumzenithal) arcs. (Other small particles, including water drops, also produce coronae.) In the half of the sky opposite the Sun, water drops produce rainbows and, surrounding the antisolar point, glories. The heiligenschein is not an atmospheric phenomenon, but like the glory is a bright area in the vicinity of the antisolar point.

Because the rainbow is the most famous, most beautiful, and most complex of these apparitions, I begin with rainbows and devote the greater part of this article to them. Also, if you understand the rainbow, it is easy to understand halos, sundogs, circumhorizontal arcs, circumzenithal arcs, and pillars.

Rainbows

The rainbow has challenged natural philosophers over the centuries, including Aristotle, Roger Bacon, Theodoric of Freiberg, René Descartes, Sir Isaac Newton, Edmund Halley, Thomas Young, Sir George Airy, and Gustav Mie. It was Descartes (1596–1650) who first understood the basic geometry of the rainbow, and it was Newton (1642–1727) who first understood the origin of the colours of the rainbow. In 1803, 1838, and 1908, Young, Airy, and Mie, respectively, gave successively more accurate treatments of the influence of the wave nature of light on the structure of the rainbow. Recently, Alistair Fraser and Raymond Lee, using the power of the computer, provided additional insights concerning the physics of the rainbow. A few poets, including Keats and Goethe, have derided science for analyzing the rainbow, but understanding only deepens one's admiration for the beauty and subtle nature of this phantom.

The Shape of a Raindrop: The shape of a raindrop is relevant for rainbows. Surface tension arising from molecular attraction shrinks raindrops into the shape with the least surface area per unit volume—a sphere. (Raindrops resemble teardrops only after they have crashed against a surface such as a windowpane.) Aerodynamic forces deform large raindrops into a hamburger-bun shape with the short axis vertical, but an average raindrop is essentially spherical.

The Origin of the Rainbow: Sunlight is refracted and reflected by a raindrop (see Figure 1). The *primary* rainbow involves two refractions (where the light ray enters and leaves the drop) and *one* internal reflection. A portion of a ray that enters a drop head-on is deviated through 180° by the internal reflection, but when the ray is shifted off-centre, the reflection produces a smaller deviation. When the ray is shifted 86% of the way toward grazing the drop (as in Figure 1), because of the increasing refraction, a *minimum angle of deviation* of approximately 138° is reached. This *stationary* angle concentrates some of the light leaving a raindrop after one reflection near this direction. Dispersion associated with the two refractions makes the minimum angle vary with wavelength, resulting in a spectrum. This interplay of sunlight with single raindrops

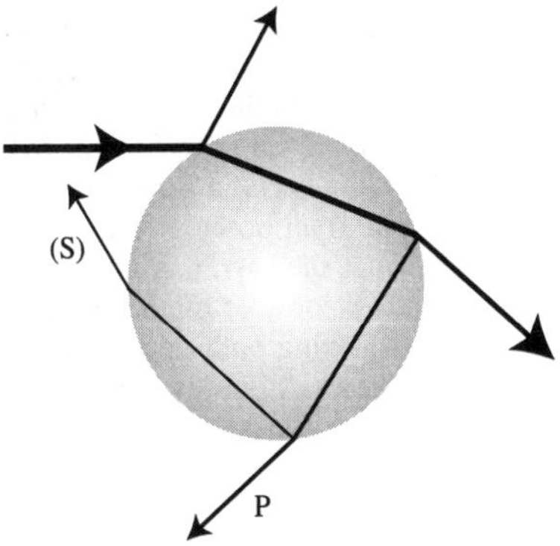

Figure 1 *The path of a ray of sunlight interacting with a spherical raindrop is displayed. The ray is shown entering the drop at 86% of the drop radius from head-on entry, causing ray P, exiting after one internal reflection, to be at a minimum angle of deviation of 138° and contributing to the primary rainbow. Ray (S) exiting after two internal reflections is close to but not at the minimum deviation for the secondary rainbow (231°); the ray entering the drop must be shifted closer to grazing incidence (to 95% of the drop radius) before a minimum deviation of 231° is attained. Rays undergoing three or more reflections within the drop are not shown, and neither is chromatic dispersion in the three rays exiting the drop. The widths of the various rays give an approximate indication of their relative intensities.*

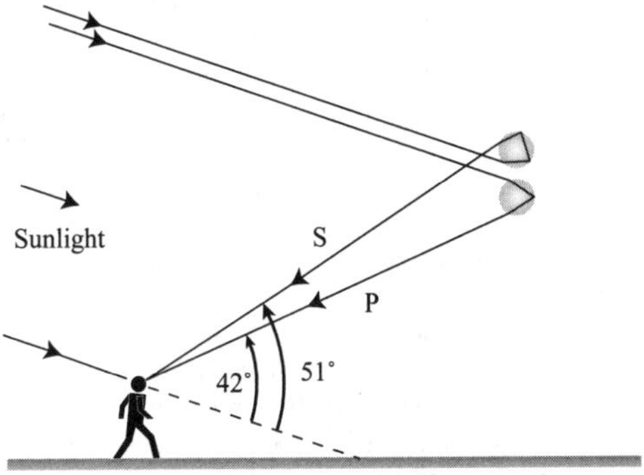

Figure 2 *Two raindrops are shown, greatly magnified, each with a ray of sunlight striking it such that the exiting ray is at the minimum angle of deviation and heading toward the observer. The drop with one internal reflection is contributing light to the observer's primary rainbow, and the drop with two internal reflections is contributing to the observer's secondary rainbow. Other drops (not shown) located along the rays P and S contribute in the same fashion to the two rainbows, and the whole array has rotational symmetry about the dashed line, the extended shadow of the observer's head. The observer, looking from the apices of these conical shells, sees two, circular, coloured bands of light.*

in the sky is symmetric about an axis extending from the Sun through the eye of the observer; thus the circular arc of a rainbow is centred on that axis. To look at the primary rainbow, the observer's eyes must be turned toward 138° + 180° = 318° or 42° from the antisolar point, the shadow of the observer's head (see Figure 2).

To Predict Where a Rainbow Might Appear: If the Sun is shining where you are, with the Sun at your back extend your arms together straight out in front of you, splay your fingers and thumbs horizontally, and touch the tips of your thumbs together. Close one eye and align the tip of one little finger with the shadow of your head. As you tilt your hands, the tip of the other little finger will trace out the location of the primary rainbow in the sky. (A double hand-span at arm's length subtends approximately 40°, about the same as the 42° angular radius of the primary rainbow.)

Rainbows: None, Semicircular, and Circular: Don't expect to see a rainbow in the sky at midday in tropical latitudes, or at midday in spring or summer at higher latitudes. The Sun has to be less than 42° above the horizon for the top of the primary rainbow to be above the horizon (see Figure 2). At sunrise or sunset, the antisolar centre of a rainbow is at the horizon, resulting in a semicircular rainbow that meets the horizon at 90°. From an airplane, or by spraying a garden hose, it is possible to see a complete circular rainbow at any time of day, provided there are many water drops and sunlight in the entire region 42° from the antisolar point.

A Rainbow Is Not a Bow: Angle, not distance, determines which raindrops send rainbow light to an observer's eye. Hence, the raindrops contributing to a rainbow lie in a conical shell with its tip at the observer's eye, and its axis coinciding with the extended shadow of the observer's head (see Figure 2). Only those parts of the conical shell having both raindrops and sunlight contribute to the rainbow. Thus, in spatial extent, a rainbow is like an immense, mouse-nibbled, ice-cream cone (sans ice cream). From the perspective of the observer located at the tip of this fragmented conical shell, a rainbow *looks* like a section of a flat circular arc or bow, but the only place a flat bow exists is on the observer's retina. Despite how rainbows are sometimes depicted in art and advertising, a rainbow cannot be viewed obliquely (it always appears circular), and it always has the same immense angular size. (Its 84° diameter spans almost one-quarter of the entire horizon.)

A Filled Cone of Light: Sunlight strikes an entire hemisphere of a raindrop, so in the case of the emerging rays that have undergone one internal reflection, sunlight is deviated over the entire range of possible angles, from 180° to the stationary, minimum, frequency-dependent angle of approximately 138°. Hence the conical shell of enhanced brightness that constitutes the primary rainbow is the outer surface of a filled cone of light (the portion thereof that lies above the observer's horizon) that brightens the disk of sky lying within the primary rainbow. Refractive dispersion occurs at all deviation angles less than 180° down to the approximate 138° minimum, but because of overlap, colours are perceived only near 138° where the overlap is not complete and the frequency-dependent stationary angle enhances the luminance, thereby creating the primary rainbow.

Your Rainbow: A rainbow is located at a particular angle relative to the Sun–observer axis (see Figure 2). When the observer moves, the axis moves, and the rainbow moves. The observer's shadow moves too, but a rainbow is subtler than a shadow; you can see someone else's shadow, but you cannot see their rainbow. Each observer has his or her own private rainbow. Although an observer's eyes image different rainbows, the two rainbows are in the same parallel direction, so when the images fuse, the observer sees one rainbow at infinity. Obviously a rainbow is not an object in the normal sense of the word; it is a pattern of light specific to the observer. Unlike the case of a normal object like a tree, there are as many rainbows as there are observers. If there is no observer, there is no rainbow; only raindrops in the sky, each raindrop independently scattering sunlight symmetrically about its own Sun-raindrop axis.

The Secondary Rainbow: If conditions are favourable (lots of rain and sunlight, and a dark sky background), a secondary rainbow will be visible. The *secondary* rainbow involves *two* internal reflections in each raindrop (see Figure 1). A light ray that enters a drop head-on is deviated through 360° by the two internal reflections, but when the ray is shifted off-centre the reflections produce a smaller deviation. When the ray is shifted 95% of the way toward grazing the drop, because of the increasing refraction, a minimum angle of deviation of approximately 231° is reached. This stationary angle concentrates some of the light leaving a raindrop after two reflections near this direction. Dispersion associated with the two refractions makes the minimum angle vary with wavelength, resulting in a spectrum. To look at the secondary rainbow, the observer's eyes must be turned toward $231^\circ + 180^\circ = 411^\circ$ or 51° from the antisolar point (see Figure 2). Thus the secondary rainbow lies $(51^\circ - 42^\circ) = 9^\circ$ outside of the primary rainbow (9° is about one fist-width at arm's length).

Width of the Secondary Rainbow: A light ray contributing to the secondary rainbow enters a raindrop closer to the edge of the raindrop than does a light ray contributing to the primary rainbow. Consequently, the amount of refraction and associated spectral dispersion are greater. The additional reflection from the curved inner surface of the raindrop further increases the dispersion, making the spectrum of the secondary bow about 60% wider than that of the primary bow (after taking the 0.5° diameter of the Sun into account).

Reversed Spectra: A light ray contributing to the primary rainbow enters the side of a raindrop nearest the convex side of the rainbow, is deviated through 138°, and exits near the opposite side of the drop heading toward the observer (see Figure 2). Long wavelengths are refracted least, emerging at a steeper angle to the rainbow axis, so the convex side of the primary rainbow appears red. A light ray contributing to the secondary rainbow is deviated through 231°. To reach the observer, the ray must rotate through the raindrop in the *opposite* sense to the path followed by the primary rainbow ray. Long wavelengths are refracted least, emerging at a shallower angle to the rainbow axis, so the concave side of the secondary rainbow appears red. Thus the spectral sequences are reversed, with the red of both bows bordering upon the space that is between the bows.

Alexander's Dark Band: The two rays, P and S, shown in Figure 2 undergo minimum deviations of 138° and 231°, the first approaching its minimum counter-clockwise, the other clockwise. Therefore there is a 138° + 231° – 360° = 9° gap into which such rays cannot enter. Thus the sky between the bows is darker than elsewhere, a feature called *Alexander's Dark Band* after Alexander of Aphrodisias, a Greek philosopher who drew attention to it c. AD 200. The "dark" band is only moderately darker than the region beneath the primary rainbow because of three sources of light between the bows: skylight, external reflections off raindrops (see Figure 1), and diffraction of light waves by the raindrops.

The Tertiary Rainbow: Edmund Halley (1656–1742) first calculated that light rays exiting a raindrop after *three* reflections have a minimum angle of deviation of 318°, placing the *tertiary* rainbow only 42° from the Sun. For at least 2000 years, people had been looking for a tertiary rainbow in the vicinity of the primary and secondary rainbows. They had been looking in the wrong part of the sky! The luminance (surface brightness) of the secondary rainbow is less than that of the primary, and the luminance of the tertiary rainbow is less than that of the secondary because of three effects: (1) Light rays contributing to successively higher-order rainbows strike raindrops closer to grazing incidence, causing a greater fraction of the light to reflect without entering the drops; (2) Some light exits the drops at each internal reflection leaving less for higher-order rainbows; (3) Rainbow width increases as the order increases, spreading the light over a greater area. There is little hope of seeing the faint tertiary rainbow because it is almost invariably overwhelmed by two sources of white light in that region of the sky (see Figure 1): (a) *Most* of the sunlight entering raindrops passes through without being internally reflected and illuminates the sunward half of the sky. (The lack of a stationary angle in the deviation of these bright, unreflected rays is why there is no "zero-order" rainbow.); (b) Sunlight externally reflected from raindrops. The quaternary rainbow, fainter again than the tertiary, also occurs in the bright sunward half of the sky, about 44° from the Sun. Higher-order rainbows also occur, but usually only the primary and secondary bows are visible in the sky (see www.atoptics.co.uk/rainbows/ord34.htm).

Banding Beneath: The concave side of a primary rainbow may display two or three narrow bands, called *supernumerary bows* or *supernumerary arcs*. They are caused by the interference of two emerging parallel light rays that have entered a raindrop slightly nearer to and farther from grazing incidence than a ray that undergoes minimum deviation. The two paths have different lengths causing interference. Similar pairs of rays emerging at various angles produce the supernumerary bow pattern. British physicist Thomas Young (1773–1829) was the first to present this explanation, although more accurate descriptions involving diffraction were later provided by British Astronomer Royal, Sir George Airy (1801–1892); German physicist Gustav Mie (1868–1957); and Canadian meteorologist Alistair Fraser (in 1983).

Hamburger Buns and a Pot of Gold: The hamburger-bun distortion of raindrops with increasing drop size has the greatest effect on the top part of a rainbow because light rays in that region traverse a vertical cross section of a raindrop. The distortion has two consequences for the rainbow:

First, the distortion substantially increases the minimum deviation angle such that light from large raindrops of various diameters is spread into a white haze beneath the primary rainbow. Only spherical drops (diameters of about 0.5 mm and smaller) contribute to the upper part of a rainbow, often causing it to be less bright and its colours less vivid than in the lower part of the bow (assuming the Sun is low in the sky so the lower part of the rainbow is at a steep angle to the horizon). In the lower part, drops of all sizes present circular cross sections to light rays that are redirected toward the observer. Thus *all* drops contribute to the lower part of the rainbow, making it the brightest part when there is a heavy rainfall with a wide range of drop sizes. As Lee and Fraser surmise in their book *The Rainbow Bridge*, the bright glow of vivid colours near the end of the rainbow may be the origin of the pot-of-gold myth.

Second, the distortion-induced modification in the shift of the position of supernumerary bows with drop size causes distinct supernumerary bows to occur only for raindrops having diameters in the range of about 0.4 to 0.8 mm, and only in the upper part of a rainbow. The contributions of larger and smaller drops are blurred due to overlap. A bright rainbow *without* supernumerary bows typically involves a heavy rain shower during which there is a wide range of drop diameters. Drops in the 0.4 to 0.8 mm range are present, but the bright area beneath the primary rainbow caused by larger raindrops obscures their otherwise distinct supernumerary bows.

Beware of Sunglasses: The reflection that rainbow light undergoes inside a raindrop occurs very near *Brewster's angle* at which light reflected from a nonmetallic surface becomes 100% polarized (named in honour of Scottish physicist Sir David Brewster (1781–1868), who discovered this phenomenon). Thus the light of a rainbow is almost 100% polarized. The direction of polarization (the direction of the electric field) is tangent to the bow, which for the upper part of a rainbow has the same orientation as that of partially polarized light reflecting from the dash of a car, a highway, or a body of water. Polarizing sunglasses are designed to block polarized light from the latter three sources and will obliterate a rainbow!

Rainbows at Night: Observations of lunar rainbows are rare. The Moon is bright enough to produce a noticeable rainbow only when it is near its full phase. Also, people are usually indoors at night, and when they do step outside it is often into a light-polluted environment, which rules out any chance of seeing a lunar rainbow. Even when conditions are favourable, few people would notice a lunar rainbow because it is usually too dim to activate colour vision and therefore appears white.

Not a Good Spectrum: The rainbow is often cited as the paragon of a white-light spectrum. However, five factors make the rainbow spectrum inferior to that produced by a laboratory spectroscope: (1) The minimum property of the stationary angle that produces a rainbow means that light of each wavelength is spread over larger angles, resulting in some overlap of the spectral colours; (2) The Sun is not a point source of light. The 0.5° spread of its rays smears the rainbow spectrum; (3) Sunlight reflected from the front of the raindrops and skylight from behind dilutes the colours making them less saturated; (4) The increase in the minimum angle of deviation associated with aerodynamic drop distortion (significant for drop diameters of 0.5 mm and larger) causes additional spectral smearing in the upper part of a rainbow; (5) Diffraction broadening results in further overlap of the spectral colours, particularly for small raindrops. In the case of fog or cloud (drop diameters in the range 0.01 to 0.1 mm), diffraction broadening causes the various colours to overlap sufficiently to produce a white rainbow, called a *fogbow*. Also known as a *cloudbow*, it may sometimes be seen from an airplane, a large white arc moving along on a cloud layer below the airplane.

Fog and Flashlight: A dark, foggy night provides an opportunity to see the stationary angle that is the key to a primary rainbow. Place a bright, well-collimated flashlight on the ground with its beam directed vertically upward into the fog. Step back a short distance and examine the vertical shaft of light. Look for a bright patch about 40° from the zenith. Fog droplets at that position preferentially redirect the light downward toward your eyes. Diffraction causes the stationary angle to deviate somewhat from the nominal 42° produced by larger drops. Diffraction broadening may make the faint patch of light from the secondary bow undetectable. It will be located about 54° from the zenith, below the fragment of the primary bow.

Rainbow Light on the Moon: The greater part of Earth's albedo is due to clouds. An observer on the Moon would see Earth brighten noticeably for several hours when the Sun–Earth–Moon angle is near 40° and the cloud droplets provide a 2°-diameter fragment of a cloudbow. At this point, the Moon is in its crescent phase, about three days from new, and earthshine will be enhanced. At Sinus Iridum, the Bay of Rainbows, twice each lunar night the plains and surrounding mountains are bathed in the light of a tattered fragment of a white primary rainbow enveloping Earth. Unfortunately, as viewed from Earth at such times, the substantial glare from the fat, sunlit, lunar crescent, plus scattering of moonlight in Earth's atmosphere and in the observer's eyes or camera tends to obscure the enhanced earthshine.

We Are Part of the Rainbow: Although rain and sunlight have been part of Earth's environment for four billion years, coloured rainbows occurred quite recently with the appearance of animals possessing colour vision. Our visual world with its brightness and colours occurs within our skull. Nevertheless, by some feat of mental projection we think that our visual world coincides spatially with the external world. Thus we confuse the neural rainbow with the external rainbow, and naively attribute the indescribable colours of the former to the latter. Three centuries ago, Sir Isaac Newton, aware of this overpowering illusion, wrote: "The rays to speak properly are not coloured. In them there is nothing else than a certain power and disposition to stir up a sensation of this or that colour." Yet, even today, most people regard the cone cells of the retina as "colour receptors," as if colours existed in the external world. They speak of "the true colours of moonbows and nebulae revealed by time-exposure photographs," unaware that they are attributing a unique property of the neural photograph in their brain to the external photograph in their hands, and subsequently to moonbows and nebulae in the sky. The eye does not detect the colours of the rainbow; the brain creates them. *We* are part of the rainbow, its most beautiful part.

Halos

Under normal conditions of temperature and pressure, the wave and statistical properties of electrons impose hexagonal crystalline structure on water ice. When sunlight interacts with ice crystals in the frosty sky, it translates the atomic architecture into macroscopic aerial patterns of striking symmetry.

Small ice crystals suspended in the air can have a variety of shapes, including multi-crystalline fragments in which the sixfold symmetry is not obvious, rods that resemble pieces of a hexagonal pencil, flat six-sided plates, and snowflakes with their elegant symmetry.

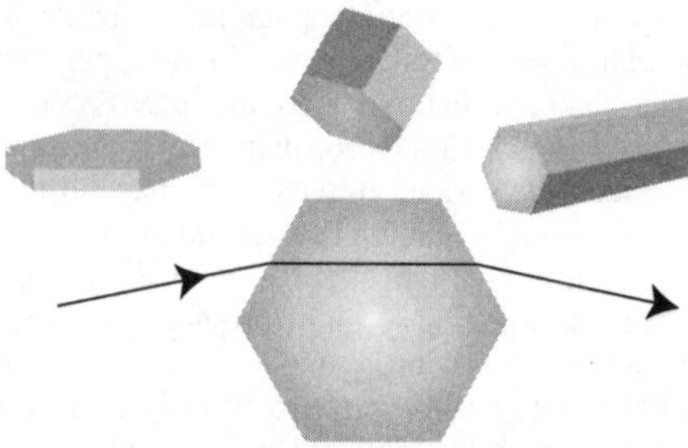

FIGURE 3 *The bottom diagram shows a light ray undergoing a net minimum deviation of 22° when it refracts symmetrically through alternate sides of a hexagonal ice crystal (in effect, a 60° ice prism). The top three diagrams show hexagonal ice crystals having, from left-to-right, increasing length-to-width ratios: a plate, a block, and a pencil. When falling, aerodynamic forces cause the plate and the pencil to orient horizontally, as shown. The block and clusters of crystals can have any orientation. Plates produce sundogs (refraction) and pillars (reflection). Randomly oriented crystals produce halos (refraction). Pencils produce pillars (reflection) and tangent arcs (refraction).*

FIGURE 4 *A schematic diagram of a 22° halo with sundogs, and a corona and pillar adjacent to the Sun low near the horizon in the centre. Hexagonal ice crystals are in the sky: plates (refraction/sundogs, reflection/pillar); blocks (refraction/halo); and both types of crystal (diffraction/corona). The absence of an upward-curving tangent arc at the top of the halo indicates that pencil crystals are not present.*

Alternate sides of a hexagonal ice crystal form a 60° prism (see Figure 3). Light passing through this prism is deviated by the two refractions, the angle of deviation being a minimum (about 22°) when the passage is symmetric, with equal refractions at the two surfaces. As in the case of minimum deviation in a water drop, a significant fraction of the light passing through randomly oriented 60° ice prisms is deviated by approximately 22°, enhancing the brightness at that angle.

Adjacent sides of a hexagonal crystal form a 120° prism, but light cannot pass through such a prism; the light undergoes total internal reflection at the second surface. Opposite sides of a hexagonal crystal are parallel and, like a windowpane, provide no net deviation. End faces of the crystal form 90° prisms with the sides; light passing through a 90° ice prism undergoes a minimum deviation of about 46° when the passage is symmetric.

Crystals having lengths about equal to their widths (called "blocks"; see Figure

3) or clusters of two or more single crystals assume random orientations as they fall. Consequently, the refraction of light rays toward an observer by such crystals has symmetry about the Sun–observer axis, and the observer sees a *halo* of light in the sky, centred on the Sun and having an angular radius of 22° (about one hand-span from the Sun at arm's length; see Figure 4). More rarely, refraction in 90° randomly oriented prisms results in an immense but fainter 46° halo, concentric with the 22° halo. Like the rainbow, a halo is not a circular hoop but a fragmented conical structure seen from its apex. Moonlight can also produce halos, particularly if the Moon is bright, near its full phase.

Because the 22° stationary angle of deviation is a minimum, the halo has a relatively sharp inner edge and a diffuse outer edge, the sky being brighter on the convex side of the halo. Because the deviation is least at the red end of the spectrum, the inner edge of a halo may appear reddish; however, ice crystals are not as optically perfect as raindrops, so the spectral colours of halos are not as pronounced as in rainbows.

The first person to understand the geometry of the 22° halo (i.e. minimum deviation in 60° ice prisms) was the French scientist Edme Mariotte (1620–1684). Sir Isaac Newton, apparently independently, arrived at the same explanation when writing his book *Opticks* (1704), but abandoned it in the published editions in favour of an erroneous explanation by the Dutch physicist Christiaan Huygens (1629–1695). Mariotte's theory was largely ignored for more than a century until revived by Thomas Young in 1807.

The ice crystals that produce halos are often in the leading edge of a low-pressure system, so a halo is a fairly reliable sign that within 24 hours the weather will be overcast and possibly stormy.

Sundogs

Like a small twig or leaf falling from a tree, pencil crystals and flat crystals such as snowflakes and plates are dynamically stable when oriented horizontally as they fall, maximizing air resistance (see Figure 3). If ice crystals in the air are predominately plates, only those crystals at the same altitude as the Sun can refract light to the observer (provided the Sun is low in the sky), resulting in two bright spots 22° on either side of the Sun (see Figure 4). Called *sundogs* or *parhelia*, under favourable conditions these spots can be almost too bright to look at. Although sundogs appear as spots in the sky, the contributing 60° ice prisms lie along the arms of a 44° "V" with the observer's eye at its vertex.

Rays passing nonsymmetrically through 60° plate prisms are deviated more than 22°, resulting in tails or smearing of the sundogs away from the Sun (see Figure 4). Also, like the 22° halo, sundogs often display a hazy spectrum with red on their sunward side.

Sundogs (or *moondogs*, if the Moon is the light source) may appear singly or in pairs (plate crystals) and may be accompanied by a 22° halo (randomly oriented crystals in addition to plates). Or only a 22° halo may be present (only randomly oriented crystals, or if plates are also present the Sun is too high in the sky for its rays to access the 60° prisms of these horizontally oriented crystals). If the Sun is moderately high in the sky (altitude ~30°), thick plates can still result in sundogs, but the skew rays involved displace the sundogs somewhat farther than 22° from the Sun.

Circumhorizontal and Circumzenithal Arcs

Closely related to the rare 46° halo, produced by refraction through the 90° faces of randomly oriented crystals, are two uncommon arcs, produced by refraction through the 90°faces of horizontally oriented plates. The 46° minimum deviation corresponds to the incident and exiting light rays making an almost grazing angle of 22° with the crystal faces.

If the incident ray enters a vertical face, the Sun must be at an altitude near 68° and the arc so formed will be only 22° above the horizon—a circumhorizontal arc —bright and rainbow-hued, with its red edge uppermost. Skew rays account for the extent of the arc perpendicular to the vertical plane containing the Sun and observer. Unlike a rainbow, it is not concentric with the observer's shadow, and it is in the same half of the sky as the Sun. If the Sun is much higher or lower, the arc is diffuse and dim, and cannot exist at all if the altitude of the Sun is much less than 60°. Thus the circumhorizontal arc cannot be seen at latitudes more than about 50° from the equator, and at that latitude only at solar noon near the summer solstice.

If the incident ray enters a horizontal face, the Sun must be relatively low in the sky at an altitude near 22°, and the arc so formed will be high in the sky, 68° above the horizon—a circumzenithal arc—bright and rainbow-hued, with its red edge lowermost, resembling an upside-down rainbow. Unlike the circumhorizontal arc, there are no geographical restrictions on a circumzenithal arc; a 22°-altitude Sun can occur anywhere.

Pillars

In cold weather when the Sun or Moon is near or just below the horizon, a vertical column or *pillar* of light sometimes is seen, extending upward from the Sun or Moon (see Figure 4). On winter nights, tall narrow pillars sometimes extend into the sky, the light sources being unshielded streetlights, often not in direct line of sight. Pillars (also known as *snow pillars*) are caused by plate crystals and/or snowflakes with their mirror-like faces oriented horizontally in the air. Reflections from pencil crystals can also produce pillars. *All* these miniature mirrors throughout the sky reflect light, but only those lying near the vertical plane passing through the light source and an observer reflect light toward the observer; hence the observer sees a vertical pillar. The crystals producing the pillar are located between the light source and the observer.

When sundogs accompany a Sun pillar, plate crystals provide at least some of the mirrors causing the pillar. When a short, upward-curving arc tangent to the top of a 22° halo accompanies a Sun pillar, reflections off the sides of pencil crystals contribute to the pillar, the *tangent arc* being due to refraction in the 60° prisms of the horizontally oriented pencils.

Coronae

In the presence of thin high cloud, hazy bright rings may closely surround the Sun or Moon, a pattern called a *corona* (not to be confused with the solar corona, the hot outer atmosphere of the Sun itself). Lying within several diameters of the Sun or Moon (see Figure 4), a corona often displays pale colours, including a reddish outer border—the reverse of the refraction-based reddish *inner* border of halos and sundogs. The red-reversal indicates that the corona is caused not by refraction but by diffraction scattering of light waves.

The scattering bodies are usually cloud droplets, but can be small ice crystals or even pollen grains. The smaller the scattering bodies, the larger the corona; the more uniform their size, the more obvious the ring structure. Thin clouds passing near the Sun or Moon may display a colourful iridescence associated with evaporation-induced variations in drop size, although in the case of the Sun the display may be too bright to view. Very small particles, such as are injected high into the atmosphere by volcanic eruptions, result in a large corona called a *Bishop's Ring*.

When cloud droplets are involved, a corona is caused by light rays that graze the sides of the water drops without entering the drops, and by rays that pass directly through the drops. The theory describing diffraction scattering is complex, and it is not possible to give a simple explanation of the structure and size of the corona. Note that the corona involves scattering of each light ray by only one drop; scattering by multiple drops eliminates the iridescence and structure of the corona.

Glories

The *glory* resembles the corona and is also caused by diffraction scattering of light waves by fog or cloud droplets; however, the glory occurs on the opposite side of the sky, surrounding the antisolar point. Like the corona, the angular size of the glory (seldom more than a few degrees) varies inversely with the size of the scattering drops. Despite the similarity of the corona and the glory, it is easy to remember which is which: the corona is in the same part of the sky as the solar corona (assuming the Sun, not the Moon, to be the light source of the corona).

Usually seen from an airplane on a cloud layer below, the glory appears as a ring-like pattern of hazy colours centred on the observer's position in the shadow of the airplane. If the cloud layer is sufficiently far from the plane, the plane's shadow (then penumbral only) will not be visible. Mountain climbers sometimes see a glory in a cloud (fog) layer below them. If the fog is close, the climber's shadow, distorted by perspective, will appear to the climber as a dark cavity in the fog with its head centred in the glory, a strange apparition called *the spectre of the Brocken* after a mountain in Germany where the phenomenon has often been observed.

In religious art, the rings or disks of light surrounding the heads of saintly figures were likely inspired by observations of the glory, and possibly the heiligenschein (see below). Certainly it flatters an observer to see an aureole surrounding the shadow of one's own head and not those of others!

The glory involves scattering of a light ray by one drop, whereas a white cloud involves scattering of a light ray by more than one drop—which is why clouds are otherwise white. As in the case of the corona, the theory describing the glory is complex, and it is not possible to give a simple explanation of the structure and size of the glory. Light waves moving along the surface of small water drops and reflections within the drops are both involved.

Heiligenschein

Heiligenschein (German for "holy light") refers to a diffuse colourless glow surrounding the shadow of the observer's head when that shadow is projected on a rough surface or on vegetation covered in dewdrops. Unlike the patterns described above, the heiligenschein is not an atmospheric phenomenon; however, like the glory, it surrounds the antisolar point, so it should be mentioned.

A rough surface appears brightest when viewed in the antisolar direction because the shadows associated with the roughness are hidden behind the objects casting the shadows. For example, on a sunny day, a person walking past shrubbery or a field of grass will see a glowing aura surrounding the shadow of his or her head. A forest viewed from an airplane displays a bright patch surrounding the shadow of the airplane. In the case of vegetation covered in dewdrops, the spherical drops redirect the incident light whence it came, enhancing the brightness associated with hidden shadows. Tiny glass spheres imbedded in highway-marker paint or on automobile license plates do the same. If the Moon had a perfectly diffuse matte surface, at full phase it would provide π times more light than at quarter phase when it is half illuminated; however, because of heiligenschein, at full phase the Moon provides more than ten times as much light—the multitude of shadows on the lunar surface are hidden, and impact-produced glass beads littering the lunar surface redirect sunlight toward Earth. When Saturn is near opposition, heiligenschein enhances the brightness of its rings.

Some people call the hidden shadow phenomenon *the opposition effect*, and restrict the term *heiligenschein* to the glow caused by dewdrops, glass spheres, or similar optics. However, etymologically, heiligenschein fits both contributions. Also, in the case of dewdrops, hidden shadows usually contribute too.

Concluding Thoughts

None of these apparitions—rainbows, halos, sundogs, circumhorizontal arcs, circumzenithal arcs, pillars, coronae, glories, and heiligenschein—are objects in the normal sense of the word. They are patterns of light specific to the individual observer. Anyone who understands them will find the world to be a more interesting place.

References

Benn, C.R., “Rainbows, Haloes, and Earthshine,” *The Observatory 114*, No. 1120 (1994), p. 115.
Boyer, C.B., *The Rainbow: From Myth to Mathematics*, Princeton University Press, 1987.
Fraser, A.B., “Why Can the Supernumerary Bows Be Seen in a Rain Shower?” *J. Opt. Soc. Am. 73* (1983), p. 1626.
Greenler, R., *Rainbows, Halos, and Glories*, Cambridge University Press, 1980.
Lee, R.L., Jr., “Mie Theory, Airy Theory, and the natural rainbow,” *Appl. Opt. 37* (1998), p. 1506.
Lee, R.L., Jr. and Fraser, A.B., *The Rainbow Bridge*, Pennsylvania State University Press, 2001.
Minnaert, M., *Light and Colour in the open air*, Bell and Sons, 1940.
Newton, I., *Opticks* (4th ed. 1730), Dover Publications, 1952.
Nussenzveig, H.M., “The Theory of the Rainbow,” *Sci. Am. 236* (4) (1977), p. 116.
Shapiro, A.E., “Newton and Huygens’ Explanation of the 22° Halo,” *Centaurus 24* (1980), p. 273.
Walker, J., “Rainbows in a Water Drop,” *Sci. Am.*, July 1977, p. 138.
Walker, J., “Mysteries of Rainbows,” *Sci. Am.*, June 1980, p. 174.
Wright, W.D., *The Rays are not Coloured*, Adam Hilger Ltd., London, 1967.

Websites:

www.atoptics.co.uk
www.meteoros.de/haloe.htm
www.philiplaven.com/index1.html

TIMES OF SUNRISE AND SUNSET

The table on the following two pages gives the times of sunrise and sunset at 4-day intervals for locations ranging from 20° to 60° north latitude. "RISE" and "SET" correspond to the upper limb of the Sun appearing at the horizon for an observer at sea level. The times are local mean time (LMT) for the Greenwich meridian (i.e. UT at 0° longitude), although for North American observers the stated values may be read directly as LMT at the observer's position with an error less than 1 min. The table may be interpolated linearly for both nontabular latitudes and dates, and can be extrapolated beyond the 20° and 60° latitude limits a few degrees without significant loss of accuracy.

It is a common misconception that extreme values for sunrise and sunset times occur on the shortest and the longest days of the year. That is not the case and is due to the tilt of Earth's spin axis to the axis of its orbit and to Earth's varying speed along its elliptical orbit (as Kepler described in his second law). At mid-northern latitudes, the earliest sunset occurs early in December and the latest sunrise in early January whereas the shortest day (in the sense of hours of daylight) is Dec. 21 or 22. For more information see *Sky & Telescope*, December 1988, p. 674 and July 1972, p. 20, and an article by Terence Hicks in *JRASC, 88*, p. 86, February 1994. Online, see the information on the *Astronomical Applications* page of www.usno.navy.mil/USNO.

The standard time of an event at a particular location must take account of the observer's longitude relative to his or her standard meridian (see STANDARD TIME ZONES on p. 45. The table below lists the latitude and the longitude correction (in minutes of time) for a number of cities in Canada and the United States. For example, to find the time of sunset in Saskatoon on 2017 Jun. 16: the latitude is 52°, and from the table the time of sunset at 0° longitude is 20:24 UT (after interpolating for date and latitude). Thus, at Saskatoon the time of sunset will be approximately 20:24 LMT. Saskatoon is in the Central time zone (C) and is 67 min of time west of the standard meridian for this zone (90° W). Thus, sunset in Saskatoon will occur at 21:31 CST (Central Standard Time)—note that Saskatchewan does not observe Daylight Saving Time. The longitude correction for any location may be found by converting the difference between the longitude of the place and that of its standard meridian to time (1° = 4 min of time), the correction being + if the place is west of its standard meridian, – if east. **Note**: Due to a difference in elevation between the observer and the actual horizon, the observed time may differ by several minutes from the predicted time.

Canadian Cities						American Cities		
Belleville	44°	+10E	Québec	47°	–15E	Atlanta	34°	+37E
Calgary	51°	+36M	Regina	50°	+58C	Boston	42°	–16E
Charlottetown	46°	+12A	Resolute	75°	+20C	Chicago	42°	–10C
Corner Brook	49°	+22N	Rimouski	48°	–26E	Cincinnati	39°	+38E
Edmonton	54°	+34M	Saint John	45°	+24A	Denver	40°	0M
Halifax	45°	+14A	St. John's	48°	+1N	Fairbanks	65°	+50A
Hamilton	43°	+20E	Sarnia	43°	+29E	Flagstaff	35°	+27M
Kelowna	50°	–3P	Saskatoon	52°	+67C	Kansas City	39°	+18C
Kingston	44°	+6E	Sudbury	47°	+24E	Los Angeles	34°	–7P
Kitchener	43°	+22E	Thunder Bay	48°	+57E	Miami	26°	+21E
London	43°	+25E	Toronto	44°	+18E	Minneapolis	45°	+13C
Moncton	46°	+19A	Vancouver	49°	+12P	New Orleans	30°	0C
Montréal	46°	–6E	Victoria	48°	+13P	New York	41°	–4E
Niagara Falls	43°	+16E	Whitehorse	61°	+60P	San Francisco	38°	+10P
Ottawa	45°	+3E	Windsor, Ont.	42°	+32E	Seattle	48°	+9P
Pangnirtung	66°	+23A	Winnipeg	50°	+29C	Tucson	32°	+24M
Prince George	54°	+11P	Yellowknife	62°	+38M	Washington	39°	+8E

SUNRISE AND SUNSET, 2017 JANUARY–JUNE
UNIVERSAL TIME AT GREENWICH MERIDIAN

Latitude:	+20°		+30°		+35°		+40°		+45°		+50°		+55°		+60°	
Event:	RISE	SET	RISE	SET	RISE	SET	RISE	SET	RISE	SET	RISE	SET	RISE	SET	RISE	SET
Jan.–2	6:34	17:30	6:55	17:09	7:07	16:57	7:21	16:43	7:38	16:27	7:58	16:06	8:25	15:39	9:03	15:01
2	6:35	17:33	6:56	17:12	7:08	17:00	7:22	16:46	7:38	16:30	7:58	16:10	8:25	15:44	9:02	15:07
6	6:37	17:35	6:57	17:15	7:09	17:03	7:22	16:50	7:38	16:34	7:58	16:15	8:23	15:49	8:59	15:14
10	6:37	17:38	6:57	17:18	7:08	17:07	7:22	16:54	7:37	16:39	7:56	16:20	8:20	15:55	8:54	15:21
14	6:38	17:41	6:57	17:22	7:08	17:11	7:20	16:58	7:35	16:43	7:53	16:25	8:17	16:02	8:49	15:30
18	6:38	17:43	6:56	17:25	7:07	17:15	7:19	17:03	7:33	16:49	7:50	16:31	8:12	16:09	8:43	15:39
22	6:38	17:46	6:55	17:29	7:05	17:19	7:16	17:07	7:30	16:54	7:46	16:38	8:07	16:17	8:35	15:49
26	6:37	17:48	6:53	17:32	7:03	17:23	7:14	17:12	7:26	16:59	7:41	16:44	8:01	16:25	8:27	15:59
30	6:36	17:51	6:51	17:36	7:00	17:27	7:10	17:17	7:22	17:05	7:36	16:51	7:54	16:33	8:18	16:09
Feb. 3	6:35	17:53	6:49	17:39	6:57	17:31	7:07	17:22	7:17	17:11	7:30	16:58	7:47	16:42	8:09	16:20
7	6:33	17:55	6:46	17:42	6:54	17:35	7:02	17:26	7:12	17:17	7:24	17:05	7:39	16:50	7:59	16:30
11	6:31	17:57	6:43	17:46	6:50	17:39	6:58	17:31	7:07	17:22	7:18	17:12	7:31	16:58	7:49	16:41
15	6:29	17:59	6:40	17:49	6:46	17:43	6:53	17:36	7:01	17:28	7:10	17:19	7:22	17:07	7:38	16:51
19	6:27	18:01	6:36	17:52	6:42	17:47	6:48	17:41	6:55	17:34	7:03	17:25	7:13	17:15	7:27	17:02
23	6:24	18:03	6:32	17:55	6:37	17:50	6:42	17:45	6:48	17:39	6:55	17:32	7:04	17:23	7:16	17:12
27	6:21	18:04	6:28	17:58	6:32	17:54	6:36	17:50	6:41	17:45	6:47	17:39	6:55	17:32	7:04	17:22
Mar. 3	6:18	18:06	6:24	18:00	6:27	17:57	6:30	17:54	6:34	17:50	6:39	17:46	6:45	17:40	6:52	17:33
7	6:15	18:07	6:19	18:03	6:22	18:01	6:24	17:58	6:27	17:56	6:31	17:52	6:35	17:48	6:41	17:43
11	6:12	18:08	6:15	18:06	6:16	18:04	6:18	18:03	6:20	18:01	6:22	17:59	6:25	17:56	6:29	17:53
15	6:08	18:10	6:10	18:08	6:11	18:08	6:12	18:07	6:13	18:06	6:14	18:05	6:15	18:04	6:17	18:02
19	6:05	18:11	6:05	18:11	6:05	18:11	6:05	18:11	6:05	18:11	6:05	18:11	6:05	18:12	6:05	18:12
23	6:01	18:12	6:00	18:13	5:59	18:14	5:59	18:15	5:58	18:16	5:56	18:18	5:55	18:20	5:52	18:22
27	5:58	18:13	5:55	18:16	5:54	18:17	5:52	18:19	5:50	18:21	5:48	18:24	5:44	18:27	5:40	18:32
31	5:55	18:14	5:51	18:18	5:48	18:21	5:46	18:23	5:43	18:27	5:39	18:30	5:34	18:35	5:28	18:42
Apr. 4	5:51	18:15	5:46	18:21	5:43	18:24	5:39	18:27	5:35	18:32	5:30	18:37	5:24	18:43	5:16	18:51
8	5:48	18:16	5:41	18:23	5:37	18:27	5:33	18:31	5:28	18:37	5:22	18:43	5:14	18:51	5:04	19:01
12	5:44	18:17	5:37	18:25	5:32	18:30	5:27	18:35	5:21	18:42	5:13	18:49	5:04	18:59	4:52	19:11
16	5:41	18:19	5:32	18:28	5:27	18:33	5:21	18:39	5:14	18:47	5:05	18:55	4:54	19:06	4:40	19:21
20	5:38	18:20	5:28	18:30	5:22	18:37	5:15	18:44	5:07	18:52	4:57	19:02	4:45	19:14	4:29	19:31
24	5:35	18:21	5:24	18:33	5:17	18:40	5:09	18:48	5:00	18:57	4:49	19:08	4:35	19:22	4:17	19:41
28	5:33	18:22	5:20	18:35	5:12	18:43	5:04	18:52	4:54	19:02	4:42	19:14	4:26	19:30	4:06	19:51
May 2	5:30	18:24	5:16	18:38	5:08	18:46	4:59	18:56	4:48	19:07	4:35	19:20	4:18	19:37	3:55	20:01
6	5:28	18:25	5:13	18:41	5:04	18:50	4:54	19:00	4:42	19:12	4:28	19:26	4:09	19:45	3:44	20:10
10	5:26	18:27	5:10	18:43	5:01	18:53	4:50	19:04	4:37	19:17	4:21	19:32	4:01	19:53	3:34	20:20
14	5:24	18:29	5:07	18:46	4:57	18:56	4:46	19:07	4:32	19:21	4:15	19:38	3:54	20:00	3:25	20:30
18	5:23	18:30	5:05	18:48	4:54	18:59	4:42	19:11	4:28	19:26	4:10	19:44	3:47	20:07	3:15	20:39
22	5:22	18:32	5:03	18:51	4:52	19:02	4:39	19:15	4:24	19:30	4:05	19:49	3:41	20:13	3:07	20:48
26	5:21	18:33	5:01	18:53	4:50	19:05	4:36	19:18	4:21	19:34	4:01	19:54	3:35	20:20	2:59	20:56
30	5:20	18:35	5:00	18:55	4:48	19:07	4:34	19:21	4:18	19:38	3:57	19:58	3:31	20:25	2:52	21:04
Jun. 3	5:20	18:37	4:59	18:58	4:47	19:10	4:33	19:24	4:16	19:41	3:54	20:02	3:27	20:30	2:46	21:11
7	5:20	18:38	4:58	18:59	4:46	19:12	4:31	19:27	4:14	19:44	3:52	20:06	3:24	20:35	2:42	21:17
11	5:20	18:39	4:58	19:01	4:46	19:14	4:31	19:29	4:13	19:47	3:51	20:09	3:22	20:38	2:38	21:22
15	5:20	18:41	4:59	19:03	4:46	19:16	4:31	19:31	4:13	19:48	3:50	20:11	3:20	20:41	2:36	21:25
19	5:21	18:42	4:59	19:04	4:46	19:17	4:31	19:32	4:13	19:50	3:50	20:12	3:20	20:43	2:36	21:27
23	5:22	18:42	5:00	19:05	4:47	19:18	4:32	19:33	4:14	19:51	3:51	20:13	3:21	20:43	2:36	21:28
27	5:23	18:43	5:01	19:05	4:48	19:18	4:33	19:33	4:15	19:51	3:53	20:13	3:23	20:43	2:39	21:27

Noctilucent clouds: *During summer twilight, particularly in the latitude range 53°–60° (in either hemisphere) look for silver-blue, cirrus-like clouds low in the polar sky. These are ice clouds about 80 km high, catching the Sun's light long after it sets (see the newly revised* www.rasc.ca/handbook/supplements*).*
From notes by Mark Zalcik and Mike Boschat.

SUNRISE AND SUNSET, 2017 JULY–DECEMBER
UNIVERSAL TIME AT GREENWICH MERIDIAN

Latitude:	+20°		+30°		+35°		+40°		+45°		+50°		+55°		+60°	
Event:	**RISE**	**SET**	**RISE**	**SET**	**RISE**	**SET**	**RISE**	**SET**	**RISE**	**SET**	**RISE**	**SET**	**RISE**	**SET**	**RISE**	**SET**
Jul. 1	5:24	18:43	5:03	19:05	4:50	19:18	4:35	19:33	4:17	19:50	3:55	20:12	3:26	20:42	2:42	21:25
5	5:26	18:44	5:04	19:05	4:52	19:17	4:37	19:32	4:20	19:49	3:58	20:11	3:29	20:39	2:47	21:21
9	5:27	18:43	5:06	19:04	4:54	19:17	4:40	19:31	4:23	19:48	4:01	20:09	3:34	20:36	2:53	21:16
13	5:28	18:43	5:08	19:03	4:56	19:15	4:42	19:29	4:26	19:45	4:05	20:05	3:39	20:32	3:00	21:10
17	5:30	18:42	5:10	19:02	4:59	19:13	4:45	19:27	4:29	19:42	4:10	20:02	3:44	20:27	3:08	21:03
21	5:31	18:41	5:13	19:00	5:01	19:11	4:49	19:24	4:33	19:39	4:15	19:57	3:50	20:21	3:16	20:55
25	5:33	18:40	5:15	18:58	5:04	19:08	4:52	19:20	4:38	19:35	4:20	19:52	3:57	20:15	3:25	20:47
29	5:34	18:38	5:17	18:55	5:07	19:05	4:56	19:17	4:42	19:30	4:25	19:47	4:04	20:08	3:34	20:37
Aug. 2	5:36	18:36	5:20	18:52	5:10	19:02	4:59	19:13	4:46	19:25	4:31	19:41	4:11	20:01	3:43	20:28
6	5:37	18:34	5:22	18:49	5:13	18:58	5:03	19:08	4:51	19:20	4:37	19:34	4:18	19:53	3:53	20:17
10	5:38	18:32	5:24	18:46	5:16	18:54	5:07	19:03	4:56	19:14	4:42	19:27	4:25	19:44	4:02	20:07
14	5:40	18:29	5:27	18:42	5:19	18:49	5:11	18:58	5:01	19:08	4:48	19:20	4:33	19:35	4:12	19:56
18	5:41	18:26	5:29	18:38	5:22	18:45	5:14	18:52	5:05	19:02	4:54	19:12	4:40	19:26	4:22	19:44
22	5:42	18:23	5:31	18:34	5:25	18:40	5:18	18:47	5:10	18:55	5:00	19:05	4:48	19:17	4:31	19:33
26	5:43	18:20	5:34	18:29	5:28	18:35	5:22	18:41	5:15	18:48	5:06	18:56	4:55	19:07	4:41	19:21
30	5:44	18:17	5:36	18:25	5:31	18:29	5:26	18:35	5:20	18:41	5:12	18:48	5:03	18:57	4:50	19:09
Sep. 3	5:45	18:13	5:38	18:20	5:34	18:24	5:30	18:28	5:24	18:33	5:18	18:40	5:10	18:47	5:00	18:57
7	5:46	18:10	5:40	18:15	5:37	18:18	5:33	18:22	5:29	18:26	5:24	18:31	5:18	18:37	5:09	18:45
11	5:47	18:06	5:42	18:10	5:40	18:13	5:37	18:15	5:34	18:18	5:30	18:22	5:25	18:27	5:19	18:33
15	5:47	18:03	5:45	18:05	5:43	18:07	5:41	18:09	5:39	18:11	5:36	18:13	5:32	18:17	5:28	18:21
19	5:48	17:59	5:47	18:00	5:46	18:01	5:45	18:02	5:43	18:03	5:42	18:05	5:40	18:06	5:37	18:09
23	5:49	17:55	5:49	17:55	5:49	17:55	5:49	17:55	5:48	17:56	5:48	17:56	5:47	17:56	5:47	17:57
27	5:50	17:52	5:51	17:50	5:52	17:50	5:52	17:49	5:53	17:48	5:54	17:47	5:55	17:46	5:56	17:44
Oct. 1	5:51	17:48	5:53	17:45	5:55	17:44	5:56	17:42	5:58	17:40	6:00	17:38	6:03	17:36	6:06	17:32
5	5:52	17:45	5:56	17:41	5:58	17:38	6:00	17:36	6:03	17:33	6:06	17:30	6:10	17:26	6:15	17:20
9	5:53	17:41	5:58	17:36	6:01	17:33	6:04	17:30	6:08	17:26	6:12	17:21	6:18	17:16	6:25	17:08
13	5:54	17:38	6:01	17:31	6:04	17:28	6:08	17:23	6:13	17:19	6:19	17:13	6:26	17:06	6:35	16:57
17	5:55	17:35	6:03	17:27	6:08	17:23	6:13	17:17	6:18	17:12	6:25	17:05	6:34	16:56	6:44	16:45
21	5:57	17:32	6:06	17:23	6:11	17:18	6:17	17:12	6:24	17:05	6:32	16:57	6:42	16:47	6:54	16:34
25	5:58	17:29	6:09	17:19	6:15	17:13	6:21	17:06	6:29	16:59	6:38	16:49	6:50	16:38	7:05	16:23
29	6:00	17:27	6:12	17:15	6:18	17:09	6:26	17:01	6:34	16:52	6:45	16:42	6:58	16:29	7:15	16:12
Nov. 2	6:02	17:25	6:15	17:12	6:22	17:05	6:30	16:56	6:40	16:47	6:51	16:35	7:06	16:20	7:25	16:01
6	6:04	17:23	6:18	17:09	6:26	17:01	6:35	16:52	6:45	16:41	6:58	16:29	7:14	16:13	7:35	15:51
10	6:06	17:22	6:21	17:07	6:30	16:58	6:39	16:48	6:51	16:36	7:05	16:23	7:22	16:05	7:45	15:42
14	6:08	17:20	6:24	17:04	6:33	16:55	6:44	16:44	6:56	16:32	7:11	16:17	7:30	15:58	7:56	15:33
18	6:11	17:20	6:28	17:03	6:37	16:53	6:49	16:41	7:02	16:28	7:18	16:12	7:38	15:52	8:06	15:24
22	6:13	17:19	6:31	17:01	6:41	16:51	6:53	16:39	7:07	16:25	7:24	16:08	7:46	15:46	8:15	15:16
26	6:16	17:19	6:34	17:00	6:45	16:49	6:57	16:37	7:12	16:22	7:30	16:04	7:53	15:41	8:24	15:10
30	6:18	17:19	6:37	17:00	6:49	16:48	7:02	16:36	7:17	16:20	7:35	16:02	8:00	15:38	8:33	15:04
Dec. 4	6:21	17:20	6:41	17:00	6:52	16:48	7:06	16:35	7:21	16:19	7:41	16:00	8:06	15:34	8:41	14:59
8	6:23	17:21	6:44	17:00	6:55	16:48	7:09	16:35	7:25	16:18	7:45	15:58	8:11	15:32	8:48	14:56
12	6:25	17:22	6:46	17:01	6:59	16:49	7:12	16:35	7:29	16:18	7:49	15:58	8:16	15:31	8:54	14:54
16	6:28	17:24	6:49	17:02	7:01	16:50	7:15	16:36	7:32	16:19	7:53	15:59	8:20	15:32	8:58	14:53
20	6:30	17:25	6:51	17:04	7:04	16:52	7:18	16:38	7:35	16:21	7:55	16:00	8:23	15:33	9:01	14:54
24	6:32	17:27	6:53	17:06	7:05	16:54	7:20	16:40	7:37	16:23	7:57	16:02	8:24	15:35	9:03	14:56
28	6:34	17:30	6:55	17:09	7:07	16:56	7:21	16:42	7:38	16:26	7:58	16:05	8:25	15:38	9:03	15:00
32	6:35	17:32	6:56	17:11	7:08	16:59	7:22	16:45	7:38	16:29	7:59	16:09	8:25	15:42	9:02	15:05

TWILIGHT

Twilight is the interval of time in the morning or evening when the Sun is below the horizon yet perceptibly contributes to sky glow. There are three geometrical definitions for the end of evening twilight or the start of morning twilight: (1) *Civil twilight*—centre of the Sun 6° below the horizon, brightest stars and planets visible, marks start and end of night for the purposes of aviation and artificial lighting of ordinary outdoor activities; (2) *Nautical twilight*—centre of the Sun 12° below the horizon, horizon indistinct; (3) *Astronomical twilight*—centre of the Sun 18° below the horizon, negligible solar component of sky glow. The following table gives the start of morning and the end of evening astronomical twilight in UT at 0° longitude. For observers in North America the times may be handled in the same way as those of sunrise and sunset (see p. 205).

Latitude:	+20°		+30°		+35°		+40°		+45°		+50°		+55°		+60°	
	Morn.	Eve.	Morn.	Eve.	Morn.	Eve.	Morn.	Eve.	Morn.	Eve.	Morn.	Eve.	Morn.	Eve.	Morn.	Eve.
Jan. 0	5:16	18:50	5:30	18:36	5:37	18:29	5:44	18:22	5:52	18:15	6:00	18:07	6:08	17:58	6:18	17:48
10	5:20	18:56	5:32	18:43	5:39	18:37	5:45	18:30	5:52	18:24	5:59	18:17	6:06	18:09	6:15	18:01
20	5:21	19:01	5:32	18:50	5:38	18:45	5:43	18:40	5:48	18:34	5:54	18:29	5:59	18:24	6:05	18:18
30	5:20	19:07	5:29	18:58	5:33	18:54	5:37	18:50	5:41	18:46	5:44	18:43	5:48	18:40	5:51	18:37
Feb. 9	5:18	19:11	5:24	19:05	5:26	19:03	5:29	19:00	5:30	18:59	5:31	18:58	5:32	18:58	5:31	18:58
19	5:13	19:15	5:16	19:12	5:17	19:11	5:17	19:11	5:17	19:12	5:15	19:13	5:12	19:17	5:07	19:22
Mar. 1	5:06	19:18	5:06	19:19	5:05	19:20	5:04	19:22	5:01	19:25	4:56	19:30	4:49	19:37	4:40	19:47
11	4:59	19:22	4:55	19:25	4:52	19:28	4:48	19:33	4:42	19:39	4:34	19:47	4:24	19:58	4:08	20:14
21	4:50	19:25	4:43	19:32	4:38	19:37	4:31	19:44	4:22	19:53	4:11	20:05	3:55	20:21	3:32	20:45
31	4:41	19:28	4:30	19:39	4:22	19:47	4:13	19:56	4:01	20:08	3:45	20:24	3:24	20:47	2:51	21:20
Apr. 10	4:31	19:32	4:17	19:47	4:07	19:57	3:55	20:09	3:39	20:25	3:19	20:46	2:49	21:16	2:01	22:06
20	4:22	19:36	4:04	19:55	3:51	20:07	3:36	20:23	3:17	20:42	2:50	21:10	2:10	21:51	0:41	23:34
30	4:14	19:41	3:51	20:04	3:37	20:18	3:18	20:37	2:54	21:02	2:20	21:37	1:21	22:38	—	—
May 10	4:07	19:47	3:41	20:13	3:24	20:30	3:02	20:52	2:33	21:22	1:48	22:07	—	—	—	—
20	4:01	19:52	3:32	20:22	3:12	20:41	2:47	21:07	2:13	21:42	1:13	22:43	—	—	—	—
30	3:58	19:58	3:26	20:30	3:04	20:51	2:36	21:20	1:56	22:01	0:24	23:41	—	—	—	—
Jun. 9	3:56	20:02	3:22	20:36	3:00	20:59	2:29	21:30	1:44	22:16	—	—	—	—	—	—
19	3:57	20:06	3:22	20:40	2:59	21:04	2:28	21:35	1:40	22:23	—	—	—	—	—	—
29	4:00	20:07	3:25	20:41	3:02	21:05	2:31	21:35	1:44	22:22	—	—	—	—	—	—
Jul. 9	4:04	20:06	3:31	20:39	3:09	21:01	2:40	21:30	1:57	22:13	—	—	—	—	—	—
19	4:09	20:03	3:38	20:34	3:18	20:54	2:52	21:20	2:14	21:57	1:04	23:04	—	—	—	—
29	4:14	19:58	3:47	20:26	3:29	20:44	3:05	21:06	2:34	21:38	1:43	22:27	—	—	—	—
Aug. 8	4:19	19:51	3:55	20:15	3:40	20:31	3:20	20:50	2:53	21:16	2:15	21:54	0:58	23:06	—	—
18	4:24	19:43	4:04	20:03	3:50	20:16	3:34	20:33	3:12	20:54	2:42	21:23	1:55	22:09	—	—
28	4:28	19:34	4:12	19:50	4:01	20:01	3:47	20:14	3:30	20:31	3:06	20:54	2:32	21:27	1:32	22:25
Sep. 7	4:31	19:24	4:19	19:36	4:10	19:45	4:00	19:55	3:46	20:09	3:28	20:26	3:03	20:51	2:24	21:29
17	4:34	19:14	4:25	19:23	4:19	19:29	4:11	19:37	4:01	19:47	3:47	20:00	3:29	20:18	3:01	20:45
27	4:37	19:05	4:32	19:10	4:27	19:14	4:22	19:19	4:15	19:26	4:05	19:36	3:52	19:48	3:33	20:07
Oct. 7	4:39	18:56	4:37	18:58	4:35	19:00	4:32	19:02	4:28	19:07	4:22	19:13	4:13	19:21	4:00	19:34
17	4:42	18:49	4:43	18:47	4:43	18:47	4:42	18:48	4:41	18:49	4:37	18:52	4:33	18:57	4:25	19:04
27	4:45	18:43	4:50	18:38	4:51	18:36	4:52	18:35	4:53	18:34	4:53	18:34	4:51	18:35	4:48	18:38
Nov. 6	4:49	18:38	4:56	18:31	4:59	18:27	5:02	18:24	5:05	18:22	5:07	18:19	5:09	18:17	5:10	18:16
16	4:53	18:36	5:03	18:26	5:08	18:21	5:12	18:17	5:17	18:12	5:21	18:08	5:26	18:03	5:30	17:59
26	4:58	18:36	5:10	18:24	5:16	18:18	5:22	18:12	5:28	18:07	5:34	18:00	5:40	17:54	5:48	17:46
Dec. 6	5:04	18:38	5:17	18:25	5:24	18:18	5:31	18:11	5:38	18:04	5:45	17:57	5:53	17:49	6:02	17:40
16	5:09	18:42	5:23	18:28	5:31	18:21	5:38	18:14	5:45	18:06	5:53	17:58	6:02	17:49	6:12	17:39
26	5:14	18:47	5:28	18:33	5:36	18:26	5:43	18:18	5:50	18:11	5:58	18:03	6:07	17:54	6:18	17:44
Jan. 5	5:18	18:53	5:32	18:39	5:38	18:32	5:45	18:26	5:52	18:19	6:00	18:11	6:08	18:03	6:17	17:54

SKY BRIGHTNESS AT MIDNIGHT

BY ROY BISHOP

Astronomers generally desire dark skies, free of moonlight and man-made light pollution. As mentioned on the previous page, the beginning or end of *astronomical twilight* corresponds to the centre of the Sun being 18° below the horizon. At that point the amount of sunlight scattered by the upper layers of Earth's atmosphere is negligible; that is, it is less than the combined illuminance (about 2×10^{-3} lux) from starlight, airglow, and zodiacal light, the three main contributors to the light of the "dark" night sky.

For observers in countries at high latitudes (e.g. the United Kingdom, Norway, southern Argentina and Chile, and most of Canada), around the time of the summer solstice the Sun always lies less than 18° below the horizon, and the sky does not get dark at night. This "midnight twilight" phenomenon can be displayed in a graph as a function of latitude and time of year.

The following diagram indicates the brightness of the sky at local midnight at any time of the year for any latitude north of 45°N or south of 45°S. Below the lower curve the natural sky is dark. Between the two curves twilight prevails. Above the upper curve the Sun is in the sky. Place names in roman type (left-hand side) are in the Northern Hemisphere; place names in *italic* type (right-hand side) are in the *Southern Hemisphere*. On the horizontal axis use the roman-type months for the former, *italic*-type months for the latter. The diagram is simplified slightly in that the months are assumed to be of equal duration, and the seasonal pattern of months and summer solstices for Earth's two hemispheres are assumed to be identical except for a 6-month phase shift.

The latitude of the Arctic and Antarctic Circles (90° subtract the obliquity of the ecliptic = 66°34′) is indicated by the dashed line. This line is *not* tangent to the Midnight Sun curve because at midnight on the summer solstice at either the Arctic or the Antarctic Circle the Sun is above the horizon. Atmospheric refraction raises the apparent Sun about 34′ above the true Sun. Also, rise/set is defined as the top limb of the Sun at a sea-level horizon; thus the 16′ semidiameter of the Sun must also be taken into account. To see the top limb of the Sun on the horizon at local midnight on the summer solstice, an observer must be 34′ + 16′ = 50′ south of the Arctic Circle (or north of the Antarctic Circle), at latitude 65°44′.

By running a horizontal line across the chart at a selected latitude, the reader can determine the approximate dates when midnight twilight and, possibly, midnight Sun begin and end for any locality at north or south latitudes above 48.6°, the lower limit for midnight twilight on the summer solstice. (Remarkably, when rounded to the nearest degree, the latter figure is the latitude of the longest east–west international border: the 2000-km-long 49th parallel between the United States and western Canada.)

Some examples: The diagram shows that Earth's poles are astronomically dark for less than three months of the year. At Grise Fiord, a village on Ellesmere Island and Canada's northern-most community, the sky is never dark from about Mar. 10 until early October, and the midnight Sun lasts from late April until mid-August. Cape Horn at midnight is bathed in dim Antarctic twilight from early November until early February. Even at the latitude of Vancouver there is a period of almost a month each year when the sky never gets astronomically dark. Although the midnight sky should be dark at all latitudes below the lower curve, that is no longer the case in or near populated areas where the natural night sky is immersed in a perpetual twilight: the baleful pall of light pollution (see p. 79). For such areas the TWILIGHT table on the previous page is irrelevant.

SKY BRIGHTNESS AT MIDNIGHT

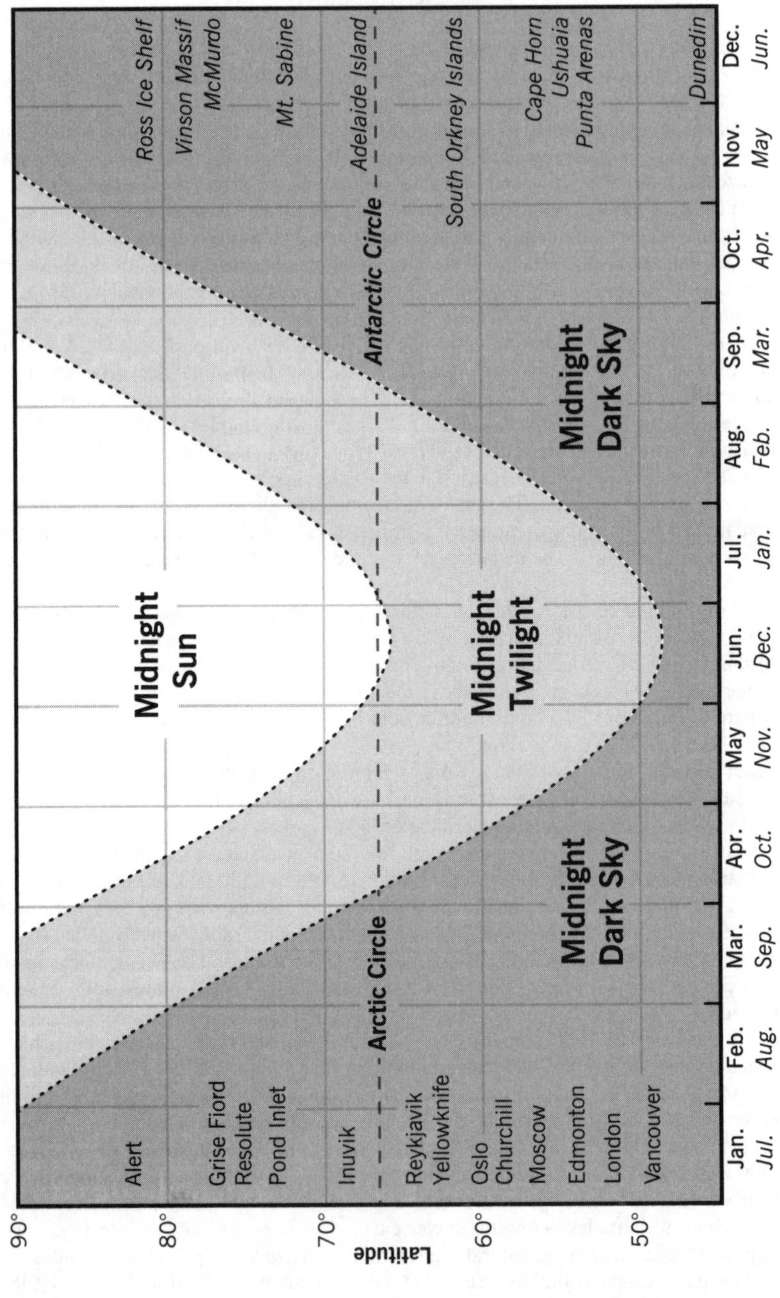

Diagram by Roy Bishop, drawn by Michael Gatto

PLANETS AND SATELLITES

THE PLANETS IN 2017

BY MURRAY PAULSON

INTRODUCTION

You would think that with the Internet and today's technology, you would never need a telescope. But nothing replaces that "being there" moment at the eyepiece when, with persistent effort, you see those subtle details obscured by distance and atmosphere revealed for fleeting moments. Seeing the changing face of the planets in real time is something that many of us find alluring. We get to be explorers in that last frontier, and we get to see the beauty of our neighbouring planets firsthand. Sometimes we even discover something new and point it out to the rest of the world, like the famous impacts in Jupiter's atmosphere. There is still a role for amateurs to play in discovery.

Optics: When observing the planets, it is important to minimize optical aberrations. To get the most out of your observing sessions, use high magnification with high-quality optics. If you are unable to change the optics, make sure they are clean and well-collimated. If you are considering a change, the best telescopes for the planets are high-quality refractors. The cost of these telescopes may be prohibitive, and "large" refractor apertures are only around 200 mm. The aperture is limited, but quality optics provide for astounding views. There are other high-end optical systems to choose from: Maksutovs, Dall–Kirkhams, and optimized Newtonians work very well.

Also important is resolution. One of the axioms of optics is: the larger the diameter of the telescope, the higher the resolution (see TELESCOPE PARAMETERS, p. 49 and TELESCOPE EXIT PUPILS, p. 50). In the world of amateur planetary imaging, some of the best work is being done with the larger, commercial, Schmidt–Cassegrain telescopes (SCTs) of aperture 300–400 mm. There are some excellent quality, larger SCTs that, when coupled with image-processing software, can do amazing things. Software can produce excellent images by stretching the contrast that central

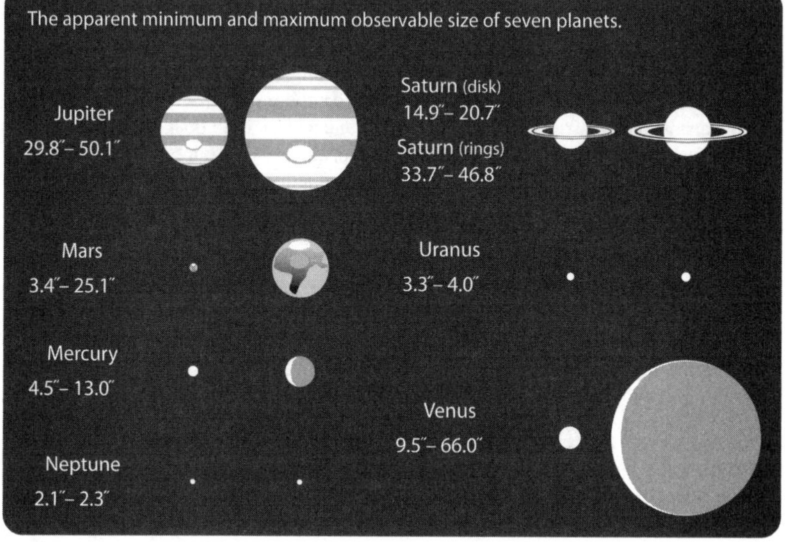

Illustration by Michael Gatto

obstructions tend to reduce. There are also good-quality Newtonian telescopes and other Cassegrain designs. To evaluate telescope quality for planetary work, H.R. Suiter's book *Star Testing Astronomical Telescopes: A Manual for Optical Evaluation and Adjustment* (Willmann–Bell, Inc., Richmond, 2nd Ed., 2009) provides the appropriate tools.

With a high-quality telescope, you need good eyepieces. The general rule is: the higher the quality and the fewer optical elements, the better. Every surface scatters light, and the features on the planets are subtle. Orthoscopic eyepieces are the benchmark for planetary eyepieces, with Zeiss "orthos" at the top of the scale. These eyepieces produce very clean, high-contrast images. There are other manufacturers that produce Abbe Orthos, notably Takahashi and University optics, but a few others make a variation on the orthoscopic design that have observers praising them. Try a variety of eyepieces when you can (e.g. at star parties) to see how they work for you. Be critical of what you see, and note the contrast and the colour each eyepiece lends to its subject. Then check your wallet! If you are using a non-driven telescope, a wide, flat-field eyepiece like the Tele Vue Nagler or Ethos is indispensable, because the large fields of view of these eyepieces give you ample time to observe at high power before having to re-position the telescope. An alternative is the Nikon NAV SW series, with oculars exhibiting very little distortion or false colour. The view in these eyepieces is sharp to the edge of the field. The next step is get a drive for the telescope, which gives the observer uninterrupted time to concentrate on the planetary image and to discern the details. My best view of Mars was with a bino-viewer. The use of both eyes gives your eyes and brain the chance to combine the image and ignore "floaters" and other visual defects. It is more expensive to purchase the viewer and the extra eyepieces, but it is effective.

Cleanliness of eyepieces and diagonals is also important. These surfaces are close to the observer, and will contribute the most degradation to image contrast if they are not clean. Do your homework before you clean your eyepieces, and make sure you do not damage them in the cleaning process (see **www.skyandtelescope.com/howto/diy**, for example).

The next factor to consider is the optical tube. If the telescope is warmer than the surrounding air, the warm air rising from the optical surfaces in the tube assembly will mix with the cold ambient air, causing localized turbulence, which degrades the image. Adequate thermal equalization of the telescope is critical for good images. The general rule is: the smaller the thermal mass, the shorter the cool-down period. To avoid long cool-down periods, some amateurs use a cooling fan to flush the heat out of the telescope or to blow cool air onto the mirror. Closed-tube assemblies will limit the mixing of the warm and cool air, and they do not cool quite as fast as an open-tube assembly.

The last of the aberrations is the atmosphere. Local heat sources, such as furnace flues, warm cars, paved parking lots, and even someone standing near the telescope, will cause heat plumes that could degrade the seeing. One way of ascertaining whether there are thermal sources affecting the seeing is to defocus your telescope while observing a bright star, and examine the image for any slow-moving anomalous structure. This movement is evidence of a heat plume aberrating the star's image. You may have to move the telescope. Sometimes the atmosphere is just not cooperative, and the jet stream or some other phenomenon will bloat the planet's image to resemble a fuzzy tennis ball. The defocused image will show a river of structure moving in one direction across it. There is not much you can do but try again on another night.

Daytime observing: The inner planets are often very close to the horizon after sunset, and this puts the observer at a disadvantage. Down that low, the shimmering of the atmosphere obscures the fine details on the inner planets. Just finding Mercury is a challenge in the twilight. Daytime observing of the inner planets is possible, but it does take some equipment and planning. The easiest way is to use a Go To telescope. Failing that, use a polar-aligned equatorial mount with setting circles. Both options will get the telescope aimed in the right area of the sky. Note: if the sky is hazy, the task of finding the planet in the daytime becomes significantly more difficult, or next to impossible.

Mars, Jupiter, and Saturn are observable in the daytime hours, so you are not limited to just the inner planets: the outer planets are more challenging, but fun to find. It is especially fun to observe a planetary conjunction in the daytime. My favourites have been Venus and Jupiter, and Mercury and Venus.

It is difficult to locate and acquire focus on planets in the daytime sky, so the recommended procedure is to first set up the telescope with a solar filter and a low-power eyepiece, then focus on the Sun. Once you have a good focus on the Sun, lock the focuser, if possible. (One can also use calibrated or marked focusers, or simply use the same eyepiece/focuser combination from the previous night's observing session.)

Do not remove the solar filter yet. **Do not hunt for planets within 5° of the Sun, because of the hazard that accidental unfiltered exposure to the Sun poses.** Remember that blindness is not a desirable observing attribute! (See VIEWING A SOLAR ECLIPSE—A WARNING, p. 145.) If you are not using a Go To scope, set the coordinates on the mount to the Sun's position, and then move off to the location of the planet you are hunting. With the Go To, just enter the command to go to the planet. **Now it is safe to remove the solar filter.** To make absolutely sure that the Sun is not in the field of view, pass your hand over the eyepiece to see if it is safe, then look.

The resolution of the eye is acute only near the centre of vision, so if you are not looking directly at the planet, you probably will not see it, and you will have to scan the field of view to find it. With Venus, this is not a problem, but it is with Mercury and the outer planets. Once the planet is in the field of view, centre it and try higher-power eyepieces. Parfocal eyepieces provide easy eyepiece exchange with minimal refocusing. A light-orange filter like the Wratten #21 darkens the light-blue sky and improves the contrast.

If the planet is not in the field, either there is an error in your mount alignment or the planet is very low in contrast. You can scan for the planet, being very careful about sweeping toward the Sun. **Do not sweep too far!** The second choice is to try to improve the mount alignment. Try the drift alignment method (see p. 70) on the Sun or obtain a better north–south reference. The atmosphere heats up throughout the day, so it is most stable in the morning. Objects in the foreground, such as asphalt parking lots, may affect the seeing. If possible, for best stability, observe over grass or water.

Drawing the planets is encouraged (see ASTRONOMICAL SKETCHING, p. 88). I now mostly image the planets, but I am glad for the time I put in to drawing them. Drawing compels the observer to critically observe the planet. This is a worthwhile activity because it gives you multiple opportunities to observe the details that appear in the fleeting moments of good seeing, and this effort teaches your eye and brain how to see the subtle features. You become a much better observer. As a bonus, drawing also provides a record of what you saw during that session, for future reference.

For drawing, use a pair of soft and hard pencils (e.g. an HB and an H), a logbook, and a template (www.astromax.org/activities/2003/mars2003/sketching.htm). Mars is typically drawn with a 42-mm circular template, corresponding to the 6792-km (~4200-mile) diameter of Mars. The templates for other planets can be of a convenient size, but do not make them too small. Jupiter and Saturn need an oblate template to make them easier to draw. Draw major features first, then fill in the little details as you see them. Jupiter rotates very rapidly, and the features will visibly shift over a 20-min interval. It is very important that you record the time and date on the drawing, as well as the aperture and eyepiece you are using, filters (if any), the general observing conditions, and your name and location. The Association of Lunar and Planetary Observers is interested in amateur contributions and is happy to receive amateur drawings.

Editor's Note: All dates are UT and some events, as viewed from North America, may occur on the evening of the previous date. Check THE SKY MONTH BY MONTH (p. 98) for exact times, especially for phenomena involving the Moon.

MERCURY

Mercury is a planet of extremes: It is the smallest of the eight planets, it is closest to the Sun and therefore the fastest moving, and it is nearly the hottest planet. Mercury also has the longest solar day, lasting two of its orbital periods, or 176 days. In the peak of its "noonday" heat, Mercury's surface warms to 427 °C, and on the far side the temperature goes down to –163 °C. The coldest place is deep in the shadows of craters near the poles, –183 °C. These extremes give the planet a temperature range of 610 C°.

Mercury has an orbital period of 87.96 days and rotates on its axis every 58.65 days, locked in a 3:2 resonance with its orbital period around the Sun. This is due to the high eccentricity of its orbit, in which perihelic tidal forces dominate the spin period. Accordingly, every elongation is different, ranging from 18° to 28°. Mercury's orbit has a high inclination of 7.0°, which can place it well above or below the ecliptic during a given apparition. Since Mercury never strays more than 28° from the Sun, it is only visible near the horizon at dusk or dawn.

Most people have never seen Mercury, because the window of opportunity is so narrow near dusk and dawn (they may have seen it, and not realized it!). That fact, coupled with the general poor quality of the atmosphere close to the horizon, makes daytime observation of Mercury the better option, when the planet is higher in the sky and you are looking through less atmosphere. If you can observe early in the day, thermal effects are reduced. (Try observing over a body of water during the daytime, when the air and water temperatures are not too different, leading to improved

MERCURY—EVENTS FOR 2017

Date	Event	Elong. from Sun °	Ang. Dia. ″	Mag.	Date	Event	Elong. from Sun °	Ang. Dia. ″	Mag.
Jan. 19	GEW	24 W	6.7	–0.2	Jul. 30	GEE	27 E	7.7	+0.3
Mar. 7	SC	2 S			Aug. 26	IC	4 S		
Apr. 1	GEE	19 E	7.5	–0.2	Sep. 12	GEW	18 W	7.2	–0.4
Apr. 20	IC	2 S			Oct. 8	SC	1 N		
May 17	GEW	26 W	8.3	+0.4	Nov. 24	GEE	22 E	6.6	–0.4
Jun. 21	SC	1 N			Dec. 13	IC	2 N		

GEE = Greatest Elongation East; GEW = Greatest Elongation West; IC = Inferior Conjunction; SC = Superior Conjunction

MERCURY—ELONGATION AND APPARENT SIZE DURING 2017

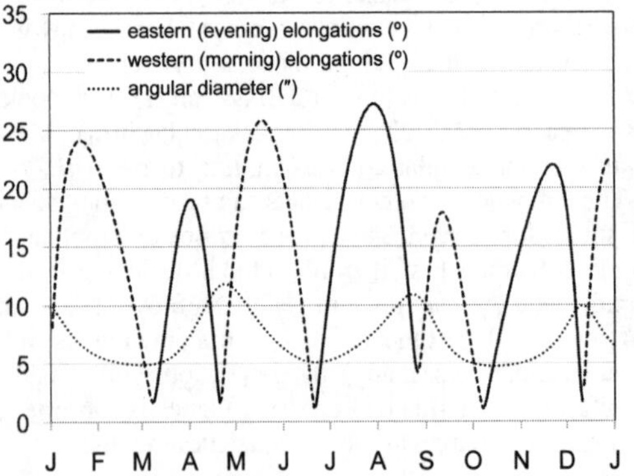

Elongation is plotted in degrees and angular diameter in arcseconds. The first day of each month is marked on the horizontal axis. Visibility depends not only on the elongation but also on the angle between the ecliptic and the horizon. See the table on the facing page for the most favourable views.

seeing.) One difficulty of observing Mercury in twilight is that the high luminance of the planet makes the subtle markings difficult to see. By observing in the daytime, when Mercury is higher than the Sun, the luminance contrast is less, which makes the markings easier to see for Northern Hemisphere observers.

Any telescope equipped with Go To or setting circles can be used to find Mercury (see the daytime observing tips on p. 212). Details on Mercury can be seen in a 130-mm telescope using high magnifications of 1.5× to 3.0× per millimetre of diameter. A red or an orange filter (Wratten #21) can be used to boost the contrast with the blue of the sky. Anecdotally, the best phases to see the subtle details on the planet are between mid-gibbous and a wide crescent, near the greatest elongations. Views of Mercury with 250-mm Maksutovs show surprising detail.

Mercury's mean synodic period (time between successive inferior conjunctions) is 115.88 days, so there are generally three opportunities to see it both after sunset and in the dawn sky every year. The angle of the ecliptic makes fall-evening and spring-morning apparitions at higher latitudes very poor—in both Northern and Southern Hemispheres—because the ecliptic is almost parallel to the horizon, and Mercury sets shortly after the Sun, or rises shortly before the Sun, in bright twilight. One disparity is that the Southern Hemisphere gets the better of the fall-morning and spring-evening elongations, because the inclination of Mercury's orbit to the ecliptic provides a more favourable geometry for Southern Hemisphere observers.

This year starts off with Mercury emerging from an inferior conjunction with the Sun into the morning sky. It will brighten as it reaches its greatest elongation west (GEW; see p. 20 for geometry and terminology) on Jan. 19, when it rises 1.5 h before the Sun. The apparition is aided by its placement above the ecliptic and 24° elongation from the Sun. Mercury shows a 6.7″ slight gibbous phase and shines at mag. –0.2. It falls to the next superior conjunction on Mar. 6, but this leads us to the best evening apparition of 2017. On the way up to the greatest eastern elongation (GEE), we

MERCURY—MOST FAVOURABLE VIEWS IN 2017
FROM NORTHERN LATITUDES:
March/April (Evening)—*May (Morning)*

Date 0h UT	**Magnitude**	**Angular Diameter** ″	**%** **Illuminated**	**Elongation from Sun** °	**Altitude at 45° N at sunset/*sunrise*** °
Mar. 22	–1.1	5.8	77	15 E	24
26	–0.9	6.3	63	18 E	28
30	–0.5	7.1	47	19 E	31
Apr. 03	+0.1	7.9	32	18 E	31
May 9	*+1.1*	*9.8*	*23*	*23 W*	*14*
13	*+1.4*	*9.0*	*32*	*25 W*	*16*
17	*+0.6*	*8.3*	*39*	*26 W*	*18*
21	*–1.4*	*7.6*	*46*	*25 W*	*18*

SOME CONJUNCTIONS INVOLVING MERCURY IN 2017

Date (UT)	Planet/Star	Separation	Date (UT)	Planet/Star	Separation
Jan. 25	Moon	3.0° N	*Jun. 28*	*Mars*	*0.8° S*
Apr. 28	*Uranus*	*0.1° N*	Jul 25	Moon	0.9° S
Jun. 16	*Ceres*	*0.7° S*	Sep. 16	Mars	0.1° S

N = object north of Mercury, S = object south of Mercury, *italics = close to Sun*

see –0.8 mag. Mercury pass a mag. 5.8 Uranus. They are 2.1° apart on Mar. 26. On Apr. 1, we have the GEE where a 7.7″, 40% illuminated Mercury sits 19° from the Sun and sets 2 h after it does, due to the very steep spring evening ecliptic. This is the fast part of Mercury's orbit, and it zips back to the Sun in just under three weeks to its next inferior conjunction on Apr. 20. Mercury arrives at a GEW 25.8° from the Sun on May 17, but it is in the unfavourable morning ecliptic, compounded with the planet 3.5° below the ecliptic. It will be a great apparition from the Southern Hemisphere. Mercury's next superior conjunction is on the summer solstice, Jun. 21, where it passes only 50′ above the Sun.

On Jun. 28, –1.8-mag. Mercury passes 46′ above 1.7-mag. Mars. They are only 8.7° away from the Sun. It will be a good hunt to see Mercury, but the real challenge is to see Mars. An absolutely pristine sky is a prerequisite. On that hopeful note, we go into the Jul. 30 GEE with a very poor angle on the evening ecliptic. This is the greatest elongation of 2017—very unfavourable in northern countries but spectacular from the Southern Hemisphere, where it sets 2h 10 min after sunset. Mercury's return to inferior conjunction is at a leisurely pace and arrives on Aug. 26. From here, we head out to the best morning apparition of 2017 in the northern countries on Sep. 12. The fall morning ecliptic tips up steeply to the horizon, and despite the 18° elongation, Mercury sets 1:45 after the Sun. On Sep. 16, Mercury and Mars pass only 3.3′ apart. This is a spectacular close conjunction and worthy of the morning hunt. In eastern North America the pair sit 18′ apart 20 min before sunrise, and as we move to the west coast, they close to within 11′. To see them at their closest approach of 3.2′, you need to be in Japan or Australia. On Sep. 18, we get a nice gathering of a slender crescent Moon rising just ahead of Mars and Mercury. Mercury will shine at mag. –1.0 and Mars at mag. 1.8, making the trio a great photo opportunity. Mercury disappears into the Sun's glare and is at superior conjunction on Oct. 8.

We have another iffy conjunction of Mercury and Jupiter on Oct. 18, where Mercury at mag. –0.9 and Jupiter at mag. –1.7, sit 56′ apart, but only 6.6° from the Sun. This one is difficult and I put it up as a challenge for those so inclined. We next move on to the Nov. 23 GEE, but again we are plagued with the shallow fall ecliptic compounded with Mercury 2.5° below it. On Dec. 13 UT (Dec. 12 local), Mercury passes 1.8° above the Sun in inferior conjunction. The last elongation of the year culminates on Jan. 1 and is a respectable morning apparition. Mercury will set 1:50 after the Sun.

VENUS

Known as both the morning star and the evening star, Venus has impressed us throughout the ages with the brilliance and purity of its light. Ranging in magnitude from –4.9 to –3.8, Venus is bright enough to cast a visible shadow. If you know when and where to look, it is visible to the naked eye in full daylight.

In the pre-spacecraft era, people thought that our sister planet might bear habitable zones somewhat like Earth. Nothing could be further from the truth. The surface temperature on Venus is a fairly constant 460 °C, under a runaway greenhouse effect. The dense carbon dioxide atmosphere has a pressure of over 9000 kPa (92 atm) at the surface and a density of 65 kg/m^3, 6.5% the density of water and about 60 times that of Earth's atmosphere. Wind friction would be serious on Venus.

Thick sulphur dioxide clouds with sulphuric acid droplets veil the surface of Venus; little light reaches the surface. Occasional detail is seen in the cloud structure in amateur telescopes, but for the most part it appears as a featureless white disk. The subtle structure in the cloud tops is difficult to observe, but too few observers even give it a try. The best times to look are from just between thick crescent and

VENUS—ELONGATION AND APPARENT SIZE DURING 2017

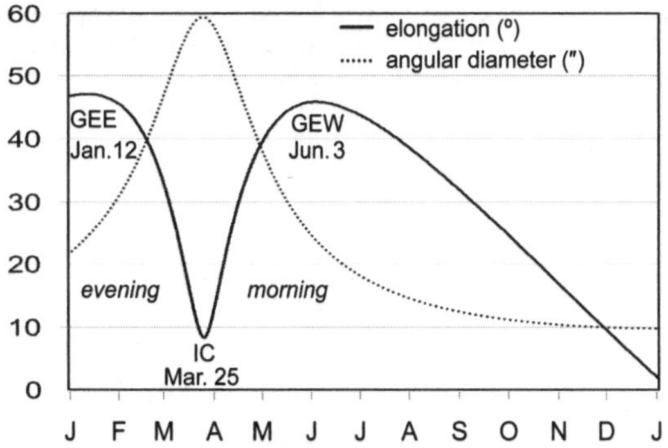

Elongation is plotted in degrees and apparent angular diameter in arcseconds. The first day of each month is marked on the horizontal axis.

mid-gibbous phases. A violet filter can enhance the visibility of atmospheric structure, and imaging through a UV filter will show cloud details. The Association of Lunar and Planetary Observers is interested in your images of Venus seen this way.

Never far from the Sun, Venus may be found in a telescope during the daytime, when high in the sky, far from the deleterious effects of our thick near-horizon atmosphere. The daytime sky is favourable for viewing the bright disk of Venus, because of the lower luminance contrast. This is a popular daytime activity at star parties (see the discussion on daytime planet viewing in the INTRODUCTION of this section, p. 212).

Venus culminates in its greatest elongation east on Jan. 12 at 47.1° from the Sun. In a wonderful coincidence, it is joined by Neptune with closest approach visible in Newfoundland of 21.6′ an hour after sunset. On the west coast, the pair will move off to 24.5′ separation at an hour after sunset. They should be visible in a high-power eyepiece with a brilliant mag. –4.6, 25″, 51% illuminated Venus at dichotomy and a diminutive 2.2″ Neptune shining at mag. 7.9. It will make for an interesting sight. Venus moves onward and downward to the Mar. 25 inferior conjunction, where it will pass 8.3° above the Sun. It will be 1% illuminated at the time and shining at mag. –4.2. In an eyepiece, you will see a delicate 59.3″ crescent that is well worth the hunt.

Post-conjunction, Venus proceeds to the morning sky where it spends the remainder of 2017. There is a fine conjunction with the Moon on the morning of May 22, and a conjunction with Uranus on Jun. 3. Venus and Uranus rise 2 h before the Sun separated by 1.8°, with Uranus above and following Venus. Uranus will sport a mag. –5.9, 3.2″ blue-green disk and Venus will have a 50% illuminated mag. –4.4 disk. They will make a pretty pair in a rich-field scope or your favourite pair of binoculars. greatest elongation west is on Jun. 3, giving a second dichotomy in the first half of 2017.

On the morning of Jul. 20, Venus and the Moon join up in the morning sky well placed for observers in North America. On Oct. 5, we are treated to a grand close conjunction of Venus and Mars. They will be 16.7′ apart in eastern North America, shrinking to a 13.4′ separation at the west coast. The minimum separation of 12′ will be observable in the eastern Pacific islands. They will be further apart the further east you are, observing them one-half hour before sunrise. The last interesting conjunction will be the Nov. 13 Venus–Jupiter event. On the east coast, they rise 1 h before the Sun and will be spaced 16.6′ apart; they will separate the further west you are, and by the time they are visible on the west coast, they will be 23′ apart. They will only be 14° from Sun, so find a clear eastern horizon! I have seen the pair in the daytime on a cool but clear February afternoon. It was a memorable experience.

At the close of the year, Venus is too close to the Sun to be easily observed as it heads toward superior conjunction in early January.

MARS

Mars is a planet that inspires us, a place we could anticipate walking on and exploring, a destination where our grandchildren may go. A web of imagined canals has ensnared us, and generations of observers and scientists have devoted their lives to the study of the Red Planet. Despite the unveiling of the mysteries of Mars, with neither Martians nor canals to be found, many of us are still infatuated with the planet.

About every 2 years and 50 days, on average, we renew our acquaintance with Mars, as Earth—on the inside track—overtakes the fourth planet. Over the roughly 15-year cycle between extreme close approaches near perihelion, there are seven oppositions with diverse separations (see OPPOSITIONS OF MARS on p. 220). The Martian day is about 3% longer than our day; this results in us observing the same central meridian of Mars about 38 min later on successive nights. Equivalently, the longitude of the centre of the Martian disk reduces by 9.5° per Earth day. Accordingly, near opposition, the same surface features will be visible at the same time of night 41 days later. When the view is near its best, you can expect to enjoy two full rotations of Mars in stroboscopic form.

Mars is accompanied by two small moons, Deimos and Phobos, discovered by Asaph Hall in 1877 with the 66-cm (26-in.) refractor at the U.S. Naval Observatory. These two moons undoubtedly are captured minor planets, given their angular shape and proximity to the asteroid belt. Deimos is the smaller, at 16 × 12 km, and completes one orbit in 30.3 h. Phobos, at 26 × 22 km, orbits Mars in a speedy 7.7 h. Viewed from the Martian surface, Phobos would rise in the west and set in the east. Detecting this pair is a real challenge, because Mars outshines them by 13 to 14 magnitudes, and they never venture very far from the planet. Observe near opposition with an occulting-bar eyepiece to block out the brilliance of the Martian disk (see p. 25), using lots of magnification and a finder chart, so you know where to look.

Observing Mars: As mentioned in last year's Handbook, Mars passes Neptune in an extremely close conjunction on the night of Dec. 31 (local)/Jan. 1, where they pass only 70″ apart at 6:53 UT. We are in a period of close conjunctions and this is the first of three over the next eight years. All of them are 2.1′ to 1.0′ at closest approach. Then nothing closer than 10′ for the next 50 years. The closest approach will be visible in the Hawaiian Islands, where they sit 20° above the horizon. What a way to welcome in the New Year! Two days later, a five-day-old Moon occults Mars only 3.5° above the horizon and 20 min before they set. Back to our cold, hard reality, we will see the pair set 10.5′ apart in Halifax, and on the west coast they are 3.6′ apart. Two days later, we miss the Mars occultation because they set before closing together. Mars is heading toward the Sun and Venus is headed away to its elongation; the two planets sit conspicuously in the evening sky over January and February. Their closest approach is on Feb. 3 where they are 5.4° apart. Mars and Venus are joined by a four-day-old crescent Moon on the night of Feb. 1 (Jan. 31 local). On the night of Feb. 26, Mars passes 34′ above Uranus and they sit far enough from the Sun to look good in a high-powered field. Mars will be a 4.6″, mag. –1.3 ruddy disk and Uranus will present a 3.4″, mag. –5.9 bluish disk. It should make for a very nice view in a scope. We get a few more wide conjunctions with the Moon as summer approaches, and on Jul. 26, Mars comes to its conjunction with the Sun. On the morning of Sep. 18, we get a conjunction of a narrow crescent Moon, Mars, and Mercury (see p. 214, Mercury). Two weeks later on Oct. 5, we get a close conjunction with Venus (see p. 217). Mars continues up the morning sky with a nice lunar conjunction on the morning of Oct. 17, when the two pass just under 1° apart. Closest approach is visible from the east coast to Winnipeg; at the west coast the pair has separated to 1.6°. Mars closes the year as it approaches Zubenelgenubi (α Libra) and Jupiter.

The subtle details on Mars can be enhanced by colour filters. The one essential filter is the orange Wratten #21, which improves the contrast between the darker

continued on p. 222

MARS JULY 2016

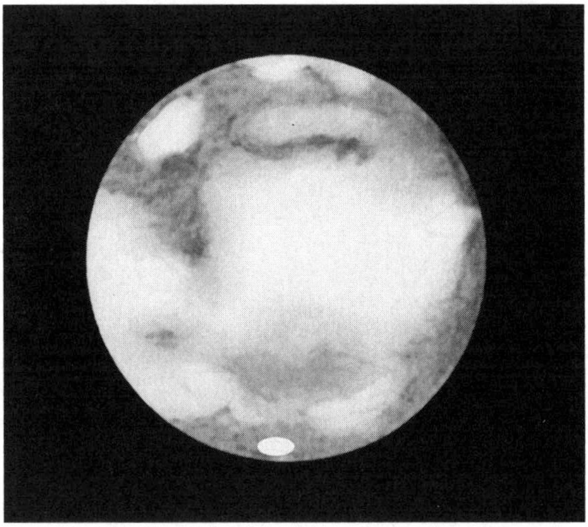

Denis Fell sketched Mars on 2016 Jul. 29 from his home in Kennedy, Saskatchewan, as the Red Planet receded from Earth (or Earth left it behind). He describes the event as "Average evening, major features still well defined at this diameter; much transient detail in the north polar region, depending on seeing." He used an 80-mm f/15 Achromat telescope with Tele Vue *Bandmate* Mars A & B filters.

He says "Observers don't need to have a large expensive telescope to see this level of detail or record it with pencil and paper, even a 60-mm telescope will do."

MARS—OBSERVING CIRCUMSTANCES IN 2017

Date 0h UT	Distance au	Dec °	Mag.	Equatorial Diam. ″	% Illum.	Rotation Axis PA °	Rotation Axis Incl. °
Jan. 1	1.684	–9.6	0.9	5.7	90	345	–25
Feb. 1	1.372	–14.9	1.1	5.1	93	332	–26
Mar. 1	1.078	–18.4	1.3	4.6	95	324	–23
Dec. 1	1.438	–17.3	1.7	4.3	95	36	22

Data are provided on the first of the month if Mars is >40° from the Sun, plus mid-month if **Equatorial Diam.** *≥10″. The position angle (***PA***) of the rotation axis is measured counterclockwise from celestial north (clockwise in telescopes having an odd number of reflections); the inclination (***Incl.***) of the rotation axis to the plane of the sky is positive if the north pole is tipped toward Earth. 2017 is an "off" year.*

OPPOSITIONS OF MARS, 2010–2022

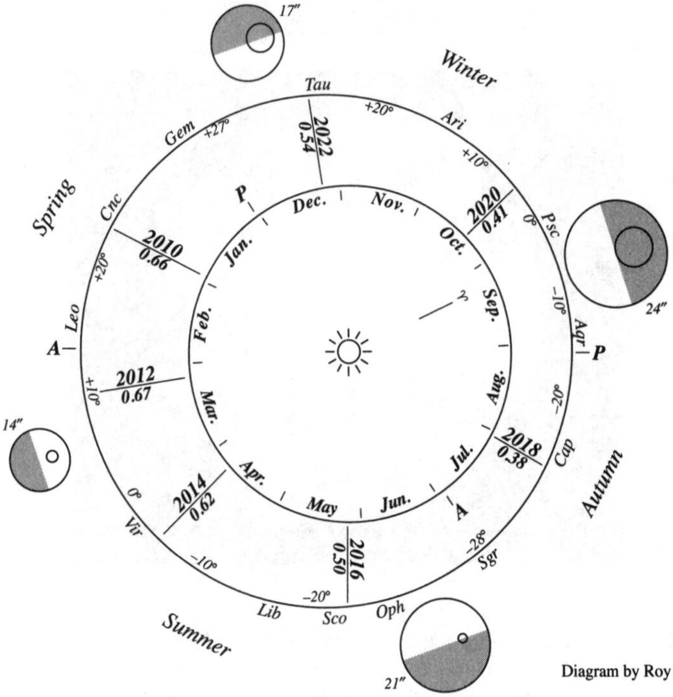

Diagram by Roy Bishop

The above diagram represents the orbits of Earth and Mars as viewed from the north ecliptic pole. Straight lines link simultaneous positions of the two planets for seven successive oppositions of Mars, beginning with that of the year 2010. The separation of the two planets (in astronomical units) at the various oppositions is indicated beside each of the connecting lines. The months inside of Earth's orbit indicate the position of Earth during the year (both planets orbit counterclockwise). For each orbit, two tick marks labelled A and P indicate the aphelion point and the perihelion point, respectively. The direction of the vernal equinox is shown (toward the late-September position of Earth). Around the orbit of Mars is indicated its declination (ranges between +27° and −28°) and the constellation in which Mars resides when at opposition.

Four views of Mars are shown: at its two equinoxes and two solstices. These views show the portion of Mars illuminated by the Sun, the location and approximate size of its north polar cap, and the apparent size of Mars (labelled in arcseconds) for oppositions occurring at these points in its orbit. The seasons of the Martian northern hemisphere are indicated around the outer margin of the diagram, and are very nearly one season ahead of those on Earth at the same orbital position. (For the southern hemisphere of Mars, the season and the configuration of the south polar cap are the same as those of the diametrically opposite view.) Note that the maximum angular diameter Mars can attain (25″) occurs near its perihelion, at a late-August opposition.

As an example of the information that can be read from this diagram: next year's opposition of Mars will occur in late July with Mars located near declination −25° in the constellation Capricornus, 0.38 au from Earth, and about 23″ in diameter. It will be autumn in the Martian northern hemisphere and the south polar cap will be visible.

MAP OF MARS

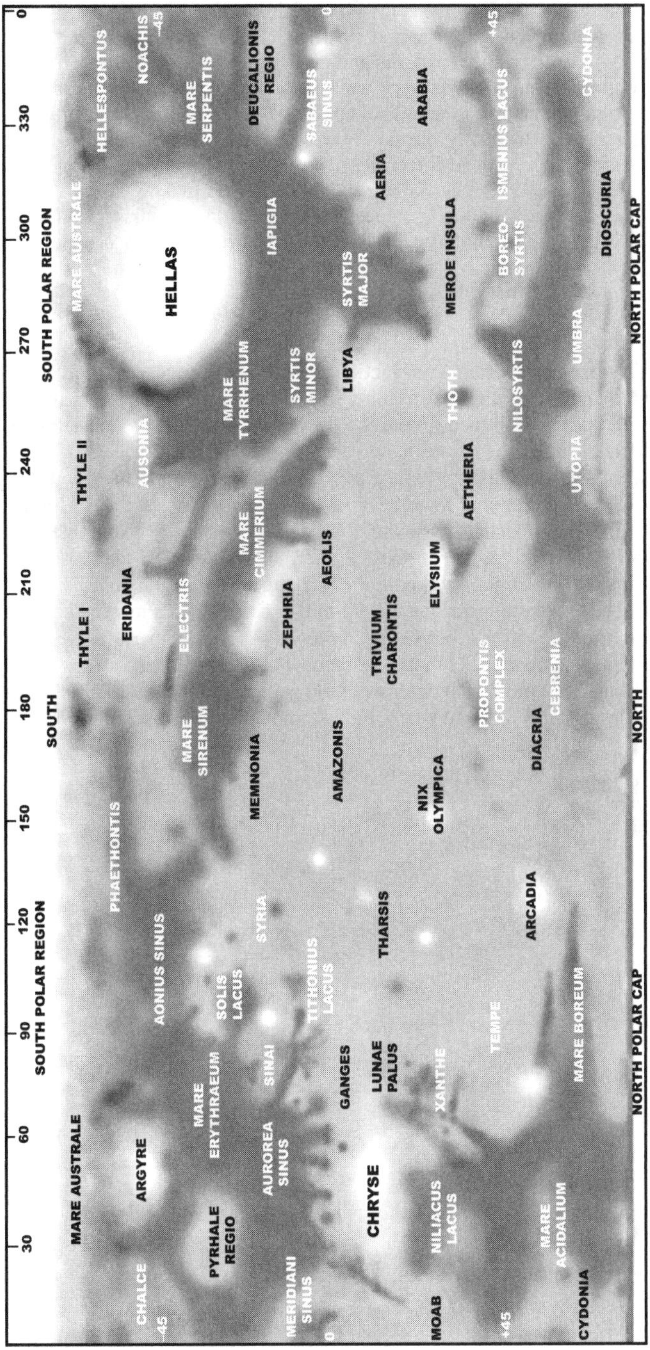

This map has south at top and north at bottom, and represents the view through a telescope having an even number (0, 2, 4) of reflections. It was computer-generated by Daniel Troiani, using all the data (CCD images, drawings, and photographs) from the Mars section of the Association of Lunar and Planetary Observers (ALPO) during the 2001 apparition. The map is intended to represent the appearance of Mars, as viewed from Earth through moderate-sized telescopes, during favourable apparitions, or electronic images that have been digitally processed. For recent observations of Mars, visit the Mars section of the ALPO website, alpo-astronomy.org.

maria and the lighter, rust-coloured deserts. The #21 is not too dense for smaller-aperture telescopes. For 200-mm and larger apertures, a red filter provides the maximum contrast. Yellow and green filters enhance the view of dust-storm activity, and a green filter enhances the view of ground haze and frost. The Hellas, Elysium, and Argyre basins occasionally have frost on their floors and may be quite bright. Blue light does not penetrate the atmosphere of Mars very well, so atmospheric details and clouds are enhanced by blue and violet filters. The surface is not usually visible in deep-blue or violet filters, but occasionally, during the "blue clearing" phenomenon, surface features will be visible through these filters. Remember that the morning side of Mars is the following side in the telescope eyepiece. I do recommend looking at Mars without filters as well. I have noticed white clouds against the salmon pink of the region north of Mare Sirenum–Cimmerium, which I would not have noticed had I used my orange filter.

JUPITER

Other than Venus when near inferior conjunction, Jupiter is the largest planet to view in a telescope, with an angular diameter ranging from 44″ in 50″ at opposition. Jupiter moves just over 30° per year in its orbit around the Sun, visiting a new constellation of the zodiac about every year.

Jupiter does not have a solid surface; however, unlike Venus, it has high-contrast, semi-stationary cloud features that have been observed for many centuries. Jupiter rotates on its axis in 9 h 51 m, slightly slower toward the poles, easily noticeable over a period of half an hour. In fact, when drawing Jupiter, sketch the major features in the first 10 min, because their locations will noticeably change if you dwell on it. Then fill in the details relative to the major features. A 50-mm telescope will show the equatorial belts, the polar hoods, and the four Galilean moons. A 75-mm aperture telescope will easily show the shadows of the moons and some structure in the various cloud belts. Fifty years ago, my old 50-mm refractor showed a brick-red Great Red Spot (GRS), but now the spot has faded to a very light salmon pink, so you need a 90-mm

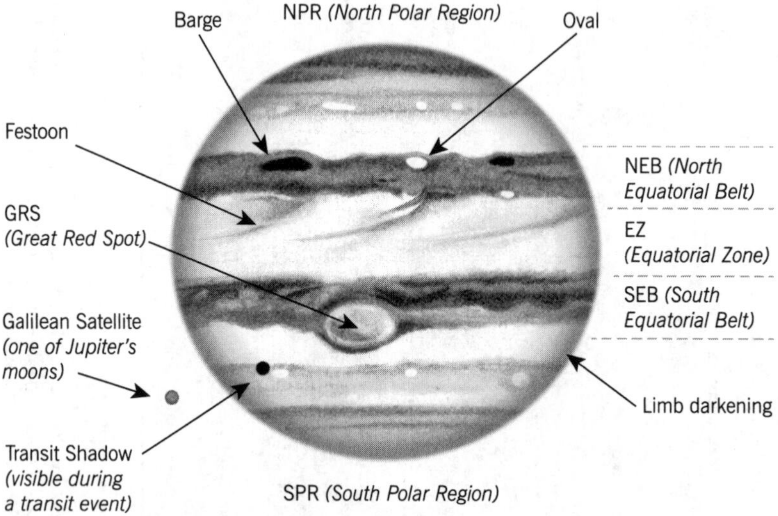

This composite drawing by Michael Gatto illustrates and names the principal observable features of Jupiter, including one of the Galilean satellites and its shadow.

refractor just to see it, under good conditions. Over the last year, it has been determined that the GRS has been shrinking for quite some time. In the 1800s, the spot was estimated to have been 41 000 km in its long axis, whereas present day measurements by the *Hubble Space Telescope* show it to be only 16 500 km in length. It is notable that recent amateur observations have determined that the spot has experienced an acceleration in its rate of shrinkage. We may bear witness to the disappearance of the Great Red Spot in our lifetime. Jupiter's belts are dynamic and occasionally disappear only to reappear again a few year later. If the GRS disappears, it may be a long time before a similar long-lived major feature emerges. Stay tuned.

The views of Jupiter in 125-mm to 175-mm apochromatic refractors or high-quality 200-mm to 320-mm obstructed apertures are spectacular. Wait for those rare moments of excellent seeing, and you will be rewarded. These apertures (with high-quality optics, properly collimated) will reveal the ovals, festoons, and many structures recorded in the best images of Jupiter. With a 130-mm refractor at magnifications above 200x, the contrast on Jupiter starts to get soft. Larger apertures have a higher magnification threshold and will improve the contrast, colour, and amount of fine detail visible on Jupiter. In the last few years, several long-lived white ovals and additional red spots have been observed in Jupiter's southern regions, while the north equatorial belt has shown more dark markings along its margins. Because some of Jupiter's cloud features are coloured, you can improve contrast and visibility by observing with colour filters. The contrast of red spots and the belt features improves with a green filter, and the bluish festoons will darken with an orange or a red filter.

Jupiter is one of the better planets for imaging. The most recent generation of video imagers has improved the quality of amateur planet images. It is now easy to get images that push the limits of the optical system, and the dynamic range of the image can be stretched to reveal low-contrast details. Amateurs are producing images nearly as good as those from Hubble, and they are making discoveries such as "Red Spot, Jr." and impacts in Jupiter's atmosphere. As deep-sky observers search for locations with the darkest skies, leading imagers seek observing locations with stable atmospheres.

This year marks Jupiter at its apogee opposition and it will show the smallest disk at opposition in 12 years. The year starts off with Jupiter 4.5° above Spica (α Virgo), and it is headed east toward its stationary point where it will start retrograde motion on Feb. 6. On Jan. 19 (the night of Jan. 18–19), we are treated to a conjunction of the Moon and Jupiter as they rise an hour after midnight—the Moon passes 2° above Jupiter. On Apr. 7, Jupiter comes to its aphelic opposition and will display a 44″ disk at mag. −2.5. It is currently at −5.5° declination but still culminates at a reasonable altitude for northern latitudes. Jupiter's perihelic oppositions are halfway around the sky in Pisces and do not favour either hemisphere, unlike those of Mars. At opposition, Jupiter's moons are at their largest apparent diameter for the year and readily recognizable in a telescope.

This year's data: Io 1.1″, Europa 1.0″, Ganymede 1.6″, and Callisto 1.5″.

On Jun. 3, a waxing gibbous Moon passes 1.5° above Jupiter an hour before sunset. Try to find it in the daytime sky with the Moon to help you locate the gas planet and set your eyes' focal plane. You may need to find it in binoculars first. A few days later, on Jun. 9, Jupiter is at its westernmost stationary point 3.1° below Porima, γ Vir. From there it travels east again, and on Jul. 28, we get a crescent Moon joining Jupiter. The closest approach of 2.3° is visible in the east coast, and the pair separate further west; they are 3.4° apart on the west coast of North America. On Oct. 19 (18 local), Mercury and Jupiter pass 56′ apart, but only 6.6° from the Sun in the evening sky. Due to our unfavourable fall ecliptic, this is only observable from south of the equator and is a challenge in the daytime sky (see Mercury, p. 214). On Oct. 26, Jupiter is in conjunction with the Sun, and just over two weeks later, on Nov. 13, is in conjunction with

JUPITER—TABLE OF DAILY CENTRAL MERIDIANS, 2017

Date 0h UT	System I	System II	Date 0h UT	System I	System II	Date 0h UT	System I	System II	Date 0h UT	System I	System II	Date 0h UT	System I	System II
JANUARY			**MARCH**			**MAY**			**JULY**			**SEPTEMBER**		
1	217.1	335.1	1	176.4	204.2	1	96.0	18.3	1	5.6	182.6	1	63.0	126.9
2	15.0	125.3	2	334.5	354.6	2	254.0	168.6	2	163.4	332.7	2	220.6	276.9
3	172.9	275.6	3	132.5	145.0	3	51.9	319.0	3	321.2	122.8	3	18.3	66.9
4	330.8	65.8	4	290.5	295.4	4	209.9	109.3	4	118.9	272.9	4	176.0	217.0
5	128.6	216.1	5	88.5	85.8	5	7.8	259.6	5	276.7	63.1	5	333.6	7.0
6	286.5	6.3	6	246.6	236.2	6	165.8	50.0	6	74.4	213.2	6	131.3	157.0
7	84.4	156.6	7	44.6	26.6	7	323.8	200.3	7	232.2	3.3	7	288.9	307.0
8	242.3	306.8	8	202.6	177.0	8	121.7	350.6	8	29.9	153.4	8	86.6	97.1
9	40.2	97.1	9	0.7	327.4	9	279.7	140.9	9	187.6	303.5	9	244.3	247.1
10	198.1	247.4	10	158.7	117.8	10	77.6	291.2	10	345.4	93.6	10	41.9	37.1
11	356.0	37.6	11	316.8	268.2	11	235.5	81.6	11	143.1	243.7	11	199.6	187.2
12	153.9	187.9	12	114.8	58.6	12	33.5	231.9	12	300.8	33.8	12	357.2	337.2
13	311.8	338.2	13	272.8	209.0	13	191.4	22.2	13	98.6	183.9	13	154.9	127.2
14	109.7	128.5	14	70.9	359.4	14	349.3	172.5	14	256.3	334.0	14	312.6	277.3
15	267.6	278.8	15	228.9	149.8	15	147.3	322.8	15	54.0	124.1	15	110.2	67.3
16	65.6	69.0	16	27.0	300.2	16	305.2	113.1	16	211.8	274.2	16	267.9	217.3
17	223.5	219.3	17	185.0	90.7	17	103.1	263.3	17	9.5	64.3	17	65.5	7.4
18	21.4	9.6	18	343.0	241.1	18	261.0	53.6	18	167.2	214.4	18	223.2	157.4
19	179.3	159.9	19	141.1	31.5	19	58.9	203.9	19	324.9	4.5	19	20.9	307.4
20	337.2	310.2	20	299.1	181.9	20	216.8	354.2	20	122.6	154.6	20	178.5	97.4
21	135.2	100.5	21	97.2	332.3	21	14.7	144.5	21	280.3	304.7	21	336.2	247.5
22	293.1	250.8	22	255.2	122.7	22	172.6	294.7	22	78.0	94.7	22	133.8	37.5
23	91.0	41.1	23	53.3	273.1	23	330.5	85.0	23	235.8	244.8	23	291.5	187.5
24	249.0	191.4	24	211.3	63.5	24	128.4	235.3	24	33.5	34.9	*(too close to Sun)*		
25	46.9	341.7	25	9.3	214.0	25	286.3	25.5	25	191.2	185.0	**NOVEMBER**		
26	204.9	132.0	26	167.4	4.4	26	84.2	175.8	26	348.9	335.0	26	303.4	71.1
27	2.8	282.4	27	325.4	154.8	27	242.1	326.0	27	146.6	125.1	27	101.1	221.2
28	160.8	72.7	28	123.5	305.2	28	40.0	116.3	28	304.3	275.2	28	258.8	11.3
29	318.7	223.0	29	281.5	95.6	29	197.8	266.5	29	102.0	65.3	29	56.6	161.4
30	116.7	13.3	30	79.5	246.0	30	355.7	56.8	30	259.7	215.3	30	214.3	311.5
31	274.6	163.6	31	237.6	36.4	31	153.6	207.0	31	57.4	5.4			

Date 0h UT	System I	System II	Date 0h UT	System I	System II	Date 0h UT	System I	System II	Date 0h UT	System I	System II	Date 0h UT	System I	System II
FEBRUARY			**APRIL**			**JUNE**			**AUGUST**			**DECEMBER**		
1	72.6	314.0	1	35.6	186.8	1	311.4	357.2	1	215.1	155.5	1	12.0	101.6
2	230.5	104.3	2	193.7	337.2	2	109.3	147.4	2	12.7	305.5	2	169.8	251.7
3	28.5	254.6	3	351.7	127.6	3	267.1	297.7	3	170.4	95.6	3	327.5	41.8
4	186.5	45.0	4	149.7	278.1	4	65.0	87.9	4	328.1	245.6	4	125.2	191.9
5	344.4	195.3	5	307.8	68.5	5	222.8	238.1	5	125.8	35.7	5	283.0	342.0
6	142.4	345.7	6	105.8	218.9	6	20.7	28.3	6	283.5	185.8	6	80.7	132.1
7	300.4	136.0	7	263.8	9.3	7	178.5	178.5	7	81.2	335.8	7	238.5	282.2
8	98.4	286.4	8	61.9	159.7	8	336.4	328.7	8	238.9	125.9	8	36.2	72.4
9	256.3	76.7	9	219.9	310.1	9	134.2	118.9	9	36.5	275.9	9	194.0	222.5
10	54.3	227.1	10	17.9	100.5	10	292.0	269.1	10	194.2	66.0	10	351.7	12.6
11	212.3	17.4	11	176.0	250.9	11	89.8	59.3	11	351.9	216.0	11	149.5	162.7
12	10.3	167.8	12	334.0	41.2	12	247.7	209.5	12	149.6	6.1	12	307.2	312.8
13	168.3	318.1	13	132.0	191.6	13	45.5	359.7	13	307.3	156.1	13	105.0	103.0
14	326.3	108.5	14	290.0	342.0	14	203.3	149.9	14	104.9	306.2	14	262.7	253.1
15	124.3	258.9	15	88.0	132.4	15	1.1	300.1	15	262.6	96.2	15	60.5	43.2
16	282.3	49.2	16	246.1	282.8	16	158.9	90.3	16	60.3	246.2	16	218.2	193.4
17	80.3	199.6	17	44.1	73.2	17	316.7	240.4	17	218.0	36.3	17	16.0	343.5
18	238.3	350.0	18	202.1	223.6	18	114.5	30.6	18	15.6	186.3	18	173.8	133.6
19	36.3	140.3	19	0.1	14.0	19	272.3	180.8	19	173.3	336.4	19	331.5	283.8
20	194.3	290.7	20	158.1	164.3	20	70.1	330.9	20	331.0	126.4	20	129.3	73.9
21	352.3	81.1	21	316.1	314.7	21	227.9	121.1	21	128.6	276.5	21	287.1	224.0
22	150.3	231.5	22	114.1	105.1	22	25.7	271.3	22	286.3	66.5	22	84.9	14.2
23	308.3	21.8	23	272.1	255.4	23	183.5	61.4	23	84.0	216.5	23	242.6	164.3
24	106.3	172.2	24	70.1	45.8	24	341.3	211.6	24	241.6	6.6	24	40.4	314.5
25	264.4	322.6	25	228.1	196.2	25	139.0	1.7	25	39.3	156.6	25	198.2	104.6
26	62.4	113.0	26	26.1	346.5	26	296.8	151.9	26	197.0	306.6	26	356.0	254.8
27	220.4	263.4	27	184.1	136.9	27	94.6	302.0	27	354.6	96.7	27	153.8	44.9
28	18.4	53.8	28	342.0	287.2	28	252.4	92.2	28	152.3	246.7	28	311.6	195.1
			29	140.0	77.6	29	50.1	242.3	29	310.0	36.8	29	109.3	345.3
			30	298.0	227.9	30	207.9	32.4	30	107.6	186.8	30	267.1	135.4
												31	64.9	285.6

Venus in the much more favourable morning sky (see Venus, p. 216). On the morning of Dec. 14, the Moon rises with Jupiter and is visible all across North America. Jupiter spends the balance of the year in Libra and passes close to Zubenelgenubi, as Mars chases it in flight.

The Galilean moons of Jupiter are frequently involved in eclipses, occultations, and transits; these events are easy to observe in amateur telescopes. For a complete listing of events, see PHENOMENA OF THE GALILEAN SATELLITES on p. 230.

Experienced amateurs should consider trying to observe Himalia, a small body that shines dimly at mag. 15.1 (near opposition). Its orbit is highly inclined, with a 250-day period, and the satellite may be found as much as 1° away from Jupiter, so it is a bit of an observing challenge. Canadian amateur Alan Whitman has spotted Himalia in a 400-mm Newtonian reflector.

JUPITER—DAILY CENTRAL MERIDIANS AND TIME OF TRANSIT OF GREAT RED SPOT

The table on the facing page can be used to calculate the longitude of the central meridian of the observed disk of Jupiter throughout 2017, except for the interval Sep. 24–Nov. 25, when Jupiter is too close to the Sun to observe. System I is the most rapidly rotating region between the middle of the North Equatorial Belt and the middle of the South Equatorial Belt. System II applies to the rest of the planet, from the equatorial belts to the poles. The rotation rate of System I is 36.577 ± 0.008 °/h and that of System II is 36.259 ± 0.008 °/h. These figures, together with the closest tabular value, can be used to determine the longitude of a system's central meridian for any given date and time (UT) of observation. **Example:** At 9:00 p.m. CDT Jul. 18 = 2:00 UT Jul. 19, the longitude of the central meridian of System I is

$$324.9 + (36.577 \times 2) = 398.1°;$$

putting this angle in the range 0°–360° by subtracting 360° leaves a longitude of 38.1°± 0.01°.

The table may also be used to estimate when the Great Red Spot (GRS) will cross the central meridian of Jupiter's disk. (Based on drift measurements, the GRS is predicted to be near longitude 255.0° in System II on 2017 Jan. 0, drifting by about +14.5° per year. See jupos.privat.t-online.de for an up-to-date value.)

Example: Suppose an observer in Montréal is viewing Jupiter on the evening of Mar. 31 (time zone: EDT, −4h). At 0h UT Apr. 1 (20h EDT Mar. 31), the table gives 186.8° for the longitude of the central meridian in System II. Ignoring GRS drift, a further rotation of 255.0°– 186.8°= 68.2° will bring the GRS to the central meridian, which takes place 68.2°÷ 36.259°/ h = 1.88h = 1 h 53 min later. Thus the GRS will transit at 1:53 UT Apr. 1 = 21:53 EDT Mar. 31. (Correcting for the annual drift in GRS longitude would add 14.5° × 3/12 ÷ 36.259°/h = 0.10h, or 6 min to the transit time.) By timing a transit of the GRS and using the table, you can update its longitude for yourself. Alternatively, you can use a specialized GRS transit calculator, such as www.skyandtelescope.com/observing/objects/planets/3304091.html.

JUPITER AND SATURN IN 2017

	Jupiter		Saturn		
Date UT	Mag.	Equatorial Diameter ″	Mag.	Equatorial Diameter ″	Ring Inclination °
Jan. 1.0	−1.9	35	+0.5	15	26.6
Feb. 1.0	−2.1	39	+0.5	16	26.7
Mar. 1.0	−2.3	42	+0.5	16	26.7
Apr. 1.0	−2.5	44	+0.4	17	26.7
May 1.0	−2.4	43	+0.2	17	26.7
Jun. 1.0	−2.3	40	+0.1	18	26.7
Jul. 1.0	−2.0	37	+0.1	18	26.7
Aug. 1.0	−1.9	34	+0.3	17	26.7
Sep. 1.0	−1.7	32	+0.4	17	26.7
Oct. 1.0	−1.7	31	+0.5	16	26.6
Nov. 1.0	−1.7	31	+0.5	15	26.6
Dec. 1.0	−1.8	31	+0.5	15	26.6
Jan. 1.0	−1.8	33	+0.5	15	26.5

SATURN

Saturn is the second-largest planet in the Solar System, with a maximum equatorial angular diameter of 21″ (excluding the rings). The ringed planet takes 29.4 y to orbit the Sun, and moves only 12.2° per year in its eastward journey along the ecliptic. Saturn is the most oblate of the planets, with a polar/equatorial diameter ratio of 0.9.

With its incredible system of rings, Saturn is possibly the most spectacular planet in the Solar System. The rings subtend 42″–47″ near opposition, and are visible even in steadied (or image-stabilized) high-power binoculars and small spotting scopes. Saturn's rings are composed mostly of ice particles of sizes ranging from dust to boulders, in complex subsystems of rings within rings. The more you zoom in on the rings, the more structure there is to see. The *Cassini* probe has found fine structure right down to the limits of its image resolution.

Visually, in earthbound telescopes, the rings divide into three distinct sectors (see facing page). The outer (A) ring is separated from the first inner (B) ring by the Cassini Division, which J.D. Cassini discovered in 1675. The Cassini Division is visible in a 50-mm telescope, yet it is only 0.8″ wide at opposition. The A ring itself is divided by the Encke Gap, a very fine division about one-fifth of the way between the outer edge of the ring and the Cassini Division. The Encke Gap is extremely difficult to observe and requires a large aperture (250 mm or greater), high-quality optics, and high magnification (~500x), which in turn demands excellent atmospheric seeing. There is also a minimum in luminance called the Encke minimum, about halfway between the outer edge of the A ring and the Cassini Division. This is easier to see and is often confused with the Encke Gap.

The next ring inward is the B ring, which is the broadest and brightest of the rings. The inner edge of this ring fades a bit in brightness and often appears to have a stranded nature, like grooves in a vinyl record. The inner edge sometimes exhibits spokes in the ansae (the part of the rings seen on either side of the planet). You need high magnification and a very clean optical system to see these subtle features. They may only be visible on one side of the planet.

The innermost ring is the Crepe Ring (also called the C ring). It goes largely unnoticed because it is so dim in comparison to the outer two rings and the glare from Saturn. It is a ghostly ring about the same width as the A ring, and it appears dark where it passes in front of the planet. It looks like a shadow cast on the planet, but it is actually blocking the planet's reflected light from our view. A very clean optical system is essential to get a good view of the Crepe Ring. Contrast-robbing dust and debris on eyepiece and diagonal surfaces have a pronounced effect, because they are close to the eye. You know you have seen the Crepe Ring when you notice that the black space within the ansae next to the ball of the planet is only slightly darker than the Crepe Ring.

At a distance of 9.5 au from the Sun, Saturn does not receive enough solar energy to sustain as lively an atmosphere as that of Jupiter. There are a few belts, and the occasional storm or outbreak of activity. The average observer will see an equatorial-region belt and the dark polar hood, but not much else. The experienced observer may see much more, but the details are subtle. White spots have been seen in the south tropical zone, and a south equatorial disturbance was recorded in 2009. In late 2010, a dramatic storm appeared in the north temperate zone, and the white spot spread and was followed for many months in 2011. These subtle phenomena are more readily captured with a camera.

Saturn tips its north pole and rings up at their maximum of 27° toward us this year, and if you look carefully you can see the north pole of Saturn in line with the Cassini Division. Try to see any sign of the south hemisphere through the division at the other end of the rings. Saturn starts off the year in Sagittarius, and on Apr. 5 it is stationary, changing direction and starting retrograde motion west, then crossing into Scorpius on May 18. This year's opposition on Jun. 15 is close to aphelion. Saturn's 18.4″ disk shines at mag. 0.0 from its 9-au distance. Compare this to its perihelic

SATURN—MAIN RING FEATURES VISIBLE FROM EARTH

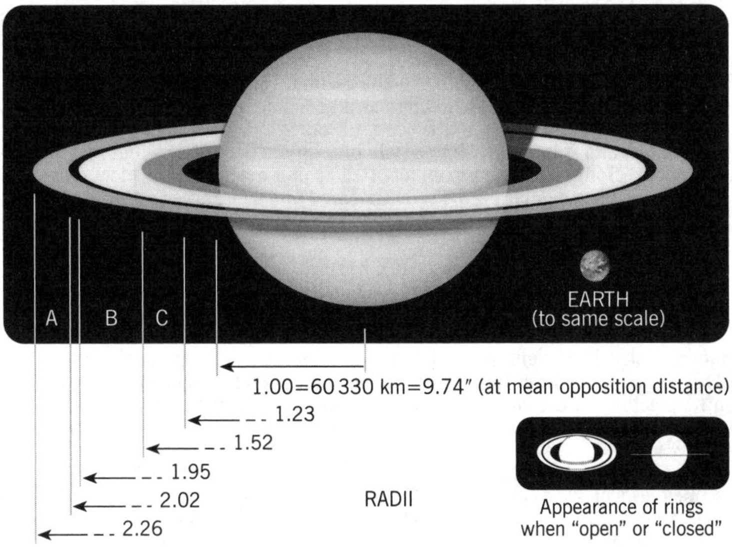

SATURN'S RING SYSTEM—MAIN STRUCTURAL REGIONS

Ring	Radius**	Discoverer
D	1.11 – 1.23	*Voyager 1* (1980)
C*	1.23 – 1.52	W.C. & G.P. Bond, W.R. Dawes (1850)
B*	1.52 – 1.95	Galileo (1610), C. Huygens (1659),
A*	2.02 – 2.26	J.D. Cassini (1675)
F	2.33	*Pioneer 11* (1979)
G	2.8	*Voyager 1* (1980)
E	3. – 8.	W.A. Feibelman (1966)

* *Visible from Earth; also, the tenuous E ring can be detected when Saturn's ring system appears edge-on.*

** *In units of Saturn's equatorial radius (60 330 km)*

Diagram by Roy Bishop/Michael Gatto

20.7″ in 2032. This year's apparition sits just over the heart of the Milky Way and favours the Southern Hemisphere. It will offer Messier hunters a lovely Solar System object as an alternative during the summer star parties. On Aug. 25, Saturn arrives at its second stationary point and turns back in prograde motion to the east. In the latter part of November, Saturn moves back into Sagittarius. On Dec. 21, the Ringed Planet joins the Sun in conjunction on the winter solstice.

Saturn has 62 natural satellites, of which 8 are visible in amateur telescopes. Of those, only Titan shows a disk in large telescopes. At opposition this year, Titan presents a 0.8″ disk; the others, less than 0.25″.

The satellite Iapetus (mag. 10.6–12.5) is tidally locked to Saturn, with its leading hemisphere as dark as coal, and the other side quite white. (The actual albedos are 0.05 and 0.5, respectively.) Because of this, when Iapetus is near elongation on the west side of Saturn, it is almost two magnitudes brighter than it is on the east side. The 79.3-day orbit of Iapetus takes it as far as 9.1′ from Saturn. It is directly north of Saturn on Mar. 10, May 28, and Aug. 14, and directly south on Apr. 18, Jul. 5, and Sep. 22. Since it is displaying both faces at these times, it will shine at an intermediate magnitude (see CONFIGURATION OF SATURN'S BRIGHTEST SATELLITES on p. 237).

URANUS

Uranus is the faintest of the planets visible to the naked eye and the third-largest overall, yet its tremendous distance means that its maximum angular diameter is only 4.0″. Uranus's orbital period is 84.4 y, and it moves along the ecliptic only about 4.3°/y. William Herschel discovered Uranus in 1781 with a 160-mm reflector, but it had been recorded by earlier observers, who charted it as a star. At mag. 5.7, it would require a clear and transparent sky for a successful naked-eye sighting. Binoculars easily reveal Uranus, and it blossoms into a pale blue-green disk under high magnification in a telescope. Some observers have reported seeing details on the planet, even with amateur-sized instruments. Fred Price, in *The Planet Observer's Handbook*, states that the only features seen on the planet are the two faint belts and that you need at least a 250-mm telescope to see these.

Uranus starts out 2017 just 30′ east of ζ Psc and sets after midnight. It is well placed for a winter observation shining at mag. 5.8 and displays a 3.5″ blue-green disk. Uranus moves into conjunction with the Sun on Apr. 14 and will disappear from us for the most part until late summer, with one exception. On Jun. 3, Uranus is joined by Venus in the morning sky. The bright mag. –4.4 beacon of Venus will help you find the pair (see p. 216). Aug. 2 marks the turn to retrograde motion and Uranus starts moving west from its position on the east side of Pisces, where it sits just over 1° above ο Psc, a 4.3-mag. star. Uranus comes to opposition on Oct. 19, shines at mag. 5.7 and its disk will grow to 3.7″.

The Uranian satellite system is within reach of medium-to-large amateur telescopes, especially at opposition. This year at opposition, the moons Titania and Oberon are mag. 14.0 and 14.1, respectively, and their orbits describe an ellipse with the long axis 10° clockwise rotated from RA north. Titania's orbit is 33″ by 20″ and Oberon's is 44″ by 26″. These brighter, more-distant satellites may be seen in telescopes as small as 250 mm under good conditions. The inner moons suffer from Uranus's glare. The fainter moons, Ariel (mag. 14.3) and Umbriel (mag. 15.0), are closer to Uranus (11″–15″ major axis), and a greater challenge. Use planetarium software to generate a finder chart for the evening you choose to search for these objects. To separate the satellites from the planet, use as much magnification as the conditions will bear; ensure a clean eyepiece. With these measures, and possibly an occulting-bar eyepiece, the observation should be possible in telescopes of aperture 300–430 mm.

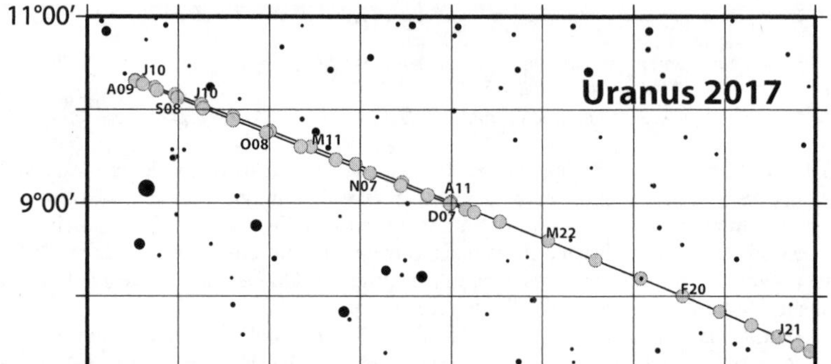

The two charts on this page and the next use the astrometric UCAC4 catalogue. The UCAC4 lists model fitted photometric magnitudes (579-642 nm). The bright star located near the chart left centre is ο Psc listed as 4.25 visual magnitude. The charts' ephemerides are generated using the JPL Horizons Web-Interface. Uranus is plotted as a gray circle of visual magnitude 5.8. The chart limiting magnitude is 9.5 according to the UCAC4. The chart is generated using the open source Generic Mapping Tools (GMT5.1.2) under Mac OS 10.10.5 (chart by Ian Cameron).

NEPTUNE

Neptune is the outermost planet in the Solar System, with a maximum angular diameter of only 2.4″. It was found at Berlin Observatory by Johann Galle on 1846 Sep. 23, near a position calculated from irregularities in the motion of Uranus; credit for this prediction has historically been shared by Urbain le Verrier of France and John Couch Adams of England, but le Verrier is the real champion here (see tinyurl.com/j23quw3). Neptune was at aphelion in 1959, at mag. 7.9. Its next perihelion, at mag. 7.7, is in 2041, in Aries.

In 2017, Neptune has a number of conjunctions with the Moon and planets. It starts off with the New Year's Eve spectacular Dec. 31–Jan. 1 conjunction with Mars (see p. 217). On Jan. 3 (2nd local), Neptune is occulted by a 5-day-old Moon, but this is only visible on the west coast of North America and further west. Then, on Jan. 12, Venus and Neptune pass less than a lunar diameter apart (see Venus p. 216). Neptune sinks into the twilight over the next two months and is in conjunction with the Sun on Mar. 2. By Jun. 15, Neptune is at its stationary point and begins its retrograde motion. At this time, it sits 2.5° east of mag. –3.7 λ Aqr, moving westward over the summer and fall months. On Sep. 5, Neptune is at opposition, where it shines at mag. 7.8 and shows a tiny 2.4″ blue disk. This is a perfectly good time to hunt for Triton. On Nov. 22, Neptune is at its second stationary point and it turns eastward in prograde motion, ending the year 30′ southeast of λ Aqr.

Neptune's one large moon, Triton, is within easy reach of medium-sized amateur telescopes (250+ mm). Triton is easier to find than any of the satellites of Uranus, primarily because it is brighter than those bodies, but also because Neptune is two magnitudes fainter than Uranus, so its glare is much reduced. At opposition, Triton is mag. 13.6, and from our perspective, its orbit describes a fat ellipse with a minor radius of 12″ and a major radius of 17″. Neptune's north pole is tipped away from Earth at 25.5°, so Triton appears to move in a counter-clockwise direction around its primary.

Editor's note: Neptune is notoriously difficult to observe for most amateurs, as its great distance and blue colour mean that not much reflected light reaches Earth. To see the planet requires more magnification than binoculars provide, so a telescope is a must.

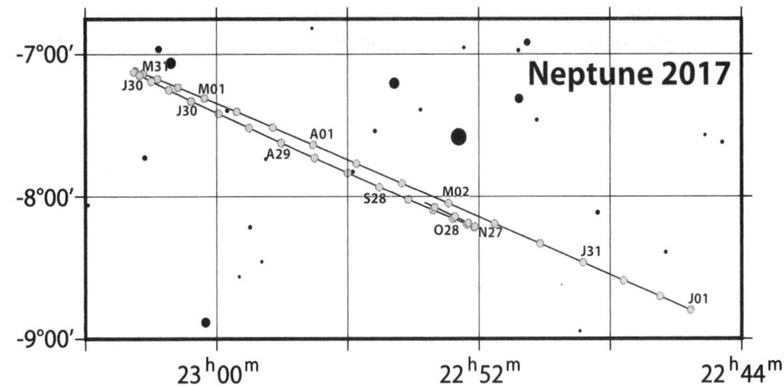

The bright star located near the chart centre is lambda Aqr listed as 3.7 visual magnitude. Neptune is plotted as a gray circle corresponding to visual magnitude 8. The chart limiting magnitude is 9.5 (chart by Ian Cameron).

PHENOMENA OF THE GALILEAN SATELLITES

BY PATRICK KELLY

The table on the following six pages gives the various transits, occultations, and eclipses of the four great satellites of Jupiter during January–mid-September and mid-December 2017. Jupiter is not well-placed for observing from mid-September to mid-December, as it is in conjunction with the Sun on Dec. 21. Double-shadow transits are indicated in **bold**. Double-satellite transits are indicated in *italics*. When a bold and italic event are close that often indicates that two moons and two shadows can simultaneously be seen on Jupiter. Since the satellite phenomena are not instantaneous but take up to several minutes, the predicted times are for the middle of each event. The predictions were generated by the Institut de Mécanique Céleste et de Calcul des Ephémérides in Paris.

Satellites designations are: I = Io II = Europa III = Ganymede IV = Callisto

Events abbreviations are:

Ec = eclipse Oc = occultation Tr = satellite transit Sh = shadow transit
I = ingress E = egress D = disappearance R = reappearance

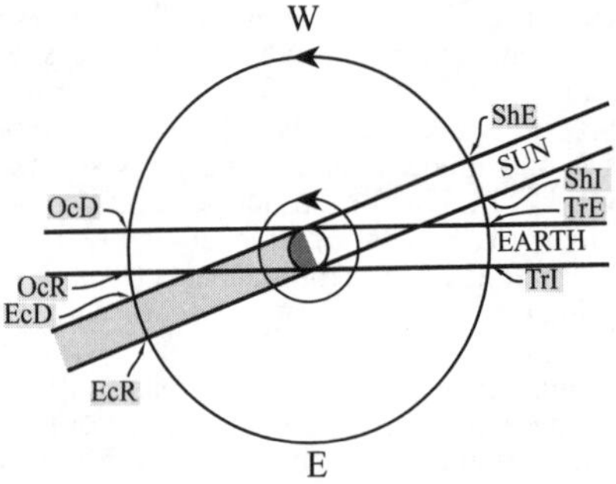

The general motion of the satellites and the successive phenomena are shown in the diagram at right, which is a view of Jupiter and the orbit of one of its satellites, looking down from the north side. Satellites move from east to west across the face of the planet and from west to east behind it (here "east" and "west" are used in the sense of the observer's sky, not in the Jovian sense). Before opposition, shadows fall to the west, and after opposition, to the east (as in the diagram).

The sequence of phenomena for the outer satellite shown in the diagram, counterclockwise beginning at the lower right, is transit ingress (TrI), transit egress (TrE), shadow ingress (ShI), shadow egress (ShE), occultation disappearance (OcD), occultation reappearance (OcR), eclipse disappearance (EcD), and eclipse reappearance (EcR). The actual sequence will depend on the actual Sun–Jupiter–Earth angle and the size of the satellite's orbit.

Over 3/4 of the phenomena listed will **not** be visible from any one location because they occur when Jupiter is near or below the horizon or when daylight interferes. In practice, an observer usually knows when Jupiter will be conveniently placed in the night sky; if not, consult THE SKY MONTH BY MONTH section (p. 95). The table can then be scanned to see if there are any events during the intended observing period. For example, an observer in Halifax would know that Jupiter is well placed near midnight in March and April as Jupiter is at opposition on Apr. 7. If planning to observe from 21:00 on Apr. 21 to 4:00 ADT on Apr. 22 (3 h behind UT), scanning the table for events in the interval Apr. 22 from 0:00 to 7:00 UT would find four events, beginning at 22:13 ADT when Ganymede begins a transit, followed 1 h and 14 min later by its shadow appearing on Jupiter's surface. About an hour later, at 0:22 on Apr. 22, Ganymede's transit ends and at 1:51 Ganymede's shadow egresses. The configuration of the four Galilean satellites during that night is given in the diagram on the right-hand side of p. XX in the THE SKY MONTH BY MONTH section.

A total of 1718 events (319 eclipse, 315 occultation, 542 shadow, and 542 transit) appear in the table, an average of one event every 3 h 52 min.

SATELLITES OF JUPITER, UT OF 2017 GEOCENTRIC PHENOMENA

Day	UT	Sat.	Event
JANUARY			
0	5:39	I	EcD
	9:03	I	OcR
	11:48	II	ShI
	14:14	II	TrI
	14:19	II	ShE
	16:39	II	TrE
1	1:06	III	EcD
	2:59	I	ShI
	3:48	III	EcR
	4:11	I	TrI
	5:11	I	ShE
	6:10	III	OcD
	6:22	I	TrE
	8:31	III	OcR
2	0:07	I	EcD
	3:31	I	OcR
	6:50	II	EcD
	11:48	II	OcR
	21:27	I	ShI
	22:40	I	TrI
	23:40	I	ShE
3	0:51	I	TrE
	18:35	I	EcD
	22:00	I	OcR
4	1:05	II	ShI
	3:32	II	TrI
	3:36	II	ShE
	5:57	II	TrE
	15:00	III	ShI
	15:56	**I**	**ShI**
	17:09	I	TrI
	17:39	III	ShE
	18:08	I	ShE
	19:19	I	TrE
	20:05	III	TrI
	22:22	III	TrE
5	13:03	I	EcD
	16:28	I	OcR
	20:08	II	EcD
6	1:06	II	OcR
	10:24	I	ShI
	11:37	I	TrI
	12:36	I	ShE
	13:48	I	TrE
7	7:32	I	EcD
	10:57	I	OcR
	14:22	II	ShI
	16:50	II	TrI
	16:53	II	ShE
	19:14	II	TrE
8	4:52	I	ShI
	5:04	III	EcD
	6:06	I	TrI
	7:04	I	ShE
	7:44	III	EcR
	8:16	I	TrE
	10:13	III	OcD
	12:30	III	OcR
9	2:00	I	EcD
	5:25	I	OcR
	9:26	II	EcD
	14:24	II	OcR
	23:21	I	ShI
10	0:34	I	TrI
	1:33	I	ShE
	2:45	I	TrE
	20:28	I	EcD
	23:53	I	OcR
11	3:39	II	ShI
	6:07	II	TrI
	6:09	II	ShE
	8:31	II	TrE
	17:49	I	ShI
	18:58	**III**	**ShI**
	19:02	I	TrI
	20:01	I	ShE
	21:13	I	TrE
	21:35	III	ShE
12	0:05	III	TrI
	2:19	III	TrE
	14:56	I	EcD
	18:22	I	OcR
	22:43	II	EcD
13	1:16	II	EcR
	3:41	II	OcR
	12:17	I	ShI
	13:31	I	TrI
	14:29	I	ShE
	15:41	I	TrE
14	9:24	I	EcD
	12:50	I	OcR
	16:55	II	ShI
	19:24	II	TrI
	19:26	II	ShE
	21:47	II	TrE
15	6:46	I	ShI
	7:59	I	TrI
	8:57	I	ShE
	9:02	III	EcD
	10:09	I	TrE
	11:41	III	EcR
	14:12	III	OcD
	16:26	III	OcR
16	3:53	I	EcD
	7:18	I	OcR
	12:01	II	EcD
	16:58	II	OcR
17	1:14	I	ShI
	2:27	I	TrI
	3:26	I	ShE
	4:37	I	TrE
	22:21	I	EcD
18	1:46	I	OcR
	6:12	II	ShI
	8:41	II	TrI
	8:43	II	ShE
	11:04	II	TrE
	19:42	I	ShI
	20:55	I	TrI
	21:54	I	ShE
	22:55	III	ShI
	23:05	I	TrE
19	1:32	III	ShE
	4:02	III	TrI
	6:13	III	TrE
	16:49	I	EcD
	20:14	I	OcR
20	1:18	II	EcD
	6:14	II	OcR
	14:11	I	ShI
	15:23	I	TrI
	16:22	I	ShE
	17:33	I	TrE
21	11:17	I	EcD
	14:42	I	OcR
	19:29	II	ShI
	21:57	II	TrI
	21:59	II	ShE
22	0:19	II	TrE
	8:39	I	ShI
	9:51	I	TrI
	10:51	I	ShE
	12:01	I	TrE
	12:59	III	EcD
	15:37	III	EcR
	18:06	III	OcD
	20:17	III	OcR
23	5:46	I	EcD
	9:10	I	OcR
	14:36	II	EcD
	19:29	II	OcR
24	3:07	I	ShI
	4:19	I	TrI
	5:19	I	ShE
	6:29	I	TrE
25	0:14	I	EcD
	3:37	I	OcR
	8:46	II	ShI
	11:13	II	TrI
	11:16	II	ShE
	13:34	II	TrE
	21:35	I	ShI
	22:47	I	TrI
	23:47	I	ShE
26	0:57	I	TrE
	2:53	III	ShI
	5:29	III	ShE
	7:55	III	TrI
	10:02	III	TrE
	18:42	I	EcD
	22:05	I	OcR
27	3:53	II	EcD
	8:44	II	OcR
	16:04	I	ShI
	17:15	I	TrI
	18:15	I	ShE
	19:25	I	TrE
28	13:10	I	EcD
	16:33	I	OcR
	22:03	II	ShI
29	0:27	II	TrI
	0:33	II	ShE
	2:49	II	TrE
	10:32	I	ShI
	11:42	I	TrI
	12:44	I	ShE
	13:52	I	TrE
	16:56	III	EcD
	19:33	III	EcR
	21:56	III	OcD
30	0:03	III	OcR
	7:39	I	EcD
	11:01	I	OcR
	17:10	II	EcD
	21:58	II	OcR
31	5:00	I	ShI
	6:10	I	TrI
	7:12	I	ShE
	8:20	I	TrE
FEBRUARY			
1	2:07	I	EcD
	5:28	I	OcR
	11:20	II	ShI
	13:42	II	TrI
	13:50	II	ShE
	16:03	II	TrE
	23:29	I	ShI
2	0:38	I	TrI
	1:40	I	ShE
	2:47	I	TrE
	6:51	III	ShI
	9:25	III	ShE
	11:43	III	TrI
	13:47	III	TrE
	20:35	I	EcD
	23:56	I	OcR
3	6:28	II	EcD
	11:12	II	OcR
	17:57	I	ShI
	19:05	I	TrI
	20:09	I	ShE
	21:15	I	TrE
4	15:03	I	EcD
	18:23	I	OcR
5	0:37	II	ShI
	2:56	II	TrI
	3:07	II	ShE
	5:17	II	TrE
	12:25	I	ShI
	13:33	I	TrI
	14:37	I	ShE
	15:42	I	TrE
	20:53	III	EcD
	23:29	III	EcR
6	1:41	III	OcD
	3:46	III	OcR
	9:32	I	EcD
	12:50	I	OcR
	19:45	II	EcD
7	0:25	II	OcR
	6:53	I	ShI
	8:00	I	TrI
	9:05	I	ShE
	10:10	I	TrE
8	4:00	I	EcD
	7:18	I	OcR
	13:54	II	ShI
	16:09	II	TrI
	16:24	II	ShE
	18:30	II	TrE
9	1:22	I	ShI
	2:27	I	TrI
	3:33	I	ShE
	4:37	I	TrE
	10:49	III	ShI
	13:22	III	ShE
	15:27	III	TrI
	17:28	III	TrE
	22:28	I	EcD
10	1:45	I	OcR
	9:02	II	EcD
	13:38	II	OcR
	19:50	I	ShI
	20:54	I	TrI
	22:02	I	ShE
	23:04	I	TrE
11	16:57	I	EcD
	20:12	I	OcR
12	3:11	II	ShI
	5:22	II	TrI
	5:41	II	ShE
	7:43	II	TrE
	14:18	I	ShI
	15:21	I	TrI
	16:30	I	ShE
	17:31	I	TrE
13	0:51	III	EcD
	3:26	III	EcR
	5:22	III	OcD
	7:24	III	OcR
	11:25	I	EcD
	14:39	I	OcR
	22:20	II	EcD
14	2:50	II	OcR
	8:47	I	ShI
	9:49	I	TrI
	10:58	I	ShE
	11:58	I	TrE
15	5:53	I	EcD
	9:06	I	OcR
	16:28	II	ShI
	18:35	II	TrI
	18:58	II	ShE
	20:55	II	TrE
16	3:15	I	ShI
	4:16	I	TrI
	5:27	I	ShE
	6:25	I	TrE
	14:46	III	ShI
	17:19	III	ShE
	19:05	III	TrI
	21:04	III	TrE
17	0:22	I	EcD
	3:33	I	OcR
	11:37	II	EcD

I = Io II = Europa III = Ganymede IV = Callisto

SATELLITES OF JUPITER, UT OF 2017 GEOCENTRIC PHENOMENA (cont)

FEBRUARY (cont)			
17	16:02	II	OcR
	21:43	I	ShI
	22:43	I	TrI
	23:55	I	ShE
18	0:52	I	TrE
	18:50	I	EcD
	22:00	I	OcR
19	5:45	II	ShI
	7:46	II	TrI
	8:15	II	ShE
	10:06	II	TrE
	16:11	I	ShI
	17:09	I	TrI
	18:23	I	ShE
	19:19	I	TrE
20	4:50	III	EcD
	7:23	III	EcR
	8:59	III	OcD
	10:58	III	OcR
	13:18	I	EcD
	16:27	I	OcR
21	0:54	II	EcD
	5:13	II	OcR
	10:40	I	ShI
	11:36	I	TrI
	12:51	I	ShE
	13:46	I	TrE
22	7:46	I	EcD
	10:54	I	OcR
	19:03	II	ShI
	20:58	II	TrI
	21:32	II	ShE
	23:18	II	TrE
23	5:08	I	ShI
	6:03	I	TrI
	7:20	I	ShE
	8:13	I	TrE
	18:43	III	ShI
	21:15	III	ShE
	22:38	III	TrI
24	0:35	III	TrE
	2:15	I	EcD
	5:20	I	OcR
	14:11	II	EcD
	18:23	II	OcR
	23:36	I	ShI
25	0:30	I	TrI
	1:48	I	ShE
	2:39	I	TrE
	20:43	I	EcD
	23:47	I	OcR
26	8:20	II	ShI
	10:08	II	TrI
	10:49	II	ShE
	12:28	II	TrE
	18:05	I	ShI
	18:56	I	TrI
	20:16	I	ShE
	21:06	I	TrE
27	8:48	III	EcD
	11:20	III	EcR
	12:30	III	OcD
	14:28	III	OcR
	15:12	I	EcD
	18:14	I	OcR
28	3:28	II	EcD
	7:33	II	OcR
	12:33	I	ShI
	13:23	I	TrI
	14:45	I	ShE
	15:32	I	TrE
MARCH			
1	9:40	I	EcD
	12:40	I	OcR
	21:38	II	ShI
	23:19	II	TrI
2	0:07	II	ShE
	1:39	II	TrE
	7:01	I	ShI
	7:49	I	TrI
	9:13	I	ShE
	9:59	I	TrE
	22:41	III	ShI
3	1:11	III	ShE
	2:06	III	TrI
	4:03	III	TrE
	4:08	I	EcD
	7:07	I	OcR
	16:46	II	EcD
	20:43	II	OcR
4	1:29	I	ShI
	2:16	I	TrI
	3:41	I	ShE
	4:25	I	TrE
	22:37	I	EcD
5	1:33	I	OcR
	10:55	II	ShI
	12:28	II	TrI
	13:24	II	ShE
	14:48	II	TrE
	19:58	I	ShI
	20:42	I	TrI
	22:10	I	ShE
	22:52	I	TrE
6	12:46	III	EcD
	15:18	III	EcR
	15:57	III	OcD
	17:05	I	EcD
	17:55	III	OcR
	20:00	I	OcR
7	6:03	II	EcD
	9:52	II	OcR
	14:26	I	ShI
	15:09	I	TrI
	16:38	I	ShE
	17:18	I	TrE
8	11:33	I	EcD
	14:26	I	OcR
9	0:13	II	ShI
	1:38	II	TrI
	2:42	II	ShE
	3:58	II	TrE
	8:54	I	ShI
	9:35	I	TrI
	11:06	I	ShE
	11:44	I	TrE
10	2:38	III	ShI
	5:08	III	ShE
	5:31	III	TrI
	6:02	I	EcD
	7:28	III	TrE
	8:52	I	OcR
	19:20	II	EcD
	23:00	II	OcR
11	3:23	I	ShI
	4:01	I	TrI
	5:35	I	ShE
	6:11	I	TrE
12	0:30	I	EcD
	3:19	I	OcR
	13:30	II	ShI
	14:47	II	TrI
	15:59	II	ShE
	17:07	II	TrE
	21:51	I	ShI
	22:27	I	TrI
13	0:03	I	ShE
	0:37	I	TrE
	16:44	III	EcD
	18:59	I	EcD
	19:14	III	EcR
	19:20	III	OcD
	21:18	III	OcR
	21:45	I	OcR
14	8:37	II	EcD
	12:09	II	OcR
	16:19	I	ShI
	16:53	I	TrI
	18:31	I	ShE
	19:03	I	TrE
15	13:27	I	EcD
	16:11	I	OcR
16	2:48	II	ShI
	3:55	II	TrI
	5:17	II	ShE
	6:16	II	TrE
	10:48	I	ShI
	11:19	I	TrI
	13:00	I	ShE
	13:29	I	TrE
17	6:37	III	ShI
	7:56	I	EcD
	8:53	III	TrI
	9:06	III	ShE
	10:37	I	OcR
	10:50	III	TrE
	21:54	II	EcD
18	1:17	II	OcR
	5:16	I	ShI
	5:46	I	TrI
	7:28	I	ShE
	7:55	I	TrE
19	2:24	I	EcD
	5:03	I	OcR
	16:05	II	ShI
	17:03	II	TrI
	18:34	II	ShE
	19:24	II	TrE
	23:44	I	ShI
20	0:12	I	TrI
	1:56	I	ShE
	2:21	I	TrE
	20:41	III	EcD
	20:52	I	EcD
	23:29	I	OcR
21	0:38	III	OcR
	11:11	II	EcD
	14:24	II	OcR
	18:13	I	ShI
	18:38	I	TrI
	20:25	I	ShE
	20:47	I	TrE
22	15:21	I	EcD
	17:55	I	OcR
23	5:23	II	ShI
	6:12	II	TrI
	7:52	II	ShE
	8:32	II	TrE
	12:41	I	ShI
	13:04	I	TrI
	14:53	I	ShE
	15:13	I	TrE
24	9:49	I	EcD
	10:35	III	ShI
	12:11	III	TrI
	12:22	I	OcR
	13:03	III	ShE
	14:10	III	TrE
25	0:28	II	EcD
	3:32	II	OcR
	7:10	I	ShI
	7:30	I	TrI
	9:21	I	ShE
	9:39	I	TrE
26	4:18	I	EcD
	6:48	I	OcR
	18:41	II	ShI
	19:19	II	TrI
	21:09	II	ShE
	21:40	II	TrE
27	1:38	I	ShI
	1:55	I	TrI
	3:50	I	ShE
	4:05	I	TrE
	22:46	I	EcD
28	0:40	III	EcD
	1:14	I	OcR
	3:56	III	OcR
	13:45	II	EcD
	16:39	II	OcR
	20:06	I	ShI
	20:21	I	TrI
	22:18	I	ShE
	22:31	I	TrE
29	17:15	I	EcD
	19:40	I	OcR
30	7:59	II	ShI
	8:27	II	TrI
	10:28	II	ShE
	10:48	II	TrE
	14:35	I	ShI
	14:47	I	TrI
	16:47	I	ShE
	16:57	I	TrE
31	11:43	I	EcD
	14:06	I	OcR
	14:33	III	ShI
	15:28	III	TrI
	17:00	III	ShE
	17:28	III	TrE
APRIL			
1	3:02	II	EcD
	5:46	II	OcR
	9:03	I	ShI
	9:13	I	TrI
	11:15	I	ShE
	11:23	I	TrE
2	6:12	I	EcD
	8:32	I	OcR
	21:17	II	ShI
	21:34	II	TrI
	23:45	II	ShE
	23:56	II	TrE
3	3:32	I	ShI
	3:39	I	TrI
	5:43	I	ShE
	5:49	I	TrE
4	0:40	I	EcD
	2:58	I	OcR
	4:38	III	EcD
	7:14	III	OcR
	16:20	II	EcD
	18:53	II	OcR
	22:00	I	ShI
	22:05	I	TrI
5	0:12	I	ShE
	0:15	I	TrE
	19:09	I	EcD
	21:24	I	OcR
6	10:35	II	ShI
	10:42	II	TrI
	13:03	II	ShE
	13:04	II	TrE
	16:28	I	ShI
	16:31	I	TrI
	18:40	I	ShE
	18:41	I	TrE
7	13:38	I	EcD
	15:50	I	EcR
	18:31	III	ShI
	18:43	III	TrI
	20:45	III	TrE
	20:57	III	ShE
8	5:37	II	EcD
	8:04	II	EcR

I = Io II = Europa III = Ganymede IV = Callisto

SATELLITES OF JUPITER, UT OF 2017 GEOCENTRIC PHENOMENA (cont)

Day	UT	Sat	Event
APRIL (cont)			
8	10:57	I	ShI
	10:57	I	TrI
	13:07	I	TrE
	13:09	I	ShE
9	8:05	I	OcD
	10:19	I	EcR
	23:49	II	TrI
	23:53	II	ShI
10	2:12	II	TrE
	2:21	II	ShE
	5:23	I	TrI
	5:25	I	ShI
	7:33	I	TrE
	7:37	I	ShE
11	2:31	I	OcD
	4:47	I	EcR
	8:27	III	OcD
	11:04	III	EcR
	18:45	II	OcD
	21:21	II	EcR
	23:49	I	TrI
	23:54	I	ShI
12	1:59	I	TrE
	2:06	I	ShE
	20:57	I	OcD
	23:16	I	EcR
13	12:57	II	TrI
	13:11	II	ShI
	15:20	II	TrE
	15:39	II	ShE
	18:14	I	TrI
	18:22	I	ShI
	20:25	I	TrE
	20:34	I	ShE
14	15:23	I	OcD
	17:44	I	EcR
	21:57	III	TrI
	22:29	III	ShI
15	0:03	III	TrE
	0:54	III	ShE
	7:52	II	OcD
	10:38	II	EcR
	12:40	I	TrI
	12:51	I	ShI
	14:51	I	TrE
	15:02	I	ShE
16	9:49	I	OcD
	12:13	I	EcR
17	2:05	II	TrI
	2:29	II	ShI
	4:28	II	TrE
	4:57	II	ShE
	7:06	I	TrI
	7:19	I	ShI
	9:17	I	TrE
	9:31	I	ShE
18	4:15	I	OcD
	6:42	I	EcR
	11:43	III	OcD
18	15:02	III	EcR
	20:59	II	OcD
	23:55	II	EcR
19	1:32	I	TrI
	1:48	I	ShI
	3:43	I	TrE
	3:59	I	ShE
	22:41	I	OcD
20	1:10	I	EcR
	15:13	II	TrI
	15:48	II	ShI
	17:36	II	TrE
	18:16	II	ShE
	19:58	I	TrI
	20:16	I	ShI
	22:09	I	TrE
	22:28	I	ShE
21	17:07	I	OcD
	19:39	I	EcR
22	1:13	III	TrI
	2:27	III	ShI
	3:22	III	TrE
	4:51	III	ShE
	10:06	II	OcD
	13:12	II	EcR
	14:24	I	TrI
	14:45	I	ShI
	16:35	I	TrE
	16:56	I	ShE
23	11:33	I	OcD
	14:07	I	EcR
24	4:20	II	TrI
	5:06	II	ShI
	6:44	II	TrE
	7:33	II	ShE
	8:51	I	TrI
	9:13	I	ShI
	11:01	I	TrE
	11:25	I	ShE
25	5:59	I	OcD
	8:36	I	EcR
	15:00	III	OcD
	19:00	III	EcR
	23:13	II	OcD
26	2:29	II	EcR
	3:17	I	TrI
	3:42	I	ShI
	5:27	I	TrE
	5:53	I	ShE
27	0:25	I	OcD
	3:05	I	EcR
	17:29	II	TrI
	18:25	II	ShI
	19:54	II	TrE
	20:52	II	ShE
	21:43	I	TrI
	22:10	I	ShI
	23:53	I	TrE
28	0:22	I	ShE
	18:52	I	OcD
	21:33	I	EcR
29	4:30	III	TrI
	6:26	III	ShI
	6:42	III	TrE
	8:48	III	ShE
	12:20	II	OcD
	15:46	II	EcR
	16:09	I	TrI
	16:39	I	ShI
	18:20	I	TrE
	18:50	I	ShE
30	13:18	I	OcD
	16:02	I	EcR
MAY			
1	6:38	II	TrI
	7:43	II	ShI
	9:02	II	TrE
	10:10	II	ShE
	10:35	I	TrI
	11:07	I	ShI
	12:46	I	TrE
	13:19	I	ShE
2	7:44	I	OcD
	10:31	I	EcR
	18:18	III	OcD
	20:33	III	OcR
	20:35	III	EcD
	22:58	III	EcR
3	1:28	II	OcD
	5:02	I	TrI
	5:03	II	EcR
	5:36	I	ShI
	7:12	I	TrE
	7:47	I	ShE
4	2:11	I	OcD
	4:59	I	EcR
	19:47	II	TrI
	21:02	II	ShI
	22:12	II	TrE
	23:28	I	TrI
	23:29	II	ShE
5	0:05	I	ShI
	1:39	I	TrE
	2:16	I	ShE
	20:37	I	OcD
	23:28	I	EcR
6	7:51	III	TrI
	10:07	III	TrE
	10:25	III	ShI
	12:47	III	ShE
	14:36	II	OcD
	17:54	I	TrI
	18:19	II	EcR
	18:33	I	ShI
	20:05	I	TrE
	20:44	I	ShE
7	15:04	I	OcD
	17:57	I	EcR
8	8:56	II	TrI
	10:20	II	ShI
	11:22	II	TrE
	12:21	I	TrI
8	12:46	II	ShE
	13:02	I	ShI
	14:31	I	TrE
	15:13	I	ShE
9	9:30	I	OcD
	12:26	I	EcR
	21:40	III	OcD
	23:58	III	OcR
10	0:33	III	EcD
	2:55	III	EcR
	3:45	II	OcD
	6:47	I	TrI
	7:30	I	ShI
	7:36	II	EcR
	8:58	I	TrE
	9:41	I	ShE
11	3:57	I	OcD
	6:54	I	EcR
	22:07	II	TrI
	23:39	II	ShI
12	0:33	II	TrE
	1:14	I	TrI
	1:59	**I**	**ShI**
	2:05	II	ShE
	3:25	I	TrE
	4:10	I	ShE
	22:24	I	OcD
13	1:23	I	EcR
	11:15	III	TrI
	13:34	III	TrE
	14:24	III	ShI
	16:44	III	ShE
	16:54	II	OcD
	19:41	I	TrI
	20:27	I	ShI
	20:53	II	EcR
	21:51	I	TrE
	22:38	I	ShE
14	16:51	I	OcD
	19:52	I	EcR
15	11:17	II	TrI
	12:57	II	ShI
	13:43	II	TrE
	14:07	I	TrI
	14:56	**I**	**ShI**
	15:23	II	ShE
	16:18	I	TrE
	17:07	I	ShE
16	11:17	I	OcD
	14:20	I	EcR
17	1:05	III	OcD
	3:27	III	OcR
	4:32	III	EcD
	6:04	II	OcD
	6:53	III	EcR
	8:34	I	TrI
	9:24	I	ShI
	10:10	II	EcR
	10:45	I	TrE
	11:35	I	ShE
18	5:44	I	OcD
	8:49	I	EcR
19	0:28	II	TrI
	2:16	II	ShI
	2:55	II	TrE
	3:01	I	TrI
	3:53	**I**	**ShI**
	4:42	II	ShE
	5:12	I	TrE
	6:04	I	ShE
20	0:11	I	OcD
	3:18	I	EcR
	14:43	III	TrI
	17:05	III	TrE
	18:24	III	ShI
	19:14	II	OcD
	20:43	III	ShE
	21:28	I	TrI
	22:22	I	ShI
	23:27	II	EcR
	23:39	I	TrE
21	0:32	I	ShE
	18:38	I	OcD
	21:47	I	EcR
22	13:39	II	TrI
	15:34	II	ShI
	15:55	*I*	*TrI*
	16:07	II	TrE
	16:50	**I**	**ShI**
	18:00	II	ShE
	18:06	I	TrE
	19:01	I	ShE
23	13:05	I	OcD
	16:15	I	EcR
24	4:35	III	OcD
	7:00	III	OcR
	8:24	II	OcD
	8:32	III	EcD
	10:22	I	TrI
	10:52	III	EcR
	11:19	I	ShI
	12:33	I	TrE
	12:44	II	EcR
	13:29	I	ShE
25	7:33	I	OcD
	10:44	I	EcR
26	2:52	II	TrI
	4:49	*I*	*TrI*
	4:54	II	ShI
	5:19	II	TrE
	5:47	**I**	**ShI**
	7:00	I	TrE
	7:19	II	ShE
	7:58	I	ShE
27	2:00	I	OcD
	5:13	I	EcR
	18:15	III	TrI
	20:39	III	TrE
	21:35	II	OcD
	22:22	III	ShI
	23:16	I	TrI
28	**0:16**	**I**	**ShI**
	0:40	III	ShE
	1:27	I	TrE

I = Io II = Europa III = Ganymede IV = Callisto

SATELLITES OF JUPITER, UT OF 2017 GEOCENTRIC PHENOMENA (cont)

Day	UT	Sat.	Phen.
MAY (cont)			
28	2:01	II	EcR
	2:26	I	ShE
	20:27	I	OcD
	23:42	I	EcR
29	16:04	II	TrI
	17:44	*I*	*TrI*
	18:12	II	ShI
	18:32	II	TrE
	18:45	**I**	**ShI**
	19:54	I	TrE
	20:37	II	ShE
	20:55	I	ShE
30	14:55	I	OcD
	18:10	I	EcR
31	8:10	III	OcD
	10:37	III	OcR
	10:47	II	OcD
	12:11	I	TrI
	12:32	III	EcD
	13:13	I	ShI
	14:22	I	TrE
	14:51	III	EcR
	15:19	II	EcR
	15:24	I	ShE
JUNE			
1	9:22	I	OcD
	12:39	I	EcR
2	5:18	II	TrI
	6:38	*I*	*TrI*
	7:31	II	ShI
	7:42	**I**	**ShI**
	7:46	II	TrE
	8:49	I	TrE
	9:52	I	ShE
	9:56	II	ShE
3	3:50	I	OcD
	7:08	I	EcR
	21:51	III	TrI
	23:59	II	OcD
4	0:18	III	TrE
	1:06	I	TrI
	2:11	I	ShI
	2:21	**III**	**ShI**
	3:16	I	TrE
	4:21	I	ShE
	4:36	II	EcR
	4:37	III	ShE
	22:17	I	OcD
5	1:37	I	EcR
	18:31	II	TrI
	19:33	*I*	*TrI*
	20:39	I	ShI
	20:49	**II**	**ShI**
	21:00	II	TrE
	21:44	I	TrE
	22:49	I	ShE
	23:14	II	ShE
6	16:45	I	OcD
	20:06	I	EcR
7	11:49	III	OcD
	13:12	II	OcD
	14:01	I	TrI
	14:19	III	OcR
	15:08	I	ShI
	16:12	I	TrE
	16:32	III	EcD
	17:18	I	ShE
	17:53	II	EcR
	18:50	III	EcR
8	11:13	I	OcD
	14:34	I	EcR
9	7:46	II	TrI
	8:29	*I*	*TrI*
	9:36	I	ShI
	10:09	**II**	**ShI**
	10:15	II	TrE
	10:39	I	TrE
	11:47	I	ShE
	12:33	II	ShE
10	5:40	I	OcD
	9:03	I	EcR
11	1:32	III	TrI
	2:25	II	OcD
	2:56	*I*	*TrI*
	4:00	III	TrE
	4:05	I	ShI
	5:07	I	TrE
	6:15	I	ShE
	6:20	III	ShI
	7:10	II	EcR
	8:35	III	ShE
12	0:08	I	OcD
	3:32	I	EcR
	21:01	II	TrI
	21:24	*I*	*TrI*
	22:34	I	ShI
	23:27	**II**	**ShI**
	23:29	II	TrE
	23:35	I	TrE
13	0:44	I	ShE
	1:51	II	ShE
	18:36	I	OcD
	22:01	I	EcR
14	15:33	III	OcD
	15:39	II	OcD
	15:52	I	TrI
	17:02	I	ShI
	18:03	I	TrE
	18:05	III	OcR
	19:12	I	ShE
	20:27	II	EcR
	20:32	III	EcD
	22:48	III	EcR
15	13:04	I	OcD
	16:30	I	EcR
16	10:17	II	TrI
	10:20	*I*	*TrI*
	11:31	I	ShI
	12:31	I	TrE
	12:46	**II**	**ShI**
	12:46	II	TrE
16	13:41	I	ShE
	15:10	II	ShE
17	7:32	I	OcD
	10:58	I	EcR
18	4:48	I	TrI
	4:53	II	OcD
	5:17	*III*	*TrI*
	6:00	I	ShI
	6:59	I	TrE
	7:48	III	TrE
	8:10	I	ShE
	9:44	II	EcR
	10:19	III	ShI
	12:33	III	ShE
19	2:01	I	OcD
	5:27	I	EcR
	23:16	I	TrI
	23:32	*II*	*TrI*
20	0:28	I	ShI
	1:27	I	TrE
	2:01	II	TrE
	2:04	**II**	**ShI**
	2:38	I	ShE
	4:28	II	ShE
	20:29	I	OcD
	23:56	I	EcR
21	17:44	I	TrI
	18:08	II	OcD
	18:57	I	ShI
	19:21	III	OcD
	19:55	I	TrE
	20:37	II	EcD
	20:37	II	OcR
	21:07	I	ShE
	21:54	III	OcR
	23:01	II	EcR
22	0:31	III	EcD
	2:47	III	EcR
	14:57	I	OcD
	18:25	I	EcR
23	12:12	I	TrI
	12:49	*II*	*TrI*
	13:26	I	ShI
	14:23	I	TrE
	15:19	II	TrE
	15:24	**II**	**ShI**
	15:36	I	ShE
	17:47	II	ShE
24	9:26	I	OcD
	12:54	I	EcR
25	6:40	I	TrI
	7:24	II	OcD
	7:54	I	ShI
	8:51	I	TrE
	9:08	III	TrI
	9:53	II	OcR
	9:55	II	EcD
	10:04	I	ShE
	11:40	III	TrE
	12:18	II	EcR
	14:19	III	ShI
	16:32	III	ShE
26	3:54	I	OcD
	7:22	I	EcR
27	1:09	I	TrI
	2:06	*II*	*TrI*
	2:23	I	ShI
	3:20	I	TrE
	4:33	I	ShE
	4:36	II	TrE
	4:42	II	ShI
	7:05	II	ShE
	22:22	I	OcD
28	1:51	I	EcR
	19:37	I	TrI
	20:40	II	OcD
	20:52	I	ShI
	21:48	I	TrE
	23:01	I	ShE
	23:09	II	OcR
	23:12	II	EcD
	23:13	III	OcD
29	1:35	II	EcR
	1:48	III	OcR
	4:30	III	EcD
	6:45	III	EcR
	16:51	I	OcD
	20:20	I	EcR
30	14:06	I	TrI
	15:20	I	ShI
	15:24	*II*	*TrI*
	16:16	I	TrE
	17:30	I	ShE
	17:54	II	TrE
	18:01	II	ShI
	20:24	II	ShE
JULY			
1	11:20	I	OcD
	14:49	I	EcR
2	8:34	I	TrI
	9:49	I	ShI
	9:56	II	OcD
	10:45	I	TrE
	11:59	I	ShE
	12:26	II	OcR
	12:29	II	EcD
	13:02	III	TrI
	14:53	II	EcR
	15:35	III	TrE
	18:18	III	ShI
	20:31	III	ShE
3	5:48	I	OcD
	9:18	I	EcR
4	3:03	I	TrI
	4:18	I	ShI
	4:42	*II*	*TrI*
	5:14	I	TrE
	6:27	I	ShE
	7:12	II	TrE
	7:20	II	ShI
	9:42	II	ShE
5	0:17	I	OcD
	3:46	I	EcR
5	21:31	I	TrI
	22:46	I	ShI
	23:13	II	OcD
	23:42	I	TrE
6	0:56	I	ShE
	1:43	II	OcR
	1:47	II	EcD
	3:10	III	OcD
	4:10	II	EcR
	5:45	III	OcR
	8:30	III	EcD
	10:43	III	EcR
	18:46	I	OcD
	22:15	I	EcR
7	16:00	I	TrI
	17:15	I	ShI
	18:01	*II*	*TrI*
	18:11	I	TrE
	19:25	I	ShE
	20:31	II	TrE
	20:39	II	ShI
	23:01	II	ShE
8	13:15	I	OcD
	16:44	I	EcR
9	10:29	I	TrI
	11:44	I	ShI
	12:30	II	OcD
	12:40	I	TrE
	13:53	I	ShE
	15:00	II	OcR
	15:04	II	EcD
	17:01	III	TrI
	17:27	II	EcR
	19:35	III	TrE
	22:18	III	ShI
10	0:29	III	ShE
	7:44	I	OcD
	11:13	I	EcR
11	4:57	I	TrI
	6:12	I	ShI
	7:08	I	TrE
	7:20	II	TrI
	8:22	I	ShE
	9:50	II	TrE
	9:57	II	ShI
	12:20	II	ShE
12	2:13	I	OcD
	5:42	I	EcR
	23:26	I	TrI
13	0:41	I	ShI
	1:37	I	TrE
	1:48	II	OcD
	2:51	I	ShE
	4:18	II	OcR
	4:21	II	EcD
	6:44	II	EcR
	7:10	III	OcD
	9:47	III	OcR
	12:30	III	EcD
	14:42	III	EcR
	20:42	I	OcD
14	0:10	I	EcR
	17:55	I	TrI

I = Io II = Europa III = Ganymede IV = Callisto

SATELLITES OF JUPITER, UT OF 2017 GEOCENTRIC PHENOMENA (cont)

JULY (cont)			
14	19:10	I	ShI
	20:06	I	TrE
	20:40	II	TrI
	21:19	I	ShE
	23:09	II	TrE
	23:16	II	ShI
15	1:38	II	ShE
	15:11	I	OcD
	18:39	I	EcR
16	12:24	I	TrI
	13:38	I	ShI
	14:35	I	TrE
	15:06	II	OcD
	15:48	I	ShE
	17:36	II	OcR
	17:39	II	EcD
	20:01	II	EcR
	21:03	III	TrI
	23:37	III	TrE
17	2:17	III	ShI
	4:27	III	ShE
	9:40	I	OcD
	13:08	I	EcR
18	6:53	I	TrI
	8:07	I	ShI
	9:04	I	TrE
	9:59	II	TrI
	10:17	I	ShE
	12:29	II	TrE
	12:34	II	ShI
	14:57	II	ShE
19	4:09	I	OcD
	7:37	I	EcR
20	1:22	I	TrI
	2:36	I	ShI
	3:33	I	TrE
	4:25	II	OcD
	4:45	I	ShE
	6:55	II	OcR
	6:56	II	EcD
	9:19	II	EcR
	11:16	III	OcD
	13:52	III	OcR
	16:30	III	EcD
	18:42	III	EcR
	22:38	I	OcD
21	2:06	I	EcR
	19:51	I	TrI
	21:04	I	ShI
	22:02	I	TrE
	23:14	I	ShE
	23:20	II	TrI
22	1:50	II	TrE
	1:53	II	ShI
	4:15	II	ShE
	17:08	I	OcD
	20:34	I	EcR
23	14:20	I	TrI
	15:33	I	ShI
	16:32	I	TrE
23	17:43	I	ShE
	17:44	II	OcD
	22:36	II	EcR
24	1:08	III	TrI
	3:43	III	TrE
	6:16	III	ShI
	8:25	III	ShE
	11:37	I	OcD
	15:03	I	EcR
25	8:49	I	TrI
	10:02	I	ShI
	11:01	I	TrE
	12:11	I	ShE
	12:40	II	TrI
	15:10	II	TrE
	15:12	II	ShI
	17:34	II	ShE
26	6:06	I	OcD
	9:32	I	EcR
27	3:19	I	TrI
	4:30	I	ShI
	5:30	I	TrE
	6:40	I	ShE
	7:04	II	OcD
	11:53	II	EcR
	15:24	III	OcD
	18:00	III	OcR
	20:30	III	EcD
	22:40	III	EcR
28	0:36	I	OcD
	4:01	I	EcR
	21:48	I	TrI
	22:59	I	ShI
	23:59	I	TrE
29	1:09	I	ShE
	2:02	II	TrI
	4:30	II	ShI
	4:32	II	TrE
	6:52	II	ShE
	19:05	I	OcD
	22:29	I	EcR
30	16:17	I	TrI
	17:28	I	ShI
	18:29	I	TrE
	19:37	I	ShE
	20:24	II	OcD
31	1:11	II	EcR
	5:17	III	TrI
	7:52	III	TrE
	10:15	III	ShI
	12:23	III	ShE
	13:35	I	OcD
	16:58	I	EcR
AUGUST			
1	10:47	I	TrI
	11:56	I	ShI
	12:58	I	TrE
	14:06	I	ShE
	15:23	II	TrI
	17:49	II	ShI
	17:53	II	TrE
	20:10	II	ShE
2	8:04	I	OcD
	11:27	I	EcR
3	5:16	I	TrI
	6:25	I	ShI
	7:27	I	TrE
	8:35	I	ShE
	9:44	II	OcD
	14:28	II	EcR
	19:35	III	OcD
	22:11	III	OcR
4	0:30	III	EcD
	2:34	I	OcD
	2:39	III	EcR
	5:56	I	EcR
	23:46	I	TrI
5	0:54	I	ShI
	1:57	I	TrE
	3:04	I	ShE
	4:45	II	TrI
	7:07	II	ShI
	7:15	II	TrE
	9:29	II	ShE
	21:03	I	OcD
6	0:25	I	EcR
	18:15	I	TrI
	19:22	I	ShI
	20:26	I	TrE
	21:32	I	ShE
	23:05	II	OcD
7	3:45	II	EcR
	9:29	III	TrI
	12:03	III	TrE
	14:14	III	ShI
	15:33	I	OcD
	16:22	III	ShE
	18:53	I	EcR
8	12:45	I	TrI
	13:51	I	ShI
	14:56	I	TrE
	16:01	I	ShE
	18:07	II	TrI
	20:26	II	ShI
	20:36	II	TrE
	22:47	II	ShE
9	10:03	I	OcD
	13:22	I	EcR
10	7:14	I	TrI
	8:20	I	ShI
	9:26	I	TrE
	10:30	I	ShE
	12:26	II	OcD
	17:03	II	EcR
	23:49	III	OcD
11	2:25	III	OcR
	4:29	III	EcD
	4:33	I	OcD
	6:37	III	EcR
	7:51	I	EcR
12	1:44	I	TrI
	2:48	I	ShI
	3:55	I	TrE
12	4:58	I	ShE
	7:30	II	TrI
	9:44	II	ShI
	9:59	II	TrE
	12:06	II	ShE
	23:02	I	OcD
13	2:20	I	EcR
	20:13	I	TrI
	21:17	I	ShI
	22:25	I	TrE
	23:27	I	ShE
14	1:48	II	OcD
	6:20	II	EcR
	13:45	III	TrI
	16:18	III	TrE
	17:32	I	OcD
	18:14	III	ShI
	20:21	III	ShE
	20:48	I	EcR
15	14:43	I	TrI
	15:46	I	ShI
	16:55	I	TrE
	17:56	I	ShE
	20:52	II	TrI
	23:02	II	ShI
	23:21	II	TrE
16	1:24	II	ShE
	12:02	I	OcD
	15:17	I	EcR
17	9:13	I	TrI
	10:14	I	ShI
	11:24	I	TrE
	12:24	I	ShE
	15:09	II	OcD
	19:38	II	EcR
18	4:05	III	OcD
	6:32	I	OcD
	6:40	III	OcR
	8:28	III	EcD
	9:46	I	EcR
	10:35	III	EcR
19	3:42	I	TrI
	4:43	I	ShI
	5:54	I	TrE
	6:53	I	ShE
	10:15	II	TrI
	12:21	II	ShI
	12:44	II	TrE
	14:42	II	ShE
20	1:02	I	OcD
	4:14	I	EcR
	22:12	I	TrI
	23:12	I	ShI
21	0:24	I	TrE
	1:22	I	ShE
	4:31	II	OcD
	8:55	II	EcR
	18:02	III	TrI
	19:32	I	OcD
	20:35	III	TrE
	22:13	III	ShI
	22:43	I	EcR
22	0:19	III	ShE
	16:42	I	TrI
	17:40	I	ShI
	18:54	I	TrE
	19:50	I	ShE
	23:38	II	TrI
23	1:39	II	ShI
	2:07	II	TrE
	4:00	II	ShE
	14:02	I	OcD
	17:12	I	EcR
24	11:12	I	TrI
	12:09	I	ShI
	13:23	I	TrE
	14:19	I	ShE
	17:54	II	OcD
	22:13	II	EcR
25	8:24	III	OcD
	8:32	I	OcD
	10:58	III	OcR
	11:41	I	EcR
	12:27	III	EcD
	14:34	III	EcR
26	5:42	I	TrI
	6:38	I	ShI
	7:53	I	TrE
	8:48	I	ShE
	13:01	II	TrI
	14:57	II	ShI
	15:30	II	TrE
	17:18	II	ShE
27	3:02	I	OcD
	6:09	I	EcR
28	0:12	I	TrI
	1:06	I	ShI
	2:23	I	TrE
	3:16	I	ShE
	7:16	II	OcD
	11:30	II	EcR
	21:32	I	OcD
	22:22	III	TrI
29	0:38	I	EcR
	0:54	III	TrE
	2:13	III	ShI
	4:18	III	ShE
	18:41	I	TrI
	19:35	I	ShI
	20:53	I	TrE
	21:45	I	ShE
30	2:25	II	TrI
	4:15	II	ShI
	4:53	II	TrE
	6:36	II	ShE
	16:02	I	OcD
	19:07	I	EcR
31	13:11	I	TrI
	14:03	I	ShI
	15:23	I	TrE
	16:14	I	ShE
	20:39	II	OcD

I = Io II = Europa III = Ganymede IV = Callisto

SATELLITES OF JUPITER, UT OF 2017 GEOCENTRIC PHENOMENA (cont)

Day	UT	Sat.	Event
SEPTEMBER			
1	0:48	II	EcR
	10:32	I	OcD
	12:45	III	OcD
	13:35	I	EcR
	15:17	III	OcR
	16:26	III	EcD
	18:32	III	EcR
2	7:41	I	TrI
	8:32	I	ShI
	9:53	I	TrE
	10:42	I	ShE
	15:49	II	TrI
	17:34	II	ShI
	18:17	II	TrE
	19:54	II	ShE
3	5:02	I	OcD
	8:04	I	EcR
4	2:11	I	TrI
	3:01	I	ShI
	4:23	I	TrE
	5:11	I	ShE
	10:02	II	OcD
	14:05	II	EcR
	23:32	I	OcD
5	2:33	I	EcR
	2:44	III	TrI
	5:14	III	TrE
	6:12	III	ShI
	8:16	III	ShE
	20:41	I	TrI
	21:29	I	ShI
	22:53	I	TrE
	23:40	I	ShE
6	5:12	II	TrI
	6:51	II	ShI
	7:40	II	TrE
	9:12	II	ShE
	18:02	I	OcD
	21:01	I	EcR
7	15:11	I	TrI
	15:58	I	ShI
	17:23	I	TrE
	18:08	I	ShE
	23:26	II	OcD
8	3:23	II	EcR
	12:32	I	OcD
	15:30	I	EcR
	17:09	III	OcD
	19:39	III	OcR
	20:26	III	EcD
	22:31	III	EcR
9	9:41	I	TrI
	10:27	I	ShI
	11:53	I	TrE
	12:37	I	ShE
	18:36	II	TrI
	20:10	II	ShI
9	21:04	II	TrE
	22:30	II	ShE
10	7:02	I	OcD
	9:59	I	EcR
11	4:12	I	TrI
	4:55	I	ShI
	6:23	I	TrE
	7:06	I	ShE
	12:49	II	OcD
	16:40	II	EcR
12	1:33	I	OcD
	4:27	I	EcR
	7:06	III	TrI
	9:35	III	TrE
	10:10	III	ShI
	12:14	III	ShE
	22:42	I	TrI
	23:24	I	ShI
13	0:54	I	TrE
	1:34	I	ShE
	8:00	II	TrI
	9:27	II	ShI
	10:28	II	TrE
	11:48	II	ShE
	20:03	I	OcD
	22:56	I	EcR
14	17:12	I	TrI
	17:52	I	ShI
	19:24	I	TrE
	20:03	I	ShE
15	2:13	II	OcD
	5:58	II	EcR
	14:33	I	OcD
	17:24	I	EcR
	21:34	III	OcD
(too close to Sun)			
DECEMBER			
16	13:22	II	EcD
	15:53	I	EcD
	17:19	II	OcR
	18:51	I	OcR
17	13:05	I	ShI
	13:54	I	TrI
	15:15	I	ShE
	16:04	I	TrE
18	4:04	III	EcD
	5:58	III	EcR
	7:25	III	OcD
	8:11	II	ShI
	9:18	III	OcR
	9:48	II	TrI
	10:21	I	EcD
	10:27	II	ShE
	12:05	II	TrE
	13:21	I	OcR
19	7:34	I	ShI
	8:24	I	TrI
	9:44	I	ShE
	10:34	I	TrE
20	2:40	II	EcD
	4:50	I	EcD
	6:42	II	OcR
	7:50	I	OcR
21	2:02	I	ShI
	2:53	I	TrI
	4:12	I	ShE
	5:04	I	TrE
	17:50	III	ShI
	19:42	III	ShE
	21:22	III	TrI
	21:28	II	ShI
	23:10	*II*	*TrI*
	23:12	III	TrE
	23:18	I	EcD
	23:44	II	ShE
22	1:26	II	TrE
	2:20	I	OcR
	20:30	I	ShI
	21:23	I	TrI
	22:41	I	ShE
	23:33	I	TrE
23	15:58	II	EcD
	17:46	I	EcD
	20:06	II	OcR
	20:49	I	OcR
24	14:59	I	ShI
	15:53	I	TrI
	17:09	I	ShE
	18:03	I	TrE
25	8:02	III	EcD
	9:55	III	EcR
	10:44	II	ShI
	11:46	III	OcD
	12:14	I	EcD
	12:32	II	TrI
	13:00	II	ShE
	13:36	III	OcR
	14:48	II	TrE
	15:19	I	OcR
26	9:27	I	ShI
	10:23	I	TrI
	11:37	I	ShE
	12:33	I	TrE
27	5:16	II	EcD
	6:43	I	EcD
	9:29	II	OcR
	9:48	I	OcR
28	3:56	I	ShI
	4:52	I	TrI
	6:06	I	ShE
	7:02	I	TrE
	21:48	III	ShI
	23:39	III	ShE
29	0:01	II	ShI
	1:11	I	EcD
	1:43	III	TrI
	1:54	*II*	*TrI*
	2:17	II	ShE
	3:29	III	TrE
	4:09	II	TrE
	4:18	I	OcR
	22:24	I	ShI
	23:22	I	TrI
30	0:34	I	ShE
	1:32	I	TrE
	18:34	II	EcD
	19:39	I	EcD
	22:47	I	OcR
	22:52	II	OcR
31	16:53	I	ShI
	17:52	I	TrI
	19:03	I	ShE
	20:02	I	TrE
32	12:00	III	EcD
	13:17	II	ShI
	13:52	III	EcR
	14:07	I	EcD
	15:15	II	TrI
	15:33	II	ShE
	16:05	III	OcD
	17:17	I	OcR
	17:30	II	TrE
	17:51	III	OcR

I = Io II = Europa III = Ganymede IV = Callisto

CONFIGURATIONS OF SATURN'S BRIGHTEST SATELLITES

BY LARRY D. BOGAN

The diagrams on the following three pages give the relative locations of Saturn's five brightest satellites for February through October 2017. Saturn resides in southern Ophiuchus this year and is in opposition with the Sun on Jun. 15 and in conjunction on Dec. 21. The names and magnitudes of these satellites, in order of increasing distance from Saturn, are Enceladus 11.8, Tethys 10.3, Dione 10.4, Rhea 9.7, and Titan 8.4.

The curves in the diagrams show the elongations of the satellites from Saturn for day 0.0 UT to day 32.0 UT for each month. The dashed curves represent Enceladus and Dione, the first and third out from Saturn. The narrow, central, vertical band represents the disk of Saturn, and the wider band the outer edge of Saturn's A ring. At the top of each monthly diagram is a scale drawing of Saturn, its rings, and the orbits of four of the five brightest satellites as seen through an inverting telescope (in the Northern Hemisphere). South is up. No orbit is shown for Enceladus, the innermost satellite, because of the small size of the scale drawing. Due to its faintness and proximity to the bright rings, Enceladus is best seen when near a maximum elongation, but even then good seeing, good optics, and an aperture of at least 200 mm are required.

During 2017, we see Saturn and its satellites from north of the ring plane. The apparent ring tilts for 2017 have a minimum of 26.6° in February and a maximum of 27.0° in October. The direction of motion of the satellites, as viewed with a telescope having an even number (0, 2, 4,...) of reflections in its optics, is counter-clockwise. An arrow has been placed on the orbit of Titan to indicate all satellite orbit revolution directions.

A particular configuration of the satellites may be determined by drawing a horizontal line across the monthly curves at the time (UT) of interest. The intersection of this line with the curves gives the relative elongations of the satellites. Project these elongations onto the drawing of the orbits at the top of the diagram. The east side of the A ring vertical band has been extended up to the drawing to facilitate transfer of each elongation. A millimetre scale, a pair of dividers, or a strip of paper on which to mark enables one to do this quickly and accurately.

The direction of the orbital motion of a satellite determines on which side of its orbit (north or south) a satellite is located. Note the movement of the satellite along the diagram curves past elongation as it revolves around Saturn to determine whether to put the satellite on the north or south side of the orbit. The February diagram shows an example configuration for Feb. 6 at 6:00 a.m. EST (11h UT).

Greatest Elongations and Conjunctions for Iapetus

The magnitude of Iapetus is comparable to the five plotted satellites, but it varies from 10.2 (western elongation) to 11.9 (eastern elongation). This satellite's orbit is about 2.9 times the size of Titan's and is tilted 15° to Saturn's ring plane; its period is 79.33 days. Iapetus is easiest to find near conjunctions, when it is just north or south of Saturn. The table below lists times (UT) of greatest elongations and conjunctions during 2017. Use "east is least and west is best" to remember the brightest elongation.

Eastern Elong.	Inferior Conj.	Western Elong.	Superior Conj.
Jan. 10	Jan. 28 20 h	Feb. 19	Mar. 11 14 h
Mar. 31	Apr. 18 21 h	May 09	May 29 13 h
Jun. 17	Jul. 06 05 h	Jul. 26	Aug. 15 22 h
Sep. 04	Sep. 23 08 h	Oct. 14	Nov. 04 02 h
Nov. 24	Dec. 13 06 h		

Note: Stellarium *for Mac, Linux, or Windows, a freeware computer program, displays the configuration of Saturn's satellites on your computer. It can be downloaded at* www.stellarium.org.

CONFIGURATIONS OF SATURN'S SATELLITES
2017 FEBRUARY–APRIL

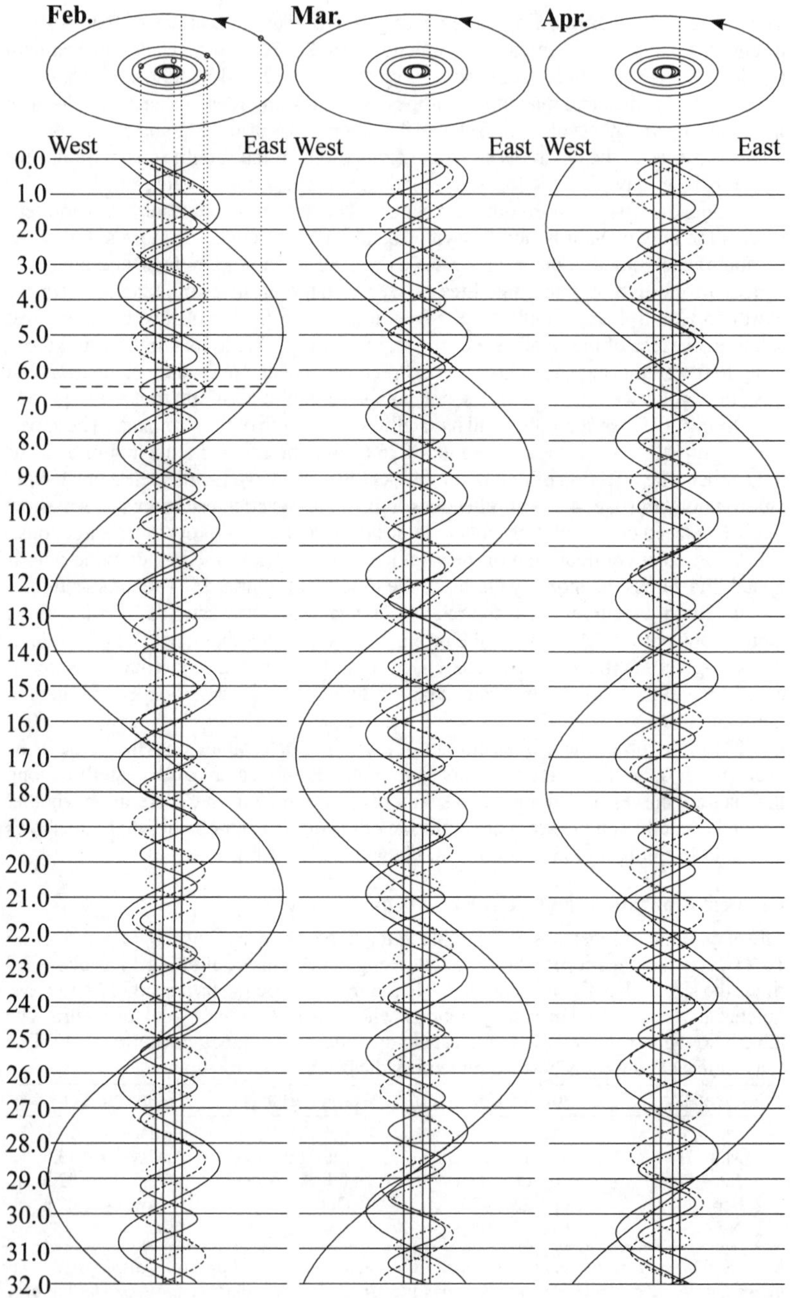

CONFIGURATIONS OF SATURN'S SATELLITES
2017 MAY–JULY

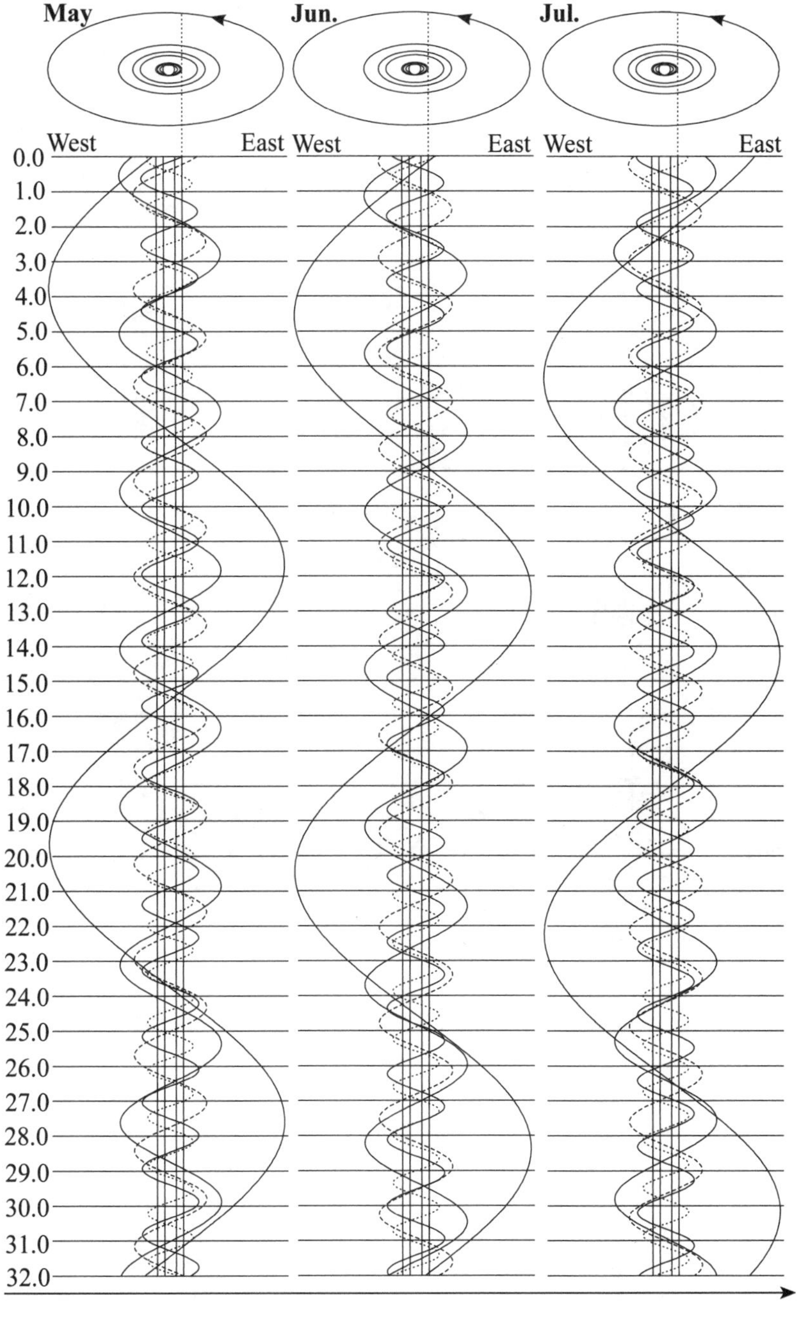

CONFIGURATIONS OF SATURN'S SATELLITES
2017 AUGUST–OCTOBER

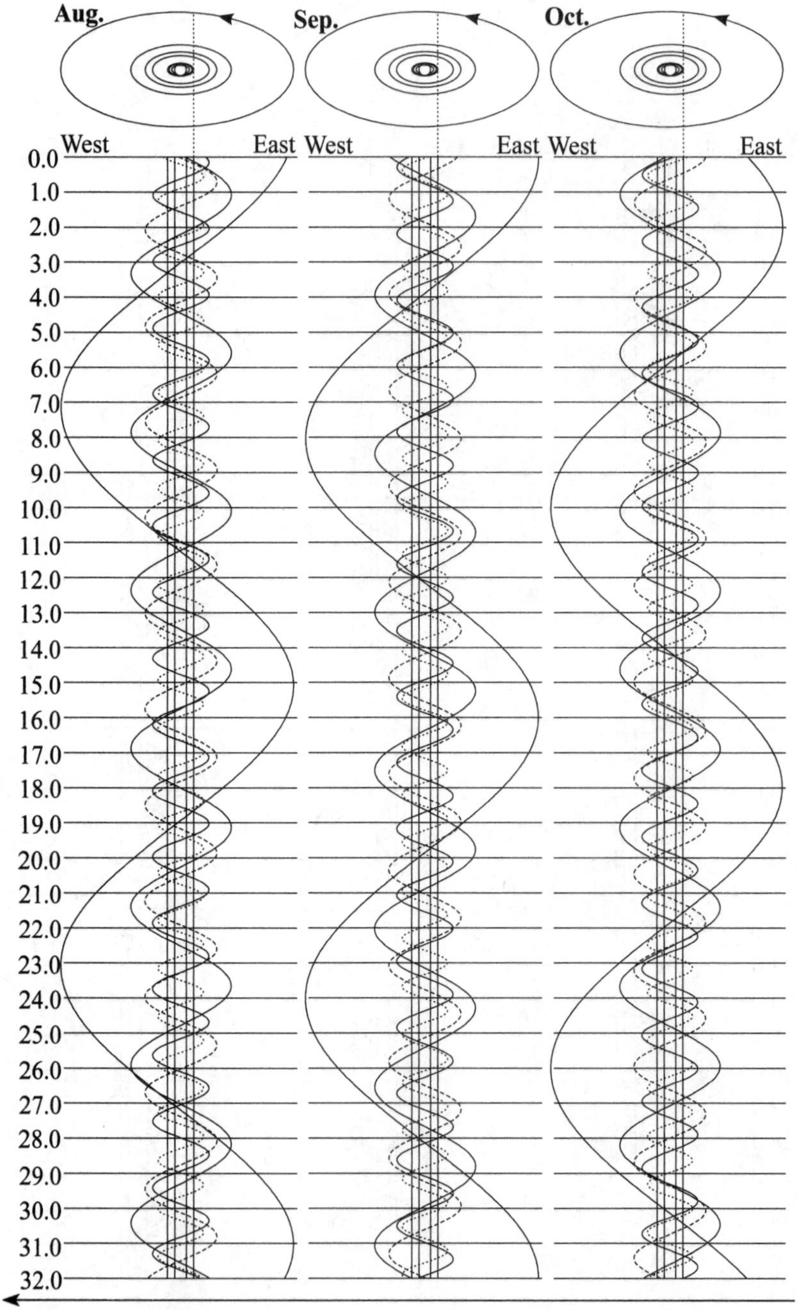

DWARF AND MINOR PLANETS

THE DWARF PLANETS

Classification of Solar System Bodies

The classification of Solar System bodies has been a rough ride on the pathway of astronomical history, and our destination may still be over the scientific horizon. At the start of the 19th century, the known Solar System included the Sun, the Earth and Moon, the classic five naked-eye planets, the "new" planet Uranus, a handful of natural satellites, and some comets. In quick succession, the "planets" 1 Ceres (1801), 2 Pallas (1802), 3 Juno (1804), and 4 Vesta (1807) were discovered between the orbits of Mars and Jupiter. In 1882, by which time many more small bodies had been discovered, these were reclassified as *asteroids*, numbered serially according to their discovery date. (Today, the designation *minor planet* is preferred over *asteroid*.)

Along the way, the planet Neptune (1846) was discovered and eventually Pluto (1930) became accepted as the ninth planet, even though it has a highly inclined and eccentric orbit relative to the other planets, and is smaller than the Moon and several natural satellites of other planets.

By 2006, the rate of discovery of Pluto-like *trans-Neptunian objects* (TNOs) prompted the International Astronomical Union (IAU) to controversially re-classify Pluto as a *dwarf planet*, numbered 134340 Pluto, followed by 1 Ceres; within two years these two were joined by three more TNOs (see below). The details may be found on the IAU webpage www.iau.org/public/pluto/ and in Mike Brown's informative book *How I Killed Pluto and Why It had it Coming* (Random House, 2012).

Currently, the IAU recognizes three principal planetary categories: (1) planets, (2) dwarf planets, and (3) small Solar System bodies. The **planets** are the traditional eight bodies: Mercury, Venus, Earth, Mars, Jupiter, Saturn, Uranus, and Neptune. The **dwarf planets** are 1 Ceres, 134340 Pluto, 136199 Eris, 136108 Haumea, and 136472 Makemake (with 50000 Quaoar, 90377 Sedna, and 9040 Orcus being strongly considered). In plain terms, planets and dwarf planets are round, but dwarf planets are considered too small to have significant gravitational effect on other bodies (other than their satellites, if they have any). **Small Solar System bodies** are everything else, other than satellites: minor planets in the asteroid belt or elsewhere (including most TNOs), and comets. What distinguishes dwarf planets from minor planets is *roundness*: dwarf planets are round, while minor planets are irregular in shape. Such systems of classification are governed by scientific convention, and are subject to change.

1 CERES

Ceres was the first dwarf planet to be discovered, but it is the smallest, and the brightest, only because its orbit lies within the asteroid belt between Mars and Jupiter, while the others are all beyond Neptune. This close proximity makes it readily observable, even in binoculars (at opposition). In early 2017, Ceres is in the evening sky in Pisces, gradually dimming from mag. 7.4, until swallowed up in the Sun's glare in March. During the latter part of the year, Ceres gradually brightens in prograde motion near Pollux (β Gem) in the morning sky, beginning to retrograde in late December, and reaching a maximum of mag. 6.9 at opposition in early 2018 (see the finder chart on the next page and the ephemeris on p. 246). In 2015, the *Dawn* spacecraft orbited Ceres and thoroughly mapped the surface, which appears to be largely water ice.

FINDER CHART FOR 1 CERES

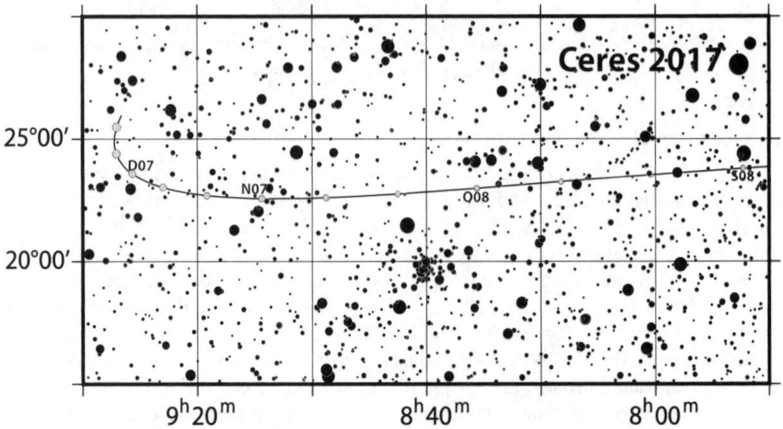

The bright star located near the chart top right is Pollux listed as 1.15 visual magnitude. The open cluster Praesepe is near the lower chart centre. See caption for Pluto at right for resource attribution (chart by Ian Cameron).

134340 PLUTO

BY MURRAY PAULSON

Pluto's mean distance from the Sun is 39.3 au, but its highly eccentric orbit currently locates it much closer, about 33.36 au in 2017. At its last perihelion in 1989, Pluto shone at mag. 13.6, a state it will not revisit until the 23rd century. As Pluto moves away from perihelion, it is slowly fading. Clyde Tombaugh discovered Pluto in 1930, when it was 42.3 au distant at mag. 15.3. It will be another 39 years before Pluto becomes this faint again. In July of 2015, we looked in wonder at the first close-up views of Pluto's surface from *New Horizons*. Over the ensuing year we have been treated to many images of this intriguing world at the edge of the Kuiper belt.

Pluto is 2370 km in diameter, only twice that of its largest moon, Charon (1208 km). It has retrograde rotation of period 6.39 days, synchronous with Charon's revolution. Pluto also has four smaller satellites, Nix, Hydra, Kerberos, and Styx, the last discovered in July 2012. These four satellites are all less than 100 km in diameter and dimmer than mag. 23.

The year starts off with Pluto in conjunction with the Sun on Jan. 6. When I first viewed it in 1988, it was in conjunction with the Sun on Nov. 4. It was also near perihelion and much easier to find at mag. 13.6. This year it is down in the deep south of Sagittarius located about 7° east of the handle of the Teapot. Pluto comes to opposition on Jul. 10 and will shine at mag. 14.2. It will sit just 1.8° east of mag. 2.9 π Sgr. It will be a tough hunt looking through all that atmosphere low to the horizon, so you will need a scope 10″ or larger and very good sky conditions to find it. I encourage you to try a smaller aperture for the fun of the chase. There will be no lack of background stars to use for star hopping. (Check the finder chart at right.) Pluto will come to conjunction with the Sun early in the new year.

Now, if finding Pluto isn't enough of a challenge, see if you can spot it in a mid-sized refractor. The observation is possible in a 125–130-mm refractor, but the transparency and seeing must both be very good. One year, I challenged RASC Edmonton Centre member Alister Ling to find it in his 125-mm APO, and I tackled it with my 94-mm Brandon refractor. Pluto was much higher at that time. Alister achieved the observation with relative ease, but the smaller aperture of 94 mm made it a very tough hunt for me. I found it, but with great difficulty, eyestrain, and over an hour of painstaking star hopping. I welcome any comments or stories of your hunt.

FINDER CHART FOR 134340 PLUTO

BY IAN CAMERON

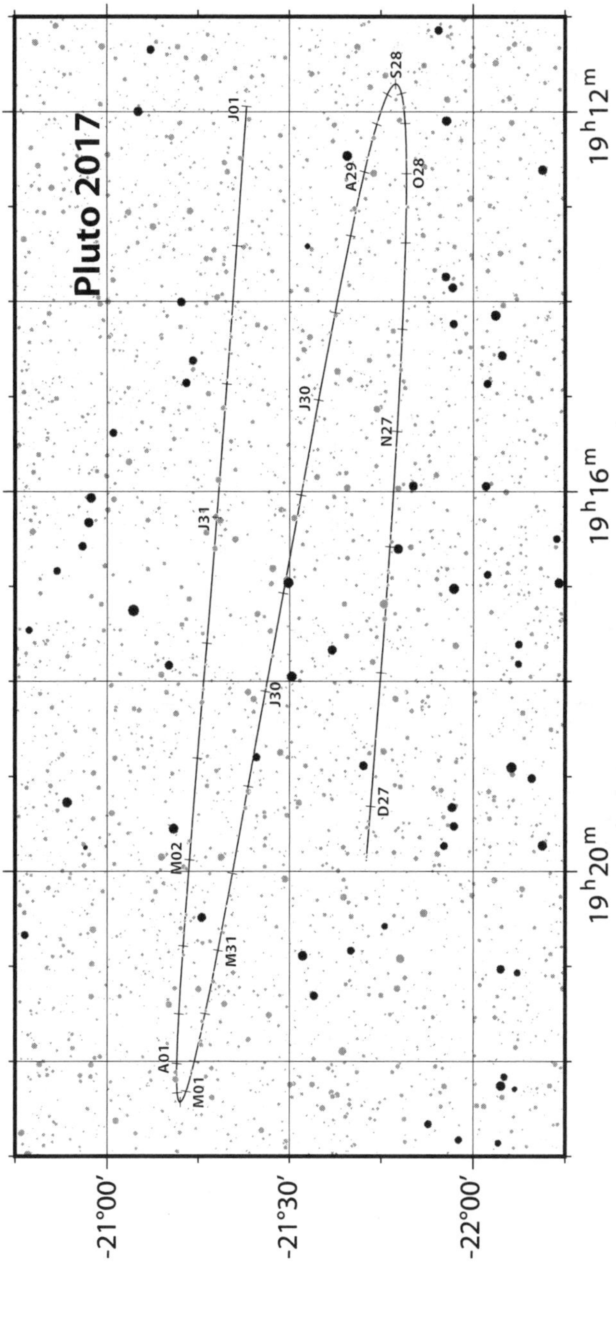

This chart uses the astrometric UCAC4 catalogue. The UCAC4 lists model fitted photometric magnitudes (579–642 nm). The brighter stars to 9.5 magnitudes, indicated by the dark circles, are from Uranometria 2000 (Vol. 2, Chart 341). The bright star located at chart centre is listed as 8.36 visual magnitude in the UCAC4. The Pluto ephemeris is generated using the JPL Horizons Web-Interface. Pluto is at opposition with magnitude 14.2 on Jul. 10. The chart limiting magnitude is 15 according to the UCAC4. The chart is generated using the open source Generic Mapping Tools (GMT5.1.2) under Mac OS 10.10.5 (chart by Ian Cameron).

THE BRIGHTEST MINOR PLANETS

The following two pages contain ephemerides for those minor planets (identified by number and name) that reach mag. 9.7 or brighter during 2017 and are positioned more than 60° from the Sun. The table is ordered by opposition date, shown in the headers, along with the opposition magnitude. In the table, **Mag.** is visual magnitude. The ephemeris for the *dwarf planet* 1 Ceres is included here in keeping with tradition, but more information and a finder chart can be found in the THE DWARF PLANETS, on p. 241. See p. 23 for the current orbital elements of the 25 brightest minor planets (by absolute magnitude) and 3 dwarf planets.

Observers can make their own finder charts by plotting the coordinates on a suitable star atlas with equinox J2000.0. Those with computer planetarium software can obtain orbital elements in several popular electronic formats from the Minor Planet Center (www.minorplanetcenter.net/iau/MPEph/MPEph.html).

FEATURE MINOR PLANET: 6 HEBE

Discovered in 1847, 6 Hebe was the sixth asteroid found, one of two discovered by Karl Ludwig Hencke. The name, proposed by Carl Friedrich Gauss, is for the goddess of youth in Greek mythology. It is thought that Hebe is the source of H chondrite meteorites, accounting for about 40% of all meteorites striking Earth.

Residing in main asteroid belt, Hebe contains around half a percent of the belt's mass. Even though it is relatively large, the high density means that Hebe does not rank very high by volume. The high density means it is quite different than most minor planets of its size, which tend to be loosely bound "rubble piles."

Hebe is the fifth-brightest object in the asteroid belt after Vesta, Ceres, Iris, and Pallas, with an opposition magnitude of +8.3.

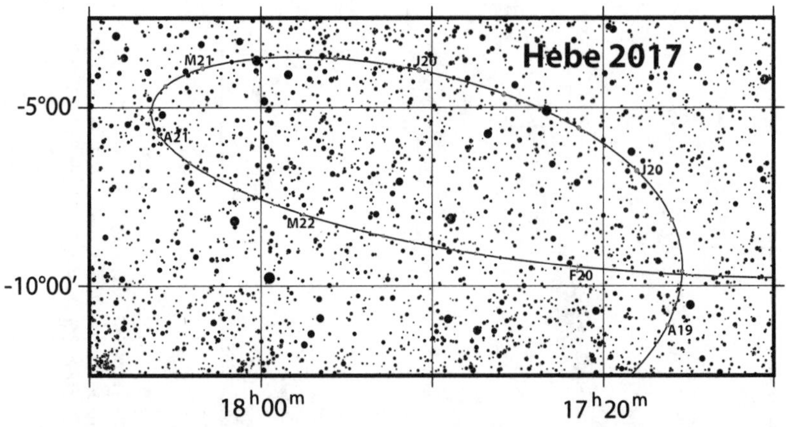

This chart uses the astrometric UCAC4 catalogue. The UCAC4 lists model fitted photometric magnitudes (579–642nm). The bright star located near the chart lower left is ν Oph listed as 3.3 visual magnitude. The Hebe ephemeris is generated using the JPL Horizons Web-Interface. Hebe is plotted as a gray circle of visual magnitude varying from 11.4 to 9.2. The chart limiting magnitude is 12.5 according to the UCAC4. The chart is generated using the open source Generic Mapping Tools (GMT5.1.2) under Mac OS 10.10.5. (Chart by Ian Cameron.)

EPHEMERIDES FOR THE BRIGHTEST MINOR PLANETS IN 2017

BY DANIEL W.E. GREEN

Date 0h TT	RA (2000) h m	Dec ° ′	Mag.
18 Melpomene 2015 Oct. 23, mag. 8.0			
Jan. 7	2 22.57	−00 41.3	9.7
4 Vesta Jan. 18, mag. 6.2			
Jan. 7	8 13.77	+22 15.0	6.5
17	8 03.38	+23 17.4	6.2
27	7 52.53	+24 15.2	6.4
Feb. 6	7 42.64	+25 03.2	6.6
16	7 34.95	+25 38.9	6.8
26	7 30.24	+26 02.3	7.0
Mar. 8	7 28.85	+26 14.3	7.2
18	7 30.73	+26 16.5	7.4
28	7 35.59	+26 10.0	7.5
Apr. 7	7 43.08	+25 55.4	7.7
17	7 52.78	+25 32.8	7.8
27	8 04.31	+25 02.4	7.9
May 7	8 17.34	+24 23.9	8.0
17	8 31.56	+23 37.4	8.0
27	8 46.73	+22 42.7	8.1
Jun. 6	9 02.65	+21 40.0	8.1
14 Irene Feb. 18, mag. 9.0			
Jan. 17	10 48.82	+20 19.5	9.7
27	10 46.63	+21 44.4	9.4
Feb. 6	10 41.39	+23 17.5	9.2
16	10 33.76	+24 47.7	9.0
26	10 24.85	+26 02.9	9.0
Mar. 8	10 16.15	+26 53.1	9.2
18	10 09.11	+27 13.5	9.4
28	10 04.76	+27 04.5	9.6
15 Eunomia Feb. 20. mag. 9.2			
Jan. 17	10 28.03	+00 08.8	9.7
27	10 21.37	−00 08.1	9.5
Feb. 6	10 12.85	−00 08.5	9.3
16	10 03.30	+00 05.7	9.2
26	9 53.68	+00 31.2	9.3
Mar. 8	9 45.02	+01 03.4	9.5
18	9 38.13	+01 37.0	9.7
9 Metis Feb. 22, mag. 9.0			
Jan. 27	10 57.47	+16 22.7	9.5
Feb. 6	10 50.97	+17 30.4	9.3
16	10 42.16	+18 39.5	9.1
26	10 32.20	+19 39.9	9.1
Mar. 8	10 22.53	+20 23.2	9.3
29 Amphitrite Mar. 3, mag. 9.1			
Feb. 6	11 22.07	+07 29.9	9.7
16	11 14.77	+07 58.5	9.5
26	11 05.75	+08 33.0	9.2
Mar. 8	10 56.06	+09 07.5	9.2
18	10 46.87	+09 36.1	9.5
29 Amphitrite (continued)			
28	10 39.18	+09 54.4	9.7
41 Daphne Mar. 8, mag. 9.6			
Mar. 8	11 06.52	−00 04.9	9.6
18	10 59.70	+02 20.2	9.7
6 Hebe Jun. 7, mag. 9.2			
May 17	18 08.83	−04 05.2	9.7
27	18 02.98	−03 42.6	9.5
Jun. 6	17 54.95	−03 35.6	9.3
16	17 45.46	−03 47.3	9.2
26	17 35.49	−04 19.0	9.2
Jul. 6	17 26.18	−05 09.7	9.3
16	17 18.53	−06 16.4	9.4
26	17 13.29	−07 34.7	9.5
Aug. 5	17 10.90	−09 00.5	9.7
40 Harmonia Jun. 23, mag. 9.3			
Jun. 16	18 16.47	−22 47.9	9.7
26	18 05.60	−23 13.7	9.4
10 Hygiea Jun. 29, mag. 9.1			
May 27	18 58.60	−23 57.4	9.9
Jun. 6	18 53.47	−23 54.2	9.7
16	18 46.39	−23 51.1	9.5
26	18 38.07	−23 46.9	9.2
Jul. 6	18 29.46	−23 40.6	9.3
3 Juno Jul. 2, mag. 9.7			
Jul. 6	18 37.39	−05 08.7	9.7
89 Julia Sep. 8, mag. 9.0			
Aug. 5	23 13.72	+06 50.7	9.6
15	23 07.00	+08 29.7	9.4
25	22 57.63	+09 47.9	9.1
Sep. 4	22 46.69	+10 41.4	9.0
14	22 35.66	+11 09.8	9.0
24	22 26.09	+11 16.4	9.2
Oct. 4	22 19.25	+11 08.9	9.4
2 Pallas Oct. 29, mag. 8.2			
Jul. 16	2 29.25	+00 20.7	9.7
26	2 40.72	−00 36.2	9.6
Aug. 5	2 51.24	−01 52.4	9.4
15	3 00.59	−03 29.5	9.3
25	3 08.48	−05 28.8	9.1
Sep. 4	3 14.59	−07 50.4	8.9
14	3 18.64	−10 32.7	8.7
24	3 20.31	−13 31.8	8.6
Oct. 4	3 19.39	−16 40.3	8.4
14	3 15.88	−19 47.5	8.3
24	3 10.02	−22 40.6	8.2
Nov. 3	3 02.43	−25 06.0	8.2

EPHEMERIDES FOR THE BRIGHTEST MINOR PLANETS IN 2017

Date 0h TT	RA (2000) h m	Dec ° ′	Mag.
2 Pallas (continued)			
Nov. 13	2 54.07	–26 53.3	8.2
23	2 46.02	–27 56.8	8.3
Dec. 3	2 39.38	–28 16.3	8.4
13	2 34.94	–27 56.2	8.5
23	2 33.16	–27 03.0	8.6
7 Iris		***Oct. 30, mag. 6.9***	
Jul. 6	1 01.80	+13 09.7	9.6
16	1 17.44	+15 06.6	9.5
26	1 32.29	+16 56.7	9.3
Aug. 5	1 46.05	+18 38.3	9.1
15	1 58.41	+20 09.7	8.9
25	2 08.89	+21 28.9	8.7
Sep. 4	2 16.99	+22 33.2	8.4
14	2 22.18	+23 19.4	8.2
24	2 23.97	+23 43.6	7.9
Oct. 4	2 22.19	+23 41.6	7.6
14	2 17.17	+23 10.6	7.3
24	2 09.87	+22 11.2	7.0
Nov. 3	2 01.96	+20 49.8	6.9
13	1 55.22	+19 18.7	7.2
23	1 51.13	+17 51.9	7.5
Dec. 3	1 50.55	+16 41.3	7.7
13	1 53.67	+15 53.1	8.0
23	2 00.26	+15 28.7	8.3
Jan. 2	2 09.93	+15 26.3	8.5
44 Nysa		***Nov. 3, mag. 9.6***	
Oct. 24	2 51.26	+09 40.4	9.7
Nov. 3	2 41.94	+08 50.5	9.6
13	2 32.25	+08 06.6	9.7
349 Dembowska		***Dec. 1, mag. 9.6***	
Nov. 23	4 33.82	+29 25.8	9.6
Dec. 3	4 23.53	+29 30.6	9.6
Dec. 13	4 13.62	+29 25.4	9.7
20 Massalia		***Dec. 17, mag. 8.4***	
Nov. 3	6 07.49	+22 39.2	9.7
13	6 07.34	+22 33.2	9.4

Date 0h TT	RA (2000) h m	Dec ° ′	Mag.
20 Massalia (continued)			
Nov. 23	6 03.42	+22 27.7	9.2
Dec. 3	5 56.09	+22 22.3	8.9
13	5 46.32	+22 16.0	8.6
23	5 35.62	+22 08.6	8.6
Jan. 2	5 25.85	+22 01.0	8.9
8 Flora		***2018 Jan. 2, mag. 8.2***	
Oct. 24	7 06.44	+17 52.8	9.7
Nov. 3	7 15.30	+17 46.2	9.6
13	7 20.80	+17 48.3	9.4
23	7 22.46	+18 02.4	9.2
Dec. 3	7 20.04	+18 30.7	9.0
13	7 13.67	+19 12.9	8.7
23	7 04.04	+20 05.8	8.5
Jan. 2	6 52.62	+21 03.4	8.2
1 Ceres*		***2018 Jan. 31, mag. 6.9***	
Jan. 7	1 36.62	+02 26.4	8.7
17	1 42.49	+03 45.3	8.8
27	1 50.06	+05 09.4	8.9
Feb. 6	1 59.13	+06 37.2	8.9
16	2 09.50	+08 07.0	9.0
	too close to Sun		
Sep. 24	8 10.31	+23 22.0	8.8
Oct. 4	8 25.43	+23 05.1	8.8
14	8 39.62	+22 49.9	8.7
24	8 52.71	+22 38.6	8.6
Nov. 3	9 04.50	+22 33.3	8.5
13	9 14.76	+22 36.7	8.3
23	9 23.20	+22 51.3	8.2
Dec. 3	9 29.52	+23 19.4	8.0
13	9 33.39	+24 02.6	7.8
23	9 34.51	+25 01.3	7.6
Jan. 2	9 32.67	+26 13.6	7.4

**dwarf planet, see p. 241*

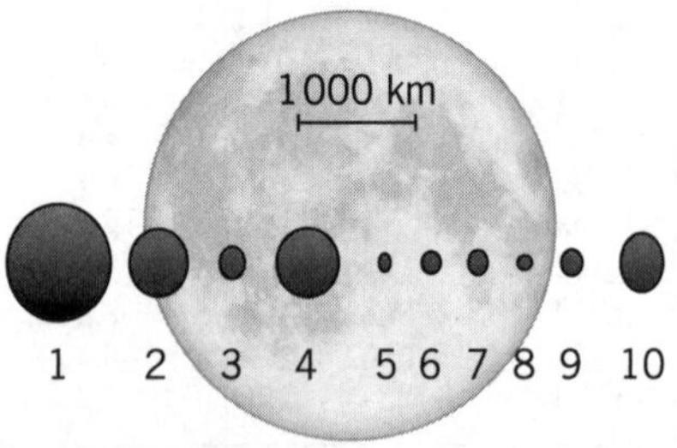

Relative sizes of the Moon and the first 10 sub-planets discovered: 1 Ceres, 2 Pallas, 3 Juno, 4 Vesta, 5 Astraea, 6 Hebe, 7 Iris, 8 Flora, 9 Metis, and 10 Hygeia (illustration by Michael Gatto, after Vystrix Nexoth).

PLANETARY OCCULTATIONS

BY DAVID W. DUNHAM, JAMES STAMM, PAUL MALEY, STEVE PRESTON, DEREK BREIT, SCOTT DONNELL, EDWIN GOFFIN, AND DAVID HERALD

Introduction

As major, dwarf, and minor planets (with their moons) move across the sky, they occasionally pass directly between an observer and a distant star, producing an *occultation*. Astronomers have learned much about Solar System bodies by carefully monitoring the changing apparent brightness of stars during the immersion and emersion phases of occultations. If the occulting body does not have an atmosphere, the occultation is virtually instantaneous; if there is an atmosphere, it causes the star's disappearance and reappearance to occur gradually. If a planet has rings or other debris in its environs, the extent and degree of transparency of this material can be precisely mapped. The rings of Uranus, the ring arcs of Neptune, and the atmosphere of Pluto were all discovered by occultation observations. If an occultation is observed at several distributed sites, the size and shape of the occulting body can be determined more accurately than by other Earth-based techniques.

Amateur astronomers can often make important contributions to occultation observing campaigns. This is particularly true for minor planet occultations, for which the paths across Earth are often very narrow and uncertain in location (due to uncertainties in both the star's position and the ephemeris of the minor planet). By recording the times of the star's disappearance and reappearance as seen from several sites (i.e. by noting the edges of the minor planet's shadow as it sweeps across Earth), the object's profile can be directly determined. Often timings of adequate accuracy can be made by visual observers using modest telescopes.

When observing an occultation, it is important that an observer know his or her location to within a fraction of a kilometre. Geographic latitude and longitude as well as the altitude of an observing site can be determined with a GPS receiver, from a high-quality topographic map, or from some map websites. If observations are to be of maximum value, the times of immersion and emersion must be determined as accurately as possible—certainly to better than 0.5 s, and better than 0.2 s for the shortest events (those less than about 10 s in duration). Photoelectric equipment with high-speed digital recording systems is well suited for this work. Attaching a low-light-level video camera to a telescope is a less expensive method for accurate timing. Visual observers using audio recorders and shortwave time-signal receivers can also make useful contributions. Even simple measurements of the duration of an occultation made with an ordinary stopwatch can be of value. CCD observers should be aware that most of these systems are incapable of timing accuracies better than about 2 s; hence visual observation may be better. Some CCD observers use the trick of turning off the telescope clock drive shortly before the predicted time and letting the images trail. The occultation will appear as a break in the trail that can be measured to about a tenth of a second if the moment the exposure is started (just after turning off the clock drive) is accurately timed.

Occultation observations are coordinated in North America by the International Occultation Timing Association (IOTA). Whether or not you are an IOTA member, IOTA wants to inform you (and others in your area) of prediction updates, if you can observe stars as dim as mag. 11. Please email the latitude and longitude (or location relative to the nearest town) of convenient observing sites, telescope size(s), and an indication of whether you are mobile to dunham@starpower.net. Individuals interested in joining IOTA should refer to LUNAR OCCULTATIONS (see p. 162). More information can be found in the *Solar System Photometry Handbook* (Willmann–Bell, Inc., 1983), *Sky & Telescope*, and occasional papers in the *Astronomical Journal*, *Icarus*, *Minor Planet Bulletin* (www.minorplanet.info), and other scientific journals.

Observations of occultations by major and minor planets, including negative observations, should be sent to reports@asteroidoccultation.com for analysis and publication by IOTA. When reporting timings, describe your geographic longitude, latitude, and altitude (to the nearest arcsecond and 30 m, respectively), telescope aperture, timing method, the start and end time of observation, an estimate of the observer's reaction time (if applicable), the accuracy of the timing, and whether the reaction time correction has been applied. The preferred report forms can be found at www.asteroidoccultation.com/observations; observational results are posted there, as well as much more useful information.

Table of Planetary Occultations

The following two-page table (see p. 250) of planetary occultations, visible from North America and Hawaii in 2017, is based on predictions by Edwin Goffin, Scott Donnell, Steve Preston, Derek Breit, and David Herald. Preston and Breit assisted Dunham and Stamm in the selection for the two-page table. There are no readily observable occultations by major planets or by their satellites for North America and Hawaii this year. There is only one occultation by a major planet worth noting, by Venus on Jan. 30 visible from Hawaii, Alaska, and at low altitude, British Columbia.

The successive columns in the table list: (1) the date and central time (UT) of the event; (2) the occulting body; (3) the apparent magnitude of the body; (4) the catalogue and number of the occulted star; (5) the star's apparent visual magnitude; (6) the star's RA and (7) Dec; (8) the expected magnitude change from the combined brightness; (9) the predicted maximum occultation duration in seconds; and (10) the approximate region from which the occultation is predicted to be visible (locations are listed chronologically from first to last). Due to uncertainties in the catalogue positions of the stars and the ephemerides of the minor planets from which these predictions are derived, the region of visibility of an occultation is uncertain, by about a path width for most of the asteroidal occultations listed. However, in late 2017, after this information was prepared in time for printing the 2017 *Observer's Handbook*, a much better stellar reference frame will become available from observations by the European Space Agency's *Gaia* astrometry spacecraft that is much improved over their *HIPPARCOS* mission of the early 1990s. Using the new *Gaia* star catalogue, along with the over 3000 previously observed asteroidal occultations (each providing a precise position relative to the new *Gaia* positional data for the star) and other new accurate CCD astrometric observations should enable us to refine the paths much more accurately than we could previously, to less than 10 km in some cases. Errors may remain, so those near but outside the paths should try to observe. It's also useful, especially for the brighter stars that produce high signal-to-noise recordings, to observe even if you are located up to about 10 path widths from the predicted path, to check for the possibility of an occultation by a previously unknown satellite of the asteroid. Updated maps and more about these events is at www.poyntsource.com/New/RASC_Events.htm.

Note that listed event times are the geocentric time of closest approach; for any specific location in North America or Hawaii, the event time can be several minutes earlier or later. A few weeks before each event, improved predictions and the latest path maps are posted at www.asteroidoccultation.com, Steve Preston's minor-planet occultation website. See www.poyntsource.com/New/Global.htm for additional useful information, including interactive maps to zoom in on the path, circumstances for dozens of stations in and near the path, and lists of stars that can be used to centre telescopes on target stars. *Occult Watcher* can be used to find other planetary occultations visible from your site (www.hristopavlov.net/OccultWatcher/publish.htm). Since *Occult Watcher* works from an interactive website, IOTA uses it to coordinate minor-planet occultation observation plans.

Alternative star numbers for some events (*) in the main table (see next two pages):

Date	Planet #	Alt. Star #	Sp.	Date	Planet #	Alt. Star #	Sp.
Jan. 31	206	TYC 1354-00834-1	K0	Sep. 11	199	TYC 1320-01092-1	B9
Feb. 5	204	TYC 4916-00244-1	G5	12	241	TYC 5233-02000-1	A2
Mar. 8	235	TYC 2469-00702-1	G5	30	751	HIP 39387	F0
Apr. 11	105	HIP 62736	K2	Oct. 23	154	TYC 0638-00660-1	G0
Jun. 6	5	TYC 6283-00014-1		Nov. 6	505	HIP 116724	F2
Jul. 1	209	TYC 7349-01278-1		9	491	TYC 4756-00238-1	F0
18	412	TYC 6263-02266-1	B8	15	1255	TYC 1240-00303-1	F0
Aug. 20	267	TYC 6391-00965-1	K0	15	420	HIP 13855	G0
Sep. 4	124	TYC 5802-01153-1	G5	23	494	HIP 48778	F8
9	732	TYC 5246-00750-1	F5				

Star catalogues are abbreviated as follows: SAO (Smithsonian Astrophysical Observatory), ZC (Robertson's Zodiacal Catalog), TYC (Tycho–2), PPM (Roeser Positions and Proper Motions), and HIP (*HIPPARCOS*). Some event stars, marked by * in the main table, have alternative star numbers, shown in the table above: **Planet #** is the dwarf- or minor-planet number and the alternative star number (**Alt. Star #**) is from the *HIPPARCOS*-mission catalogues used for the predictions on IOTA's planetary occultation websites mentioned above. Spectral types (**Sp.**) are not available for some of the stars.

Noteworthy events (marked in **bold** type in the main table on the next 2 pages):

Jan. 30: Venus's 30° disk will be 41% sunlit. Only the dark-side disappearance can be seen. SAO 146860 = HIP 117016, spectral type A0.

Mar. 11: SAO 80909 = HIP 46938 = HD 82670, sp. K5. The star's angular diameter of about 0.003″ should cause the star to disappear in 0.4 s for a central event and longer for a near-graze, so it might be measured from video or other high-speed photometric observations. There will be partial occultation zones about 4-km wide at the path edges.

Mar. 28 & **Nov. 13:** Kleopatra is the largest M-class asteroid and the most elongated large asteroid, about 4 times as long as it is wide. Radar observations around 2000 showed it to have a strange dog-bone shape, but subsequent occultation and adaptive-optics observations indicate that it may be essentially two triaxial ellipsoids joined end-to-end. Observations of this occultation will help resolve the true shape of this strange asteroid.

Apr. 10: SAO 184216 = HIP 79392, sp. A2IV. The star has a 10th-mag. companion 12" away in PA 185° that will not be occulted.

Aug. 14: SAO 59794 = HIP 34358 = HD 53686 = HR 2665, sp. K0. The star's angular diameter of 0.002″ should cause the star to disappear in 0.1 s for a central event and longer for a near-graze, so it might be measured with video. There will be partial occultation zones 6 km wide at the path edges. The path crosses central Nebraska a week before a solar eclipse there.

Aug. 23: SAO 164213 = TYC 5780–00308–1, sp. G. The path is over NW Missouri two nights after a total solar eclipse there.

Aug. 24: (849) Ara is an M-class asteroid that could support an unusual shape. Path in N Missouri three nights after solar eclipse.

Oct. 9: PPM 118757 = TYC 0644–00643–1. The star is the secondary star of a wide double; the 9.2-magnitude primary star is 19.8″ away in PA 158°; it will not be occulted.

Oct. 21 & **Nov. 14:** Observations of an occultation in 2004 Apr. 18 show that (772) Tanete may have a satellite a few hundred km away.

Nov. 21 (849) Ara, **Nov. 26** (110) Lydia, **Dec. 4** (338) Budrosa, and **Dec. 18** (161) Athor: These M-class asteroids are of special interest since they could support unusual shapes.

IOTA SELECTED LIST OF NORTH AMERICAN PLANETARY OCCULTATIONS FOR 2017

Date	UT	Occulting Body	Mag.	Star	Mag.	RA (2000) h m s	Dec ° ′ ″	ΔMag.	Dur. s	Nominal Path
Jan. 5	0:23	200 Dynamene	11.5	TYC 1921-02175-1	11.0	07 23 39.5	+29 03 53	1.0	12.0	Morehead City, NC to Tallahassee to Guadalajara
18	1:45	693 Zerbinetta	14.3	TYC 2918-01665-1	11.0	05 35 24.0	+46 36 26	3.4	7.7	James Bay to Wichita, KS to S Baja Calif. Sur
18	7:23	143 Adria	13.0	HIP 41443	9.7	08 27 11.1	+28 55 57	3.4	7.0	S New Jersey to Chicago to S Oregon
20	3:35	586 Thekla	13.4	TYC 1343-00386-1	11.2	06 54 34.6	+20 43 15	2.3	7.2	Cape Breton Is. to Thunder Bay to Salem, Oregon
21	6:09	135 Hertha	12.4	TYC 1886-00343-1	10.9	06 22 06.6	+26 19 23	1.7	9.6	Eastern Virginia to S Nebraska to N California
30	**4:50**	**Venus**	**–4.7**	**SAO 146860**	**8.2**	**23 43 17.8**	**–00 09 20**	**0.0**	**848.1**	**Hawaii to Alaska to British Columbia**
31	3:27	206 Hersilia	12.6	*SAO 96656	8.5	07 14 06.6	+19 29 18	4.1	9.9	North Carolina to Denver to Chico, California
Feb. 3	2:19	893 Leopoldina	14.5	2UCAC 33518079	10.1	05 05 40.5	+05 27 03	4.4	8.0	S Baja Calif. to Salt Lake City to Jasper, AB
5	7:15	204 Kallisto	13.0	*SAO 137771	10.2	10 46 11.0	–02 38 07	2.9	6.1	South Carolina to ne. Oklahoma to Oregon
7	1:50	739 Mandeville	11.9	TYC 0806-00344-1	11.0	08 12 25.4	+14 48 30	1.3	9.4	The Bahamas to New Orleans to Los Angeles
Mar. 3	2:34	34 Circe	13.4	TYC 1280-00058-1	10.6	04 50 00.8	+16 24 43	2.9	7.1	Sw. Washington to Winnipeg to Newfoundland
8	7:03	235 Carolina	13.9	*SAO 60640	9.0	08 12 28.5	+31 15 02	4.9	12.8	Jacksonville, FL to Dallas to Los Angeles
11	**6:31**	**1343 Nicole**	**15.2**	**SAO 80909**	**6.3**	**09 33 59.1**	**+23 27 13**	**8.9**	**3.0**	**Jacksonville, FL to San Francisco, California**
14	3:57	636 Erika	14.5	TYC 4950-00722-1	11.5	12 58 27.9	–00 45 12	3.1	5.8	Central Florida to central Texas to Los Angeles, CA
14	3:59	113 Amalthea	12.9	TYC 1878-01081-1	10.0	06 24 08.4	+22 18 13	3.0	4.3	San Diego to central Texas to Jacksonville, Florida
18	4:01	461 Saskia	15.7	TYC 1324-01960-1	9.4	05 52 45.1	+22 16 14	6.3	2.5	San Francisco to Dallas, Texas to Orlando, Florida
28	**8:28**	**216 Kleopatra**	**12.9**	**TYC 5728-01527-1**	**11.4**	**19 45 43.1**	**–10 00 49**	**1.7**	**4.4**	**Austin, Texas to Orlando, Florida**
29	2:56	304 Olga	15.2	TYC 0739-02340-1	11.5	06 22 58.2	+11 59 36	3.7	3.8	Baja California Norte to El Paso to eastern NC
30	0:56	68 Leto	12.6	TYC 2406-01895-1	10.8	05 56 18.4	+30 38 05	2.0	5.7	Grand Forks, MN to Toronto to southern Rhode Is.
Apr. 10	**9:49**	**599 Luisa**	**13.2**	**SAO 184216**	**8.5**	**16 12 09.9**	**–23 55 18**	**4.7**	**9.3**	**N NB to Atlantic City, NJ to Gainesville, Florida**
11	10:08	105 Artemis	10.8	*SAO 119629	8.9	12 51 18.5	+01 05 07	2.1	9.6	Edmonton to Boise, Idaho to San Diego, California
Jun. 6	4:45	5 Astraea	11.2	*PPM 720088	9.6	19 04 51.1	–16 50 34	1.8	12.7	Jacksonville, Florida to Albuquerque, New Mexico
21	3:24	582 Olympia	14.2	TYC 1038-01489-1	10.7	18 46 05.2	+13 42 01	3.5	3.0	Se. Labrador to Sault Ste. Marie to central Utah
Jul. 1	4:15	209 Dido	12.8	*PPM 747874	10.8	16 35 43.8	–32 27 50	2.2	20.7	St. Augustine, Fla. to Swift Current, Saskatchewan
17	2:34	205 Martha	13.2	TYC 5155-00399-1	11.4	19 55 30.8	–03 46 08	2.0	6.0	Southern New Jersey to central Kansas
18	5:04	412 Elisabetha	13.2	*PPM 733677	9.9	18 04 36.7	–20 58 51	3.4	9.8	Thunder Bay to central Baja California
Aug. 13	4:03	318 Magdalena	14.2	TYC 5774-00489-1	10.6	21 00 00.1	–10 14 18	3.6	6.6	Newfoundland to Raleigh, NC to New Orleans
14	**9:27**	**930 Westphalia**	**16.8**	**SAO 59794**	**5.9**	**07 07 22.4**	**+34 00 33**	**10.9**	**1.1**	**Tucson, Arizona to Grand Is., NE to James Bay**
20	4:00	267 Tirza	13.7	*SAO 191125	9.1	22 25 20.6	–20 01 51	4.6	5.3	Jacksonville, Florida to Baja California Sur
23	**3:55**	**834 Burnhamia**	**13.1**	**SAO 164213**	**9.1**	**21 12 25.8**	**–11 49 07**	**4.0**	**6.6**	**Timmons, Ontario to Kansas City to Baja Norte**
24	**10:49**	**849 Ara**	**14.8**	**TYC 0741-01184-1**	**10.4**	**06 34 23.1**	**+12 32 45**	**4.4**	**3.1**	**Santa Cruz, CA to Colorado Spgs. to Kansas City**
28	1:03	506 Marion	13.4	TYC 5225-00428-1	11.6	22 11 31.4	–01 14 31	2.0	6.7	Virginia Breach, Virginia to Nashville, Tennessee
Sep. 3	9:05	31 Euphrosyne	11.9	TYC 2415-01151-1	11.5	05 32 07.6	+36 49 16	1.0	9.8	Tallahassee, FL to New York, NY to Fredericton
4	5:43	124 Alkeste	11.6	*SAO 145835	9.5	22 03 08.1	–09 36 39	2.3	7.9	Norfolk to New Orleans to Brownsville, Texas
9	8:41	732 Tjilaki	13.4	*SAO 146624	8.9	23 18 00.3	–02 41 46	4.5	3.1	St. John's, Nfld to Cleveland to Big Bend, Texas

† **Bold = see the note for this event on p. 249** *See the alternate star name for this event at the top of p. 249.

IOTA SELECTED LIST OF NORTH AMERICAN PLANETARY OCCULTATIONS FOR 2017 (continued)

Date		UT	Occulting Body	Mag.	Star	Mag.	RA (2000) h m s	Dec ° ′ ″	ΔMag.	Dur. s	Nominal Path
Sep.	11	11:07	199 Byblis	15.1	*SAO 95001	9.2	05 56 04.4	+19 22 37	5.9	3.1	Los Angeles to Pueblo, Colorado to Chicago
	12	6:15	241 Germania	11.4	*SAO 146133	9.0	22 30 54.4	–00 27 46	2.5	18.0	Nutak, Labrador to Ignace, Ontario to San Jose, CA
	12	10:54	535 Montague	14.3	TYC 1271-01321-1	10.4	04 46 57.1	+17 52 29	3.9	5.8	Vancouver to Churchill, Manitoba
	30	6:34	751 Faina	13.8	*SAO 79892	9.0	08 03 08.6	+24 35 23	4.8	4.7	Tulsa to Ann Arbor, Michigan to Rigolet, Labrador
Oct.	7	9:42	56 Melete	13.7	TYC 1314-01646-1	11.2	06 09 15.7	+15 25 17	2.6	15.8	Prince Rupert to Winnipeg to Toronto to NYC
	9	**4:01**	**44 Nysa**	**10.1**	**PPM 118757**	**9.4**	**03 01 48.2**	**+10 50 48**	**1.2**	**16.0**	**Barrie, Ontario to Ft. Worth to Chihuahua, Mexico**
	21	**6:49**	**772 Tanete**	**13.9**	**TYC 2450-01220-1**	**10.1**	**07 11 11.8**	**+36 02 17**	**3.8**	**7.8**	**Baja Calif. Norte to Las Vegas to Portland, Oregon**
	23	2:34	154 Bertha	10.2	*PPM 118203	10.2	02 24 51.9	+13 53 20	2.4	12.5	Newfoundland to San Francisco, California
	25	9:23	111 Ate	11.3	TYC 1766-00900-1	11.5	02 28 47.2	+23 15 13	0.7	14.2	Cape Cod to Toronto to Minneapolis to Bend, OR
	25	9:37	319 Leona	15.4	TYC 0780-00625-1	9.7	17 57 16.0	+09 01 33	5.7	4.2	S Brit. Col. to Calgary to Hamilton, ON to Long Is.
Nov.	6	5:32	505 Cava	12.6	*SAO 165814	9.0	23 39 19.7	–17 47 29	3.6	20.7	Central Baja to Salt Lake City to Saskatoon, Sask.
	8	10:20	56 Melete	13.2	TYC 0742-01328-1	10.5	06 09 06.4	+13 32 23	2.8	17.4	Nova Scotia to Missouri to northern Baja
	9	10:52	491 Carina	13.7	*SAO 131919	9.9	05 15 33.3	–02 38 08	3.8	9.0	Eastern North Carolina to central Mexico
	11	2:42	388 Charybdis	13.5	TYC 2408-00547-1	10.0	05 37 33.6	+32 08 21	3.5	17.5	Winnipeg to Jackson, WY to Monterey, California
	12	1:32	545 Messalina	14.1	2UCAC 27012288	11.2	21 25 45.1	–13 32 51	3.0	5.4	Baja California Sur to St. Louis to Saguenay, QC
	13	**3:54**	**216 Kleopatra**	**12.0**	**TYC 5175-00471-1**	**11.8**	**20 23 51.3**	**–07 18 23**	**0.9**	**4.8**	**Salem, Oregon to Duluth, Minnesota**
	14	**10:55**	**772 Tanete**	**13.6**	**TYC 2948-00195-1**	**9.7**	**07 17 14.8**	**+40 01 59**	**3.9**	**8.6**	**Tallahassee, Florida to Detroit to James Bay**
	15	1:25	1255 Schilowa	13.7	*SAO 93384	9.2	03 19 37.6	+19 34 23	4.5	3.2	Moosonee to Wawa to Kansas City to central Baja
	15	6:44	420 Bertholda	13.0	*SAO 93211	8.9	02 58 23.8	+19 13 44	4.1	12.1	Churchill, Manitoba to central Vancouver Island
	16	1:54	1109 Tata	15.7	TYC 5229-00980-1	11.4	22 25 20.7	–04 52 54	4.3	6.4	Baja California Norte to Nashville to S New Jersey
	19	3:28	167 Urda	13.6	2UCAC 38934333	11.3	05 46 22.1	+20 12 47	2.4	4.1	Moosonee, Ontario to Thunder Bay to Fresno, CA
	19	9:39	735 Marghanna	16.0	TYC 1441-02328-1	11.1	11 46 50.5	+17 29 46	4.9	3.4	Dartmouth, NS to Milwaukee to Fresno, California
	21	**8:50**	**849 Ara**	**14.1**	**TYC 0171-02617-1**	**10.7**	**07 10 40.6**	**+04 02 17**	**3.5**	**8.6**	**Labrador to Montréal to S LA to Mexico City**
	23	6:53	494 Virtus	14.6	*SAO 81100	8.7	09 56 55.9	+20 46 37	5.9	7.0	Puerto Vallarta, Mexico to Daytona Beach, Florida
	26	**6:20**	**110 Lydia**	**12.0**	**TYC 1885-01101-1**	**11.3**	**06 14 39.4**	**+27 20 10**	**1.2**	**8.6**	**Cape Cod to Toronto to Minneapolis to Bend, OR**
	26	8:34	758 Mancunia	12.5	TYC 0033-00800-1	10.8	01 54 44.6	+03 47 01	1.9	14.3	New York City to Chicago to Salem, Oregon
Dec.	**4**	**8:25**	**338 Budrosa**	**12.5**	**TYC 1856-00889-1**	**11.2**	**05 31 09.9**	**+27 33 26**	**1.6**	**6.4**	**Ft. Pierce, Florida to Encinal, Texas to central Baja**
	7	6:18	151 Abundantia	12.8	TYC 1799-00448-1	10.9	03 39 42.4	+24 04 16	2.1	3.9	S NS to Ottawa to Fargo, ND to Portland, Oregon
	10	1:35	151 Abundantia	12.8	TYC 1798-00616-1	11.2	03 37 07.5	+24 00 15	1.8	4.1	Gander, NF to Ottawa to Hays, Kansas to Baja Norte
	11	4:50	141 Lumen	11.5	TYC 2915-01715-1	10.8	05 44 24.9	+40 04 37	1.2	14.1	S Labrador to Wawa, Ont. to Denver to San Diego
	15	4:33	53 Kalypso	13.4	TYC 4669-00354-1	11.1	00 05 21.1	–05 04 08	2.4	7.5	La Paz, Baja Sur to Houston to Charleston, SC
	18	**10:43**	**161 Athor**	**12.7**	**TYC 2431-00133-1**	**9.9**	**06 07 52.3**	**+37 09 43**	**2.9**	**3.2**	**Philadelphia to Sault Ste. Marie to NW Alaska**
	21	12:25	980 Anacostia	11.4	TYC 2405-01295-1	9.9	05 44 46.6	+31 24 36	1.7	5.8	Los Angeles to Tucson, Arizona to Laredo, Texas
	21	15:14	334 Chicago	13.3	TYC 1336-00845-1	10.9	06 24 08.3	+19 42 06	2.5	2.5	Hawaii to Japan to South Korea
	26	6:35	980 Anacostia	11.5	TYC 2404-00686-1	11.1	05 39 25.0	+30 52 26	1.0	5.9	Hawke's Bay, Nfld to Fargo, ND to San Francisco

† **Bold = see the note for this event on p. 249** *See the alternate star name for this event at the top of p. 249.

METEORS, COMETS, AND DUST

METEORS

BY MARGARET CAMPBELL–BROWN AND PETER BROWN

A *meteor* (from the Greek *meteoros*, meaning "high in the air") is the light, heat, ionization, and (occasionally) sound phenomena produced when a solid body (a *meteoroid*) collides with molecules in Earth's upper atmosphere. These collisions heat the surface of the object; then, at a height typically between 120 km and 80 km, the meteoroid begins to ablate, or lose mass. Typically, ablation takes the form of vapourization, although melting and quasicontinuous fragmentation may also contribute. It is these ablated meteoric atoms that collide with air molecules to produce atomic excitations, or ionization, leading to the emission of light we see in the night sky. Typical visual meteors are produced by meteoroids the size of a small pebble, although the relationship between mass, magnitude, and velocity is complex (Figure 1). The faintest meteors visible to the naked eye are due to meteoroids the size of the tip of a ballpoint pen; the brightest meteors are due to meteoroids whose diameters roughly match the thickness of a pen.

Larger and low-velocity meteoroids are favoured to pass through Earth's atmosphere, although rarely as a single monolithic body. When these ponderable masses reach the ground, they are called *meteorites*. At the other extreme, very small meteoroids (micrometres in size) efficiently radiate heat from their surface and do not reach ablation temperatures; such particles reach Earth's surface without having been fully ablated, although most are heated many hundreds of degrees.

Meteoroids can be divided broadly into two groups: stream and sporadic meteoroids. *Stream* meteoroids follow similar orbits around the Sun, many of which can be linked to a particular parent object, in most cases a comet. When Earth intersects the orbit of a stream, a meteor shower occurs. Since all the meteoroids in a stream move along nearly identical orbits, their paths in the atmosphere are parallel. This creates a perspective effect: the meteor trails on the celestial sphere appear to radiate from a fixed location, called the meteor *radiant*. *Sporadic* meteoroids, in contrast, are much more loosely associated and are not part of tightly grouped streams.

Meteor showers are named for the constellation from which they appear to radiate. Official rules for naming showers have been adopted by IAU commission #22 and can be found at www.ta3.sk/IAUC22DB/MDC2007/Dokumenty/shower_nomenclature.php. When several showers have radiants in the same constellation, nearby bright stars are used in naming.

The sporadic complex as seen at Earth, however, is structured and shows definite directionalities as well as annual variations in activity levels. Sporadic meteor radiants are concentrated in six major source regions throughout the sky. These sources are in fixed locations with respect to the Sun. Variations in the strengths of these sources throughout the year have been observed; it is the elevation of these sources at a particular location plus the intrinsic strength of each source at a given time of the year that determine the average background sporadic rate. Figure 2 shows the distribution of sporadic radiants in Sun-centred coordinates. The expected sporadic rate varies as a function of the altitude of the apex of Earth's way throughout the year, but is generally in the range of 8–13 meteors per hour for visual observers. The apex is the instantaneous direction of travel of Earth around the Sun; it is the point on the ecliptic that transits at 6:00 local apparent solar time (see p. 40).

In general, meteoroid streams are formed when particles are ejected from comets as they approach the Sun. The parent objects of many showers have been identified from the similarity of the orbits of the object and the stream. Cometary associations include the η-Aquariids and Orionids, which are derived from 1P/Halley; the Leonids, which originate from 55P/Tempel–Tuttle; and the Perseids, from 109P/Swift–Tuttle. Several minor planets are known to be associated with meteor streams: 3200 Phaethon linked to the Geminid stream and 2003 EH1 linked to the Quadrantid shower are the most prominent examples. All of these particles have orbits that coincide closely with that of the parent object, but their orbits are gradually shifted through radiative effects and planetary perturbations. Such effects lead to a broadening of the stream over time, resulting in an increased duration of the meteor shower as seen from Earth—older streams tend to be more long-lived—and eventually transform stream meteoroids into sporadic meteoroids.

The visual strength of a meteor shower is measured by its Zenithal Hourly Rate (ZHR), defined as the number of meteors a single average observer would see if the radiant were directly overhead and the sky dark and transparent with a limiting stellar magnitude of +6.5 (conditions that are rarely met in reality). A more physical measure is the flux of a meteoroid stream, measured in numbers of meteors of absolute brightness (referenced to a range of 100 km) brighter than +6.5 per square kilometre per second perpendicular to the radiant direction. While an observer will tend to see the largest number of meteors by looking at the shower radiant, the most useful counts are obtained by looking some distance away from the radiant.

Most data on meteor showers are currently gathered visually by amateur observers. It is crucial to observe from a dark-sky location with a clear view of the sky, and to allow at least 20 min before the start of observations to allow dark adaptation of the eyes. One should choose an area of the sky to observe, preferably with an elevation

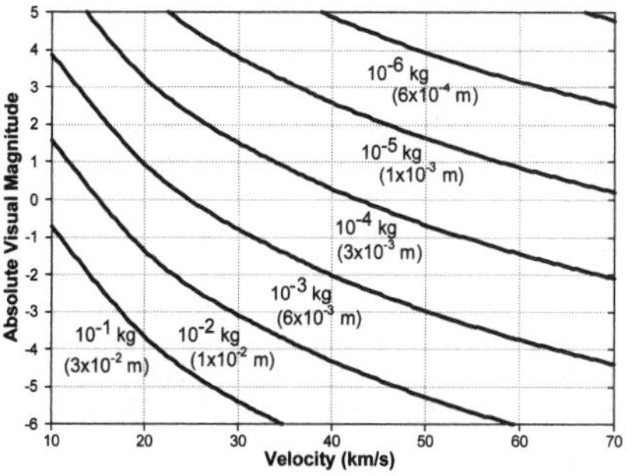

FIGURE 1 *Magnitude as a function of velocity for meteoroids of different sizes. Uncertainties in the mass scale are largest at high velocities and small masses, and may be as large as an order of magnitude in mass at the extremes.*

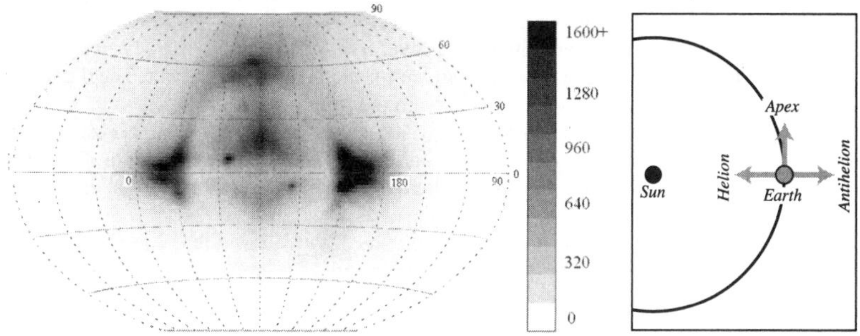

FIGURE 2 *Plot of the radiant distribution of meteors as seen by the Canadian Meteor Orbit Radar throughout the entire year, in Sun-centred ecliptic coordinates. The Sun is at (0,0), the helion, and the Earth's orbital velocity points to the centre of the plot, the apex. The antihelion point is at (180,0). The small concentrations visible near the centre of the plot are major showers (the Geminids and Eta Aquariids in particular). The intensity of the plot reflects the number of radiants per 2 deg². The rate of sporadic meteors as a function of time depends on which of the sporadic sources are above the horizon at the time of observation. The diagram at right shows the meaning of the coordinate system.*

greater than 40°. The limiting magnitude should be carefully recorded for each session, along with the UT and the centre of the field of view of the observer. The most basic observations should include an estimate of the brightness of the meteor, the time of observation, and a shower association (based on the radiant and apparent speed of the meteor). Information on collecting and reporting scientifically useful observations can be found at the International Meteor Organization's website, www.imo.net.

TABLE OF METEOR SHOWERS FOR 2017

The table lists the major visual showers as well as those detectable by radio methods during the day. Of the strongest annual showers, the Moon is favourable for the **Quadrantids**, **Orionids**, and the **Geminids**. Some models predict an enhancement in activity from the Perseids near their peak time in 2017, though the Moon will severely affect the shower's visibility.

Shower	Max Date UT	λ 2000	*D*	ZHR	θ $\times10^{-6}$	*R*	Moon %	*r*	RA h m	Dec °	*v* km/s
Quadrantids	**Jan. 3 14h**	**283.16**	**0.6**	**120**	**8.4**	**✓**	**27+**	**2.1**	**15 20**	**+49**	**43**
April Lyrids	Apr. 22 12h	32.3	1.3	20	4.6	✓	20–	2.9	18 10	+34	48
η-Aquariids	May 6 2h	45.5	5	60	6.4	>03	79+	2.4	22 30	−2	66
S δ-Aquariids	Jul. 29 4h	126	8	20	6.2	>23	35+	3.2	22 44	−16	43
Perseids	Aug. 12 19h	140.0	2	90	6.0	✓	75–	2.1	3 08	+58	60
Orionids	**Oct. 21 11h**	**208**	**2**	**20**	**2.2**	**>23**	**3+**	**2.4**	**6 20**	**+16**	**67**
S Taurids	Nov. 5 12h	223	15	10	1.0	✓	98–	2.3	3 34	+14	31
N Taurids	Nov. 12 11h	230	15	15	1.4	✓	32–	2.3	4 00	+22	30
Leonids	Nov. 17 17h	235.3	1	20	1.9	>00	1–	2.5	10 12	+22	71
Geminids	**Dec. 14 6h**	**262.2**	**1**	**120**	**11.0**	**✓**	**14–**	**2.3**	**7 28**	**+33**	**36**
Ursids	Dec. 22 15h	270.7	0.5	10	2.2	✓	13+	3.0	14 36	+75	35
S D ω-Cetids	May 6 14h	46	20	≈20	—	day	—	—	1 24	–6	36
N D ω-Cetids	May 9 17h	49	30	≈20	—	day	—	—	0 47	+19	36
D ζ-Perseids	Jun. 4 16h	74	19	≈25	—	day	—	—	3 47	+23	29
D Arietids	Jun. 9 9h	78.5	16	≈45	—	day	—	2.1	2 52	+26	41
D β-Taurids	Jun. 25 15h	94	9	≈20	—	day	—	—	5 31	+20	29
D Sextantids	Sep. 29 5h	186	12	≈20	—	day	—	—	10 17	−1	33

The column **Max Date** lists the date and hour (in Universal Time) when Earth intersects the densest part of the stream, based on the solar longitude **λ** (J2000.0) given in the third column.

The fourth column, ***D***, gives the duration of the shower in days, which is the total number of days for which the activity level is over half the maximum activity.

The **ZHR**, or Zenithal Hourly Rate, is given for the peak of the shower. The **θ** column gives the meteoroid flux at the time of maximum (see text for explanation).

The ***R*** column gives the local times for which the radiant is above the horizon for an observer at 45°N latitude (and therefore meteors from the shower are visible); a ✓ symbol indicates that the radiant is up throughout the night hours, while "day" indicates that the shower is not visible at night.

The **Moon** column gives the percent illumination of the Moon at the time of the shower peak (+ for waxing, – for waning). The population index, ***r***, at the time of the maximum is a measure of the size distribution of particles in the stream. A larger *r* value indicates an excess of small particles, while smaller *r* values indicate larger numbers of brighter meteors. A shower with a higher *r* value will therefore suffer more from background light such as moonlight or light pollution. Sporadic meteors at observable visual magnitudes have an *r* value near 3.0.

The **RA** and **Dec** columns show the position in the sky of the radiant at the time of the shower peak. The position of the radiant will vary from these values away from the time of the peak; tables published by IMO in their annual shower calendar provide details of radiant drift. The last column, ***v***, gives the apparent atmospheric speed of the meteors in the shower.

FIREBALLS
BY PHILIP MCCAUSLAND

Fireballs are exceptionally bright meteors (at least mag. −5) that are spectacular enough to light up a wide area and attract public attention. Fireballs can occur as the brightest members of some annual meteor showers, but are more often part of the sporadic meteoroid flux and so can occur at any time. The brightest fireballs are sometimes termed bolides, being visible even in daylight.

Fireballs result from the collision of meteoroids ~1 cm or more in diameter with the Earth's atmosphere. The accurate reporting of such events is therefore of great interest for understanding this poorly known impactor population of Solar System material lying in the size range between dust and small asteroids. Fast-moving fireballs are typically destroyed in the upper atmosphere (>50 km altitude). Slower-moving fireballs with initial entry velocities typically <25 km/s can penetrate more deeply into the atmosphere and are capable of delivering meteorites. Reports of these slower type of fireballs are especially useful for assisting meteorite recovery efforts, and also critically for understanding the orbit of the object before it arrived on Earth. Excellent recent Canadian examples of meteorite-dropping fireballs with calculated orbits include Tagish Lake (2000), Buzzard Coulee (2008), and Grimsby (2009).

Systematic observations of fireballs are usually made by instruments in dedicated regional or global networks, using all-sky cameras, radar, and infrasound arrays (see meteor.uwo.ca). More information on all-sky camera networks in North America can be found at www.allsky.ca. More commonly, fireball observations are made by amateur observers and members of the public who are in the right place at the right time! Eyewitness and amateur camera observations are valuable and can be reported via the Internet sites and phone numbers given below.

Fireball phenomena may include the development of a trail that persists after the event, the apparent fragmentation of the meteoroid during entry, flaring events, or a terminal burst in brightness, and occasionally reports of simultaneous "sizzling" sound that may be the result of transduced electromagnetic waves from the fireball. Meteorite-dropping fireballs in particular are often signified by reports of the persistence of "embers" after the main fireball and of a delayed sonic boom. These observations indicate that the meteoroid has likely penetrated into the lower atmosphere (<40 km altitude) and that portions of it may have survived entry to become meteorites. After entry to altitudes between ~30 and ~20 km, the meteoroid typically slows down to only 2–3 km/s, and fireball phenomena cease; thereafter any surviving fragments drop to the ground on ballistic trajectories over several minutes during a period called dark flight. Such falling objects may sometimes be heard producing whirring or popping noises by local witnesses within ~1 km of the meteorite fall. Fragments in dark flight can also often be detected in the troposphere by Doppler weather radar, which can thus assist in defining the approximate ground locations of the fallen meteorites.

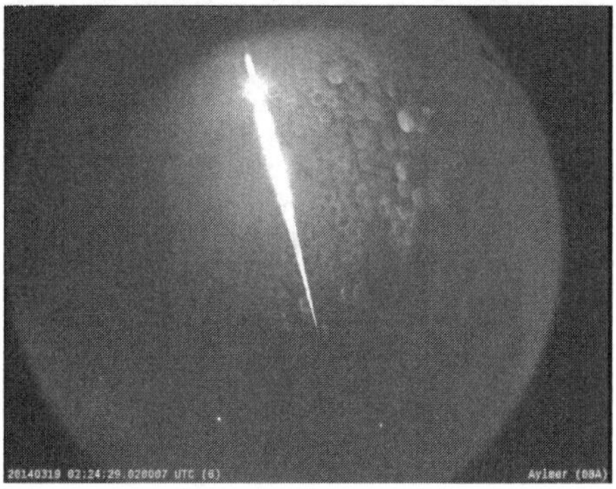

The St. Thomas fireball of 2014 Mar. 19 (UT), widely seen over southern Ontario (all-sky image from Aylmer, Ontario). To date, no fragments have been recovered.

Rapid recovery of freshly fallen meteorites—as well as their careful handling and storage—before they have been exposed for long to the terrestrial atmosphere is highly desirable. Fresh recovery allows meteorite researchers to study water-soluble minerals (such as salt), organic phases, and physical properties (such as porosity and seismic velocities) before terrestrial alteration. Rapid meteorite recovery is also essential for the study of short-lived radioactive isotopes induced by pre-fall exposure to cosmic rays; this information is highly useful for estimating the true pre-fall size of the meteoroid as well as its dynamical history before encountering the Earth.

The scientific value of a freshly fallen meteorite is significantly greater when its pre-fall orbit is known. Under favourable circumstances, visual observer data can be used to obtain an approximate atmospheric trajectory, which, coupled with satellite or video observations, can be used to derive a pre-fall orbit.

The main reasons to report the observation of a fireball are: (1) to alert meteor researchers and all-sky camera network operators to the existence of a new event; (2) to add to the global database of observed fireball events, associated with meteor showers or not; (3) to assist with possible meteorite recovery from a slow fireball event; (4) to provide trajectory information that can be used to help calculate the orbit for a recovered meteorite; (5) to rule out catastrophic events such as airplane crashes and satellite re-entries; and, (6) to help calibrate atmospheric explosions detected by infrasound arrays deployed to monitor the Comprehensive Nuclear Test Ban Treaty.

The Meteorites and Impacts Advisory Committee (MIAC) maintains an informative website, including a fireball report form for Canadian events: www.uqac.ca/miac.

Other sites where fireballs may be reported include: USA and Canada (American Meteor Society) www.amsmeteors.org/fireball/report.html, North American Meteor Network (NAMN) www.namnmeteors.org/reports.html, and Global (International Meteor Organization) fireballs.imo.net/members/imo/report_intro.

The AMS site also offers smartphone users a fireball reporting app, allowing the user to automatically provide the observing location and indicate their fireball beginning and endpoint observations by phone orientation against the sky. This has proved to be very immediate and useful in recent fireball events and is recommended: www.amsmeteors.org/members/fireball/report-a-fireball.

Reports of fireballs seen over Canada can also be faxed to the Canadian Fireball Reporting Centre c/o Phil McCausland at 519-661-3198. Reports should include the following information (making notes immediately, at least of the precise time, is recommended):

(1) The name, telephone number/email, and address of the observer(s).

(2) The time of occurrence (and uncertainty in this time); an accurate time is required to search instrumental databases.

(3) The location of the observer at the time the fireball was seen (preferably in precise longitude and latitude).

(4) The beginning and ending points of the fireball, in terms of either astronomical RA and Dec, or azimuth and degrees elevation above the horizon. Indicate whether the true beginning was observed and whether the ending point was blocked by an object on the horizon.

(5) An estimate of the apparent magnitude; or compare the fireball brightness to that of the Moon. Was the ground lit up? Did the fireball cast shadows?

(6) The duration of the fireball event and the persistent trail (if any).

(7) A qualitative description of the event (e.g. colour, flares, fragmentation, dust clouds persisting after the fireball, and sound). If sound was heard, report the time delay between the fireball and the arrival of the sound, or the precise time of the sound arrival as well as that of the fireball.

(8) The existence of any video, audio, or photographic records.

METEORITE IDENTIFICATION

BY RICHARD K. HERD AND CHRISTOPHER D.K. HERD

Meteorites are rocks from space that have fallen on Earth. Fossil meteorites are found in ancient strata; others, found at the surface, are recent arrivals or may have lain there for many thousands of years before discovery. Those witnessed to traverse Earth's atmosphere, and recovered based on those observations, are called meteorite *falls*; fewer than 1300 have ever been documented. Those with no record of arrival are meteorite *finds,* when recognized, and are far more numerous. Meteorites are named for where they are found. The Meteoritical Society (Met. Soc.) is the main worldwide organization for meteorite specialists, called *meteoriticists*. It is responsible for approval of new meteorites. Its nomenclature committee guidelines (meteoriticalsociety.org/?page_id=59) ensure that new meteorites are named to avoid confusion and ambiguity with existing meteorites, and that type specimens of all new meteorites are preserved in collections accessible to researchers.

Over 54000 meteorites are known; many more probably exist. Over 38000 are from Antarctica, over 10000 are numbered meteorites from the Saharan and Arabian deserts, and about 5500 (numbered and unnumbered) meteorites worldwide comprise the rest. See *Field Guide to Meteors and Meteorites* by O.R. Norton and L.A. Chitwood, Springer–Verlag, 2008; *Atlas of Meteorites* by M. Grady, B. Pratesi and V.M. Cecchi, Cambridge University Press, 2014; and the Meteoritical Bulletin database at: www.lpi.usra.edu/meteor. The latter allows a rapid search based on meteorite name, or any number of qualifiers.

Over 70 identified meteorites are known from Canada, but there is a backlog in describing them for Met. Soc. approval. There have been six falls since 1994: St-Robert, Québec, 1994 Jun. 14; Kitchener, Ontario, 1998 Jul. 12; Tagish Lake, British Columbia, 2000 Jan. 18; Buzzard Coulee, Saskatchewan, 2008 Nov. 20; Grimsby, Ontario, 2009 Sep. 25; and another in 2005 that is not yet official. One of the most significant recent finds is of iron meteorites associated with a late-Holocene crater near Whitecourt, Alberta, the first such recognized in Canada.

Often there is confusion over when and where meteorites have fallen or have been preserved, and also over what they are and look like, even though websites now provide ready access to meteorite research, photos, and data. All are significantly different than Earth rocks. Samples sent to experts for identification, even by other scientists, are usually "meteorwrongs"—terrestrial rocks or minerals, human-made slag, metals, alloys, or concrete—that rarely resemble meteorites.

Meteorites probably begin as streams of fragments (*meteoroids*) that are debris from collisions between larger objects. The calculated orbits of several falls intersect the asteroid belt; their ultimate origin in space and time may be elsewhere. Links have been proposed between some types or groups of meteorites and specific asteroids or asteroid types, based on the meteorites' reflectance spectra and density. For example, results from the NASA Dawn mission have strengthened a connection between some howardite-eucrite-diogenite (HED) meteorites and minor planet 4 Vesta. While the exact provenance of most meteorites is uncertain, they are an unparallelled source of information about the Solar System, from its primitive beginnings to its present. Many preserve pre-solar mineral grains made in stars that were part of our local stellar nursery. Decay products of short-lived radionuclides produced in the early Solar System and primordial organic compounds (possibly derived from cold, interstellar, molecular clouds) have been identified, yielding detailed information about the origin of the Solar System and the biological precursors of life.

The diversity of planetary bodies represented by meteorites is unmatched by planetary exploration missions. They are thus invaluable, and represent space exploration "without the commute," providing complementary information to planetary missions, and insights into the overall physical and chemical processes that have acted to form the Sun and its planets and their satellites. With increased space exploration, the current, somewhat arcane, classification schemes will undoubtedly change considerably to realistically reflect planetological contexts, as geological fieldwork provides for Earth rocks. In theory, any rocky Solar System body is a potential source of meteorites already in collections. About 115 meteorites are similar to Apollo samples, and are from the Moon (see curator.jsc.nasa.gov/antmet/lmc/index.cfm and www.meteorites.wustl.edu/lunar/moon_meteorites.htm). At least 80 meteorites are derived from Mars (see curator.jsc.nasa.gov/antmet/mmc/index.cfm and www.imca.cc/mars/martian-meteorites.htm). These meteorites, also known as the SNCs (shergottite-nakhlite-chassignite, after their main representatives, Shergotty, Nakhla, and Chassigny), are linked to the Red Planet by trapped gas within them that matches the composition of the unique Martian atmosphere, as measured by the 1976 *Viking* landers. The Martian meteorite of Tissint, Morocco, fell on 2011 Jul. 18, and represents only the 5th Martian meteorite fall and the first one in almost 50 years.

Popular ideas about when and where meteorites fall are connected with the observation of *meteors*, the brief streaks of light produced when high-speed, interplanetary particles enter Earth's upper atmosphere. Sporadic meteors and *meteor showers* do not produce meteorites; their fragile cometary debris fragments are reduced to dust high in the atmosphere. On average, Earth collects over 100 tonnes of cosmic debris per day. In contrast, stronger, larger space rocks can survive a fiery passage through the atmosphere and result in meteorites. These first appear as bright *fireballs*, are slowed to terminal speeds by atmospheric friction, and cease to show a bright trail long before they reach Earth's surface. Fireballs, which may seem very close, are usually quite high in the atmosphere, 50 km or more from the observer. Even if an extraterrestrial object does reach the surface, it is likely to plunge into the 70% that is water or to be lost among forests, jungles, or mountainous regions. In only uncommonly recorded cases have meteorites struck or landed within a few metres of humans (see "Possible Hazards of Meteorite Falls" by C.E. Spratt, *JRASC, 85* (October 1991), p. 263); the Chelyabinsk event of 2013 Feb. 15 is a rare case where the shock wave from the object's atmospheric entry caused widespread injuries. Rare meteoroids of masses exceeding many thousands of tonnes that are not slowed appreciably by Earth's atmosphere produce impact craters. Large impacts may have dramatically altered the history of life on our planet, but they do not result in meteorites—the kinetic energy is sufficiently high to vapourize the impacting body completely and to deform and melt the target area in seconds. Crater diameters are typically more than ten times the diameter of the impacting body. Glassy *tektites* found scattered over several continents may be evidence of such impacts, but they do not have meteorite compositions or characteristics, instead reflecting the composition of the target materials struck by the meteoroid.

Meteorites are divided into three groups that vary widely both in appearance and properties: *stones* or *stony meteorites*, *stony-irons*, and *irons* or *iron meteorites* (known in the past as *aerolites*, *siderolites*, and *siderites*, respectively). All usually contain metallic nickel-iron compounds (with traces of other metals) and are mildly to strongly magnetic, depending on the amount of nickel-iron relative to other minerals. Those that have lain on Earth's surface for long periods may be rusted almost beyond recognition; some require laboratory tests to confirm their identity. Specimens generally have a quite soft, dull black to brown fusion crust formed by friction during atmospheric passage; more prevalent on stones and stony-irons, the crust may have partially flaked off or been weathered away. Meteorites only rarely contain bubble-like cavities; they are never almost perfectly spherical and smooth. During atmospheric entry, only their surface is affected. Surfaces of irons and stony-irons are dimpled rather than bulbous. They rust easily so there may be no bright metal showing. Stony meteorites do not show protuberances; weathered varieties are rusty, even on broken surfaces. Fresh stony meteorites may have a whitish "concrete-like" rock interior, with bright metal specks. Their crusts are black or smoky grey, varying from quite glassy to dull; telltale lines and bubbled patches orient their flight through the air. More metallic samples may have a shield-like shape, as a result of aerodynamic sculpting, and may therefore also be oriented.

Stones are the most abundant; they resemble some terrestrial rocks but are denser. Most (called *chondrites*) consist of spheres of silicate minerals (called *chondrules*) visible on broken, cut, or polished surfaces, and scattered grains of metal. The oldest, most primitive, and least altered meteorites are found among the chondrites. Rare stony meteorites without chondrules are called *achondrites*; these are thought to be melt products from chondrites, or samples of younger volcanic planetary surfaces. In August 1996, NASA scientists announced the discovery of fossil and chemical evidence of bacterial life in the Allan Hills 84001 meteorite—an ancient achondrite from Mars. Other scientists disagree that the weight of evidence points to ancient life on Mars; however, the rock retains evidence of the conditions necessary for life in the form of minerals precipitated by warm water. This controversy has resulted in renewed interest in missions to Mars and in finding water and life on Mars and elsewhere, even in extreme conditions on Earth. Irons and stony-irons are dense, with up to equal amounts of silicates and iron. Most irons are thought to be core material of planetary bodies formed by melting chondrites, whereas stony-irons (in particular the *pallasites*) may be samples of the core-mantle boundary of such planetary bodies.

Rare *carbonaceous chondrites* are grey to black, some resembling charcoal with silicate inclusions. The dark colour is from iron oxides and sulphides. They contain a few percent carbon in very fine-grained carbonates, carbides, graphite, diamonds, and primitive organic molecules. They may have had biologically important roles in providing seeds for the origin of life; recent significant insights into this process have come from study of the unique Tagish Lake meteorite. The study of these samples, along with interplanetary dust particles and samples of Comet Wild–2 from the NASA *Stardust* mission, has become important in deciphering the origins of meteorites and, therefore, of the Solar System and everything in it. We are all composed of recycled stardust.

In Canada, expertise in meteorite identification and classification exists at several government and university institutions. The largest meteorite collections are the National Meteorite Collection, the Royal Ontario Museum collection, and the University of Alberta Meteorite Collection. The curators of these collections, and other experts on meteorite identification and research, are members of the Astromaterials Discipline Working Group (ADWG); see regional contacts at www.eas.ualberta.ca/adwg. If a suspected meteorite passes initial criteria, such as magnetic character, presence of a fusion crust, etc., digital photos are typically requested for follow-up. Further examination and any analysis may be negotiated with the expert, but an expert opinion is free of charge. Experts can assist in enabling classification of any new meteorite: anyone who has found a meteorite should consult the Met. Soc. guidelines (see meteoriticalsociety.org/?page_id=59) to ensure that the proper name is assigned and that all other requirements are followed. Meteorites of Canadian origin are subject to the provisions of the *Cultural Property Export and Import Act* and may not be exported from Canada without a permit.

METEORITE IMPACT CRATERS OF NORTH AMERICA

BY JOHN SPRAY

Earth has endured the hypervelocity impact of planetary bodies since its inception 4.6 billion years ago, as has every other planet in the Solar System. However, in contrast to the Moon, Mercury, Mars, many minor planets, and some satellites of the gas giants, the Earth shows relatively few impact craters on its surface. Currently, 188 are proven; see the Earth Impact Database (2015) at www.passc.net/EarthImpactDatabase.

The Moon's surface is saturated with craters, as is Mercury's, and over 42 000 craters have been named on Mars. Our planet's inventory is limited because Earth (like Venus) is an active planet. This means that most craters have been destroyed or buried due to plate tectonics, volcanic activity, or weathering. The interiors of the large gas planets (Jupiter, Saturn, Uranus, Neptune) are obscured, so we see no direct evidence of cratering—if there are indeed stable, solid surfaces on these planets.

Of the 188 known terrestrial craters, 60 occur in North America (see the following table), 31 of which are in Canada, 28 in the United States, and one in Mexico (see the map on p. 263). This total represents about one-third of the world inventory. North American craters range in diameter from as small as 36 m for the Whitecourt crater (Alberta), up to ~150 km for Chicxulub (Mexico). The principal criteria for determining if a geological feature is an impact structure formed by the hypervelocity impact of a meteorite or comet are listed below. Criteria are divided into megascopic (a bird's-eye/satellite scale), macroscopic (can be seen with the human eye), and microscopic (requiring a microscope):

1. Presence of *shatter cones* (conical-shaped fracture systems) that are in situ (macroscopic evidence);

2. Presence of multiple *planar deformation features* (PDFs) in minerals within in-situ rocks (microscopic evidence);

3. Presence of *high-pressure mineral polymorphs* within in-situ rocks (microscopic evidence, requiring proof via X-ray diffraction, etc.). Examples include the high-pressure polymorphs of SiO_2 (e.g. stishovite);

4. *Morphometry*. On some planetary bodies, such as the Moon and Mars, we rely on the shape of the impact structure to determine its presence and type. This is a megascopic quality (i.e. too big to be seen by the unaided human eye, thus requiring remote sensing). On Earth, recognizing impact structures solely by their morphometry can be complicated by two factors: (a) weathering, erosion, burial processes, and tectonic deformation; and (b) certain terrestrial features having comparable shape (e.g. volcanoes, salt diapirs, glacial landforms), such that a circular structure alone is insufficient to claim impact-structure status;

5. Presence of an impact-generated *melt sheet* and/or *dikes*, and impact-melt *breccias* that were generated by hypervelocity impact (macroscopic). Melt sheets may be overlain by so-called fallback breccias, and material blasted out of the crater may form ejecta blankets about the original central cavity. For large impact events, ejecta can be distributed globally (e.g. Chicxulub);

6. *Pseudotachylyte* is a rock generated by frictional melting at the macroscopic scale. Some pseudotachylytes are associated with seismic faulting (earthquakes, due to isostatic rebound and plate tectonics), so they are not exclusively impact generated; however, in association with features 1–3 above, they can be contributory criteria.

In terms of relative importance, criteria 1–3 above are definitive, with supportive evidence being added by 4–6. For well-preserved buried structures, as revealed by detailed geophysical techniques (especially seismic data), some workers consider this as strong evidence in favour of an impact origin. Normally, buried craters are verified by drilling and sampling rock for evaluation using criteria 1–3 above.

TABLE OF METEORITE IMPACT CRATERS OF NORTH AMERICA

#	Name, Location	Lat. (N) ° ′	Long. (W) ° ′	Diam.* km	Age† My	Visible Geologic Surface Expression	Features
1	Ames, Oklahoma, USA	36 15	98 12	16	470. (30)	buried 3 km	none
2	Avak, Alaska, USA	71 15	156 38	12	3–95	buried 30 m	none
3	Barringer (Meteor), Arizona, USA	35 02	111 01	1.19	0.049 (0.003)	rimmed polygonal crater	fragments of meteorite, highly shocked sandstone
4	Beaverhead, Montana, USA	44 36	113 00	60	~ 600	oval area of crushed sandstone and shatter cones	shatter cones
5	Brent, Ontario	46 05	78 29	3.8	>453	sediment-filled shallow depression	fracturing
6	Calvin, Michigan, USA	41 50	85 57	8.5	450. (10)	buried 400 m	none
7	Carswell, Saskatchewan	58 27	109 30	39	115. (10)	discontinuous circular ridge	shatter cones, breccia, impact melt
8	Charlevoix, Québec	47 32	70 18	54	342. (15)	semicircular trough, central peak	breccia, shatter cones, impact melt
9	Chesapeake Bay, Virginia, USA	37 17	76 01	90	35.5 (0.3)	buried 400–500 m, ring structure	none
10	Chicxulub, Yucatan, Mexico	21 20	89 30	150	64.98 (0.05)	buried 1 km, ring of sink holes	none (related to the K/T mass-extinction event)
11	Clearwater East, Québec	56 05	74 07	26	290. (20)	circular lake	sedimentary float
12	Clearwater West, Québec	56 13	74 30	36	290. (20)	island ring in circular lake	impact melt, breccias
13	Cloud Creek, Wyoming, USA	43 07	106 45	7	190. (30)	buried 1.1 km	none
14	Couture, Québec	60 08	75 20	8	430. (25)	circular lake	breccia float
15	Crooked Creek, Missouri, USA	37 50	91 23	7	320. (80)	oval area of disturbed rocks,	breccia, shatter cones
16	Decaturville, Missouri, USA	37 54	92 43	6	< 300	slightly oval depression shallow marginal depression	breccia, shatter cones
17	Deep Bay, Saskatchewan	56 24	102 59	13	99 (4)	circular bay	sedimentary float
18	Des Plaines, Illinois, USA	42 03	87 52	8	< 280	buried, 15–100 m	none
19	Eagle Butte, Alberta	49 42	110 30	10	< 65	minor structural disturbance	shatter cones
20	Elbow, Saskatchewan	50 59	106 43	8	395. (25)	buried, small mound	none
21	Flynn Creek, Tennessee, USA	36 17	85 40	3.8	360. (20)	sediment-filled shallow depression with small central peak	breccia, shatter cones
22	Glasford, Illinois, USA	40 36	89 47	4	< 430	buried 350 m	none
23	Glover Bluff, Wisconsin, USA	43 58	89 32	8	< 500	disturbed dolomite exposed	shatter cones
24	Gow, Saskatchewan	56 27	104 29	5	< 250	lake and central island	breccia, impact melt
25	Haughton, Nunavut	75 22	89 41	23	39	shallow circular depression	shatter cones, breccia
26	Haviland, Kansas, USA	37 35	99 10	0.015	< 0.001	excavated depression	fragments of meteorite
27	Holleford, Ontario	44 28	76 38	2.35	550. (100)	sediment-filled shallow depression	sedimentary fill
28	Ile Rouleau, Québec	50 41	73 53	4	< 300	island is central peak of submerged structure	shatter cones, breccia dykes
29	Kentland, Indiana, USA	40 45	87 24	13	< 97	central peak exposed in quarries, rest buried	breccia, shatter cones, disturbed rocks
30	La Moinerie, Québec	57 26	66 37	8	400. (50)	lake-filled depression	breccia float

*Approximate, apparent (post-erosion) rim-to-rim diameter, not including concentric features beyond the rim (e.g. both #31 and #52); also, not all craters are circular.
†Numbers in parentheses are uncertainties.

TABLE OF METEORITE IMPACT CRATERS OF NORTH AMERICA (cont)

#	Name, Location	Lat. (N) ° ′	Long. (W) ° ′	Diam.* km	Age† My	Surface Expression	Visible Geologic Features
31	Manicouagan, Québec	51 23	68 42	80–90	214. (1)	circumferential lake, central peak	impact melt, breccia
32	Manson, Iowa, USA	42 35	94 33	35	73.8 (0.3)	none, central elevation buried 30 m	none
33	Maple Creek, Saskatchewan	49 48	109 6	6	< 75	buried, small mound	disturbed rocks
34	Marquez, Texas, USA	31 17	96 18	12.7	58. (2)	circular area of disturbed rock	shatter cones
35	Middlesboro, Kentucky, USA	36 37	83 44	6	< 300	circular depression	disturbed rocks
36	Mistastin, Newfoundland/Labrador	55 53	63 18	28	36.4 (4)	elliptical lake and central island	breccia, impact melt
37	Montagnais, Nova Scotia	42 53	64 13	45	50.5 (0.8)	none, under water (115 m) and sediment	none
38	New Québec, Québec	61 17	73 40	3.44	1.4 (0.1)	rimmed, circular lake	raised rim, impact melt
39	Newporte, North Dakota, USA	48 58	101 58	3.2	< 500	none, buried 3 km	none
40	Nicholson, NWT	62 40	102 41	12.5	< 400	irregular lake with islands	breccia
41	Odessa, Texas, USA	31 45	102 29	0.168	< 0.0635	sediment-filled depression with very slight rim, 4 others buried & smaller	fragments of meteorite
42	Pilot, NWT	60 17	111 01	6	445. (2)	circular lake	fracturing, breccia float
43	Presqu'ile, Québec	49 43	74 48	24	< 500	none, heavily eroded	shatter cones
44	Red Wing, North Dakota, USA	47 36	103 33	9	200 (25)	none, buried 1.5 km	none
45	Rock Elm, Wisconsin, USA	44 43	92 14	6	< 505	circular rim depression, central dome	shatter cones, breccia
46	Saint Martin, Manitoba	51 47	98 32	40	220 (32)	none, partially buried	impact melt
47	Santa Fe, New Mexico , USA	35 45	105 56	6–13	<1200	deeply eroded, large and extensive shatter cones	breccia, shatter cones
48	Serpent Mound, Ohio, USA	39 02	83 24	8	< 320	circular area of disturbed rock, slight central peak	breccia, shatter cones
49	Sierra Madera, Texas, USA	30 36	102 55	13	< 100	central hills, annular depression, outer ring of hills	breccia, shatter cones
50	Slate Islands, Ontario	48 40	87 00	30	~ 450	islands are central peak of submerged structure	shatter cones, breccia dykes
51	Steen River, Alberta	59 30	117 38	25	91 (7)	none, buried 200 m	none
52	Sudbury, Ontario	46 36	81 11	130	1850 (3)	deformed elliptical basin	breccia, impact melt, shatter cones, breccia dykes
53	Tunnunik, NWT (*see note below*)	72 25	113 58	~ 25	130–450	heavily eroded	shatter cones
54	Upheaval Dome, Utah, USA	38 26	109 54	10	< 170	circular area of disturbed rock	breccia dykes
55	Viewfield, Saskatchewan	49 35	103 04	2.5	190 (20)	buried 1 km	none
56	Wanapitei, Ontario	46 45	80 45	7.5	37.2 (1.2)	lake-filled depression	breccia float
57	Wells Creek, Tennessee, USA	36 23	87 40	12	200 (100)	basin with central hill, inner and outer annular valleys, ridges	breccia, shatter cones
58	West Hawk Lake, Manitoba	49 46	95 11	2.44	351 (20)	circular lake	none
59	Wetumpka, Alabama, USA	32 31	86 10	6.5	81 (1.5)	arcuate outer ridge, central depression	breccia
60	Whitecourt, Alberta	54 00	115 36	0.036	<0.0011	sediment-filled circular depression with raised rim obscured by trees	fragments of meteorite

* Approximate, apparent (post-erosion) rim-to-rim diameter, not including concentric features beyond the rim (e.g. both #31 and #52); also, not all craters are circular.
†Numbers in parentheses are uncertainties. *Note: Prince Albert crater, Victoria Island, NWT, discovered in 2012, has been renamed "Tunnunik."*

MAP OF NORTH AMERICAN METEORITE IMPACT STRUCTURES

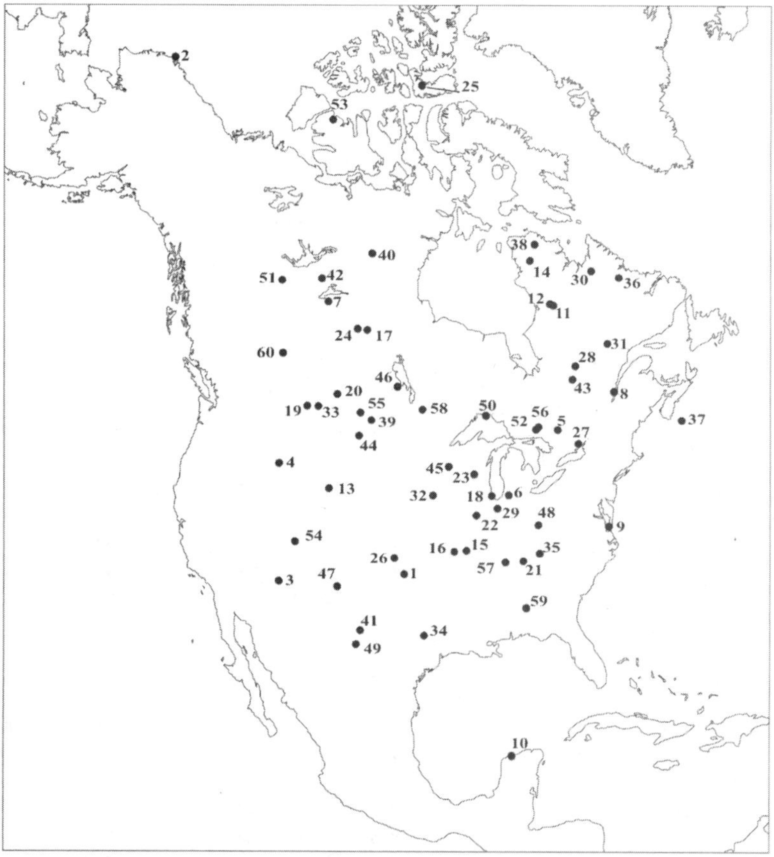

Of the 188 known impact structures identified on Earth, 60 are in North America (31 in Canada, 28 in the United States, and 1 in Mexico). These are shown on the above map; the numbers correspond to the listing in the table on the previous pages. Although the oceans cover ~70% of Earth, only two impact structures have been identified on the seafloor (Mjølnir in the Barents Sea, and #37 off the coast of Nova Scotia). Also, with the exception of structure #52, all were formed within approximately the last 10% of Earth's history. Evidence of many earlier craters has been erased by geological processes. It is possible, however, to calculate a terrestrial cratering rate by focusing only on geologically stable areas of Earth (known as cratons), with low erosion and sedimentation rates. One such area is the North American craton. Calculations indicate that Earth has received at least 10 000 impacts generating craters greater than 20 km in diameter over the last 3.5 billion years. Very early in Earth history, the impactor flux was as high as 100 times the current rate. Some of these impacts had profound influence on the evolution of life on this planet. For example, Chicxulub (#10) is linked to a mass-extinction event 65 million years ago. Some impact craters are the source of considerable economic resources. In North America, hydrocarbons are extracted from #1, 2, 6, 34, 39, 44, 49, 51, 55; #7 produces uranium; #52 is the site of a world-class nickel-copper mining camp.

COMETS IN 2017

BY DANIEL W.E. GREEN AND SYUICHI NAKANO

Listed here are observable periodic comets predicted to return to perihelion in 2017 at about mag. 18 or brighter, those one-apparition comets expected to be recovered in 2017, and a few notable fainter comets. Favourable returns are indicated in **bold**, fair returns in regular type, and poor returns in *italic* (this scheme is intended as a rough guide only). The precision of the data should allow an ephemeris computation good to about 1′. The angular elements are referred to the ecliptic and mean equinox J2000.0.

		Perihelion			Siderial	Arg.	Asc.	
		Date	Distance	Eccen.	Period	Peri.	Node	Incl.
		T	q	e	P	ω	Ω	i
Comet		TT	au		a	°	°	°
128P/Shoemaker–Holt	**Jan.**	**10.8**	**3.0559**	**0.3212**	**9.6**	**210.58**	**214.29**	**4.36**
P/2003 SQ215 (NEAT–LONEOS)		27.73	2.2802	0.5836	12.8	137.54	257.24	5.58
P/2013 YG46 (Spacewatch)		**29.49**	**1.7876**	**0.4542**	**5.9**	**242.38**	**48.91**	**7.86**
P/2007 T6 (Catalina)	**Feb.**	**15.46**	**2.2208**	**0.5039**	**9.5**	**335.9**	**102.51**	**22.18**
188P/LINEAR–Mueller		17.04	2.5651	0.4149	9.2	26.77	358.98	10.51
219P/LINEAR		20.62	2.3652	0.3525	7.0	107.41	231.03	11.53
93P/Lovas	Mar.	1.45	1.7002	0.6127	9.2	74.9	339.63	12.2
2P/Encke		**10.09**	**0.3359**	**0.8483**	**3.3**	**186.56**	**334.56**	**11.78**
172P/Yeung		**13.11**	**3.3369**	**0.2072**	**8.6**	**209.13**	**30.89**	**11.24**
73P/Schwassmann–Wachmann		16.82	0.9722	0.6855	5.4	199.39	69.66	11.24
41P/Tuttle–Giacobini–Kresak	**Apr.**	**13.91**	**1.0451**	**0.6613**	**5.4**	**62.14**	**141.07**	**9.23**
47P/Ashbrook–Jackson	**Jun.**	**10.16**	**2.8182**	**0.3171**	**8.4**	**357.67**	**356.97**	**13.03**
P/2000 S1 (Skiff)		**24.23**	**2.5361**	**0.6173**	**17.1**	**309.09**	**28.16**	**21.02**
71P/Clark		**30.21**	**1.5863**	**0.4943**	**5.6**	**208.92**	**59.44**	**9.45**
251P/LINEAR	**Jul.**	**16.5**	**1.7325**	**0.5059**	**6.6**	**31.15**	**219.41**	**23.42**
217P/LINEAR		16.54	1.2354	0.6878	7.9	246.95	125.45	12.86
259P/Garradd	**Aug.**	**4.03**	**1.809**	**0.3377**	**4.5**	**257.5**	**51.48**	**15.89**
189P/NEAT		**5.94**	**1.2134**	**0.5882**	**5.1**	**16.21**	**281.75**	**20.07**
30P/Reinmuth		19.18	1.8767	0.5021	7.3	13.29	119.7	8.13
145P/Shoemaker–Levy		31.9	1.9041	0.5408	8.4	10.37	26.81	11.26
P/2010 H2 (Vales)	**Sep.**	**15.87**	**3.0965**	**0.195**	**7.5**	**129.52**	**64.27**	**14.26**
213P/Van Ness		**24.33**	**1.9835**	**0.4075**	**6.1**	**5.56**	**311.33**	**10.38**
P/2004 T1 (LINEAR–NEAT)	**Oct.**	**13.28**	**1.716**	**0.5065**	**6.5**	**336.34**	**51.46**	**11.03**
65P/Gunn		**16.85**	**2.9101**	**0.25**	**7.6**	**213.54**	**62.02**	**9.19**
96P/Machholz		**27.96**	**0.1239**	**0.9592**	**5.3**	**14.79**	**94.25**	**58.14**
62P/Tsuchinshan	**Nov.**	**16.19**	**1.3838**	**0.5975**	**6.4**	**30.35**	**90.25**	**9.71**
236P/LINEAR		**20.15**	**1.8375**	**0.5078**	**7.2**	**119.27**	**245.67**	**16.33**
14P/Wolf	**Dec.**	**2**	**2.743**	**0.356**	**8.8**	**159.02**	**202.12**	**27.9**
139P/Vaisala–Oterma		**10.83**	**3.4144**	**0.2463**	**9.6**	**166.07**	**242.21**	**2.33**
P/2010 D1 (WISE)		18.83	2.6896	0.3544	8.5	226.14	160.81	9.63

For an explanation of these elements, see p. 22; the elements are for an epoch within 20 days of perihelion. Visit the website www.minorplanetcenter.net/iau/Ephemerides/Comets/ for up-to-date ephemerides. For observers interested in monitoring the brightness of observable comets, visit www.icq.eps.harvard.edu/CometMags.html for comet magnitude updates. To make personalized finder charts using computer planetarium software, go to www.minorplanetcenter.net/iau/MPEph/MPEph.html to retrieve downloadable orbital elements in several popular electronic formats.

OBSERVING COMETS

BY DAVID H. LEVY

Each comet has its own unique, changing appearance. Observationally, comets are very much like deep-sky objects. Even in large telescopes, an observer can confuse a comet with a galaxy or a diffuse planetary nebula. Comets near a telescope's limit are virtually impossible to spot without an accurate position extracted from a detailed atlas, such as *Uranometria* or *Millennium*. It is difficult to define a telescope's limiting magnitude for comets, because the more diffuse a comet, the more difficult it is to find. Typically, under a dark sky, a 150-mm telescope will catch a 9th-mag. comet, a 200-mm telescope will see 10th, and a 400-mm should capture a 13th-mag. comet.

If you think you have found a new comet, after confirming the observation, file a *discovery report* according to the procedure in REPORTING OF ASTRONOMICAL DISCOVERIES, p. 7. For more information on comet observing and hunting, read *David Levy's Guide to Observing and Discovering Comets* (Cambridge, 2003).

Magnitude Estimates

The brightness of the coma can be estimated using a variety of methods, the most common of which is the "In-Out" method:

(1) Study the coma until you are familiar with its "average" brightness, an easy process if the coma is of uniform brightness, but rather difficult if there is a strong central condensation.

(2) With the help of a variable-star chart or some source in which star magnitudes are listed, find a comparison star at approximately the same altitude as the comet.

(3) Defocus the star to the size of the in-focus coma.

(4) Compare the star's out-of-focus brightness with that of the coma.

Repeat the last three steps with a second star, or more if needed, until an interpolation can be made.

Physical Characteristics

An estimate of a comet's magnitude is more useful if an estimate of the coma diameter is made at the same time. An observer seeing a 3′ coma, for example, will estimate much brighter than one who sees only a 1′ coma at the same time. The simplest way of estimating coma size is to draw the coma with the embedded and surrounding field stars, and then compare the drawing to an atlas, using its scale to determine the size.

A nightly measurement of a comet's degree of condensation is a good way of studying its changing behaviour. A comet undergoing an outburst of dust from its nucleus might begin its display by showing almost overnight the development of an increased condensation. Use an integer scale from 0 to 9, where 0 means a diffuse coma with absolutely uniform brightness, 3 means a diffuse coma with gradually increasing brightness toward the centre, 6 involves a definite central condensation, and 9 refers to an almost stellar image.

Because of the changing Earth–Sun–comet geometry and the changing activity in a comet, the length and position angle of a tail should be measured. A rough way to measure the length of a tail is to sketch it and compare with a detailed atlas, as with the coma. Observers can also measure the position angle using an atlas and a protractor.

Visual Comet Hunting

The key ingredient to a successful comet search is perseverance, especially in this time of automated searches. The chances for a visual discovery have plummeted in the last few years. Although there are stories of people finding comets very quickly (Mark Whitaker discovered Comet Whitaker–Thomas 1968 V after three nights of comet hunting), these are the exception. Don Machholz searched for some 1700 hours for each of his first two comets, and I spent more than 917 hours before my first discovery. In contrast, neither Alan Hale nor Tom Bopp was comet hunting when they independently discovered what later became the Great Comet of 1997.

It is important to know the sky well before beginning a comet search program, but it is more important to know the difference between the fuzzy appearances of comets compared to galaxies, nebulae, and clusters. Observing all the objects in THE MESSIER CATALOGUE (see p. 314) provides an excellent education in what these distant objects look like, and observing as many known comets as possible is good preparation for recognizing an interloper. Generally, comets lack the bilateral symmetry of spiral galaxies and the mottled appearance of globular clusters. More important, they usually have unsharp edges, fading off into space so that it is often difficult to tell where the comet ends and the sky begins.

Although most comet hunters still use traditional star atlases to check their suspects, some are moving into a new mode of comet hunting. These hunters have attached encoders to their telescopes that allow an instant reading of the suspect's position in RA and Dec. If the telescope has been properly set up, this approach is faster. However, a sense of the nature of the fuzzy object in the field of view is still important since thousands of nonstellar objects dot the sky.

Comets may appear at any time, but they are usually found within 90° of the Sun. Good areas to search are in the evening western sky during the week after full Moon and in the morning eastern sky before dawn around new Moon. Although comet hunters differ in their approaches to searching, one way is to use an altazimuth mount and make horizontal sweeps. In the western sky, begin near the end of evening twilight at the horizon, sweep across, then return to the point of origin, move upward about half a field of view and sweep again, etc. In the morning, reverse the process.

The author bet a friend one dollar that this lovely Sun-grazing comet (ISON C/2012 S1) would get brighter than mag. 0. Technically it did, just before it disintegrated, but he did not see it that bright, so he lost. (Photo by David Levy using Obadiah, his 32-cm (12-in.) Schmidt camera)

Photographic and Electronic Comet Hunting

While still possible, it is now very difficult to discover comets photographically because the sky is so well covered by the professional surveys. With film and a wide-angle camera like a Schmidt camera, take photographs of selected areas of sky, then repeat these exposures after at least 45 min. Using a stereomicroscope or a blink microscope, it is then possible to spot moving objects. Through a stereomicroscope, the comet will appear to "float" above or "sink" below the stellar background. If a blink microscope is used, the comet will appear to jump back and forth.

Using a CCD, take at least three images of each field, then examine either visually or using a moving-object detection program. Visual inspection is like blinking, so moving objects appear to move steadily through the three pictures, then jump back and begin moving again.

Finally, it is possible to discover comets over the Internet. Since images from the *SOHO* spacecraft are made available soon after they are taken, amateur astronomers can scan these images for Sun-grazing comets. RASC member Michael Boschat won the 2001 Ken Chilton Prize for his discoveries of over 50 *SOHO* comets in this way.

Designation of Comets

The International Astronomical Union assigns each comet a unique designation that is similar to, although not identical to, the provisional designation system for minor planets (see www.minorplanetcenter.net/iau/lists/CometResolution).

The first component of the designation is a letter indicating the comet's status: C/ for a long-period comet, P/ for a periodic comet (defined as having a period of less than 200 years), X/ for a comet for which a reasonable orbit cannot be computed, and D/ for a disappeared comet. Then the year is stated, followed by the *half-month* letter. (The year is sub-divided into half-month intervals beginning with A (the first half of January) and concluding with Y (the last half of December), omitting the letter I.) Thus Comet Hale–Bopp, the first comet to be found in the second part of July 1995, is labelled C/1995 O1. Once the orbit of a periodic comet is well known, that comet receives a permanent number according to the order in which the comet's periodicity was recognized. Comet Halley—the first comet ever recognized to be periodic—is 1P/Halley. Comet Shoemaker–Levy 9, now disappeared, has the designation D/1993 F2, as it was discovered in the second half of March 1993.

Under a previous system, a comet was designated according to its order of discovery or recovery in a given year (e.g. 1982i, Comet Halley, was the ninth comet to appear in 1982). After cometary information was complete for a given year, each comet also received a Roman numeral designation based on the order of perihelion passage (e.g. Halley at its last return was also known as 1986 III). The current designation went into effect in January 1995, but it is retroactive to every previously discovered comet for which a reasonable orbit is available.

When a comet becomes well known, the vast majority of scientists, press, and public ignore the official designation, preferring instead to use more easily remembered names. Our experience with comets Hale–Bopp and Hyakutake (C/1996 B2) shows clearly that people are more comfortable with proper names. However, with two comets named Hyakutake, almost 1500 named *SOHO*, and well over 100 named LINEAR, we need to become familiar with the official designation in order to separate one comet from another (see www.cbat.eps.harvard.edu/cometnameg).

A handful of comets are named not for their discoverers, but for the persons who computed their orbits. The most famous of these is 1P/Halley, which has been well observed since at least 240 BC. It was finally identified as a comet appearing every 76 years or so by Edmund Halley in 1705. Two others are 2P/Encke and 27P/Crommelin.

In the event that the cometary nature of an object is established after it was originally given an minor planet designation, the original designation remains. When Gene and Carolyn Shoemaker and I discovered asteroid 1990 UL3 using the Palomar 18-in. telescope, for example, its orbit appeared to be more cometary than asteroidal. A few weeks after discovery, Steve Larson and I took a series of images through the Kuiper 61-in. telescope that clearly showed a tail, and the identification was changed to periodic comet Shoemaker–Levy 2. The mixed designation C/1990 UL3 applies.

Editor's Note: David Levy has discovered 23 comets: 9 by visual searches, 13 photographically at Palomar Observatory under the combined name Shoemaker–Levy, and the latest, co-discovered with Wendee Levy and Tom Glinos, by Hyperion, an automated telescope at Jarnac Observatory (at his home in Arizona): P/2010 E2 (Jarnac).

INTERPLANETARY DUST

BY ROY BISHOP

Outside of the astronomical community it is not generally realized that the inner Solar System contains a vast cloud of dust. The particles in this cloud are concentrated near the plane of the ecliptic and toward the Sun, their spatial particle density in the ecliptic falling off somewhat more rapidly than the reciprocal of their distance from the Sun. Measurements from spacecraft indicate that the cloud extends well beyond the orbit of Mars but is negligible in the vicinity of Jupiter's orbit and beyond.

The particles composing the cloud have a continuum of sizes, from pebble-sized clumps down to specks with diameters comparable to the wavelength of visible light and smaller. The smaller particles are the more numerous, although the mass distribution appears to peak near 10^{-8} kg, corresponding to a particle diameter of a few tenths of a millimetre. The total mass of the cloud is small, amounting to perhaps 10^{-14} of the mass of the Solar System. It is as if the satellites of Mars had been pulverized and spread throughout the inner Solar System.

Like the planetary system, the interplanetary dust cloud is not static; its particles generally move in orbits about the Sun. In addition, the particles undergo continual fragmentation due to collisions, sputtering associated with bombardment by the solar wind, electrostatic bursting, and sublimation. This progression toward smaller and smaller sizes is of crucial significance for the cloud, since particles with diameters appreciably less than a tenth of a millimetre have a sufficiently large surface-to-volume ratio that the radiation pressure of sunlight has a significant effect upon their motion—aberration of sunlight results in a small backward force, causing them to slowly spiral inward toward the Sun (the Poynting–Robertson Effect). During a total solar eclipse in 1983, instruments carried by a balloon detected a ringlike concentration of dust only a couple of solar diameters from the Sun. Its inner edge apparently marks the point at which solar heat vapourizes the infalling particles. The resulting tiny gas molecules, like the smallest particles of dust, are blown out of the Solar System by the dominant radiation pressure and interactions with the solar wind.

Because of the above-mentioned influences on the sizes and motions of the dust particles, the estimated mean life of a cloud particle is about 10^4 years. Since that is much less than the age of the Solar System, the cloud must be in a dynamic equilibrium—that is, it must be gaining new material as it loses the old. Part of the coma and tail of a comet is the result of significant quantities of dust ejected from its nucleus, and it is believed that short-period comets provide most of the new dust to the cloud (see *Sky & Telescope*, Jun. 2010, p. 16). Since comet nuclei are believed to consist of the undifferentiated matter from which the Solar System formed, much of the dust of the interplanetary cloud is most likely composed of this same low-density, fragile, primitive material.

To an observer on Earth the most noticeable aspect of the dust cloud is meteors—larger particles of the cloud that encounter Earth at high speeds and vapourize in the upper atmosphere. In addition, sunlight scattered by the dust cloud appears as a faint (fortunately!) glow in the vicinity of the ecliptic. The glow is brightest toward the Sun, is due primarily to particles with diameters between a few micrometres and a millimetre, and is referred to as the *zodiacal light*. A slight brightening in the sky opposite the Sun, called the *gegenschein* (German for "counterglow"), is due to a phase effect (analogous to full Moon) and also, possibly, to a concentration of dust at the L3 Lagrangian point of the Earth–Sun system. The integrated visual magnitude of the dust is about −8.5, making it the brightest Solar System object in the sky after the Sun and Moon. As astronomical objects the zodiacal light and the gegenschein are unusual in that they can be seen only with the unaided eye. Because of their large angular sizes and indistinct borders, both are invisible in binoculars or a telescope.

The Zodiacal Light

Poetic references to the zodiacal light go back several centuries (e.g. see *The Observatory, 108* (1988), p. 181). The 19th-century poet Edward FitzGerald is noted for his translation of the famous poem "Rubaiyat" by the Persian Omar Khayyam. In one of the stanzas Khayyam's reference to the morning was altered by FitzGerald into haunting references to the zodiacal light: "Dreaming when Dawn's Left Hand was in the Sky" (in mid-northern latitudes the zodiacal light and the first glow of the early autumn dawn combine to produce a large, glowing, ghostly figure having an upraised left arm); and "Before the phantom of False morning died" (the zodiacal light soon vanishes in the glow of the true dawn).

When conditions are favourable, the zodiacal light is indeed a mysterious and beautiful sight. Because the zodiacal light is brightest nearest the Sun, it is best seen within half an hour following the end of evening twilight and in the half hour prior to the beginning of morning twilight (for times of twilight, see p. 208), and when the ecliptic is at a steep angle relative to the horizon. In the tropics the ecliptic is always at a steep angle to the horizon. In mid-northern latitudes the optimum geometry occurs in the evening western sky in February and March, and in the morning eastern sky in September and October. The zodiacal light appears as a huge, softly radiant pyramid of white light with its base near the horizon and its axis centred on the zodiac (or better, the ecliptic). In its brightest parts it exceeds the luminance of the central Milky Way.

Despite its brightness, most people have not seen the zodiacal light. As mentioned above, certain times of night and year are more favourable than others. In addition, moonlight, haze, or light pollution rule out any chance of seeing this phenomenon. Even with a dark, transparent sky the inexperienced observer may confuse the zodiacal light with twilight and thus ignore it, or may not notice it because he or she is expecting a much smaller object.

The Gegenschein

The zodiacal light extends all around the zodiac with a shallow minimum in brightness some 120° to 150° from the Sun; nevertheless, this "zodiacal band" or "light bridge" is exceedingly faint and is visible only from high-altitude sites having very dark, transparent skies. However, the slight brightening in the vicinity of the antisolar point can be seen from most dark observing sites, provided the air is transparent.

The gegenschein is very faint. Haze, moonlight, bright nearby stars, planets, or light pollution will hide it completely. Most observers, including experienced ones, have not seen it. The gegenschein is sufficiently faint that, except from high-altitude sites with very dark skies, a person will not notice it without making a special effort to *look* for it. It is a ghostly apparition best seen near midnight, and in mid-northern latitudes, in the autumn or winter when the antisolar point is nearest the zenith. To avoid interference from bright stars or the Milky Way, the periods late September to early November and late January to early February are best. At these times the gegenschein is in Pisces and Cancer, respectively. It appears as a faint yet distinct, somewhat elliptical glow perhaps 10° in diameter. The luminance of the gegenschein is about 10^{-4} cd/m^2, some 10 orders of magnitude dimmer than the brightest light the human eye can tolerate.

Don't determine the antisolar point before you look—imagination is too powerful. Find the antisolar point by locating the gegenschein, and *then* check your star charts!

STARS

CONSTELLATIONS—NAMES AND ABBREVIATIONS

Nominative & Pronunciation	Genitive & Pronunciation	Abbr.	Meaning
Andromeda, ăn-drŏm′ē-dȧ	Andromedae, ăn-drŏm′ē-dē′	And	Daughter of Cassiopeia
Antlia, ănt′lĭ-ȧ	Antliae, ănt′lē-ē′	Ant	The Air Pump
Apus, ā′pŭs	Apodis, ăp′ă-dĭs	Aps	Bird of Paradise
Aquarius, ȧ-kwâr′ē-ŭs	Aquarii, ȧ-kwâr′ē-ī′	Aqr	The Water Bearer
Aquila, ȧ-kwĭl′ȧ	Aquilae, ȧ-kwĭl′e	Aql	The Eagle
Ara, ā′rȧ	Arae, ā′rē	Ara	The Altar
Aries, âr′ēz	Arietis, ȧ-rī′ē-tĭs	Ari	The Ram
Auriga, ô-rī′gȧ	Aurigae, ô-rī′jē	Aur	The Charioteer
Boötes, bō-ō′tēz	Boötis, bō-ō′tĭs	Boo	The Herdsman
Caelum, sē′lŭm	Caeli, sē′lī	Cae	The Chisel
Camelopardalis kȧ-mĕl′ō-pȧr′dȧ-lĭs	Camelopardalis kȧ-mĕl′ō-pȧr′dȧ-lĭs	Cam	The Giraffe
Cancer, kăn′sēr	Cancri, kăn′krē	Cnc	The Crab
Canes Venatici kā′nēz vē-năt′ĭ-sī	Canum Venaticorum kā′nŭm vē-năt′ĭ-kôr′ŭm	CVn	The Hunting Dogs
Canis Major, kā′nĭs mā′jēr	Canis Majoris, kā′nĭs mā-jôr′ĭs	CMa	The Big Dog
Canis Minor, kā′nĭs mī′nēr	Canis Minoris, kā′nĭs mī-ñôr′ĭs	CMi	The Little Dog
Capricornus, kăp′rĭ-kôr-nŭs	Capricorni, kăp′rĭ-kôr-nī	Cap	The Goat
Carina, kȧ-rī′-nȧ	Carinae, kȧ-rī′-nē	Car	The Keel
Cassiopeia, kăs′ĭ-ō-pē′yȧ	Cassiopeiae, kăs′ĭ-ō-pē′yē	Cas	The Queen
Centaurus, sĕn-tôr′ŭs	Centauri, sĕn-tôr′ī	Cen	The Centaur
Cepheus, sē′fē-ŭs	Cephei, sē′fē-ī′	Cep	The King
Cetus, sē′tŭs	Ceti, sē′tī	Cet	The Whale
Chamaeleon, kȧ-mē′lē-ŭn	Chamaeleontis, kȧ-mē′lē-ŏn′tĭs	Cha	The Chameleon
Circinus, sûr′sĭ-nŭs	Circini, sûr′sĭ-nī	Cir	The Compasses
Columba, kō-lŭm′bȧ	Columbae, kō-lŭm′bē	Col	The Dove
Coma Berenices kō′mȧ bĕr′ĕ-nī′sēz	Comae Berenices kō′mē bĕr′ĕ-nī′sēz	Com	Berenice's Hair
Corona Australis kō-rō′nȧ ôs-trā′lĭs	Coronae Australis kō-rō′nē ôs-trā′lĭs	CrA	The Southern Crown
Corona Borealis kō-rō′nȧ bôr′ē-ăl′ĭs	Coronae Borealis kō-rō′nē bôr′ē-ăl′ĭs	CrB	The Northern Crown
Corvus, kôr′vŭs	Corvi, kôr′vī	Crv	The Crow
Crater, krā′tēr	Crateris, krā-tēr′ĭs	Crt	The Cup
Crux, krŭks	Crucis, kro͞o′sĭs	Cru	The Cross
Cygnus, sĭg′nŭs	Cygni, sĭg′nī	Cyg	The Swan
Delphinus, dĕl-fī′nŭs	Delphini, dĕl-fī′nī	Del	The Dolphin
Dorado, dō-rȧ′dō	Doradus, dō-rȧ′dŭs	Dor	The Swordfish
Draco, drā′kō	Draconis, drā′kō′nĭs	Dra	The Dragon
Equuleus, ē-kwo͞o′lē-ŭs	Equulei, ē-kwo͞o′lē-ī′	Equ	The Little Horse
Eridanus, ē-rĭd′ȧ-nŭs	Eridani, ē-rĭd′ȧ-nī′	Eri	The River
Fornax, fôr′năks	Fornacis, fôr-nās′ĭs	For	The Furnace
Gemini, jĕm′ĭ-nī	Geminorum, jĕm′ĭ-nôr′ŭm	Gem	The Twins
Grus, grŭs	Gruis, gro͞o′ĭs	Gru	The Crane (bird)
Hercules, hûr′kū-lēz	Herculis, hûr′kū-lĭs	Her	The Son of Zeus
Horologium, hŏr′ō-lō′jĭ-ŭm	Horologii, hŏr′ō-lō′jĭ-ī	Hor	The Clock
Hydra, hī′drȧ	Hydrae, hī′drē	Hya	The Water Snake (♀)
Hydrus, hī′drŭs	Hydri, hī′drī	Hyi	The Water Snake (♂)
Indus, ĭn′dŭs	Indi, ĭn′dī	Ind	The Indian

CONSTELLATIONS—NAMES AND ABBREVIATIONS (continued)

Nominative & Pronunciation	Genitive & Pronunciation	Abbr.	Meaning
Lacerta, lȧ-sûr′tȧ	Lacertae, lȧ-sûr′tē	Lac	The Lizard
Leo, lē′ō	Leonis, lē′ō′nĭs	Leo	The Lion
Leo Minor, lē′ō mī′nẽr	Leonis Minoris lē′ō′nĭs mī-nôr′ĭs	LMi	The Little Lion
Lepus, lē′pŭs	Leporis, lĕp′ôr-ĭs	Lep	The Hare
Libra, lē′brȧ	Librae, lē′brē	Lib	The Balance
Lupus, lo͞o′pŭs	Lupi, lo͞o′pī	Lup	The Wolf
Lynx, lĭnks	Lyncis, lĭn′sĭs	Lyn	The Lynx
Lyra, lī′rȧ	Lyrae, lī′rē	Lyr	The Lyre
Mensa, mĕn′sȧ	Mensae, mĕn′sē	Men	The Table
Microscopium mī′krō-skō′pē-ŭm	Microscopii mī′krō-skō′pē-ī′	Mic	The Microscope
Monoceros, mō-nŏs′ẽr-ŏs	Monocerotis, mō-nŏs′ẽr-ō′tĭs	Mon	The Unicorn
Musca, mŭs′kȧ	Muscae, mŭs′ē	Mus	The Fly
Norma, nôr′mȧ	Normae, nôr′mē	Nor	The Square
Octans, ŏk′tănz	Octantis, ŏk′tăn′tĭs	Oct	The Octant
Ophiuchus, ō′fē-ū′kŭs	Ophiuchi, ō′fē-ū′kī	Oph	The Serpent Bearer
Orion, ō-rī′ŏn	Orionis, ôr′ē-ō′nĭs	Ori	The Hunter
Pavo, pā′vō	Pavonis, pȧ-vō′nĭs	Pav	The Peacock
Pegasus, pĕg′ȧ-sŭs	Pegasi, pĕg′ȧ-sī	Peg	The Winged Horse
Perseus, pûr′sē-ŭs	Persei, pûr′sē-ī′	Per	Rescuer of Andromeda
Phoenix, fē′nĭks	Phoenicis, fē-nī′cĭs	Phe	The Phoenix
Pictor, pĭk′tẽr	Pictoris, pĭk-tor′ĭs	Pic	The Painter
Pisces, pī′sēz	Piscium, pĭsh′ē-ŭm	Psc	The Fishes
Piscis Austrinus, pī′sĭs ôs-trī′nŭs	Piscis Austrini, pī′sĭs ôs-trī′nī	PsA	The Southern Fish
Puppis, pŭp′ĭs	Puppis, pŭp′ĭs	Pup	The Stern
Pyxis, pĭk′sĭs	Pyxidis, pĭk′sĭ-dĭs	Pyx	The Compass
Reticulum, rē-tĭk′-ū-lŭm	Reticuli, rē-tĭk′-ū-lī	Ret	The Reticle
Sagitta, sȧ-jĭt′ȧ	Sagittae, sȧ-jĭt′ē	Sge	The Arrow
Sagittarius, săj′ĭ-târ′ē-ŭs	Sagittarii, săj′ĭ-târ′ē-ī′	Sgr	The Archer
Scorpius, skôr′pē-ŭs	Scorpii, skôr′pē-ī	Sco	The Scorpion
Sculptor, skŭlp′tẽr	Sculptoris, skŭlp′tôr′ĭs	Scl	The Sculptor
Scutum, skū′tŭm	Scuti, sko͞o′tī	Sct	The Shield
Serpens, sûr′pĕnz	Serpentis, sûr-pĕn′tĭs	Ser	The Serpent
Sextans, sĕks′tănz	Sextantis, sĕks-tăn′tĭs	Sex	The Sextant
Taurus, tôr′ŭs	Tauri, tôr′ī	Tau	The Bull
Telescopium tĕl′ȧ-skō′pē-ŭm	Telescopii, tĕl′ȧ-skō′pē-ī	Tel	The Telescope
Triangulum, trī-ăng′gū-lŭm	Trianguli, trī-ăng′gū-lī′	Tri	The Triangle
Triangulum Australe trī-ăng′gū-lŭm ôs-trā′lē	Trianguli Australis trī-ăng′gū-lī′ ôs-trā′lĭs	TrA	The Southern Triangle
Tucana, to͞o-kăn′ȧ	Tucanae, to͞o-kăn′ē	Tuc	The Toucan
Ursa Major, ûr′să mā′jẽr	Ursae Majoris, ûr′sē mȧ-jôr′ĭs	UMa	The Great Bear
Ursa Minor, ûr′să mī′nẽr	Ursae Minoris, ûr′sē mī-nôr′ĭs	UMi	The Little Bear
Vela, vē′lȧ	Velorum, vē-lôr′ŭm	Vel	The Sails
Virgo, vûr′gō	Virginis, vûr′jĭn-ĭs	Vir	The Maiden
Volans, vō′lănz	Volantis, vō-lăn′tĭs	Vol	The Flying Fish
Vulpecula, vŭl-pĕk′ū-lȧ	Vulpeculae, vŭl-pĕk′ū-lē′	Vul	The Fox

ā dāte; ă tăp; â câre; ȧ gȧgȧ; ē wē; ĕ mĕt; ẽ makẽr; ī īce; ĭ bĭt; ō gō; ŏ hŏt; ô ôrb; o͞o mo͞on; ū ūnite; ŭ ŭp; û ûrn

In terms of area (based on the official IAU boundaries), of the 88 constellations the 3 largest are Hydra (1303 square degrees), Virgo (1294), and Ursa Major (1280); the 3 smallest: Sagitta (80), Equuleus (72), and Crux (68). A complete list of the areas of the constellations appears in the 1972 edition of *The Handbook of the British Astronomical Association*, and was reproduced in the June 1976 issue of *Sky & Telescope* (p. 408).

COMA BERENICES

BY CHRIS BECKETT & RANDALL ROSENFELD

...the beauteous hair, that lately shed
Refulgent beams from Berenice's head;
The lock she fondly vow'd with lifted arms,
Imploring all the powers to save from harms....
—From The Hair of Berenice, Catullus 1st c. BC
(trans. Tytler 1793)

Reigning high overhead on clear spring evenings a grouping of stars catches the attention of even casual night-sky observers. This is Coma Berenices, one of the brightest star clusters and a constellation named after an ancient queen. The main star pattern consists only of three 4th-mag. stars, which appear as an upside-down right angle, but despite the dim setting, the region includes three globular clusters and objects from all Deep-Sky Observing Certificates.

The story of Coma Berenices is rare in constellation lore, based not on myth but a real person, Queen Berenice II of Egypt, who, according to Hyginus, is said to have promised a lock of her long amber-coloured hair to Aphrodite if the king returned safe from war. Upon his return, she placed a lock in the temple; however, in the morning it was gone, making the king anxious. The quick-thinking court astrologer, Conon, to advance his career, declared that Aphrodite was so impressed with the gesture she placed the hair among the stars.

Now catalogued as the open cluster Melotte 111, from the Explore the Universe program, the cluster is still most popularly known as Coma Berenices. Ptolemy described it as a "nebulous convolution which is called Coma Berenice" located "between the outermost parts of Leo and Ursa Major," including the stars Gamma, 7, and 23 Comae Berenices, which he suggested was "shaped like a leaf."

Before Coma Berenices, the region was seen as a sheaf of wheat held aloft by Virgo. We see the transition in Bayer's 1603 Uranometria where a Wheat Sheaf is depicted on chart 5 and Berenice's Hair on chart 2, and all major astronomical charts thereafter. Spanning over 5° of sky and shining at mag. +1.8, Melotte 111 is perfect for 7× binoculars, and with many orange, or yellow-white stars, it may appear faintly golden, perhaps even amber, to the naked eye.

Coma Berenices is also home to the North Galactic Pole (NGP), an invisible location less than 0.5 degrees south of the star 31 Comae. On the way from Mel 111 be sure to stop by NGC 4565, Herschel's aptly named "Needle Galaxy." Moving 2° south from the NGP, we find NGC 4725, a spiral galaxy, unique for its solitary spiral arm. From here, M64 lies about 1/3 of the way to Alpha Comae, even though in small telescopes a dark lane is easily observed, leading to its proper name "The Black Eye Galaxy." Sharing a 2° field with Alpha Comae (Diadem), we find two globular clusters. To observe both in a small telescope, first locate 8th mag. M53, and while staring directly at this object, use averted vision to see the Challenge Object NGC 5053. Six degrees north of Alpha is a galaxy chain of Deep-Sky Gems running from NGC 5016 to the west through NGC 4685, M85, NGC 4450, finally to NGC 4340. The third globular cluster is located at the far western edge of the constellation—the easily detected but difficult to resolve NGC 4147, a masquerader in this Realm of the Galaxies.

★ The Virgo Galaxy Cluster spans both Virgo and Coma Berenices, including the northern reaches of "Markarian's Chain" of galaxies and beyond, NGC 4473, 4477, and 4459. Low-power fields of 3.5° capture M88 and M91 to the northeast, then scanning west will bring M100, M99, and M98 into view. Now try for the Challenge Object Abell 1656, the Coma Berenices Galaxy Cluster. Centred around NGC 4889 and NGC 4874 exist many tiny fuzzy specs of remote galaxies.

It is fortunate that Queen Berenice was immortalized in the sky, because soon after this event, the king died and she was murdered. Coincidentally, the philosopher Aristotle wrote about hairy stars 100 years before Berenice was queen. He used the Greek word komē, "hair of the head," to illustrate the "luminous tail of a comet," objects long thought of as portenders of doom for powerful heads of state.

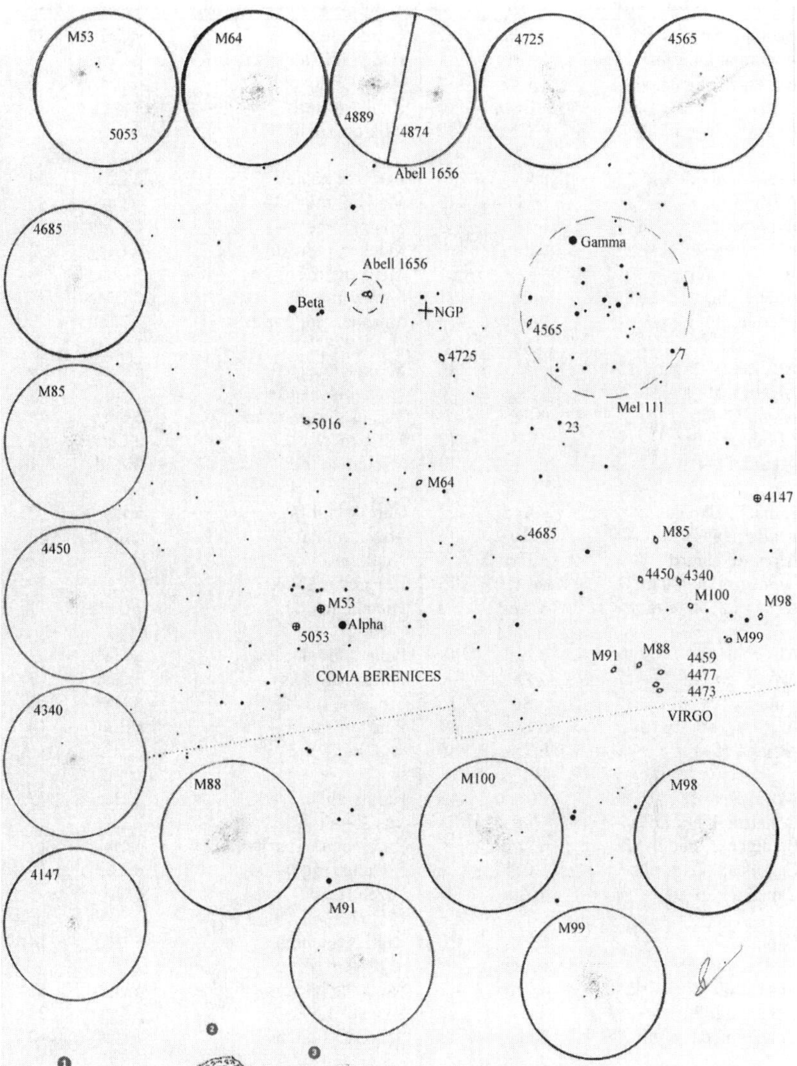

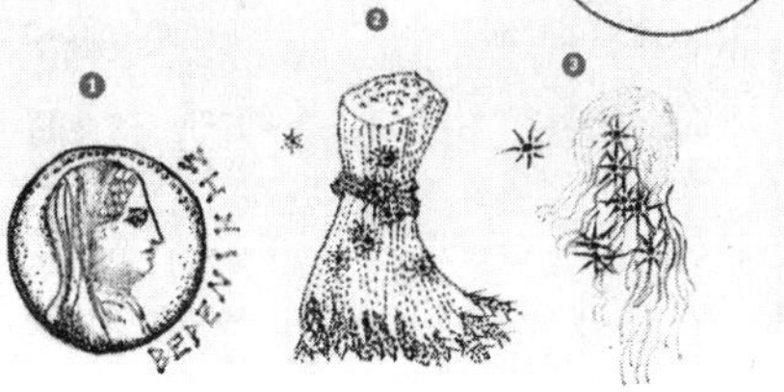

❶ Numismatic portrait of Queen Berenice II of Egypt (3rd century BC).

❷ Wheat sheaf from Bayer Uranometria (1603) chart 5.

❸ Hair from Bayer Uranometria (1603) chart 2.

Diagram by Randall Rosenfeld

FINDING LIST OF SOME NAMED STARS

Name & Pronunciation	Con.	RA	Name & Pronunciation	Con.	RA
Acamar, ā′kȧ-mȧr	θ Eri	2	Gienah, jē′nȧ	γ Crv	12
Achernar, ā′kẽr-nȧr	α Eri	1	Hadar, hăd′ar	β Cen	14
Acrux, ā′krŭks	α Cru	12	Hamal, hăm′al	α Ari	2
Adara, ȧ-dā′rȧ	ε CMa	6	Kaus Australis,	ε Sgr	18
Al Na'ir, ăl-nâr′	α Gru	22	kôs ôs-trā′lĭs		
Albireo, ăl-bĭr′ē-ō	β Cyg	19	Kochab, kō′kăb	β UMi	14
Alcor, ăl-kôr′	80 UMa	13	Markab, mȧr′kăb	α Peg	23
Alcyone, ăl-sī′ō-nē	η Tau	3	Megrez, me′grĕz	δ UMa	12
Aldebaran,	α Tau	4	Menkar, mĕn′kȧr	α Cet	3
ăl-dĕb′ȧ-rȧn			Menkent, mĕn′kĕnt	θ Cen	14
Alderamin,	α Cep	21	Merak, mē′răk	β UMa	11
ăl-dĕr′ȧ-mĭn			Merope, mĕr′ō-pē	23 Tau	3
Algeiba, ăl-jē′bȧ	γ Leo	10	Miaplacidus,	β Car	9
Algenib, ăl-jē′nĭb	γ Peg	0	mī′ȧ-plăs′ĭ-dŭs		
Algol, ăl′gŏl	β Per	3	Mintaka, mĭn-tȧ′kȧ	δ Ori	5
Alioth, ăl′ĭ-ŏth	ε UMa	12	Mira, mī′rȧ	o Cet	2
Alkaid, ăl-kād′	η UMa	13	Mirach, mī′răk	β And	1
Almach, ăl′măk	γ And	2	Mirfak, mir′făk	α Per	3
Alnilam, ăl-nī′lăm	ε Ori	5	Mizar, mi′zȧr	ζ UMa	13
Alphard, ăl′fȧrd	α Hya	9	Nunki, nŭn′kē	σ Sgr	18
Alphecca, ăl-fĕk′ȧ	α CrB	15	Peacock, pē′kŏk	α Pav	20
Alpheratz, ăl-fē′răts	α And	0	Phecda, fĕk′dȧ	γ UMa	11
Altair, ăl-târ′	α Aql	19	Polaris, pō-lâr′ĭs	α UMi	2
Ankaa, ăn′kȧ	α Phe	0	Pollux, pŏl′ŭks	β Gem	7
Antares, ăn-tā′rēs	α Sco	16	Procyon, prō′sĭ-ŏn	α CMi	7
Arcturus, ark-tū′rŭs	α Boo	14	Pulcherrima,	ε Boo	14
Atria, ā′trĭ-a	α TrA	16	pŭl-kĕr′ĭ-mȧ		
Avior, ă-vĭ-ôr′	ε Car	8	Rasalgethi,	α Her	17
Bellatrix, bĕ-lā′trĭks	γ Ori	5	rȧs′ăl-jē′thē		
Betelgeuse, bĕt′ĕl-jūz	α Ori	5	Rasalhague, rȧs′ăl-hāg	α Oph	17
Canopus, kȧ-nō′pŭs	α Car	6	Regulus, rĕg′ū-lŭs	α Leo	10
Capella, kȧp-pĕl′ȧ	α Aur	5	Rigel, rī′gĕl	β Ori	5
Caph, kăf	β Cas	0	Rigil Kentaurus,	α Cen	14
Castor, kȧs′tẽr	α Gem	7	rī′jĭl kĕn-tô′rŭs		
Cor Caroli, kôr kăr′ŏ-lī	α CVn	12	Sabik, sā′bĭk	η Oph	17
Deneb, dĕn′ĕb	α Cyg	20	Scheat, shē′ăt	β Peg	23
Denebola, dĕ-nĕb′ō-la	β Leo	11	Schedar, shĕd′ȧr	α Cas	0
Diphda, dĭf′dȧ	β Cet	0	Shaula, shô′lȧ	λ Sco	17
Dubhe, dŭb′ē	α UMa	11	Sirius, sĭr′ĭ-ŭs	α CMa	6
Elnath, ĕl′năth	β Tau	5	Spica, spī′kȧ	α Vir	13
Eltanin, ĕl-tā′nĭn	γ Dra	17	Suhail, sŭ-hāl′	λ Vel	9
Enif, ĕn′ĭf	ε Peg	21	Thuban, tho͞o′ban	α Dra	14
Fomalhaut, fō′măl-ôt	α PsA	22	Vega, vē′gȧ	α Lyr	18
Gacrux, gȧ′krŭks	γ Cru	12	Zubenelgenubi,	α Lib	14
Gemma, jĕm′ȧ	α CrB	15	zo͞o-bĕn′ĕl-jĕ-nū′bē		

Key to pronunciation at the foot of p. 271..

THE BRIGHTEST STARS

BY TOOMAS KARMO, CHRIS CORBALLY, AND RICHARD GRAY

In the following table, the 285 brightest stars (allowing for variability) are listed, reduced from previous years to allow a new subject on p. 284, SPECTROSCOPY OF STARS. An extended table is in www.rasc.ca/handbook/supplements. Data for visual doubles are for the brighter component (A); the last column describes the companion(s). Where the double is too close to be resolved conveniently, data are for combined light (AB).

Apparent Visual Magnitude (**m_V** = *V*): Apparent magnitudes, with "v" appended for variables, are from *HIPPARCOS*. (For variables, these data are occasionally in mild conflict with published magnitude ranges.) The photoelectric system is from H.L. Johnson and W.W. Morgan, *Ap. J.*, *117* (1953). The (yellow) *V* filter corresponds roughly to the response of the eye. The probable error of a *V* value is at most 0.03.

Colour Index (***B* – *V***): Since *B* on this system is the brightness of a star through a blue filter, the difference *B* – *V*, here taken from *HIPPARCOS*, measures apparent colour (as possibly reddened by interstellar dust; although, in general, *B* – *V* and spectral type are well correlated). The probable error of a *B* – *V* value is at most 0.02.

Spectral Classification (**MK Type**): The "temperature type" (O, B, A, F, G, K, M) is given first, followed by a finer subtype (0–9) and a "luminosity class" (Roman numerals I–V, with "a" or "b" added occasionally to indicate slightly brighter or fainter stars within the class). O stars are hottest, M stars coolest; Ia stars are the most luminous supergiants, III stars are giants, and V stars are dwarfs. (V stars form the largest class in the cosmos, comprising the main sequence.) Other MK symbols include "e" for hydrogen emission; "f" for broad, nonhydrogen emission in hot stars; "m" for strong metallic absorption; "n" or "nn" for unusually broad absorption (a signature of rotation); "p" for peculiarities; "s" for a mixture of broad and sharp lines; and ":" for a minor uncertainty. The types are the best available from Garrison's unpublished spectrograms and the literature. Where a single star (e.g. α CMa A) is given two types (e.g. A0 and A1), with the second type flagged "m", the first is the type that best characterizes the hydrogen lines, the second the type that best characterizes the metal lines.

Parallax (**π**), *Proper Motion* (**μ**), and *Position Angle* (**PA**): Parallaxes, in milliarcseconds (mas), proper-motion vector norms ("/y), and vector position-angles (degrees, from N through E) are derived from the *HIPPARCOS* 2007 data reduction, with a few exceptions.

Absolute Visual Magnitude (**M_V**) and *Distance in Light-Years* (***D***): Absolute magnitudes and distances are determined from parallaxes, except where a colon follows the absolute magnitude; in these cases, both quantities are determined from a calibration of the spectral classification. The absolute magnitude is left uncorrected for interstellar absorption. The appropriate correction is typically ~–0.06 mag. per 100 ly outside the Local Bubble, i.e. beyond ~100 ly.

Radial Velocity (**V_{rad}**): Radial velocities are from BSC5. "SB" indicates a spectroscopic binary, an unresolved system whose duplicity is revealed by periodic Doppler oscillations in its spectrum and for which an orbit is possibly known. If the lines of both stars are detectable, "SB2" is used; "+" and "–" indicate, respectively, motion away from and toward the observer. "V" indicates a variable velocity in a star not observable as a spectroscopic binary. (In most "V" cases, the orbit is unknown.)

Remarks: Remarks include data on variability and spectra, particulars on any companions, and traditional names. Our principal source for variability ranges is P.N. Kholopov et al., *Combined General Catalogue of Variable Stars*, 4.1 ed., 1998 (online as VizieR GCVS4). Our sources for traditional names include the Kaler online archive and Kunitzsch-with-Smart's *Short Guide to Modern Star Names* (1986). Navigation-star names are **bold**.

We thank Professor Emeritus R.F. Garrison (University of Toronto), lead author of this article for editions 1984 through 2015, for the guidance and encouragement he generously gave to us and the wider RASC family.

TABLE OF BRIGHTEST STARS

Star Name	RA (2017.5) h m	Dec ° ′	m_V	$B-V$	MK Type	π mas	M_V	D ly	μ ″/y	PA °	V_{rad} km/s	Remarks
Sun			−26.75	0.63	G2 V		4.8	8 lm				
α And	0 09.3	+29 11	2.07	−0.04	B9p IV: (HgMn)	34	−0.3	97	0.214	140	−12 SB	**Alpheratz**
β Cas	0 10.1	+59 15	2.28v	0.38	F2 III	60	1.2	55	0.554	109	+12 SB	var.: 2.25–2.31, 0.10 d Caph
γ Peg	0 14.1	+15 17	2.83v	−0.19	B2 IV	8	−2.6	400	0.009	168	+4 SB	var.: 2.78–2.89, 0.15 d Algenib
β Hyi	0 26.6	−77 09	2.82	0.62	G1 IV	134.1	3.5	24.3	2.243	82	+23	
α Phe	0 27.1	−42 13	2.40	1.08	K0 IIIb	38.5	0.3	~85	0.426	147	+75 SB	**Ankaa**
δ And A	0 40.3	+30 57	3.27	1.27	K3 III	~30.9	0.7	106	0.142	126	−7 SB	
α Cas	0 41.5	+56 38	2.24	1.17	K0 IIIa	~14.3	−2.0	230	0.060	122	−4 V?	**Shedar**
β Cet	0 44.5	−17 53	2.04	1.02	K0 III	~33.9	−0.3	96	0.235	82	+13 V?	**Diphda**
η Cas A	0 50.2	+57 54	3.46	0.59	G0 V	168	4.6	19.4	1.222	117	+9 SB	B:7.51, K4 Ve, 13.7″ PA:62°→325°, 1779→2015 Achird
γ Cas	0 57.8	+60 49	2.15v	−0.05	B0 IVnpe (shell)	5	−4.2	600	0.026	98	−7 SB	var.:1.6–3.0; B: 8.8, 2.1″, PA:255°→259°, 1888→2002 Tsih
β Phe AB	1 06.9	−46 38	3.32	0.88	G8 III	16	0.3:	150	0.088	293	−1	AB similar in light, spectrum, 0.4″
η Cet	1 09.5	−10 05	3.46	1.16	K1.5 III CN1	26.3	0.6	124	0.257	123	+12V	2 exoplanets
β And	1 10.7	+35 43	2.07	1.58	M0 IIIa	17	−1.8	200	0.209	123	+3 V	Mirach
δ Cas	1 27.0	+60 20	2.66v	0.16	A5 IV	32.8	0.2	99	0.301	99	+7 SB	ecl.? 2.68–2.76, 759 d Ruchbah
γ Phe	1 29.1	−43 14	3.41v	1.54	K7 IIIa	14	−0.9	230	0.209	185	+26 SB	irreg. var.: 3.39–3.49
α Eri	1 38.4	−57 09	0.45	−0.16	B3 Vnp (shell?)	23	−2.7	140	0.095	114	+16 V	**Achernar**
α Tri	1 54.1	+29 40	3.42	0.49	F6 IV	52	2.0	63	0.234	177	−13 SB	Mothallah
β Ari	1 55.6	+20 54	2.64	0.16	A4 V	56	1.4	59	0.148	138	−2 SB	Sheratan
ε Cas	1 55.7	+63 45	3.35	−0.15	B3 IV:p (shell)	8	−2.2	400	0.037	121	−8 V	Segin
α Hyi	1 59.3	−61 29	2.86	0.29	F0n III–IV	45	1.1	72	0.265	84	+1 V	
γ And A	2 05.0	+42 25	2.10	1.37	K3 IIb	9	−3.1	400	~0.065	~139	−12 SB	B: 5.4, B9 V, 9.5″; C: 6.2, A0 V; BC 0.3″ Almach
α Ari	2 08.2	+23 33	2.01	1.15	K2 IIIab	~49.6	0.5	66	0.240	128	−14 SB	calcium weak? exoplanet **Hamal**
β Tri	2 10.6	+35 04	3.00	0.14	A5 IV	26	0.1	130	0.154	105	+10 SB2	
ο Cet A	2 20.2	−2 54	6.47v	0.97	M5–10 IIIe	11	1.7	300	0.238	178	+64 V	LPV, 2–10; B: VZ Cet, 9.5v, Bpe, 0.5″ Mira
γ Cet AB	2 44.2	+3 19	3.47	0.09	A2 Va	41	1.5	80	0.207	225	−5 V	A: 3.57; B: 6.23, 1.9″, PA:283°→299°, 1825→2014
α UMi A	2 53.6	+89 20	1.97v	0.64	F5–8 Ib	7.5	−3.6	430	~0.046	~105?	−17 SB	low-amp. Cep., 4.0 d; B: 8.2, F3 V, 18″ **Polaris**
θ Eri A	2 58.9	−40 14	3.28	0.17	A5 IV	30	0.5	100	0.057	293	+12 SB2	B: 4.35, A1 Va, 8.4″, PA:82°→91°, 1835→2013 **Acamar**
α Cet	3 03.2	+4 09	2.54	1.63	M2 III	13	−1.9	250	0.078	188	−26 V	**Menkar**
γ Per	3 06.1	+53 34	2.91	0.72	G8 III + A2 V	13	−1.5	240	0.006	175	+3 SB2	composite spectrum
ρ Per	3 06.3	+38 54	3.32v	1.53	M4 II	11	−1.6	310	0.167	129	+28	semiregular var.: 3.3–4.0
β Per	3 09.3	+41 01	2.09v	0.00	B8 V + F:	36	−0.1	90	0.003	119	+4 SB	ecl.: 2.12–3.39, 2.9 d; composite Algol
α Per	3 25.6	+49 55	1.79	0.48	F5 Ib	~6.4	−4.2	510	0.035	138	−2 V	in open cluster **Mirfak**
δ Per	3 44.2	+47 51	3.01	−0.12	B5 IIIn	6	−3.0	500	0.050	149	+4 SB	
γ Hyi	3 47.0	−74 11	3.26	1.59	M2 III	15.2	−0.8	~214	0.126	24	+16	
η Tau	3 48.5	+24 09	2.85	−0.09	B7 IIIn	8	−2.6	400	0.048	156	+10 V?	in Pleiades Alcyone

TABLE OF BRIGHTEST STARS (continued)

Star Name	RA (2017.5) h m	Dec ° ′	m_V	$B-V$	MK Type	π mas	M_V	D ly	μ ″/y	PA °	V_{rad} km/s	Remarks	
ζ Per A	3 55.2	+31 56	2.84	0.27	B1 Ib	4	−4.0	800	0.011	150	+20 SB	B: 9.16, B8 V, 12.9″, PA:205°→209°, 1824→2012	
γ Eri	3 58.8	−13 28	2.97	1.59	M1 IIIb	16	−1.0	200	0.129	151	+62	calcium, chromium weak	Zaurak
ε Per A	3 59.0	+40 04	2.90	−0.20	B0.5 IV	5	−3.6	600	0.028	149	+1 SB2	B: 7.39, B9.5 V, 8.7″, PA:10°→10°, 1821→2012	
λ Tau A	4 01.7	+12 32	3.41v	−0.10	B3 V	7	−2.4	480	0.017	209	+18 SB2	ecl.: 3.37–3.91, 4.0 d; B: A4 IV	
α Ret A	4 14.7	−62 26	3.33	0.92	G8 II–III	20.2	−0.1	162	0.065	40	+36 SB?		
$θ^2$ Tau	4 29.7	+15 54	3.40	0.18	A7 III	22	0.1	150	0.112	104	+40 SB	in Hyades	
α Dor AB	4 34.4	−55 01	3.30	−0.08	A0p V: (Si)	19	−0.3	169	~0.059	~79?	+26	A: 3.8; B: 4.3, B9 IV; 0.3″ (2014); orbit 12 y	
α Tau A	4 36.9	+16 33	0.87v	1.54	K5 III	49	−0.7	67	0.199	161	+54 SB	irregular var.: 0.75–0.95	**Aldebaran**
$π^3$ Ori	4 50.8	+6 59	3.19	0.48	F6 V	124	3.7	26.3	0.464	89	+24 SB2		Tabit
ι Aur	4 58.1	+33 12	2.69v	1.49	K3 II	7	−3.2	500	0.016	155	+18 V	var.: 2.63–2.78	Hasseleh
ε Aur A	5 03.2	+43 51	3.03v	0.54	F0Iab? + ~B5V	<2?	−8.0:	~2000	~0.003	n.a.	−3 SB	ecl.: 2.92–3.83, 9892 d (dim ~700d)	Almaaz
ε Lep	5 06.2	−22 21	3.19	1.46	K4 III	15	−0.9	210	0.076	164	+1		
η Aur	5 07.7	+41 15	3.18	−0.15	B3 V	13	−1.2	240	0.075	155	+7 V?		Hoedus II
β Eri	5 08.7	−5 04	2.78	0.16	A3 IVn	36	0.6	89	0.112	228	−9		Cursa
μ Lep	5 13.7	−16 11	3.29V	−0.11	B9p IV: (HgMn)	18	−0.5	190	0.050	109	+28	var.: 2.97–3.41, 2 d	
β Ori A	5 15.4	−8 11	0.18	−0.03	B8 Ia	4	−6.9	900	0.001	69	+21 SB	B: 6.8, B5 V, 9″ (2011); C: 7.6; BC: 0.1″	**Rigel**
α Aur Aa+Ab	5 18.0	+46 01	0.08	0.80	G6:III + G2:III	76	−0.5	43	0.433	170	+30 SB2	composite; A: 0.6; B: 1.1, 0.0—0.1″	**Capella**
η Ori AB	5 25.4	−2 23	3.35v	−0.24	B0.5 V + B	3	−4.0	1000	~0.004?	n.a.	+20 SB2	ecl.: 3.31–3.60, 8.0 d; A: 3.6; B: 5.0, 1.8″ (2015)	
γ Ori	5 26.1	+6 22	1.64	−0.22	B2 III	13	−2.8	250	0.015	212	+18 SB?		**Bellatrix**
β Tau	5 27.4	+28 37	1.65	−0.13	B7 III	24	−1.4	130	0.175	173	+9 V		**Elnath**
β Lep A	5 29.0	−20 45	2.81	0.81	G5 II	~20.3	−0.6	160	0.086	183	−14 V?	B: 7.5, 2.7″, PA:268°→8°, 1875→2015	Nihal
δ Ori A	5 32.9	−0 17	2.25v	−0.18	O9.5 II	5	−4.4	700	0.001	137	+16 SB	ecl.: 2.14–2.26, 5.7 d	Mintaka
α Lep	5 33.5	−17 49	2.58	0.21	F0 IB	1.5	−6.6	2000	0.004	72	+24		Arneb
λ Ori A	5 36.1	+9 57	3.39	−0.16	O8 IIIf	3	−4.2	~1100	0.004	216	+34	B: 5.61, B0 V, 4.5″, PA:45°→44°, 1779→2015	Meissa
ι Ori A	5 36.3	−5 54	2.75	−0.21	O9 III	~1.4	−6.5	2000	0.001	108	+22 SB2	B: 7.3, B7 IIIp (He wk), 11.6″, PA:134°→141°, 1779→2012	
ε Ori	5 37.1	−1 12	1.69	−0.18	B0 Ia	2	−7.2	2000	0.002	118	+26 SB		**Alnilam**
ζ Tau	5 38.7	+21 09	2.97v	−0.15	B2 IIIpe (shell)	7	−2.7	400	0.020	175	+20 SB	ecl., var.: 2.88–3.17, 133 d; B: 5.0, 0.007″	
α Col A	5 40.3	−34 04	2.65	−0.12	B7 IV	12	−1.9	260	0.025	176	+35 V?		Phact
ζ Ori A	5 41.6	−1 56	1.74	−0.20	O9.5 Ib	4	−5.0	700	0.005	58	+18 SB	B: 4.2, B0 III, 2.4″, PA:152°→167°, 1822→2013	Alnitak
κ Ori	5 48.6	−9 40	2.07	−0.17	B0.5 Ia	5	−4.4	600	0.002	131	+21 V?		Saiph
β Col	5 51.6	−35 46	3.12	1.15	K1.5 III	37.4	1.0	87	0.408	8	+89 V		Wazn
α Ori	5 56.1	+7 25	0.45v	1.50	M2 Iab	7	−5.5	500	0.030	68	+21 SB	semiregular var.: 0.0–1.3	**Betelgeuse**
β Aur	6 00.8	+44 57	1.90v	0.08	A1 IV	~40.2	−0.1	81	0.056	269	−18 SB2	ecl.: 1.89–1.98, 4.0 d (mags. equal)	Menkalinan
θ Aur AB	6 00.9	+37 13	2.65	−0.08	A0p II: (Si)	~19.7	−0.9	166	~0.086	~149	+30 SB	B: 7.2, G2 V, 4.0″, PA:7°→304°, 1871→2014	
η Gem	6 15.9	+22 30	3.31v	1.60	M3 III	8	−2.0	400	~0.064	~259	+19 SB	ecl., var.: 3.2–3.9, 233 d; B: 6.2, 1.7″ (2012)	Propus
ζ CMa	6 21.0	−30 04	3.02	−0.16	B2.5 V	9.0	−2.2	360	0.008	61	+32 SB		Furud

TABLE OF BRIGHTEST STARS (continued)

Star Name	RA (2017.5) h m	Dec ° ′	m_V	$B-V$	MK Type	π mas	M_V	*D* ly	μ ″/y	PA °	V_{rad} km/s	Remarks	
β CMa	6 23.5	−17 58	1.98v	−0.24	B1 II–III	7	−3.9	~490	0.003	256	+34 SB	var.: 1.93–2.00, 0.25 d	Mirzam
μ Gem	6 24.0	+22 30	2.87v	1.62	M3 IIIab	14	−1.4	230	0.124	153	+55 V?	irregular var.: 2.75–3.02	Tejat (T. Posterior)
α Car	6 24.3	−52 42	−0.62	0.16	A9 Ib	11	−5.5	~310	0.031	41	+21		**Canopus**
ν Pup	6 38.3	−43 13	3.17	−0.10	B8 IIIn	9	−2.1	370	0.004	186	+28 SB		
γ Gem	6 38.7	+16 23	1.93	0.00	A1 IVs	30	−0.7	110	0.057	166	−13 SB		Alhena
ε Gem	6 45.0	+25 07	3.06	1.38	G8 Ib	4	−4.0	800	0.014	204	+10 SB		Mebsuta
α CMa A	6 45.9	−16 44	−1.44	0.01	A0mA1 Va	~379	1.5	8.6	~1.339	~204	−8 SB	B: 8.5, WDA; 9,6″ (2013) ; orbit 50.1 y	**Sirius**
ξ Gem	6 46.3	+12 53	3.35	0.44	F5 IV	56	2.1	58.7	0.223	211	+25 V?		Alzirr
α Pic	6 48.4	−61 58	3.24	0.22	A6 Vn	~34	0.9	100	0.252	345	+21		
τ Pup	6 50.4	−50 38	2.94	1.21	K1 III	18	−0.8	180	0.077	154	+36 SB		
ε CMa A	6 59.3	−29 00	1.50	−0.21	B2 II	8.0	−4.0	410	0.004	68	+27		**Adhara**
ο² CMa	7 03.8	−23 52	3.02	−0.08	B3 Ia	1	−6.6	3000	0.004	329	+48 SB		
δ CMa	7 09.1	−26 25	1.83	0.67	F8 Ia	2	−6.6	2000	0.005	317	+34 SB		Wezen
π Pup	7 17.8	−37 08	2.71	1.62	K3 Ib	4	−4.3	800	0.012	303	+16		
η CMa	7 24.8	−29 20	2.45	−0.08	B5 Ia	2	−6.5	2000	0.007	325	+41 V		Aludra
β CMi	7 28.1	+8 15	2.89	−0.10	B8 V	~20.2	−0.6	~162	0.064	234	+22 SB		Gomeisa
σ Pup A	7 29.8	−43 20	3.25	1.51	K5 III	17	−0.6	190	0.198	342	+88 SB	B: 8.6, G5: V, 21.5″, PA:90°→73°, 1826→2011	
α Gem A	7 35.7	+31 51	1.93	0.03	A1mA2 Va	63	0.9	52	~0.254	~234	+6 SB	orbit 445 y; max = 6.5″, in 1880;	
α Gem B	7 35.7	+31 51	2.97	0.03	A2mA5 V:	63	2.0	52	~0.254	~234	−1 SB	min = 1.8″, in 1965; 5.2″ (2015)	Castor
α CMi A	7 40.2	+5 11	0.40	0.43	F5 IV–V	285	2.7	11.5	~1.259	~215	−3 SB	B: 10.3, WD; 3.8″ (2014); orbit 41 y	**Procyon**
β Gem	7 46.4	+27 59	1.16	0.99	K0 IIIb	97	1.1	33.8	0.628	266	+3 V	exoplanet	**Pollux**
ξ Pup	7 50.0	−24 54	3.34	1.22	G6 Iab–Ib	3	−4.5	1200	0.005	260	+3 SB		Asmidiske
χ Car	7 57.2	−53 02	3.46	−0.18	B3 IVp	7	−2.3	500	0.035	304	+19 V	Si II strong	
ζ Pup	8 04.2	−40 03	2.21	−0.27	O5 Iafn	3.0	−5.4	1080	0.034	299	−24 V?		Naos
ρ Pup	8 08.3	−24 21	2.83v	0.46	F2mF5 II: (var)	51.3	1.4	64	0.095	299	+46 SB	d Del spec.; var.: 2.68–2.87, 0.14 d	
γ² Vel	8 10.1	−47 23	1.75v	−0.14	WC8 + O9 I:	3	−5.9	1100	0.012	330	+35 SB2	var.: 1.81–1.87	Regor (Al Suhail al Muhlif)
ε Car	8 22.9	−59 34	1.86v	1.20	K3:III + B2:V	5	−4.5	600	0.034	311	+2	ecl.?: 1.82–1.94	**Avior**
ο UMa A	8 31.7	+60 39	3.35v?	0.86	G5 III	~18.2	−0.3	~179	0.172	231	+20	var.?: 3.30?–3.36?	
δ Vel AB	8 45.2	−54 46	1.93	0.04	A1 Va	40	0.0	81	~0.107	~164	+ 2 V?	B: 5.0, 0.4″, PA:177°→263°, 1894→2013	Koo She
ε Hya ABC	8 47.7	+6 21	3.38	0.68	G5:III + A:	25	0.4	130	~0.232	~259	+36 SB	composite A: 3.8; B: 4.7, 0.3″ (2014); C: 7.8, 2.9″	
ζ Hya	8 56.3	+5 53	3.11	0.98	G9 II–III	~19.5	−0.4	~167	0.101	279	+23		
ι UMa A	9 00.4	+47 58	3.12	0.22	A7 IVn	~68.9	2.3	47.3	~0.491	~244	+9 SB	BC: 10.8, M1 V, 2.4″, PA:349°→82°, 1831→2012	Talitha
λ Vel	9 08.6	−43 30	2.23v	1.66	K4 Ib–IIa	6.0	−3.9	540	0.028	299	+18	var.: 2.14–2.30	Al **Suhail** al Wazn
a Car	9 11.4	−59 02	3.43v	−0.19	B2 IV–V	7	−2.3	500	0.022	312	+23 SB2	ecl.?: 3.41–3.44	HR 3659
β Car	9 13.4	−69 47	1.67	0.07	A1 III	28.8	−1.0	113	0.191	305	−5 V?		**Miaplacidus**
ι Car	9 17.6	−59 21	2.21v	0.19	A7 Ib	4.3	−4.6	800	0.022	302	+13	var.: 2.23–2.28	Aspidiske (Scutulum, Turais)

TABLE OF BRIGHTEST STARS (continued)

Star Name	RA (2017.5) h m	Dec ° ′	m_V	$B-V$	MK Type	π mas	M_V	D ly	μ ″/y	PA °	V_{rad} km/s	Remarks
α Lyn	9 22.1	+34 19	3.14	1.55	K7 IIIab	16	−0.8	~203	0.224	274	+38	
κ Vel	9 22.7	−55 05	2.47	−0.14	B2 IV–V	6	−3.8	600	0.016	315	+22 SB	
α Hya	9 28.4	−8 44	1.99	1.44	K3 II–III	18	−1.7	180	0.038	336	−4 V?	**Alphard**
N Vel	9 31.8	−57 07	3.16	1.54	K5 III	13.6	−1.2	240	0.033	280	−14	HR 3803
θ UMa	9 34.0	+51 36	3.17	0.48	F6 IV	74.2	2.5	44.0	1.088	241	+15 SB	
ε Leo	9 46.8	+23 42	2.97	0.81	G1 II	13.2	−1.4	250	0.047	259	+4 V?	Ras Elased Australis
υ Car AB	9 47.5	−65 09	2.92	0.29	A6 II	2.3	−5.3	~1400	0.028	307	+14	A: 3.01; B: 5.99, B7 III, 5.0″, PA:126°→126°, 1836→2010
η Leo	10 08.3	+16 41	3.48	−0.03	A0 Ib	3	−4.5	1300	~0.003	n.a.	+3 V	B: 4.5, 0.1″, PA:84°→309°, 1937→1993
α Leo A	10 09.3	+11 53	1.36	−0.09	B7 Vn	41	−0.6	79	0.249	271	+6 SB	**Regulus**
ω Car	10 14.2	−70 08	3.29	−0.07	B8 IIIn	9.5	−1.8	340	0.037	281	+7 V	
ζ Leo	10 17.7	+23 20	3.43	0.31	F0 IIIa	12	−1.2	270	0.020	110	−16 SB	Adhafera
q Car	10 17.7	−61 25	3.39v	1.54	K3 IIa	5.0	−3.1	660	0.026	286	+8	irregular var.: 3.36–3.44 HR 4050
λ UMa	10 18.1	+42 50	3.45	0.03	A1 IV	24	0.3	140	0.186	256	+18 V	Tania Borealis
γ Leo A	10 20.9	+19 45	2.61	1.13	K1 IIIb Fe–0.5	26	−0.3	130	~0.333	~118	−37 SB	[(has exoplanet) 4.3″ (2012); orbit 510.3 y;
γ Leo B	10 20.9	+19 45	3.16	1.42	G7 III Fe–1	26	0.2	130	~0.346	~118	−36 V	max = ~5″, around 2100 Algieba
μ UMa	10 23.4	+41 25	3.06	1.60	M0 IIIp	14	−1.2	230	0.089	293	−21 SB	Ca II emission Tania Australis
p Car	10 32.6	−61 47	3.30v	−0.09	B4 Vne	7	−2.6	500	0.021	304	+26	irregular var.: 3.27–3.37 HR 4140
θ Car	10 43.6	−64 29	2.74	−0.22	B0.5 Vp	7	−3.0	460	0.022	303	+24 SB	nitrogen enhanced
μ Vel AB	10 47.5	−49 31	2.69	1.07	G5 III + F8:V	28	−0.1	~117	0.083	131	+6 SB	A: 2.72; B: 5.92, 2.3″, PA:55°→57°, 1880→2014
β UMa	11 02.9	+56 17	2.34	0.03	A0mA1 IV–V	~40.9	0.4	80	0.088	68	−12 SB	Merak
α UMa AB	11 04.8	+61 39	1.81	1.06	K0 IIIa	27	−1.1	120	0.139	255	−9 SB	A: 1.86; B: 4.8, A8 V, 0.7″ (2013) **Dubhe**
ψ UMa	11 10.6	+44 24	3.00	1.14	K1 III	22.6	−0.2	145	0.068	246	−4 V?	
δ Leo	11 15.0	+20 26	2.56	0.13	A4 IV	56	1.3	58	0.193	132	−20 V	Zosma
θ Leo	11 15.2	+15 20	3.33	0.00	A2 IV	~19.8	−0.2	165	0.099	217	+8 V	(K-line var.) Chertan (Chort, Coxa)
λ Cen	11 36.6	−63 07	3.11	−0.04	B9.5 IIn	8	−2.4	400	0.034	258	−1 V	
β Leo	11 50.0	+14 28	2.14	0.09	A3 Va	91	1.9	36	0.511	257	0 V	**Denebola**
γ UMa	11 54.7	+53 36	2.41	0.04	A0 Van	39	0.4	83	0.108	84	−13 SB	Phecda
δ Cen	12 09.3	−50 49	2.58v	−0.13	B2 IVne	8	−2.9	400	0.050	262	+11 V	irregular var.: 2.51–2.65
ε Crv	12 11.0	−22 43	3.02	1.33	K2 III	~10.3	−1.9	320	0.072	278	+5	Minkar
δ Cru	12 16.1	−58 51	2.79v	−0.19	B2 IV	9.4	−2.3	350	0.037	254	+22 V?	var.: 2.78–2.84, 0.15 d
δ UMa	12 16.3	+56 56	3.32	0.08	A2 Van	40.5	1.4	81	0.104	86	−13 V	Megrez
γ Crv	12 16.7	−17 38	2.58	−0.11	B8 III	21	−0.8	154	0.160	278	−4 SB	sp. var.? **Gienah** Ghurab
α Cru A	12 27.6	−63 12	1.25	−0.20	B0.5 IV	10	−3.7	~320	0.037	251	−11 SB	[5.4″ (1826); 3.9″ (2015) **Acrux A**
α Cru B	12 27.6	−63 12	1.64	−0.18	B1 Vn	10	−3.3	~320	0.037?	251?	−1	PA: 114°→112°, 1826→2015 Acrux B
δ Crv A	12 30.8	−16 37	2.94	−0.01	B9.5 IVn	~37.6	0.8	87	0.252	237	+9 V	B:8.26, K2 V, 24.6″, PA: 216°→213°, 1782→2012 Algorab
γ Cru	12 32.1	−57 13	1.59v	1.60	M3.5 III	37	−0.6	89	0.267	174	+21	var.: 1.60–1.67 **Gacrux**

TABLE OF BRIGHTEST STARS (continued)

Star Name	RA (2017.5) h m	Dec ° ′	m_V	$B-V$	MK Type	π mas	M_V	D ly	μ ″/y	PA °	V_{rad} km/s	Remarks	
β Crv	12 35.3	−23 30	2.65	0.89	G5 II	22	−0.6	146	0.057	179	−8 V		Kraz
α Mus	12 38.2	−69 14	2.69v	−0.18	B2 IV–V	10.3	−2.2	320	0.042	252	+13 V	var.: 2.68–2.73, 0.090 d	
γ Cen A	12 42.5	−49 03	2.95	−0.02	A1 IV	25	−0.1	130	~0.194	~267	−6	[orbit 84 y; min = 0.2″ ; 0.4″ (2010)	
γ Cen B	12 42.5	−49 03	2.85	−0.02	A0 IV	25	−0.2	130	~0.194	~267	−6	0.2″ (2014) max = 1.7″	
γ Vir AB	12 42.5	−1 33	2.74	0.37	F1 V + F0mF2 V	85	2.4	39	~0.619	~276	−20	A: 3.48; B: 3.50; 0.8″ (2007); 2.3″ (2015)	Porrima
β Mus AB	12 47.4	−68 12	3.04	−0.18	B2 V + B2.5 V	~9.6	−2.1	340	~0.043	~258	+42 V	A: 3.51; B: 4.00, 1.0″, PA:317°→52°, 1880→2015	
β Cru	12 48.8	−59 47	1.25v	−0.24	B0.5 III	12	−3.4	300	0.046	249	+16 SB	var.: 1.23–1.31, 0.24 d	Mimosa (Becrux)
ε UMa	12 54.8	+55 52	1.76v	−0.02	A0p IV: (CrEu)	~39.5	−0.3	83	0.112	94	−9 SB?	var.: 1.76–1.78, 5.1 d	**Alioth**
δ Vir	12 56.5	+3 18	3.39	1.57	M3 III	16	−0.5	~198	0.473	264	−18 V?		Auva
α² CVn A	12 56.8	+38 13	2.85	−0.06	A0p (SiEu)	28	0.1	110	0.241	283	−3 V	B:5.6, F0 V, 19.3″, PA:234°→227°, 1777→2015	Cor Caroli
ε Vir	13 03.0	+10 52	2.85	0.93	G9 IIIab	29.8	0.2	110	0.275	274	−14 V?		Vindemiatrix
γ Hya	13 19.9	−23 16	2.99	0.92	G8 IIIa	~24.4	−0.1	134	0.081	121	−5 V?		
ι Cen	13 21.6	−36 48	2.75	0.07	A2 Va	55	1.5	59	0.352	256	0		
ζ UMa A	13 24.6	+54 50	2.23	0.06	A1 Va	40	0.1	90	0.123	100	−6 SB2	B:3.94, A1mA7 IV–V, 14.7″; period ≥ 5000 y?	Mizar
α Vir	13 26.1	−11 15	0.98v	−0.24	B1 V	13	−3.4	250	0.052	234	+1 SB2	var.: 0.95–1.05, 4.0 d; mult. 3.1, 4.5, 7.5	**Spica**
ζ Vir	13 35.6	−0 41	3.38	0.11	A2 IV	44	1.6	74	0.285	280	−13		Heze
ε Cen	13 41.0	−53 33	2.29	−0.17	B1 III	8	−3.3	400	0.019	233	+3		
η UMa	13 48.2	+49 14	1.85	−0.10	B3 V	31	−0.7	104	0.122	263	−11 SB?		**Alkaid**
ν Cen	13 50.6	−41 46	3.41	−0.22	B2 IV	~7.5	−2.2	440	0.034	233	+9 SB		
μ Cen	13 50.7	−42 34	3.47v	−0.17	B2 IV–V pne	~6.4	−2.5	510	0.031	232	+9 SB	variable shell: 2.92–3.47	
η Boo	13 55.5	+18 19	2.68	0.58	G0 IV	88	2.4	37	0.361	190	0 SB		Muphrid
ζ Cen	13 56.6	−47 22	2.55	−0.18	B2.5 IV	8.5	−2.8	380	0.073	232	+7 SB2		
β Cen AB	14 05.1	−60 27	0.58v	−0.23	B1 III	8	−4.8	400	0.041	235	+6 SB	B:3.94, A1mA7 IV–V, 0.4″; period 1500 y?	**Hadar**
π Hya	14 07.4	−26 46	3.25	1.09	K2 IIIb	~32.3	0.8	101	0.148	163	+27 V		
θ Cen	14 07.7	−36 27	2.06	1.01	K0 IIIb	55	0.8	59	0.734	225	+1		**Menkent**
α Boo	14 16.5	+19 06	−0.05	1.24	K1.5 III Fe–0.5	89	−0.3	37	2.279	209	−5 V	high space velocity	**Arcturus**
γ Boo	14 32.8	+38 14	3.04	0.19	A7 IV+	37.6	0.9	87	0.190	323	−37 V		Seginus
η Cen	14 36.6	−42 14	2.33v	−0.16	B1.5 IV pne	11	−2.5	310	0.048	227	0 SB	variable shell: 2.30–2.41	
α Cen B	14 40.8	−60 54	1.35	0.9	K1 V	750	5.7	4.3	~3.703	~283	−21 V?	[AB 7″; orbit 79.9 y; min = 2″ (1955); max 22″	
α Cen A	14 40.8	−60 54	−0.01	0.71	G2 V	750	4.4	4.3	~3.710	~277	−22 SB	C: Proxima, 12.4, M5e, 2.2°	**Rigil Kentaurus**
α Lup	14 43.1	−47 28	2.30v	−0.15	B1.5 III	7	−3.5	460	0.032	221	+5 SB	var.: 2.29–2.34, 0.26 d	
α Cir	14 43.9	−65 03	3.18	0.26	A7p (Sr)	60.4	2.1	54.1	0.303	220	+7 SB?	B: 8.6, K5 V, 15.4″, PA:263°→226°, 1826→2013	
ε Boo AB	14 45.8	+27 00	2.35	1.34	K0 II–III+A0 V	16	−1.6	200	0.044	288	−17 V	A:2.50; B:4.66, 2.9″, PA:318°→343°,1822→2010	Izar
β UMi	14 50.7	+74 05	2.07	1.46	K4 III	24.9	−0.9	131	0.035	289	+17 V	exoplanet	**Kochab**
α² Lib	14 51.8	−16 07	2.75	0.15	A3 III–IV	43	0.9	76	0.126	237	−10 SB		**Zubenelgenubi**
β Lup	14 59.7	−43 12	2.68	−0.18	B2 IV	9	−2.7	380	0.054	222	0 SB		

TABLE OF BRIGHTEST STARS (continued)

Star Name	RA (2017.5) h m	Dec ° ′	m_V	$B-V$	MK Type	π mas	M_V	D ly	μ ″/y	PA °	V_{rad} km/s	Remarks	
κ Cen	15 00.3	−42 10	3.13	−0.21	B2 V	9	−2.2	400	0.029	218	+8 SB		
σ Lib	15 05.1	−25 21	3.25v	1.67	M2.5 III	11	−1.5	290	0.083	239	−4	semiregular var.: 3.20–3.46	Brachium
ζ Lup	15 13.6	−52 10	3.41	0.92	G8 III	~27.8	0.6	117	0.133	238	−10		
δ Boo	15 16.2	+33 15	3.46	0.96	G8 III Fe–1	~26.8	0.6	122	0.140	143	−12 SB		
β Lib	15 18.0	−9 27	2.61	−0.07	B8 IIIn	~17.6	−1.2	190	0.100	259	−35 SB		Zubeneschamali
γ TrA	15 20.6	−68 45	2.87	0.01	A1 IIIn	17.7	−0.9	184	0.074	244	−3 V		
γ UMi	15 20.7	+71 46	3.00	0.06	A3 III	6.7	−2.9	490	0.025	315	−4 V		Pherkad
δ Lup	15 22.5	−40 43	3.22	−0.23	B1.5 IVn	4	−3.9	900	0.032	218	0 V?		
ε Lup AB	15 23.9	−44 45	3.37	−0.19	B2 IV–V	6	−2.6	500	~0.030	~230	+8 SB2	A: 3.56; B: 5.04, 0.2″, PA:285°→95°, 1883→2014	
ι Dra	15 25.3	+58 54	3.29	1.17	K2 III	32.2	0.8	101	0.019	334	−11	exoplanet	Edasich
α CrB	15 35.4	+26 39	2.22v	0.03	A0 IV (composite)	43	0.4	75	0.150	127	+2 SB	ecl.: 2.21–2.32, 17 d	**Alphecca**
γ Lup AB	15 36.3	−41 13	2.80	−0.22	B2 IVn	8	−2.8	400	~0.030	~212	+2 V	A: 3.5; B: 3.6, 0.8″ (2015) ; similar spectra	
α Ser	15 45.1	+6 22	2.63v?	1.17	K2 IIIb CN1	44	0.9	74	0.141	71	+3 V?	var.?	Unukalhai (Cor Serpentis)
β TrA	15 56.7	−63 29	2.83	0.32	F0 IV	~80.8	2.4	40.4	0.444	205	0		
π Sco A	15 59.9	−26 10	2.89	−0.18	B1 V + B2 V	6	−3.4	600	0.029	203	−3 SB2	A: occ. bin.: 3.4 + 4.5, 0.0003″ sep.	
T CrB	16 00.2	+25 52	10.08v	1.34	gM3: + Bep	–	0.6	2500?	0.011	329	−29 SB	recurrent nova 1866 (mag. 3), 1946 (mag. 2)	
η Lup A	16 01.3	−38 27	3.42	−0.21	B2.5 IVn	7	−2.2	440	0.033	211	+8 V	A: 3.47; B: 7.70, 15.0″, PA:22°→19°, 1834→2013	
δ Sco AB	16 01.4	−22 40	2.29	−0.12	B0.2 IVe (shell)	7	−3.6	500	~0.037	~196	−7 SB	AB: sep. < 1″; C: 4.9, B2 IV–V, 8°	Dschubba
β Sco AB	16 06.5	−19 51	2.56	−0.06	B0.5 V	8	−2.9	400	0.025	192	−1 SB	A: 2.78; B: 5.04, ~0.3″; C: 4.93, 14″	Graffias
δ Oph	16 15.3	−3 44	2.73	1.58	M1 III	~19.1	−0.9	171	0.150	198	−20 V		Yed Prior
ε Oph	16 19.2	−4 44	3.23	0.97	G9.5 IIIb	31	0.7	106	0.093	64	−10 V		Yed Posterior
σ Sco A	16 22.3	−25 38	2.91v	0.13	B1 III	5	−3.7	700	0.019	213	+3 SB	var.: 2.86–2.94, 0.25 d; B: 8.3, B9 V, 20.0″ (2013)	
η Dra A	16 24.2	+61 28	2.73	0.91	G8 IIIab	35.4	0.5	92	0.059	343	−14 SB?	B: 8.7, 4.8″, PA:150°→139°, 1843→1996	
α Sco A	16 30.5	−26 28	1.06v	1.86	M1.5 Iab	6	−5.1	600	0.026	207	−3 SB	irregular var.: 0.88–1.16; B: 5.37, 2.5″	**Antares**
β Her	16 31.0	+21 27	2.78	0.95	G7 IIIa	23	−0.4	140	0.100	261	−26 SB		Kornephoros
τ Sco	16 37.0	−28 15	2.82	−0.21	B0 V	7	−3.0	500	0.025	203	+2 V		
ζ Oph	16 38.1	−10 36	2.54	0.04	O9.5 Vn	9	−2.7	370	0.029	32	−15 V		
ζ Her AB	16 41.9	+31 34	2.81	0.65	G1 IV	93	2.7	35	~0.575	~307	−70 SB	A: 2.90; B: 5.53, G7 V, 1.3″ (2010), orbit 34 y	
η Her	16 43.5	+38 53	3.48	0.92	G7.5 IIIb Fe–1	30.0	0.9	109	0.092	157	+8 V?		
α TrA	16 50.5	−69 03	1.91	1.45	K2 IIB–IIIA	~8.4	−3.5	390	0.036	150	−3		**Atria**
ε Sco	16 51.3	−34 19	2.29	1.14	K2 III	51	0.8	64	0.666	247	−3		
μ^1 Sco	16 53.1	−38 05	3.00v	−0.20	B1.5 IVn	7	−2.9	500	0.024	206	−25 SB2	ecl.: 2.94–3.22, 1.4 d	
κ Oph	16 58.5	+9 21	3.19	1.16	K2 III	36	1.0	91	0.292	268	−56 V		
ζ Ara	17 00.1	−56 01	3.12	1.55	K4 III	7	−2.7	490	0.041	206	−6		
ζ Dra	17 08.8	+65 42	3.17	−0.12	B6 III	10	−1.8	330	0.028	314	−17 V		Aldhibah
η Oph AB	17 11.4	−15 45	2.43	0.06	A2.5 Va	37	0.3	90	~0.107	~22	−1 SB	A: 3.0; B: 3.5, A3 V, 0.6″ (2014), orbit 87.6 y	**Sabik**

TABLE OF BRIGHTEST STARS (continued)

Star Name	RA (2017.5) h m	Dec ° ′	m_V	$B-V$	MK Type	π mas	M_V	D ly	μ ″/y	PA °	V_{rad} km/s	Remarks	
η Sco	17 13.4	−43 16	3.32	0.44	F2 V:p (Cr)	~44.4	1.6	73	0.290	175	−28		
α Her AB	17 15.4	+14 22	2.78v	1.16	M5 Ib–II	9	−2.4	400	0.032	347	−33 V	semiregular var.: 2.7–4.0; B: 5.4, 4.7″	Rasalgethi
π Her	17 15.7	+36 47	3.16	1.44	K3 IIab	8.7	−2.2	380	0.027	276	−26 V?		
δ Her	17 15.8	+24 49	3.12	0.08	A1 Vann	43.4	1.3	75	~0.158	~188	−40 SB	B: 8.8, 12.7″, PA:163°→288°, 1779→2013	Sarin
θ Oph	17 23.1	−25 01	3.27v	−0.19	B2 IV	~7.5	−2.4	440	0.025	197	−2 SB	occ. bin.: 3.4, 5.4; var.: 3.25–3.31, 0.14 d	
β Ara	17 26.8	−55 33	2.84	1.48	K3 Ib–IIa	5	−3.6	600	0.027	199	0		
γ Ara A	17 26.9	−56 24	3.31	−0.15	B1 Ib	~2.9	−4.4	1100	0.016	182	−3 V	broad lines for Ib; B:10.0,18.1″, PA:324°→326°, 1835→2008	
β Dra A	17 30.8	+52 17	2.79	0.95	G2 Ib–IIa	8.6	−2.5	380	0.020	308	−20 V	B: 11.5, 4.4″, PA:13°→12°, 1889→1934	Rastaban
υ Sco	17 32.0	−37 18	2.70	−0.18	B2 IV	6	−3.5	600	0.030	185	+8 SB		
α Ara	17 33.2	−49 53	2.84	−0.14	B2 Vne	12	−1.7	300	0.075	206	0 SB		
λ Sco	17 34.8	−37 07	1.62v	−0.23	B1.5 IV	6	−4.6	600	0.032	195	−3 SB2	ecl.?, var: 1.62−1.68, 0.21 d	**Shaula**
α Oph	17 35.7	+12 33	2.08	0.16	A5 Vnn	67	1.2	49	0.247	154	+13 SB?		**Rasalhague**
θ Sco	17 38.6	−43 00	1.86	0.41	F1 III	~11	−3.0	300	0.006	119	+1		Girtab (Sargas)
κ Sco	17 43.7	−39 02	2.39v	−0.17	B1.5 III	7	−3.5	480	0.026	193	−14 SB	var.: 2.41–2.42, 0.20 d	
β Oph	17 44.3	+4 34	2.76	1.17	K2 III	~39.8	0.8	82	0.165	345	−12 V		Cebalrai
μ Her A	17 47.1	+27 43	3.42	0.75	G5 IV	~120.3	3.8	27.1	0.804	201	−16 V	BC: 9.78, 34.9″, PA:240°→249°, 1781→2010	
ι^1 Sco	17 48.8	−40 08	2.99	0.51	F2 Ia	2	−5.9	2000	0.006	180	−28SB		
G Sco	17 51.0	−37 03	3.19	1.19	K2 III	25.9	0.3	126	0.049	56	+25		HR 6630
γ Dra	17 57.0	+51 29	2.24	1.52	K5 III	21.1	−1.1	154	0.024	200	−28		**Eltanin**
ν Oph	18 00.0	−9 46	3.32	0.99	G9.5 IIIa	22	0.0	150	0.117	185	+13	2 exoplanets	
γ^2 Sgr	18 06.9	−30 25	2.98	0.98	K0 III	34	0.6	97	0.189	197	+22 SB		Nash
η Sgr A	18 18.8	−36 45	3.10v	1.5	M3.5 IIIab	22	−0.2	~146	0.211	218	+1 V?	irreg. var.: 3.05–3.12; B: 8.33, G8: IV:, 3.6″ (2010)	
δ Sgr	18 22.1	−29 49	2.72	1.38	K2.5 IIIa	9	−2.4	350	0.041	128	−20 V?		Kaus Meridionalis
η Ser	18 22.2	−2 54	3.23	0.94	K0 III–IV	54	1.9	~60.5	0.890	218	+9 V?		
ε Sgr	18 25.3	−34 22	1.79	−0.03	A0 II:n (shell?)	23	−1.4	~143	0.130	198	−15		**Kaus Australis**
λ Sgr	18 29.0	−25 25	2.82	1.02	K1 IIIb	~41.7	0.9	78	0.191	194	−43 V?		Kaus Borealis
α Lyr	18 37.5	+38 48	0.03	0.00	A0 Va	130	0.6	25.0	0.350	35	−14 V	protoplanetary debris?	**Vega**
φ Sgr	18 46.7	−26 58	3.17	−0.11	B8 III	14	−1.2	240	0.051	89	+22 SB	similar optical(?) companion, 0.1″	
σ Sgr	18 56.4	−26 16	2.05	−0.13	B3 IV	14	−2.2	230	0.056	164	−11V		**Nunki**
γ Lyr	18 59.6	+32 43	3.25	−0.05	B9 II	5	−3.1	600	0.003	290	−21 V		Sulafat
ζ Sgr AB	19 03.7	−29 51	2.60	0.06	A2 IV–V + A4:V:	37	0.4	90	n.a.	n.a.	+22 SB	A: 3.2; B: 3.5, 0.6″ (2014), orbit 21.1 y	Ascella
ζ Aql A	19 06.2	+13 53	2.99	0.01	A0 Vann	~39.3	1.0	83	0.096	184	−25 SB		
λ Aql	19 07.2	−4 51	3.43	−0.10	B9 Vnp (kB7HeA0)	26	0.5	120	0.093	192	−12 V		
τ Sgr	19 08.0	−27 39	3.32	1.17	K1.5 IIIb	27	0.5	120	0.255	191	+45 SB		
π Sgr ABC	19 10.8	−21 00	2.88	0.38	F2 II–III	6	−3.1	500	0.036	182	−10	A: 3.7; B: 3.8 0.1″ (1989); C: 6.0, AB–CD<1″?	Albaldah
δ Dra	19 12.6	+67 42	3.07	0.99	G9 III	33.5	0.7	97	0.133	46	+25 V		Nodus Secundus

TABLE OF BRIGHTEST STARS (continued)

Star Name	RA (2017.5) h m	Dec ° ′	m_V	$B-V$	MK Type	π mas	M_V	D ly	μ ″/y	PA °	V_{rad} km/s	Remarks	
δ Aql	19 26.4	+3 09	3.36	0.32	F2 IV	64	2.4	51	0.268	72	−30 SB		Deneb Okab
β Cyg A	19 31.4	+28 00	3.36	1.09	K3 II + B9.5 V	8	−2.3	430	0.009	229	−24 V	B: 5.11, 35″; Aa, Ac: Δm = 1.5, 0.4″	Albireo
δ Cyg AB	19 45.5	+45 10	2.86	0.00	B9.5 III	20	−0.7	160	~0.066	~42	−20 SB	B: 6.4, F1 V; 2.7″, PA:41°→217°, 1826→2015	
γ Aql	19 47.1	+10 39	2.72	1.51	K3 II	~8.3	−2.7	390	0.017	100	−2 V		Tarazed
α Aql	19 51.6	+8 55	0.76	0.22	A7 Vnn	195	2.2	16.7	0.660	54	−26		**Altair**
θ Aql	20 12.2	−0 46	3.24	−0.07	B9.5 III	11	−1.5	290	0.036	81	−27 SB2		
β Cap A	20 22.0	−14 44	3.05	0.79	K0: II: + A5: V:n	10	−2.0	300	0.046	81	−19 SB	A: mult.: 4.0 + 4.3 + 4.8 + 6.7, <1″	Dabih
γ Cyg	20 22.9	+40 19	2.23	0.67	F8 Ib	2	−6.5	2000	0.003	111	−8 V		Sadr
α Pav	20 27.0	−56 41	1.94	−0.12	B2.5 V	18	−1.8	180	0.086	175	+2 SB		**Peacock**
α Ind	20 38.8	−47 14	3.11	1.00	K0 III CN−1	33	0.7	98	0.083	37	−1		
α Cyg	20 42.0	+45 21	1.25	0.09	A2 Ia	2	−6.9	~1400	0.003	47	−5 SB		**Deneb**
η Cep	20 45.6	+61 54	3.41	0.91	K0 IV	70.1	2.6	46.5	0.823	6	−87		
β Pav	20 46.5	−66 08	3.42	0.16	A6 IV	~24.1	0.3	135	0.044	283	+10		
ε Cyg	20 46.9	+34 02	2.48	1.02	K0 III	44.9	0.7	73	0.486	47	−11 SB?	B: optical; C: shared p-motion, 78″	Gienah
ζ Cyg	21 13.7	+30 18	3.21	0.99	G8 IIIa Ba 0.5	23	0.0	140	0.069	175	+17 SB		
α Cep	21 19.0	+62 40	2.45	0.26	A7 Van	66.5	1.6	49.1	0.158	72	−10 V		Alderamin
β Cep	21 28.9	+70 38	3.23v	−0.20	B1 III	5	−3.4	700	0.015	56	−8 SB	var.: 3.16–3.27, 0.19 d; B: 7.8;14.1″ (2013)	Alfirk
β Aqr	21 32.5	−5 30	2.9	0.83	G0 Ib	6	−3.2	500	0.020	114	+7 V?		Sadalsuud
ε Peg	21 45.0	+9 57	2.38v	1.52	K2 Ib	5	−4.2	700	0.027	89	+5 V	irregular var.: 0.7–3.5 (flare in 1972)	**Enif**
δ Cap	21 48.0	−16 03	2.85v	0.18	A3mF2 IV:	84	2.5	38.7	0.396	139	−6 SB	occ. bin.: 2.81–3.05, 1.0 d, 3.2 + 5.2	
γ Gru	21 55.0	−37 17	3.00	−0.08	B8 IV–Vs	15	−1.1	210	0.099	98	−2 V?		
α Aqr	22 06.7	−0 14	2.95	0.97	G2 Ib	6	−3.1	~520	0.021	117	+8 V?		Sadalmelik
α Gru	22 09.3	−46 53	1.73	−0.07	B7 Vn	32	−0.7	101	0.194	139	+12		**Al Na'ir**
ζ Cep	22 11.5	+58 17	3.39	1.56	K1.5 Ib	3.9	−3.7	800	0.014	69	−18 SB		
α Tuc	22 19.7	−60 10	2.87	1.39	K3 III	16	−1.1	200	0.081	241	+42 SB		
ζ Peg	22 42.3	+10 55	3.41	−0.09	B8.5 III	16	−0.6	210	0.078	98	+7 V?		Homam
β Gru	22 43.7	−46 48	2.07v	1.61	M5 III	18	−1.6	180	0.135	92	+2	irregular var.: 2.0–2.3	
η Peg	22 43.8	+30 19	2.93	0.85	G8 II + F0 V	15	−1.2	210	0.029	153	+4 SB		Matar
δ Aqr	22 55.6	−15 44	3.27	0.07	A3 IV–V	20	−0.2	160	0.051	237	+18 V	(wk λ4481)	Skat
α PsA	22 58.6	−29 32	1.17	0.14	A3 Va	130	1.7	25.1	0.368	117	+7	imaged exoplanet	**Fomalhaut**
β Peg	23 04.6	+28 11	2.44v	1.66	M2 II–III	16.6	−1.5	~196	0.232	54	+9 V	irregular var.: 2.31–2.74	Scheat
α Peg	23 05.6	+15 18	2.49	0.00	A0 III–IV	24	−0.6	133	0.073	124	−4 SB		**Markab**
γ Cep	23 40.1	+77 44	3.21	1.03	K1 III–IV	71	2.5	46	0.135	339	−42 V?	exoplanet	Errai

SPECTROSCOPY OF STARS

BY CHRIS CORBALLY, RICHARD GRAY, AND TOOMAS KARMO

An important column is included in the table of Brightest Stars. This is the classification of the star's spectrum in terms of MK Type, after Morgan and Keenan who first developed this primary system in 1943. Its symbols are explained in the introduction to the table. The MK type is really a compact description of the star's spectrum in relation to a grid of standard stars, first covering the two dimensions of temperature type and luminosity, and then including common peculiarities that stars may show.

The MK types are useful in estimating the physical parameters of stars, along with their ages, distances, and reddenings (the amount of dust in their line of sight), which are important for galactic astronomy. The classifications identify the more astrophysically interesting stars.

Classifying spectra: The classification process for normal stars is straightforward, matching as close as possible the "look" of a star's spectrum with how it fits into a "library of standard spectra." You can either build up that library through your own spectra, which is the best way eventually, or find a library that suits the resolution of your spectra on the Internet.[1] For precise work, be careful that the stars you are using as standards are genuine MK system standards. The matching of unknown to standard spectra is made easier and more precise by using ratios of spectral features, traditionally called "absorption lines." The best features to use change, depending on the temperature type of the star. Richard Gray's Digital Spectral Classification Atlas[2] points out these features in the blue-green region of the spectrum, where the criteria are the most sensitive, while *winmk* and *xmk* are programs for comparing digital spectra on screen.[3]

Observing spectra: Slitless spectroscopy is a simple way to start obtaining one's own spectra. This involves putting a prism or diffraction grating in front of a DSLR lens or the digital imager on a telescope.[4] The spectra are of low resolution, but are sufficient to distinguish the broad MK "letter classes" of stars, to monitor variable stars, and get novae and supernovae, emission nebulae, and comets.[5] There are plenty of bright examples of these. For more detailed spectra, a spectrograph matching your telescope needs to be bought or made.[6]

Processing spectra: While a picture of a spectrum, or group of them in a crowded field, is beautiful, the science comes alive when one displays the intensity of the signal against wavelength. Extracting a 1-D digital spectrum from the 2-D image on the detector is both a science and an art, but there is abundant help on the Internet.[7] The other step for science is calibrating the pixel position against actual wavelength along the spectrum. Again look to the Internet for help in this.

What to observe: Examples of spectral interest are given under Resources 5 and 6 below. The AAVSO posts campaigns for observing objects, which often include the need for spectral data.[8] There are also interesting, bright variable stars, like Miras and B-type shell stars, that repay long-term spectroscopic observing. As John Martin remarks, "interesting" is a matter of individual taste and scientific curiosity. As these develop, you will surely become delighted with looking at your spectra and very knowledgeable about them.

A Few Resources

1 pendientedemigracion.ucm.es/info/Astrof/invest/actividad/spectra.html
2 ned.ipac.caltech.edu/level5/Gray/frames.html
3 www.appstate.edu/~grayro/MK/winmk.htm (for MS Windows)
www.appstate.edu/~grayro/spectrum/ftp/download.html
(see Auxiliary X-Windows programs for Linux and iOS versions)
4 The Star Analyzer is one such grating www.rspec-astro.com/star-analyser
John Martin's page comprehensively describes slitless spectroscopy
go.uis.edu/gratingspectra
5 Examples are at www.rspec-astro.com/sample-projects
6 Modest off-the-shelf spectrographs include the Shelyak ALPY-600, while both Christian Buil's and John Menke's websites offer advice on building your own and show their inspiring images
www.astrosurf.com/buil and www.menkescientific.com/johnspage.html
7 Start at go.uis.edu/gratingspectra
8 www.aavso.org/observing-campaigns#current

THE 50 BRIGHTEST STARS BY MAGNITUDE

This table contains the Sun and 50 other stars with an apparent magnitude brighter than mag. 2.0 that appear in the previous table. A subset of data from that table is included, although the spectral classifications have been simplified. As in the previous table, the components of visual binary stars are listed separately; their combined magnitudes appear in footnotes. Where more than one star has the same apparent magnitude, they have been sorted by right ascension. Navigation star names are **bold**.

Rank	Star Name	**RA** (2017.5) h m	**Dec** ° ′	m_V	*B* – *V*	**MK Type**	M_V	***D*** ly	
	Sun			−26.75	0.63	G2	4.8	8 lm	
1	α CMa A	6 45.9	−16 44	−1.44	0.01	A0	1.5	8.6	**Sirius**
2	α Car	6 24.3	−52 42	−0.62	0.16	A9	−5.5	~310	**Canopus**
3	α Boo	14 16.5	+19 06	−0.05	1.24	K1.5	−0.3	37	**Arcturus**
4	α Cen A	14 40.8	−60 54	−0.01	0.71	G2	4.4	4.3	**Rigil Kentaurus A**[1]
5	α Lyr	18 37.5	+38 48	0.03	0.00	A0	0.6	25.0	**Vega**
6	α Aur Aa+Ab	5 18.0	+46 01	0.08	0.80	G6+G2	−0.5	43	**Capella**
7	β Ori A	5 15.4	−8 11	0.18	−0.03	B8	−6.9	900	**Rigel**
8	α CMi A	7 40.2	+5 11	0.40	0.43	F5	2.7	11.5	**Procyon**
9	α Eri	1 38.4	−57 09	0.45	−0.16	B3	−2.7	140	**Achernar**
10	α Ori	5 56.1	+7 25	0.45v	1.50	M2	−5.5	500	**Betelgeuse**
11	β Cen AB	14 05.1	−60 27	0.58v	−0.23	B1	−4.8	400	**Hadar**
12	α Aql	19 51.6	+8 55	0.76	0.22	A7	2.2	16.7	**Altair**
13	α Tau A	4 36.9	+16 33	0.87v	1.54	K5	−0.7	67	**Aldebaran**
14	α Vir	13 26.1	−11 15	0.98v	−0.24	B1	−3.4	250	**Spica**
15	α Sco A	16 30.5	−26 28	1.06v	1.86	M1.5	−5.1	600	**Antares**
16	β Gem	7 46.4	+27 59	1.16	0.99	K0	1.1	33.8	**Pollux**
17	α PsA	22 58.6	−29 32	1.17	0.14	A3	1.7	25.1	**Fomalhaut**
18	α Cru A	12 27.6	−63 12	1.25	−0.20	B0.5	−3.7	~320	**Acrux A**[2]
19	β Cru	12 48.8	−59 47	1.25v	−0.24	B0.5	−3.4	300	Mimosa (Becrux)
20	α Cyg	20 42.0	+45 21	1.25	0.09	A2	−6.9	~1400	**Deneb**
21	α Cen B	14 40.8	−60 54	1.35	0.88	K1	5.7	4.3	Rigil Kentaurus B[1]
22	α Leo A	10 09.3	+11 53	1.36	−0.09	B7	−0.6	79	**Regulus**
23	ε CMa A	6 59.3	−29 00	1.50	−0.21	B2	−4.0	410	**Adhara**
24	γ Cru	12 32.1	−57 13	1.59v	1.60	M3.5	−0.6	89	**Gacrux**
25	λ Sco	17 34.8	−37 07	1.62v	−0.23	B1.5	−4.6	600	**Shaula**
26	γ Ori	5 26.1	+6 22	1.64	−0.22	B2	−2.8	250	**Bellatrix**
27	α Cru B	12 27.6	−63 12	1.64	−0.18	B1	−3.3	~320	Acrux B[2]
28	β Tau	5 27.4	+28 37	1.65	−0.13	B7	−1.4	130	**Elnath**
29	β Car	9 13.4	−69 47	1.67	0.07	A1	−1.0	113	**Miaplacidus**
30	ε Ori	5 37.1	−1 12	1.69	−0.18	B0	−7.2	2000	**Alnilam**
31	α Gru	22 09.3	−46 53	1.73	−0.07	B7	−0.7	101	**Al Na'ir**
32	ζ Ori A	5 41.6	−1 56	1.74	−0.20	O9.5	−5.0	700	Alnitak
33	γ^2 Vel	8 10.1	−47 23	1.75v	−0.14	WC8+O9	−5.9	1100	Al Suhail al Muhlif[3]
34	ε UMa	12 54.8	+55 52	1.76v	−0.02	A0	−0.3	83	**Alioth**
35	α Per	3 25.6	+49 55	1.79	0.48	F5	−4.2	510	**Mirfak**
36	ε Sgr	18 25.3	−34 22	1.79	−0.03	A0	−1.4	~143	**Kaus Australis**
37	α UMa AB	11 04.8	+61 39	1.81	1.06	K0	−1.1	120	**Dubhe**
38	δ CMa	7 09.1	−26 25	1.83	0.67	F8	−6.6	2000	Wezen
39	η UMa	13 48.2	+49 14	1.85	−0.10	B3	−0.7	104	**Alkaid**
40	θ Sco	17 38.6	−43 00	1.86	0.41	F1	−3.0	300	Girtab (Sargas)
41	ε Car	8 22.9	−59 34	1.86v	1.20	K3+B2	−4.5	600	**Avior**
42	β Aur	6 00.8	+44 57	1.90v	0.08	A1	−0.1	81	Menkalinan
43	α TrA	16 50.5	−69 03	1.91	1.45	K2	−3.5	390	**Atria**
44	γ Gem	6 38.7	+16 23	1.93	0.00	A1	−0.7	110	Alhena
45	α Gem A	7 35.7	+31 51	1.93	0.03	A1	0.9	52	Castor A
46	δ Vel AB	8 45.2	−54 46	1.93	0.04	A1	0.0	81	Koo She
47	α Pav	20 27.0	−56 41	1.94	−0.12	B2.5	−1.8	180	**Peacock**
48	α UMi A	2 53.6	+89 20	1.97v	0.64	F5–8	−3.6	430	**Polaris**
49	β CMa	6 23.5	−17 58	1.98v	−0.24	B1	−3.9	~490	Mirzam
50	α Hya	9 28.4	−8 44	1.99	1.44	K3	−1.7	180	**Alphard**

[1] To the unaided eye, the combined visual magnitude of Rigil Kentaurus A and B is –0.28.
[2] To the unaided eye, the combined visual magnitude of Acrux A and B is 0.68.
[3] Confusingly, Suhail **is** a navigation star name, but the star is λ Vel (Al Suhail al Wazn), not on this list.

THE NEAREST STARS

BY TODD J. HENRY

The nearest stars hold a special fascination for any of us who have gazed skyward. Astronomers study the Sun's neighbours because they are the nearest, and therefore brightest, examples of their types. For many kinds of stars, the fundamental framework of stellar astronomy is built upon direct measurements of luminosities, colours, temperatures, and masses of nearby stars. Their surrounding environments are remote destinations to explore from Earth, and any planets orbiting them could someday become outposts of humankind because the nearest stars are the first step beyond our own Solar System.

The definition of a "nearby" star system is that its distance is accurately known to be within a designated horizon. Distances may be measured geometrically, via astrometry using the technique of trigonometric parallax, or estimated using myriad combinations of photometric and spectroscopic data. Here we adopt distances based on trigonometric parallaxes only, as they are the most reliable and are independent of assumptions about the type of star under scrutiny. With modern techniques, we now know the distances to several dozen stars to better than 1% accuracy.

The list presented here includes the Sun's 51 nearest stellar neighbours and their companions within the astronomically convenient horizon of 5.0 parsecs, or 16.3 light-years (ly). The definition of a parsec, which is equivalent to 3.26 ly, is based upon the radius of the Earth's orbit: as the Earth swings around the Sun, nearby stars shift back and forth relative to more distant, background objects because of our changing perspective, much as a thumb held at arm's length will seem to shift relative to a distant background when you close one eye, then the other. This shift is called parallax. The size of the shift depends entirely upon the star's distance, and astronomers have defined the distance at which a star's parallax is 1.00″ to be 1.00 parallax-second (parsec). As the distance increases, the shift decreases inversely, i.e. parallax = 1/distance. Thus, a star at 5.00 parsecs will exhibit a trigonometric parallax of 0.200 arcseconds, or 200 milliarcseconds (mas). The shifts are slight—the parallax of the nearest star, Proxima Centauri, is 769 mas and is only about 1/2300th the width of the full Moon.

To be included in the list, a stellar system must have a trigonometric parallax of at least 200 mas with an error of less than 10 mas published in the refereed literature, meaning that the distance is known to 5% or better. There are, effectively, four broad categories of nearby star parallaxes: (1) A wonderful compendium of ground-based parallax efforts through 1995 is *The General Catalogue of Trigonometric Stellar Parallaxes* (a.k.a. the *Yale Parallax Catalog*, or *YPC*) by van Altena et al. The *YPC* includes nearly 16 000 parallax measurements of more than 8 000 stars. Stars as bright as Sirius and as faint as mag. 20 can be found in the *YPC*, with most parallaxes accurate to 3–13 mas. (2) ESA's *HIPPARCOS* space astrometry mission targeted nearly 120 000 relatively bright stars at a precision of typically 0.5–4 mas, with a compendium of results published in 1997. In 2007, van Leeuwen published a new reduction of the *HIPPARCOS* data, and those results have been used to generate the parallaxes given here. (3) Since then, several teams have continued using traditional telescopes on the ground to measure parallaxes for both new and known stars within 5 parsecs, primarily by the Allegheny, Dartmouth, RECONS, Torino, and USNO groups. (4) In space, the *Hubble Space Telescope* has been used to determine parallaxes of several of the Sun's neighbours, while measuring stellar masses or searching for exoplanets (primarily by the U. Texas group). The list presented here uses a comprehensive combination of trigonometric parallaxes from various sources to arrive at a weighted mean parallax for each system, which simply means that higher-quality parallaxes are mathematically given more weight in the averaging process. Individual component parallaxes have been combined for all systems except for the nearest one, which is, in fact, a triple including Proxima and the two components of α Centauri, A and B. The *YPC* includes 43 of the 51 extrasolar systems, while *HIPPARCOS* improved upon many of those, but added no new systems. RECONS added five of the eight remaining systems, with the latest two additions having parallaxes measured by other teams. In total, 110 different parallaxes have been used to generate the distances given. The RECONS group (www.recons.org) is keeping a tally of all trigonometric parallax efforts since the *YPC* and *HIPPARCOS*, and the reader is encouraged to contact the author about any overlooked publications (thenry@astro.gsu.edu).

Including the Sun, there are 52 known systems in the 5-parsec sphere, made up of 66 stars, 8 brown dwarfs, and 9 extrasolar planets (plus, of course, the 8 planets in the Solar System). Curiously, there are one-third more systems in the southern sky (30) than in the north (21), even though historically far more astronomical observations have been made in the northern sky. Seventeen of the systems include stellar or brown-dwarf companions, while an additional five (including the Solar System) have planets. The smallest type of star, known as red dwarfs of spectral type M, dominate our galaxy, accounting for 73% of the 5-parsec sample (48 of 66 stars—all stars without types in the list are type M, but individual spectral types are not available because of close separations in multiple systems, hence the "J" for joint in some spectral types). None of these red dwarfs is visible with the unaided eye. In some ways, our galaxy mimics an ocean full of creatures, large and small, but it is the smallest fish that dominate the population. Missing from the nearby waters are the largest whales, the most massive stars of spectral types O and B. Such stars are exceedingly rare and have lifetimes of only a few million years. The visually brightest star in the night sky is Sirius, which is the brighter star in the sixth-nearest system, and the only A-type star listed. Near Sirius in the sky is Procyon (the 15th-nearest system), nearly as bright and the only F-type star listed. Both Sirius and Procyon have white-dwarf companions that are the leftover embers of more-massive counterparts. These stars have already reinvented themselves, having changed from stars larger than Sirius and Procyon to reveal only their cores as white dwarfs by sloughing off their outer layers long ago. In the past, the light of Sirius and Procyon would be lost in the glare of their much larger, and brighter, components. In all, there are five white dwarfs, denoted by "D" in the list, nearer than 5 parsecs. The two stars most similar to our Sun are the only other two G dwarfs, α Centauri A and τ Ceti. Finally, eight stars are of K type, including α Centauri B, 61 Cygni A and B, and the naked-eye stars ε Indi, o^2 Eridani A, and ε Eridani. The latter star is particularly interesting because it is circled by a band of cold dust and at least one planet, with reports of two additional planets inferred because of gaps in the dusty disk. Other systems with planets include CD–46 11540 and CD–49 13515, each with one detected planet, and the Ross 780 (GJ 876) system, around which four planets have been found. Also worthy of note is Kapteyn's Star, which is a rare subdwarf—an ancient, subluminous star of spectral luminosity class VI—that is moving quickly through the solar neighbourhood. It has the largest radial velocity of the systems in the list, and has the second-fastest proper motion, only surpassed by Barnard's Star, the second-nearest system.

We continue to find more of the Sun's neighbours, even so close to home. Recent and ongoing sky surveys provide a wealth of solar neighbourhood candidates for those who cleverly dig through the databases for gems. DENIS (DEep Near-Infrared Survey) has provided two recent additions, the red dwarf DENIS 1048–3956 and the brown dwarf DENIS 0255–4700. To the author's knowledge, the latter object is the faintest object outside the Solar System for which an absolute visual magnitude has been measured, with $M_V = 24.44$. Following in the footsteps of Giclas and Luyten, who both did breakthrough work in studies of nearby stars via proper-motion searches, the SCR (SuperCOSMOS–RECONS) effort trawls an electronic database generated by scanning glass plates of the entire sky. The 24th-nearest system, an M/T dwarf pair known as SCR 1845–6357, was found during an early SCR search, and efforts are continuing.

In the following table, names are given in the first column with emphasis on discovery names or variable-star names, the latter if for no other reason than it gives some idea as to the system's location in the sky. Component designations within a single system are listed as A, B, or C, and are enclosed by parentheses if there are different names for individual members. Presumed planets are listed as "+nP" in the companion column, where n is the number of planets. Astrometric information is given next, including **RA** and **Dec** for equinox J2000.0, the weighted mean parallax (**π**) and its estimated error (***err***) in mas, the derived distance (**D**) in light-years, and the proper motion (**μ**) in mas/y with the position angle of the motion (**PA**) (north is 0°, east is 90°). Spectroscopic information is then listed, including the systemic radial velocity (**V_{rad}**) and spectral type (**Sp.**) for each component, when known. Photometric information is provided in the form of the visual magnitude (**m_v**), where it may be useful to know that the human eye can see to about mag. 6. The list closes with the derived absolute magnitude (**M_V**), which is a valuable measurement of an object's intrinsic brightness, and reflects how bright an object would appear if it were at a standard distance of 10 parsecs.

In the past few years, brown dwarfs very near the Sun have been found, including WISE 1049–5319AB, which currently ranks as the third-nearest system. Eight brown dwarfs are now known within 5 parsecs. Nonetheless, the stars still outnumber the brown dwarfs by 8:1, and there are more extrasolar planets known than brown dwarfs. GJ 1061, now ranked as the 21st-nearest system, remains the closest new star found to the Sun since the YPC and *HIPPARCOS* compendia. In the next few years, additional brown dwarfs will likely enter the sample—WISE 0855–0714 and DENIS 0817–6155 are the leading contenders, but require accurate parallaxes for inclusion—and now that *Gaia* observations are underway, new stars may be added as well.

In 1999, the first planet around Ross 780 was announced, and thus the first reliable exoplanet discovery within 5 parsecs made it into the *Observer's Handbook* in 2000. Other than the Sun, there are now five systems within 5 parsecs that are *reported* to have planets (these are indicated in the table by the designation "+*n*P," where *n* is the number of planets). Research on individual nearby stars has recently been reinvigorated because the nearest stellar systems are prime targets for more-sensitive exoplanet searches, and ultimately, life. The population of nearby stars remains a compelling area of research because we have yet to answer the fundamental questions, what types of stars form at what rates? and, how much mass in our galaxy can be found in stars? That so many faint, yet nearby, objects have slipped through previous surveys of our neighbourhood hints at more to come. Undoubtedly, the more complete our reconnaissance of the solar neighbourhood, the better we will understand the nature of stars that make up our galaxy, and our Sun's place among them.

★

* (See entry 2 at right.) For the fastest-moving star in the sky, Barnard's Star, the 2017.0 coordinates are RA 17h 58m 48s, Dec +4° 44′ 31″, steadily moving northward in eastern Ophiuchus.

TABLE OF NEAREST STARS

	Name		RA (2000) h m	Dec ° ′	π mas	*err* mas	*D* ly	μ mas/y	PA °	V_{rad} km/s	Sp.	m_V	M_V
	Sun	+8P									G2V	−26.72	4.83
1	Proxima Cen	(C)+1P	14 30	−62 41	768.69	0.29	4.24	3853	281.5	−16	M5.0V	11.09	15.52
	α Cen	A	14 40	−60 50	747.23	1.17	4.36	3710	277.5	−26	G2V	0.01	4.38
		B+1P	14 40	−60 50				3724	284.8	−18	K0.0V	1.34	5.71
2	Barnard's		17 58	+04 42*	545.51	0.29	5.98	10358	355.6	−111	M3.5V	9.57	13.25
3	WISE 1049−5319	A	10 49	−53 19	495.02	4.56	6.59	2787	277.5		L8.0V		
		B	10 49	−53 19							T1.0V		
4	Wolf 359		10 56	+07 01	417.46	2.03	7.78	4696	234.6	+19	M5.5V	13.53	16.64
5	Lalande 21185		11 03	+35 58	393.25	0.57	8.29	4802	186.9	−85	M2.0V	7.46	10.43
6	Sirius	A	6 45	−16 43	380.02	1.28	8.58	1339	204.1	−9	A1V	−1.43	1.47
		B	6 45	−16 43							DA2	8.44	11.34
7	BL Cet	(A)	1 39	−17 57	373.70	2.70	8.73	3368	80.4	+29	M5.5V	12.61	15.47
	UV Cet	(B)	1 39	−17 57						+32	M6.0V	13.06	15.92
8	Ross 154		18 50	−23 50	337.22	1.97	9.67	666	106.8	−10	M3.5V	10.44	13.08
9	Ross 248		23 42	+44 11	316.84	0.55	10.31	1617	177.0	−78	M5.5V	12.29	14.79
10	ε Eri	+1P	3 33	−09 27	311.22	0.09	10.48	977	271.1	+16	K2.0V	3.73	6.20
11	CD −36 15693		23 06	−35 51	305.08	0.70	10.69	6896	78.9	+9	M1.0V	7.34	9.76
12	Ross 128		11 48	+00 48	298.14	1.37	10.94	1361	153.6	−31	M4.0V	11.16	13.53
13	EZ Aqr	A	22 39	−15 18	289.50	4.40	11.27	3254	46.6	−50	M5.0VJ	13.03	15.34
		B	22 39	−15 18								13.27	15.58
		C	22 39	−15 18								15.07	17.38
14	61 Cyg	A	21 07	+38 45	286.08	0.48	11.40	5281	51.9	−66	K5.0V	5.21	7.49
		B	21 07	+38 45				5172	52.6	−64	K7.0V	6.03	8.31
15	Procyon	A	7 39	+05 13	285.17	0.64	11.44	1259	214.7	−4	F5 IV–V	0.37	2.65
		B	7 39	+05 13							DQZ	10.70	12.98
16	BD +59 1915	A	18 43	+59 38	283.83	1.46	11.49	2238	323.6	−1	M3.0V	8.90	11.17
		B	18 43	+59 38				2313	323.0	+1	M3.5V	9.69	11.96
17	GX And	(A)	0 18	+44 01	280.00	0.59	11.65	2918	81.9	+12	M1.5V	8.08	10.31
	GQ And	(B)	0 18	+44 01						+11	M3.5V	11.06	13.29
18	ε Ind	A	22 03	−56 47	276.07	0.28	11.81	4704	122.7	−40	K3.0V	4.68	6.89
		B	22 04	−56 47				4823	121.1		T1.0V		
		C	22 04	−56 46							T6.0V		
19	DX Can		8 30	+26 47	275.63	2.42	11.83	1290	242.2	−5	M6.0V	14.90	17.10
20	τ Cet		1 44	−15 56	273.97	0.17	11.91	1922	296.4	−17	G8.5V	3.49	5.68
21	GJ 1061		3 36	−44 31	271.01	1.25	11.99	831	118.8	−20	M5.0V	13.09	15.26
22	YZ Cet		1 13	−17 00	269.08	2.99	12.12	1372	61.9	+28	M4.0V	12.02	14.17
23	Luyten's		7 27	+05 14	266.23	0.66	12.25	3738	171.2	+18	M3.5V	9.85	11.98
24	SCR 1845−6357	A	18 45	−63 58	259.50	1.11	12.57	2558	74.7		M8.5V	17.40	19.47
		B	18 45	−63 58							T6.0V		
25	SO 0253+1652		2 53	+16 53	259.41	0.89	12.57	5050	137.9		M6.5V	15.14	17.21
26	Kapteyn's		5 12	−45 01	255.67	0.91	12.76	8670	131.4	+245	M2.0VI	8.85	10.89
27	AX Mic		21 17	−38 52	253.44	0.80	12.87	3455	250.6	+28	K9.0V	6.67	8.69
28	DENIS 1048−3956		10 48	−39 56	248.24	0.58	13.12	1530	229.2		M8.5V	17.39	19.37
29	Kruger 60	A	22 28	+57 42	248.06	1.39	13.15	990	241.6	−34	M3.0V	9.79	11.76
		B	22 28	+57 41							M4.0V	11.41	13.38
30	Ross 614	A	6 29	−02 49	244.44	0.92	13.34	930	131.7	+17	M4.0V	11.18	13.12
		B	6 29	−02 49							M5.5V	14.26	16.20
31	UGP 0722−0540		7 22	−05 40	242.80	2.40	13.43	970	291.3		T10.0V		
32	Wolf 1061		16 30	−12 40	234.38	1.50	13.92	1189	184.5	−21	M3.5V	10.10	11.95
33	van Maanen's		0 49	+05 23	232.70	1.81	14.02	2978	155.5	+54	DZ7	12.40	14.23
34	CD −37 15492		0 05	−37 21	230.32	0.90	14.16	6100	112.5	+23	M1.5V	8.54	10.35
35	Wolf 424	A	12 33	+09 01	227.90	4.60	14.31	1811	277.4		M5.0VJ	13.25	15.04
		B	12 33	+09 01								13.24	15.03
36	TZ Ari		2 00	+13 03	224.80	2.99	14.51	2097	147.8	−29	M4.0V	12.31	14.07
37	G 208−44	(A)	19 54	+44 25	220.93	0.94	14.78	731	143.1		M5.5VJ	13.46	15.17

TABLE OF NEAREST STARS (continued)

	Name		RA (2000) Dec h m ° ′	π mas	err mas	D ly	μ mas/y	PA °	V_{rad} km/s	Sp.	m_V	M_V
	G 208–44	(C)	19 54 +44 25								16.75	18.46
	G 208–45	(B)	19 54 +44 25							M6.0V	14.01	15.72
38	BD +68 946		17 36 +68 20	220.47	0.83	14.79	1309	194.2	–29	M3.0V	9.17	10.89
39	LHS 292		10 48 –11 20	220.30	3.60	14.81	1644	158.5	–7	M6.5V	15.73	17.45
40	CD –46 11540	+1P	17 29 –46 54	220.11	1.39	14.82	1050	146.9	–10	M2.5V	9.37	11.08
41	L 145–141		11 46 –64 50	216.12	1.09	15.09	2688	97.4		DQ6	11.50	13.17
42	Ross 780	+4P	22 53 –14 16	214.45	0.57	15.21	1174	125.1	–2	M3.5V	10.18	11.84
43	G 158–27		00 07 –07 32	213.00	3.60	15.31	2041	203.6	–42	M5.0V	13.77	15.41
44	LHS 288		10 44 –61 13	209.70	2.65	15.55	1657	348.1		M5.5V	13.90	15.51
45	BD +44 2051	(A)	11 05 +43 32	205.67	0.93	15.86	4511	282.1	+69	M1.0V	8.77	10.34
	WX UMa	(B)	11 06 +43 31				4531	281.9		M5.5V	14.44	16.01
46	BD +50 1725		10 11 +49 27	205.53	0.49	15.87	1452	249.7	–26	K7.0V	6.56	8.12
47	BD +20 2465		10 20 +19 52	204.60	2.80	15.94	506	264.0	+12	M2.5V	9.32	10.87
48	WISE 1639–6847		16 39–68	47	202.30	3.10	16.11	3156	169.3	brown dwarf		
49	CD –49 13515	+2P	21 34 –49 01	202.03	1.00	16.14	819	183.2	+4	M1.5V	8.66	10.19
50	DENIS 0255–4700		02 55 –47 01	201.37	3.89	16.20	1149	119.5		L7.5V	22.92	24.44
51	o² Eri	A	04 15 –07 39	200.65	0.23	16.26	4088	213.2	–42	K0.5V	4.43	5.94
		B	04 15 –07 39				4073	212.4		DA4	9.52	11.03
		C	04 15 –07 39							M4.0V	11.24	12.75

Editor's Note: For more information, see A.H. Batten, "Our Changing Views of the Solar Neighbourhood," *JRASC, 92* (1998), pp. 231–237, at www.rasc.ca/sites/default/files/jrasc1998-10.pdf.

SOME EASILY OBSERVABLE NEARBY STARS

This table lists some of the nearby stars from the main table that may be of interest to the observer, including all those of mag. 6 and brighter, plus three of historical interest (all red dwarfs). The stars have been re-ordered by magnitude of the primary component. The table data have been simplified—consult the original table for details.

Name		RA (2000) h m	Dec ° ′	π mas	D ly	μ ″/y	PA °	Sp.	m_V
Sun	+8P							G2	–26.7
Sirius[1]	A	6 45	–16 43	380	8.6	1.3	204	A1	–1.4
α Cen[2,3]	A	14 40	–60 50	747	4.4	3.7	278	G2	0.0
	B+1P	14 40	–60 50			3.7	285	K0.0	1.3
Procyon[4]	A	7 39	5 13	285	11.4	1.3	215	F5	0.4
τ Cet[5]		1 44	–15 56	274	11.9	1.9	296	G8.5	3.5
ε Eri[5]	+1P	3 33	–09 27	311	10.5	1.0	271	K2.0	3.7
o² Eri[6]	A	4 15	–07 39	201	16.3	4.1	213	K0.5	4.4
	B	4 15	–07 39			4.1	212	DA4	9.5
ε Ind	A	22 3	–56 47	276	11.8	4.7	123	K3.0	4.7
61 Cyg[7]	A	21 7	38 45	286	11.4	5.3	52	K5.0	5.2
	B	21 7	38 45			5.2	53	K7.0	6.0
Kapteyn's		5 12	–45 1	256	12.8	8.7	131	M2.0	8.9
Barnard's[8]		17 58	4 42	546	6.0	10.4	356	M3.5	9.6
Luyten's[9]		7 27	5 14	266	12.3	3.7	171	M3.5	9.9

[1] α CMa, see note on facing page.
[2] Rigil Kentaurus, similar to Sun, see note on p. 292.
[3] The star system nearest to Sun reported to have at least one planet.
[4] α CMi, see note on p. 291.
[5] Similar to Sun, the nearest such star visible to observers at north-temperate latitudes.
[6] B is the nearest white-dwarf star that is easily observable, see p. 304.
[7] First star to have its stellar parallax measured (Bessel, 1838).
[8] Star with the largest proper motion; second-closest star system to Sun (Barnard, 1916).
[9] Only 1.2 ly from Procyon.

DOUBLE AND MULTIPLE STARS

BY BRIAN D. MASON

Approximately 85% of stars are found in double or multiple systems. While the first detection of double systems dates back to the early 17th century, it was not until systematic work with large-aperture telescopes was done (notably by William Herschel) that the physical rather than the optical nature of these systems was ascertained. The larger the aperture of the telescope, the closer the stars that can be separated under good conditions. The resolving power in arcseconds can be estimated as $120/D$, where D is the diameter of the telescope objective in millimetres. Astronomers using long-baseline optical interferometry have measured double-star separations less than a milliarcsecond (0.001″).

The *Journal of Double Star Observations* (hereafter *JDSO*) is a good source for free information on double and multiple stars (see www.jdso.org). The double stars in the following table were selected to cover a wide variety of interests. Wide or slowly moving pairs are good for evaluating optical performance or estimating seeing. With the preponderance of inexpensive, large-aperture telescopes, the availability of interferometry for the amateur (see R. Caloi, *JDSO 4*, 111, 2008), and access to systems with larger magnitude differences (see J. Daley, *JDSO 3*, 159, 2007), closer systems have been included. The list covers many decades of separation with small and large Δm. Of the 136 listed systems, 19 have separations of 1″ or less and 23 between 1″ and 2″. At more moderate separations, there are 19 between 2″ and 3″, 19 between 3″ and 5″, 24 between 5″ and 7″, 19 between 7″and 10″, and 13 with separations greater than 10″. Of these more moderate separations, those with both small and large magnitude differences are well represented. The pairs are well distributed in RA. One-third of the objects are found south of the equator, giving adequate coverage of southern declinations. Sissy Haas (*Sky & Telescope*, September 2012) provides some excellent test objects for determining your Δm limit at a range of separations. Also, an article by Dirk Terrell (*Sky & Telescope*, August 2012) is ideal for those looking at eclipsing binaries, including pairs much closer than those listed in these tables.

Since many of the stars selected exhibit significant motion, the predicted position angles (PA) and separations are given for both 2017.0 and 2018.0. PA is the angular direction of the fainter star (B) from the brighter (A), measured counterclockwise from north (*clockwise* in an optical system having an *odd* number of reflections). Note that data for 2017.0 have been changed for some systems due to improvements in orbit calculations or more recent measurements. Also included are notes on selected systems. If no 2018.0 data are provided, there is no calculation (orbital or linear) of the motion (if any) of this double. The 2017.0 data are the most recently published.

Notes on some double and multiple stars in the table (marked with a *):

ζ Phe AB,C: While AB,C has been slowing opening up since the first (1835) measure, AB, close to an arcsecond in separation, has a visual orbit of 210y.

γ And A, BC: BC component moving fast; periastron was 2015.5.

94 Cet AB: In addition to the pair whose parameters are given in the table, the B component is also a close (a=0.064″) 740-day pair resolved with the Very Large Telescope.

ζ Ori AB: Zeta Ori A was also resolved as a close pair with the Navy Precision Optical Interferometer (NPOI) with a period of about 7.36 y. It was recently also resolved with the 4.1 m SOAR telescope.

HR 2384 AB: C is an 8th-magnitude target 12″ away at 311°. It is a close (0.5″) pair with an orbital period of 99 y. It is very likely physical, making this a visual quadruple.

α CMa AB: The companion to Sirius is a difficult target, usually observable only during periods of exceptional seeing, when you can use the highest magnification and move the primary off the field of view. The white-dwarf secondary, predicted by Bessel and first observed by Alvan Clark, remains a challenging target for visual observers. The recent book by Jay Holberg, *Sirius: Brightest Diamond in the Sky*, is excellent.

α CMi AB: Like Sirius, Procyon has a white-dwarf companion. It was first detected in 1840 by the variation in the proper motion of the star, but not resolved until 1896 by Shaeberle with the 91-cm refractor of Lick Observatory.

γ Leo AB: Two different 554-y solutions have been computed at Pulkovo Observatory. The average prediction of those is given in the table, although they differ by only 1° ±0.01″, so no determination can be made of which is better.

ξ UMa AB: Many "firsts" are associated with this system. It was one of the first discovered systems (Herschel), one of the first systems whose motion led to the discovery of the physical (rather than optical) nature of double stars (Struve), and the first to have an orbit calculated for it (Savary). Always relatively wide, with an obvious position-angle change of 6° per year, this is a system that will never fail to please, observing season to observing season.

β Mus: This bright, massive pair is classified as a "runaway pair" of the Sco–Cen Association. It is quite unusual for runaway stars to be binary; still rarer are those with periods this long.

θ Vir AB: A is a close (1.2″) pair with a long period of 695 y. However, with the first catalogued position from 1902, the orbit is still speculative.

α Com AB: Still in rapid motion; periastron was 2015.3. An eclipse was unfortunately barely missed (Muterspaugh et al., submitted to *ApJL*, 2015).

HR 5386 A,BC: BC is a close (0.24″) pair with a short (40 y) period first measured by S.W. Burnham with the Lick 36-inch.

α Cen AB: Our closest neighbour is a quick-moving double star. The brighter component is a near twin of the Sun, while the B component is cooler. According to R.G. Aitken, this pair was discovered by Father Richaud while observing a comet at Pondicherry, India, in December 1689. In 2015, AB went through a close approach from Nov. 20 to Dec. 9 (this is due to the geometry of the orbit, periastron is not until June 2035). The C component, Proxima, slightly closer to the Sun, is an extremely faint red dwarf, separated from the A component by 2.2°.

ψ Cyg AB: A is a close (0.14″) pair with a short (54-y) period first measured by Elliott Horch on the WIYN telescope.

β Cap AB: A is a close (0.07″) pair with a short (3.8-y) period first measured by Blazit et al. on the Hale 200″, while B is also a close (0.94″) pair of longer (539-y) period first measured by Burnham but attributed to Barnard. Since AB is associated by common proper motion, this is a physical and visual quadruple.

TABLE OF DOUBLE AND MULTIPLE STARS

Star	RA (2000) h	m	Dec °	′	Magnitudes comb.	A	B	2017.0 PA °	2017.0 Sep. ″	2018.0 PA °	2018.0 Sep. ″	Period y
36 And AB	00	55.0	+23	38	5.6	6.1	6.5	331	1.14	332	1.15	168
ζ Phe AB,C*	01	08.4	–55	15	4.0	4.0	8.2	242	6.76			
ϕ Psc AB	01	13.7	+24	35	4.6	4.7	9.1	221	7.80			
κ Tuc AB	01	15.8	–68	53	4.9	5.0	7.7	316	4.96	316	4.96	857
γ Ari AB	01	53.5	+19	18	3.8	4.5	4.6	0	7.36			
α Psc AB	02	02.0	+02	46	3.8	4.1	5.2	262	1.83	261	1.83	3267
γ And A,BC*	02	03.9	+42	20	2.2	2.3	5.0	63	9.75			
γ And BC	02	03.9	+42	20	5.0	5.3	6.5	128	0.09	122	0.14	64
ι Tri	02	12.4	+30	18	5.0	5.3	6.7	68	3.94			
ι Cas AB	02	29.1	+67	24	4.5	4.6	6.9	228	2.62	227	2.63	620
ι Cas AC	02	29.1	+67	24	4.5	4.6	9.1	120	7.07			
α UMi AB	02	31.8	+89	16	2.1	2.1	9.1	233	18.12			
ν Cet	02	35.9	+05	36	5.0	5.0	9.1	80	8.41			
84 Cet	02	41.2	–00	42	5.8	5.8	9.7	301	3.63			
γ Cet AB	02	43.3	+03	14	3.4	3.5	6.2	299	1.91			
ε Ari AB	02	59.2	+21	20	4.6	5.2	5.6	210	1.33	210	1.33	1216
γ Per Aa,Ab	03	04.8	+53	30	2.7	2.9	4.4	244	0.19	244	0.15	15
α For	03	12.1	–28	59	3.9	4.0	7.2	300	5.40	300	5.42	269

* See note in text.

TABLE OF DOUBLE AND MULTIPLE STARS (continued)

	RA (2000) Dec				Magnitudes			2017.0 PA	2017.0 Sep.	2018.0 PA	2018.0 Sep.	Period
Star	h	m	°	′	comb.	A	B	°	″	°	″	y
94 Cet AB*	03	12.8	−01	12	5.1	5.1	11.0	190	2.13	189	2.12	1420
HR 997	03	18.7	−18	34	5.8	5.9	8.2	122	8.07	122	8.08	linear
32 Eri AB	03	54.3	−02	57	4.5	4.8	5.9	348	6.84			
HR 1230	04	10.0	+80	42	5.2	5.6	6.3	154	0.68	155	0.67	372
ε Aur AB	05	02.0	+43	49	3.0	3.0	14.0	226	28.93			
14 Ori	05	07.9	+08	30	5.4	5.8	6.7	288	0.96	286	0.97	197
β Ori A,BC	05	14.5	−08	12	0.3	0.3	6.8	202	9.52			
14 Aur AB	05	15.4	+32	41	5.0	5.0	9.0	11	9.75			
16 Aur	05	18.2	+33	22	4.8	4.8	10.6	55	4.14			
HR 1771 AB	05	21.8	−24	46	5.1	5.4	6.6	99	3.50			
118 Tau AB	05	29.3	+25	09	5.4	5.8	6.7	209	4.76			
33 Ori AB	05	31.2	+03	18	5.4	5.7	6.7	27	1.87			
λ Ori AB	05	35.1	+09	56	3.3	3.5	5.5	44	4.46			
ζ Ori AB*	05	40.7	−01	57	1.7	1.9	3.7	167	2.18	167	2.18	1509
52 Ori	05	48.0	+06	27	5.3	6.0	6.0	222	1.20			
β Mon AB	06	28.8	−07	02	4.0	4.6	5.0	137	7.15			
β Mon AC	06	28.8	−07	02	4.2	4.6	5.4	130	9.91			
β Mon BC	06	28.8	−07	02	4.4	5.0	5.4	113	2.93			
HR 2384 AB*	06	29.8	−50	14	5.3	6.0	6.2	251	0.37	249	0.32	53
α CMa AB*	06	45.1	−16	43	−1.5	−1.5	8.5	74	10.78	72	10.94	50
12 Lyn AB	06	46.2	+59	27	4.8	5.4	6.0	66	1.91	66	1.91	908
12 Lyn AC	06	46.2	+59	27	4.8	5.4	7.1	311	8.50			
38 Gem AB	06	54.6	+13	11	4.7	4.8	7.8	143	7.32	142	7.32	1898
HR 2674	07	03.3	−59	11	5.5	5.8	6.8	86	1.41			
δ Gem	07	20.1	+21	59	3.5	3.6	8.2	229	5.47	229	5.45	1200
α Gem	07	34.6	+31	53	1.6	1.9	3.0	54	5.18	53	5.25	460
HR 2949 AB	07	38.8	−26	48	3.8	4.4	4.6	317	10.20			
α CMi AB*	07	39.3	+05	14	0.4	0.4	10.8	304	4.31	310	4.48	41
χ Gem	07	44.4	+24	24	3.7	3.7	8.2	241	7.24			
ζ Cnc AB	08	12.2	+17	39	4.9	5.3	6.3	13	1.13	10	1.13	60
ζ Cnc AB,C	08	12.2	+17	39	4.6	4.9	6.3	65	5.93	65	5.93	1115
HR 3432	08	37.3	−62	51	5.5	5.5	11.0	237	5.76			
ι Cnc	08	46.7	+28	46	4.0	4.1	6.0	308	30.13			
ε Hya AB,C	08	46.8	+06	25	3.4	3.5	6.7	308	2.82	309	2.82	589
ι UMa A,BC	08	59.2	+48	03	3.1	3.1	9.2	102	1.95	106	1.94	2084
σ^2 UMa AB	09	10.4	+67	08	4.8	4.9	8.9	347	4.40	347	4.43	970
38 Lyn AB	09	18.8	+36	48	3.8	3.9	6.1	224	2.54			
HR 3752	09	25.5	−61	57	5.8	5.8	9.6	330	8.77			
ψ Vel	09	30.7	−40	28	3.6	3.9	5.1	126	1.10	129	1.08	34
11 Lmi	09	35.7	+35	49	4.8	4.8	12.5	50	6.49	50	6.52	201
γ Sex AB	09	52.5	−08	06	5.1	5.4	6.4	41	0.52	40	0.51	78
γ Leo AB*	10	20.0	+19	50	2.1	2.4	3.6	127	4.73	127	4.73	554
μ Vel	10	46.8	−49	25	2.7	2.8	5.7	56	2.39	57	2.40	149
54 Leo	10	55.6	+24	45	4.3	4.5	6.3	112	6.72			
ξ UMa AB*	11	18.2	+31	32	3.8	4.3	4.8	166	1.93	161	2.01	60
ν UMa AB	11	18.5	+33	06	3.5	3.5	10.1	145	7.77			
57 UMa AB	11	29.1	+39	20	5.3	5.4	10.7	354	5.46			
α^1 Cru AB	12	26.6	−63	06	0.6	1.3	1.6	112	3.90			
24 Com	12	35.1	+18	23	4.8	5.1	6.3	270	20.06			
γ Vir AB	12	41.7	−01	27	2.8	3.5	3.5	2	2.55	0	2.69	169
β Mus*	12	46.3	−68	06	3.0	3.5	4.0	62	0.85	63	0.84	194
θ Vir AB*	13	09.9	−05	32	4.4	4.4	9.4	342	6.82			
α Com AB*	13	10.0	+17	32	4.4	4.9	5.5	192	0.43	192	0.50	26
ζ Uma AB	13	23.9	+54	56	2.0	2.2	3.9	153	14.45			
84 Vir	13	43.1	+03	32	5.5	5.6	8.3	228	2.64			
τ Boo	13	47.3	+17	27	4.5	4.5	11.1	70	1.50	74	1.43	964
HR 5386 A,BC*	14	23.4	+08	27	4.8	5.0	6.8	195	6.22			
φ Vir AB	14	28.2	−02	14	4.9	4.9	10.0	112	5.26			
α Cen AB*	14	39.6	−60	50	−0.3	0.0	1.3	315	4.15	327	4.46	80
π^1 Boo	14	40.7	+16	25	4.5	4.9	5.8	113	5.42			

* See note in text.

TABLE OF DOUBLE AND MULTIPLE STARS (continued)

Star	RA (2000) h	m	Dec °	′	Magnitudes comb.	A	B	2017.0 PA °	2017.0 Sep. ″	2018.0 PA °	2018.0 Sep. ″	Period y
ζ Boo AB	14	41.1	+13	44	3.8	4.5	4.6	288	0.37	286	0.33	125
ε Boo AB	14	45.0	+27	04	2.4	2.6	4.8	343	2.89			
ξ Boo AB	14	51.4	+19	06	4.6	4.8	7.0	300	5.47	299	5.39	152
44 Boo	15	03.8	+47	39	4.8	5.2	6.1	74	0.68	80	0.53	210
π Lup	15	05.1	−47	03	3.8	4.6	4.6	64	1.64			
η CrB AB	15	23.2	+30	17	5.0	5.6	6.0	225	0.53	238	0.46	42
δ Ser AB	15	34.8	+10	32	3.8	4.2	5.2	172	3.97	172	3.97	1038
$ζ^2$ CrB	15	39.4	+36	38	4.6	5.0	5.9	307	6.36			
$ι^1$ Nor AB	16	03.5	−57	47	4.7	5.2	5.8	115	0.17	67	0.16	27
ξ Sco AB	16	04.4	−11	22	4.3	5.2	4.9	7	1.10	9	1.11	46
ξ Sco AC	16	04.4	−11	22	5.0	5.2	7.3	43	7.53	43	7.53	1514
11 Sco AB	16	07.6	−12	45	5.7	5.8	9.8	263	2.79			
χ Her AB	16	08.1	+17	03	4.8	5.1	6.2	14	27.03	14	27.00	linear
σ CrB AB	16	14.7	+33	52	5.2	5.6	6.5	239	7.21	239	7.23	726
ρ Oph AB	16	25.6	−23	27	4.6	5.1	5.7	337	2.87	337	2.86	2398
α Sco	16	29.4	−26	26	0.9	1.0	5.4	277	2.58	277	2.57	1218
λ Oph AB	16	30.9	+01	59	3.8	4.2	5.2	43	1.42	44	1.41	129
HR 6246 AB	16	49.6	+13	16	5.7	5.7	10.0	44	5.21			
μ Dra AB	17	05.3	+54	28	4.9	5.7	5.7	1	2.54	0	2.56	812
η Oph AB	17	10.4	−15	44	2.4	3.1	3.3	230	0.55	229	0.53	88
α Her AB	17	14.6	+14	23	3.3	3.5	5.4	103	4.64	103	4.64	3600
36 Oph AB	17	15.3	−26	36	3.9	4.3	5.1	140	5.05	140	5.06	471
HR 6426 AB	17	19.0	−34	59	6.0	6.4	7.4	115	0.77	80	0.53	42
41 Ara AB	17	19.1	−46	38	5.6	5.6	8.9	258	10.55	258	10.62	953
95 Her	18	01.5	+21	36	4.3	4.9	5.2	257	6.37			
τ Oph AB	18	03.1	−08	11	4.8	5.3	5.9	288	1.52	288	1.51	257
70 Oph AB	18	05.5	+02	30	4.1	4.2	6.2	124	6.43	124	6.50	88
HR 6749–50	18	06.8	−43	25	4.9	5.7	5.7	359	1.74	359	1.74	450
59 Ser AB	18	27.2	+00	12	5.3	5.4	7.6	320	3.75			
HR 6997 AB	18	36.6	+33	28	5.4	5.4	9.4	201	6.85			
$ε^1$ Lyr AB	18	44.3	+39	40	4.8	5.2	6.1	345	2.33	345	2.32	1725
$ε^2$ Lyr CD	18	44.3	+39	40	4.6	5.3	5.4	75	2.39	75	2.39	724
β Cyg AB	19	30.7	+27	58	2.9	3.2	4.7	54	34.28			
16 Cyg AB	19	41.8	+50	32	5.3	6.0	6.2	133	39.76	133	39.78	13513
δ Cyg AB	19	45.0	+45	08	2.8	2.9	6.3	217	2.74	216	2.75	918
ε Dra	19	48.2	+70	16	3.9	4.0	6.9	21	3.24			
π Aql AB	19	48.7	+11	49	5.8	6.3	6.8	105	1.46			
ζ Sge AB,C	19	49.0	+19	09	5.0	5.0	9.0	311	8.44			
ψ Cyg AB*	19	55.6	+52	26	4.9	5.0	7.5	177	2.78			
16 Vul	20	02.0	+24	56	5.2	5.8	6.2	127	0.85	127	0.85	1201
χ Cep AB	20	08.9	+77	43	4.4	4.4	8.3	120	7.21			
β Cap AB*	20	21.0	−14	47	3.1	3.2	6.1	267	205.40			
β Del AB	20	37.5	+14	36	3.7	4.1	5.0	184	0.28	199	0.26	27
52 Cyg	20	45.6	+30	43	4.2	4.2	8.7	70	6.02			
γ Del	20	46.7	+16	07	3.9	4.4	5.0	265	8.94	265	8.92	3249
HR 8040 AB	20	58.5	+50	28	5.5	5.9	6.8	25	1.99			
ε Equ AB	20	59.1	+04	18	5.4	6.0	6.3	280	0.12	274	0.06	101
12 Aqr AB	21	04.1	−05	49	5.6	5.8	7.5	196	2.45			
τ Cyg AB	21	14.8	+38	03	3.7	3.8	6.6	197	0.96	192	0.98	50
μ Cyg AB	21	44.1	+28	45	4.5	4.8	6.2	323	1.52	324	1.50	789
λ Oct	21	50.9	−82	43	5.4	5.6	7.3	63	3.48			
30 Peg AB	22	20.5	+05	47	5.4	5.4	11.5	17	6.37			
Kruger 60 AB	22	28.0	+57	42	9.7	9.9	11.4	262	1.49	244	1.60	45
$ζ^2$ Aqr AB	22	28.8	−00	01	3.7	4.3	4.5	162	2.29	161	2.31	487
δ Cep AB	22	29.2	+58	25	4.0	4.2	6.1	282	21.75			
o Cep AB	23	18.6	+68	07	4.8	5.0	7.3	223	3.37	223	3.37	1505
72 Peg	23	34.0	+31	20	5.1	5.7	6.1	105	0.57	106	0.58	492
σ Cas AB	23	59.0	+55	45	4.9	5.0	7.2	326	3.07			

*See note in text.

CARBON STARS

BY RON OSTROMECKI AND RICHARD HUZIAK

Carbon stars are variable, late-stage red giants with periodicities ranging from around 70 days to over 400 days. Carbon in the outer atmosphere of the star absorbs blue light, resulting in the red appearance. Magnitude estimation can be tricky because of a phenomenon called the Purkinje effect, which can lead to overstating the brightness of the star. The newer spectral classification C encompasses the older classifications J, N, and R.

	RA (2000) **Dec**		**Tycho 2**		
Star	h m	° ′	**Δ*m*$_V$**	***B–V***	**Spec.**
WZ Cas	0 01.3	+60 21	6.8–7.7	2.8	C9,2JLi
SU And	0 04.6	+43 33	8.0–8.5	2.81	C6,4
ST Cas	0 17.5	+50 17	9.0–10.0	2.48	C4,4
VX And	0 19.9	+44 43	7.5–9.7	5.59	C4,5J
NQ Cas	0 24.6	+54 18	9.1–9.8	1.83	C4,5J
AQ And	0 27.5	+35 35	7.7–9.5	3.65	C5,4
W Cas	0 54.9	+58 34	7.8–12.5	3.6	C7,1e
Z Psc	1 16.1	+25 46	6.4–7.5	2.86	C7,2
WW Cas	1 33.5	+57 45	9.1–11.7	2.1	C5,5
R Scl	1 27.0	−32 33	5.7–8.1	4.4	C6,5ea
V Ari	2 15.0	+12 14	8.2–8.9	2.15	C5p,5
R For	2 29.3	−26 06	7.5–13.0	2.21	C4,3e
HD 16115	2 35.1	−9 27	8.15	1.21	C2,3
DY Per	2 35.3	+56 09	10.5–16.0	2.0	C4,5
V623 Cas	3 11.4	+57 54	7–3–8.0	2.3	C4,5J
Y Per	3 27.7	+44 11	8.1–11.3	2.52	C4,3e
V466 Per	3 41.5	+51 30	7.6–9.1	4.25	C5,5
U Cam	3 41.8	+62 39	7.5–9.0	3.95	C5.5e
AC Per	3 45.1	+44 47	9.0–9.6:	3.09	C6,3
UV Cam	4 05.9	+61 48	7.5–7.7	2.26	C5,3
T Cae	4 47.3	−36 13	7.7–8.7	2.59	C6,4
ST Cam	4 51.2	+68 10	6.7–8.0	3.38	C5,4
TT Tau	4 51.5	+28 32	7.9–9.0	2.3	C7,4
SU Tau	5 49.1	+19 04	9.1–18.0	1.1	C1,0
V346 Aur	4 52.6	+38 30	9.3–9.8	3.56	C8,1J
R Lep	4 59.6	−14 48	5.5–11.7	4.93	C7,6e
EL Aur	5 03.4	+50 38	8.7–9.2	3.4	C5,4
W Ori	5 05.4	+1 11	5.5–6.9	3.81	C5,4
TX Aur	5 09.1	+39 0	8.5–9.2	3.71	C5,4
SY Eri	5 09.8	−5 31	7.8–9.1	2.62	C6,3
UV Aur	5 21.8	+32 31	7.3–10.9	2.1	C7,2Jep
S Aur	5 27.1	+34 09	8.2–13.3	1.81	C4–5
RT Ori	5 33.2	+7 09	7.6–8.6	2.97	C6,4
SZ Lep	5 35.8	−25 44	7.4–7.9	2.4	C7,3
S Cam	5 41.0	+68 48	8.1–10.9	2.95	C7,3e
TU Tau	5 45.2	+24 25	7.7–8.8	2.75	C5,4
Y Tau	5 45.7	+20 42	6.4–7.3	3.44	C6.5,4e
FU Aur	5 48.1	+30 38	8.5–9.2	2.77	C7,2
TU Gem	6 10.9	+26 01	6.9–8.0	3.36	C6,4
GK Ori	6 17.7	+8 31	9.5–11	2.0	C4–5
V Aur	6 24.0	+47 42	8.5–13	3.87	C6,2e
BL Ori	6 25.5	+14 43	5.9–6.6	2.55	C6,3
RV Aur	6 34.7	+42 30	9.9–10.4:	3.47	C4,5
UU Aur	6 36.5	+38 27	5.1–6.6	3.1	C6,3
VW Gem	6 42.1	+31 27	8.1–8.5	2.68	C5,4
GY Mon	6 53.2	−4 35	8.1–9.1:	2.64	C6,3
NP Pup	6 54.4	−42 22	6.2–6.5	2.5	C–R3
RV Mon	6 58.4	+6 10	6.9–7.7	3.2	C5,3
V614 Mon	7 01.0	−3 15	7.0–7.4	1.96	C4,5J
RY Mon	7 06.9	−7 33	7.5–9.2	4.38	C6,5:
W CMa	7 08.1	−11 55	6.3–7.1	2.66	C6,3
R CMi	7 08.7	+10 01	7.5–11.6	2.55	C7,1Je
BM Gem	7 21.0	+24 60	8.9–10.0:	2.8	C5,4J
RU Cam	7 21.7	+69 40	8.1–9.8	1.16	C2,2e
BE CMa	7 23.6	−22 58	9.3–9.8:	2.46	C5,5J
NQ Gem	7 31.9	+24 30	7.4–8.2:	2.27	C6,2e
W CMi	7 48.8	+5 24	8.7–9.0	3.23	C7,2
RT Pup	8 05.3	−38 47	8.2–9.1	2.43	C6,2
RU Pup	8 07.5	−22 55	8.3–8.5:	3.61	C5,4
RY Hya	8 20.1	+2 46	8.3–11.1	3.77	C6,4e
AC Pup	8 22.7	−15 55	8.9–10.1	3.04	C5,4
YY Pyx	8 28.2	−27 15	9.0–9.7	4.52	C
UZ Pyx	8 46.6	−29 44	7.0–7.6	2.39	C5,5J
X Cnc	8 55.4	+17 14	5.7–6.9	3.37	C5,4
T Cnc	8 56.7	+19 51	7.6–10.5	4.32	C4,7
RT UMa	9 18.4	+51 24	8.6–9.6	3.69	C4,4
Y Hya	9 51.1	−23 01	6.2–7.4	4.17	C5,4
SZ Car	9 59.9	−60 13	7.2–7.8	2.81	C
AB Ant	10 11.9	−35 19	6.6–7.1	2.47	C6,3
U Hya	10 37.6	−13 23	4.6–5.4	2.8	C6.5,3
VY UMa	10 45.1	+67 25	5.7–6.3	2.59	C6,3
TZ Car	10 46.1	−65 37	8.7–9.1	2.43	C
V Hya	10 51.6	−21 15	6.0–12.3	5.55	C6,3e
SY Car	11 15.6	−57 56	8.8–9.0	2.48	C
S Cen	12 24.6	−49 26	8.1–8.6	2.04	C4,5
SS Vir	12 25.2	+0 46	6.0–9.6	4.2	C6,3e
Y CVn	12 45.1	+45 26	4.9–5.9	3.4	C5,4J
RU Vir	12 47.3	+4 09	8.1–14.2	4.5	C8,1e
RY Dra	12 56.4	+65 60	5.9–8.0	3.7	C4,5J
TT CVn	12 59.4	+37 49	8.0–8.6	1.99	C3,5CH
R CrB	15 48.6	+28 09	5.7–15.2	1.9	C0,0
V CrB	15 49.5	+39 34	6.9–12.6	3.12	C6,2e
RR Her	16 04.2	+50 30	8.1–9.4	3.0	C6.5e
V Oph	16 26.7	−12 26	7.3–11.6	4.38	C6,3e
SU Sco	16 40.6	−32 23	8.6–<13.0:	3.36	C5,5
TW Oph	17 29.7	−19 28	8.5–9.4	4.34	C5,5
SZ Sgr	17 44.9	−18 39	8.4–8.8	2.89	C7,3
SX Sco	17 47.5	−35 42	8.7–9.8	3.82	C5,4
T Dra	17 56.4	+58 13	7.2–13.5	2.7	C7,2e
FO Ser	18 19.4	−15 37	8.4–8.7	2.03	C4,5
SS Sgr	18 30.4	−16 54	9.6–10.2	3.82	C3,4
T Lyr	18 32.3	+36 60	7.5–9.2	5.46	C6,5
HK Lyr	18 42.8	+36 58	7.5–8.4	3.5	C7,4
RV Sct	18 44.4	−13 13	8.7–9.1	2.63	C4,4
S Sct	18 50.3	−7 54	6.6–7.3	3.32	C6,4
UV Aql	18 58.5	+14 22	8.6–9.8:	4.39	C5,4–5
V Aql	19 04.4	−5 41	6.7–7.2	4.0	C5,4
V1942 Sgr	19 19.2	−15 55	6.7–7.2	2.73	C6,4
UX Dra	19 21.6	+76 34	5.9–7.1	2.91	C7,3
AW Cyg	19 28.8	+46 03	8.2–9.2	3.87	C4,5
AQ Sgr	19 34.3	−16 22	7.0–7.4	3.26	C7,4
TT Cyg	19 41.0	+32 37	7.2–8.0	2.6	C5,4e
AX Cyg	19 57.2	+44 16	7.7–8.9	4.4	C4,5
V1469 Aql	20 01.1	+9 31	8.4–8.5:	2.04	C
SV Cyg	20 09.5	+47 52	8.5–9.8	3.15	C7.4
RY Cyg	20 10.4	+35 57	8.5–10.3	2.82	C5,5
RS Cyg	20 13.4	+38 44	6.5–9.5	2.8	C8,2e
RT Cap	20 17.1	−21 19	6.8–8.0	4.42	C6,4
WX Cyg	20 18.6	+37 27	8.8–13.2	2.59	C8,2JLi
U Cyg	20 19.6	+47 54	5.9–12.1	2.81	C8,2e
V778 Cyg	20 36.1	+60 05	10.2–11.4	3.2	C4,5J
BD Vul	20 37.3	+26 29	9.3–12.7	3.74	C7,3e
V Cyg	20 41.3	+48 08	7.7–13.9	4.04	C6,3e
S Cep	21 35.2	+78 37	7.4–12.9	4.45	C7,4e
V460 Cyg	21 42.0	+35 31	5.6–6.5	2.75	C6,4
RV Cyg	21 43.3	+38 01	7.8–8.4	4.52	C6,4e
RX Peg	21 56.4	+22 52	8.6–9.8	3.18	C4,4J
RZ Peg	22 05.9	+33 30	7.6–13.6	2.65	C9,1e
DG Cep	22 44.2	+61 44	8.7–9.7	3.17	C6,4
TV Lac	22 56.1	+54 14	8.7–9.5:	2.94	C4,5
VY And	23 01.8	+45 53	9.6–11.8	3.81	C4,4J
EW And	23 27.0	+49 31	8.8–9.4	3.33	C7,3
ST And	23 38.8	+35 46	7.7–11.8	3.53	C5,3e
TX Psc	23 46.4	+3 29	4.8–5.2	2.78	C7,2

COLOURED DOUBLE STARS

BY MICHEL DUVAL

The list of *coloured* double stars in the following table is limited to the most beautiful pairs and those pairs most easily viewed by beginning observers in small instruments (75-mm to 150-mm objective diameter).

Subjective appreciations are suggested regarding beauty (!!!—very beautiful, !!—beautiful, !—nice) and the difficulty of visually separating the pairs in the telescope (T—tight, VT—very tight, F—faint).

The abbreviations used for colours are: B—Blue, E—Emerald, G—Green, Gd—Gold, L—Lilac, O—Orange, R—Red, T—Topaz, V—Violet, W—White, and Y—Yellow. Different observers may perceive colours differently depending on their eye physiology, telescope optics, and local seeing conditions.

The coloured double stars β Cyg, α CVn, and ε Boo are better known as Albireo, Cor Caroli ("Heart of Charles"), and Izar, respectively.

An online supplement to this table at www.rasc.ca/handbook/supplements contains pairs that may be easier to observe with higher magnifications and/or larger instruments. A section has been added to this supplement for the 2017 edition showing the differences between perceptions of colours by our eyes and by photos taken at various sensitivities and time exposures. François Chevrefils of the Centre francophone de Montréal de la SRAC and Alan Whitman are thanked for reviewing this table and its supplement.

TABLE OF COLOURED DOUBLE STARS

	RA (2000) Dec			Magnitudes		Sep.	Colour		Notes	
Star	h	m	° ′	A	B	″	A	B	Beau.	Diff.
WINTER										
Σ 163 Cas	1	51	+64 51	6.8	9.1	34	O	B	!!	F
λ Ari	1	58	+23 36	5.0	6.7	37	Y	B	!!	
γ And	2	04	+42 19	2.3	5.4	10	O	B	!!!	
66 Cet	2	13	−2 24	5.7	7.7	16	O	B	!	F
59 And	2	11	+39 02	6.0	6.7	17	Y	B	!!	
η Per	2	51	+55 53	3.8	8.5	28	O	B	!!	F
32 Eri	3	54	−2 57	4.8	5.9	7	T	B	!!!	T
ε Per	3	58	+40 01	3.0	9.0	9	Y	G		VT
φ Tau	4	20	+27 21	5.1	7.5	49	Y	B		F
χ Tau	4	22	+25 38	5.4	8.5	19	Y	G		F
Σ 627 Ori	5	00	+3 37	6.6	7.0	21	Y	G	!!	
ρ Ori	5	13	+2 52	4.6	8.5	7	O	B	!	F
Σ 680 Tau	5	19	+20 08	6.0	10.0	9	Y	B		F
σ Ori	5	39	−2 37	3.9	6.5	42	O	B	!!	
26 Aur	5	39	+30 30	6.0	8.0	12	Y	B	!	F
ε Mon	6	24	+4 36	4.5	6.5	13	Y	B	!	F
5 Lyn	6	27	+58 25	5.2	9.8	32	Y	B	!	F
20 Gem	6	32	+17 47	6.3	6.9	20	Y	B	!	
38 Gem	6	54	+13 11	5.0	7.8	7	Y	B	!!	T
h3945 CMa	7	17	− 23 19	4.8	5.8	27	Y	B	!!!	
δ Gem	7	20	+21 59	3.5	8.5	6	Y	R	!!	T
κ Gem	7	44	+24 24	3.6	8.1	7	O	B		F, VT
Σ 1149 CMi	7	49	+3 13	7.8	9.2	22	Y	B	!	F
Σ 1183 Mon	8	06	−9 14	6.2	7.8	31	Y	G	!	F
ι Cnc	8	47	+28 46	4.0	6.6	31	Y	B	!!	

TABLE OF COLOURED DOUBLE STARS (continued)

Star	RA (2000) h	m	Dec ° ′	Magnitudes A	B	Sep. ″	Colour A	B	Notes Beau.	Diff.
SPRING										
Σ 1321 UMa	9	14	+52 41	8.0	8.0	18	Y	B		
Σ 1360 Leo	9	30	+10 35	8.0	9.0	14	B	G		
6 Leo	9	32	+9 43	5.4	9.3	37	O	G		
γ Leo	10	20	+19 50	2.4	3.6	5	O	Y		VT
35 Sex	10	43	+04 45	6.9	8.4	7	O	B		
54 Leo	10	56	+24 45	4.3	6.3	6	Y	B	!	T
88 Leo	11	32	+14 22	6.4	9.1	15	Y	B	!	F
2 CVn	12	16	+40 40	5.9	8.7	11	Gd	B		
17 Vir	12	22	+05 18	6.6	10.0	21	B	O		
24 Com	12	35	+18 23	5.1	6.3	20	Gd	B	!!	
32 Cam	12	49	+83 25	5.0	6.0	21	Y	B		
35 Com	12	53	+21 15	5.2	9.8	28	Y	B		
α CVn	12	56	+38 19	2.9	5.6	19	B	G	!!!	
ε Boo	14	45	+27 04	2.6	4.8	3	O	B		VT
ξ Boo	14	51	+19 06	4.8	7.0	6	Y	O		VT
ζ CrB	15	39	+36 38	5.0	6.0	6	Y	B	!!!	
SUMMER										
β Sco	16	05	−19 48	2.6	4.9	14	B	O	!	
κ Her	16	08	+17 03	5.0	6.0	28	Y	R	!	
α Her	17	15	+14 23	3.5	5.4	5	R	G	!	VT
ψ Dra	17	42	+72 09	4.9	6.1	30	Y	L	!	
95 Her	18	01	+21 36	5.0	5.1	6	G	B	!!	T
59 Ser	18	27	+0 12	5.4	7.7	4	Y	G	!!	VT
ζ Lyr	18	45	+37 36	4.3	5.9	44	Y	G	!!	
o Dra	18	51	+59 23	4.8	7.8	34	Gd	L	!!	F
11 Aql	18	59	+13 37	5.3	9.3	19	Y	B	!!	
β Cyg	19	31	+27 58	3.1	5.1	35	Y	B	!!!	
57 Aql	19	54	−8 14	6.0	6.0	36	Y	G	!!	
17 Cyg	19	46	+33 44	5.0	9.0	26	R	B	!	F
OΣ 394 Cyg	20	00	+36 25	7.0	10.0	11	O	B		
26 Cyg	20	01	+50 06	5.0	9.0	41	Y	B		F
31 Cyg	20	13	+46 44	4.0	7.0	107	O	B	!!	
σ Cap	20	19	−19 07	5.4	9.4	56	O	B	!	F
52 Cyg	20	45	+30 43	4.0	9.0	6	Y	B		
AUTUMN										
γ Del	20	47	+16 07	4.4	5.0	9	O	G	!	T
1 Peg	21	22	+19 48	4.2	7.6	36	O	V		
h 1647 Peg	21	29	+22 11	6.1	10.2	41	O	B		
β Cep	21	29	+70 34	3.2	8.6	13	W	B	!	T
41 Aqr	22	14	−21 04	5.6	6.7	5	Y	B		VT
δ Cep	22	29	+58 25	4.2	6.1	41	Y	B	!!	
Σ 2978 Peg	23	07	+32 50	6.4	7.5	8	Y	B	!	
57 Peg	23	10	+8 41	5.1	9.7	32	Y	B		F
Σ 2991 Peg	23	13	+11 04	6.0	10.0	33	Y	B	!	F
Ψ[1] Aqr	23	16	−9 05	4.5	10.0	49	Y	B	!	
94 Aqr	23	19	−13 27	5.3	7.0	12	Y	G	!!	
OΣΣ 254 Cas	00	01	+60 21	7.6	8.7	57	R	B	!!	
Σ 3053 Cas	00	02	+66 06	5.9	7.3	15	O	B		
42 Psc	00	22	+13 29	6.4	10.3	29	T	E		
12 Cet	00	30	−3 57	6.0	10.8	12	Y	B		
55 Psc	00	39	+21 26	5.6	8.5	7	O	B	!!	F
η Cas	00	49	+57 49	3.5	7.2	13	W	G	!	
Σ 80 Cet	00	59	+0 47	8.0	9.0	28	Y	B		

VARIABLE STARS

BY STELLA KAFKA AND ELIZABETH O. WAAGEN

Variable stars are stars whose brightness changes on timescales from minutes to years. They reveal many stellar properties. Depending upon their type, variables can tell us their age, mass, radius, temperature, luminosity, internal and external structure, composition, and evolutionary history. Systematic observation of variable stars is an area in which amateur astronomers can make a valuable contribution to astronomy.

For beginning observers, simplified charts of the fields of four different types of bright variable stars are shown below (see www.aavso.org for authoritative versions). On each chart the magnitudes (with decimal point omitted) of several suitable comparison stars are shown. A brightness estimate of the variable is made using two comparison stars, one brighter, one fainter than the variable. The magnitude, date, and time of each observation are recorded. When a number of observations have been made, a graph of magnitude versus date can be plotted. The shape of this *light curve* depends upon the type of variable. Further information about variable-star observing is available from the American Association of Variable Star Observers (AAVSO), 49 Bay State Road, Cambridge MA 02138, USA (email: aavso@aavso.org).

Table 1 is a list of long-period variables, brighter than mag. 8.0 at maximum and north of –20°. The first column (the Harvard designation of the star) gives the position for the year 1900: the first four characters give the hours and minutes of right ascension, the next three the declination in degrees. The **Max.** column gives the mean maximum magnitude. The **Min.** column gives the mean minimum magnitude. The period (**Per.**) is in days. **Epoch** gives the predicted date of the earliest maximum occurring this year; by adding multiples of the period to this epoch, the dates of subsequent maxima can be found. These variables may reach maximum two or three

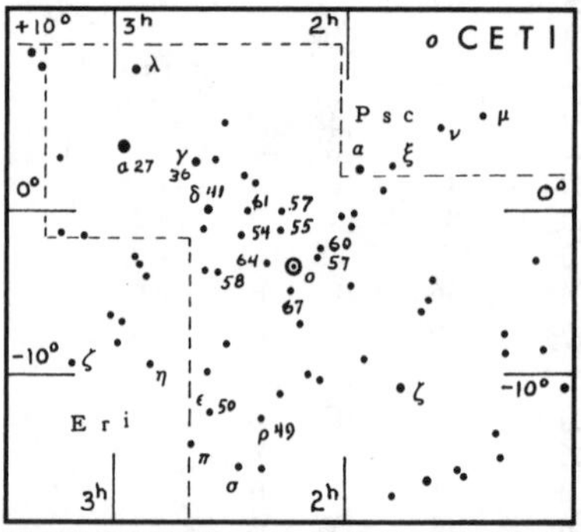

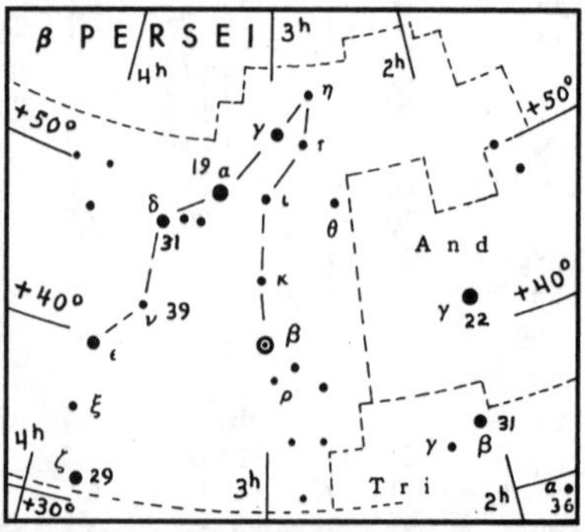

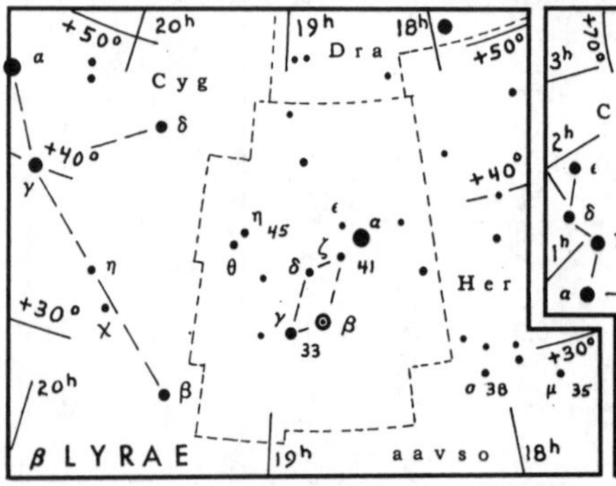

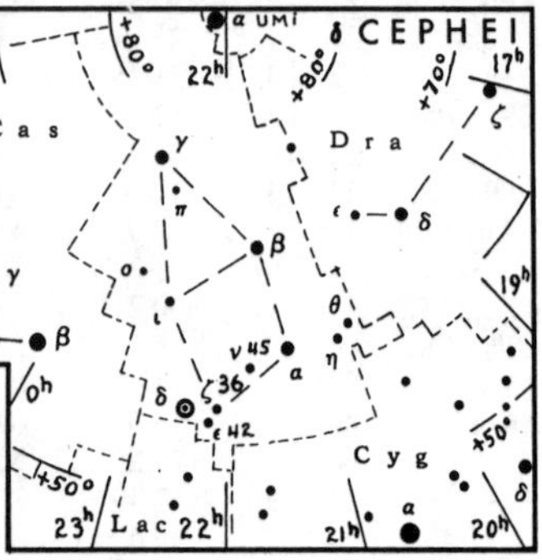

TABLE 1—LONG-PERIOD VARIABLE STARS NORTH OF −20°

Variable		Max. m_v	Min. m_v	Per. d	Epoch 2017	Variable		Max. m_v	Min. m_v	Per. d	Epoch 2017
0017+55	T Cas	7.9	11.9	445	Apr. 23	1425+39	V Boo	7.0	11.3	260	Jan. 21
0018+38	R And	6.9	14.3	409	Jun. 13	1432+27	R Boo	7.2	12.3	223	Jul. 13
0211+43	W And	7.4	13.7	396	Feb. 14	1517+31	S CrB	7.3	12.9	361	Aug. 20
0214–03A	o Cet	3.4	9.3	332	Feb. 15	1546+39	V CrB	7.5	11.0	358	Sep. 20
0228–13	U Cet	7.5	12.6	235	Apr. 26	1546+15	R Ser	6.9	13.4	356	Jun. 30
0231+33	R Tri	6.2	11.7	267	Aug. 24	1606+25	RU Her	8.0	13.7	485	Sep. 26
0430+65	T Cam	8.0	13.8	373	Oct. 19	1621+19	U Her	7.5	12.5	406	Jul. 12
0455–14	R Lep	6.8	9.6	427	May 29	1621–12	V Oph	7.5	10.2	297	May 9
0509+53	R Aur	7.7	13.3	458	———	1632+66	R Dra	7.6	12.4	246	Apr. 14
0549+20A	U Ori	6.3	12.0	368	Apr. 22	1647+15	S Her	7.6	12.6	307	May 29
0617–02	V Mon	7.0	13.1	340	Jul. 24	1702–15	R Oph	7.6	13.3	306	Aug. 1
0653+55	R Lyn	7.9	13.8	379	Sep. 18	1717+23	RS Her	7.9	12.5	220	May 6
0701+22A	R Gem	7.1	13.5	370	Feb. 16	1805+31	T Her	8.0	12.8	165	Mar. 3
0703+10	R CMi	8.0	11.0	338	May 3	1811+36	W Lyr	7.9	12.2	198	May 3
0727+08	S CMi	7.5	12.6	333	Apr. 10	1833+08	X Oph	6.8	8.8	329	May 4
0811+12	R Cnc	6.8	11.2	362	Jul. 21	1901+08	R Aql	6.1	11.5	270	Feb. 10
0816+17	V Cnc	7.9	12.8	272	May 28	1910–17	T Sgr	8.0	12.6	395	Mar. 12
0848+03	S Hya	7.8	12.7	257	Apr. 11	1910–19	R Sgr	7.3	12.5	270	Apr. 6
0850–08	T Hya	7.8	12.6	289	Mar. 3	1934+49	R Cyg	7.5	13.9	426	Mar. 15
0939+34	R LMi	7.1	12.6	372	Apr. 26	1940+48	RT Cyg	7.3	11.8	190	May 17
0942+11	R Leo	5.8	10.0	310	Apr. 30	1946+32	χ Cyg	5.2	13.4	408	Oct. 29
1037+69	R UMa	7.5	13.0	302	Jun. 29	2016+47	U Cyg	7.2	10.7	463	Nov. 7
1214–18	R Crv	7.5	13.8	317	Oct. 17	2044–05	T Aqr	7.7	13.1	202	Jun. 8
1220+01	SS Vir	6.8	8.9	364	Apr. 26	2108+68	T Cep	6.0	10.3	388	May 27
1231+60	T UMa	7.7	12.9	257	Jun. 9	2137+53	RU Cyg	8.0	9.4	233	Mar. 25
1233+07	R Vir	6.9	11.5	146	Mar. 1	2301+10	R Peg	7.8	13.2	378	Apr. 25
1239+61	S UMa	7.8	11.7	226	Jan. 28	2307+59	V Cas	7.9	12.2	229	May 13
1315+46	V CVn	6.8	8.8	192	Jul. 11	2315+08	S Peg	8.0	13.0	319	Sep. 19
1327+06	S Vir	7.0	12.7	375	Apr. 13	2338–15	R Aqr	6.5	10.3	387	May 18
1344+40	R CVn	7.7	11.9	329	Oct. 24	2353+50	R Cas	7.0	12.6	430	Apr. 26
1425+84	R Cam	8.3	13.2	270	Sep. 25	2357–15	W Cet	7.6	14.4	351	Apr. 19

weeks before or after the epoch and may remain at maximum for several weeks. This table has been prepared with AAVSO observations.

Table 2 lists stars that are representative of some other types of variables. Data for preparation of predicted maxima of Cepheids are from the online edition of the General Catalogue of Variable Stars (www.sai.msu.su/groups/cluster/gcvs/gcvs), except for δ Cep, which are from www.aavso.org/vsx, the AAVSO International Variable Star Index (VSX); data for eclipsing binaries are from the Mt. Suhora Observatory, Cracow Pedagogical University Database (www.as.up.krakow.pl/ephem; J. M. Kreiner, 2015) and for β Per, from VSX; and the determination of the maximum of RR Lyr is based on elements from J.-F. Le Borgne (2015, private communication).

DESCRIPTION OF VARIABLE-STAR TYPES

Variable stars can be divided into two main classes: intrinsic variables, in which the variation is due to changes of a single star, and extrinsic variables, in which the variation is due to interaction of multiple stars or objects within a stellar system. There are many cases of overlapping variability types, such as a Mira pulsating variable as part of an eclipsing binary system. Intrinsic variables fall into three main classes: (1) pulsating stars, in which periodic expansion and contraction of the stellar surface occur; (2) eruptive variables, in which solarlike flares occur; and (3) rotating stars, in which shape distortion or star spots cause variation. Extrinsic variables consist of two main classes: (4) binary systems, in which variability is caused by orbital motion or mass transfer; and (5) cataclysmic variables, in which accretion onto a compact object can cause it to go into outburst. With modern detectors, about 1% of all stars

TABLE 2—OTHER TYPES OF VARIABLE STARS

Variable		Min. m_V	Max. m_V	Type	Spectral Class	Period d	Epoch 2017 UT
0053+81	U Cep	6.7	9.8	Ecl.	B7Ve + G8III-IV	2.493086	Jan. 1.98*
0301+40	β Per	2.1	3.3	Ecl.	B8V + G8III	2.86736	†
0355+12	λ Tau	3.5	4.0	Ecl.	B3V + A4IV	3.952934	Jan. 2.94*
0416+19	T Tau	9.6	10.8	INT	F8Ve-K1IV-Ve(T)		
0530–05	T Ori	9.5	12.3	INA	B8-A3EpV		
0539+09	FU Ori	8.7	9.8	FU	F2peI-II		
0619+07	T Mon	5.6	6.6	Cep	F7Iab-K1Iab+A0V	27.024649	Jan. 2.86
0658+20	ζ Gem	3.6	4.2	Cep	F7Ib-G3Ib	10.149806#	Jan. 8.40
0749+22	U Gem	8.6	15.5	UGSS	Pec(UG) + M4.5V		
1846+33	β Lyr	3.4	4.3	Ecl.	B8II-IIIep	12.940617#	Jan. 10.61*
1922+42	RR Lyr	6.9	8.0	RR Lyr	A5.0-F7.0	0.5674#	Jan. 1.10
1946+35	CI Cyg	8.9	12.2	ZAND	Pec Bep + M5III		
1947+00	η Aql	3.5	4.3	Cep	F6Ib-G4Ib	7.176641	Jan. 4.61
2138+43	SS Cyg	8.0	12.5	UGSS	K5V + (Pec)UG		
2225+57	δ Cep	3.5	4.4	Cep	F5Ib-G1Ib	5.36627	Jan. 1.66

* Minimum # Changing period; revised for 2017.

† Algol; predictions for all minima in 2017 are given in THE SKY MONTH BY MONTH section (p. 98).

are found to be variable. Brief and general descriptions of the major types in each class are given below.

(1) Pulsating Variables

δ *Scuti* stars are variables that have both radial and nonradial pulsation modes with periods of 0.01–0.2 day and amplitudes from barely measurable to nearly a full magnitude. They are of A–F spectral types. Typical representative: CY Aquarii.

Cepheids are variables that pulsate with periods of 1–70 days. They have high luminosity, and the amplitude of light variation ranges from 0.1 to 2 magnitudes. The prototypes of the group, classical Cepheids, are located in open clusters and obey the well-known period-luminosity relation. They are of late F spectral class at maximum and G to K at minimum. The later (cooler) the spectral class of a classical Cepheid at minimum, the longer is its period. Typical representative of classical Cepheids: δ Cephei.

RR Lyrae stars are giant variables with periods of 0.2–1.2 days and amplitude of light variation between 0.5 and 2 magnitudes. They are usually of spectral class A. About 20% of RR Lyrae stars exhibit the Blazhko effect (a long-term variation in period and amplitude), including the prototype of the class itself, RR Lyrae.

RV Tauri stars are supergiant variables with a characteristic light curve of alternating deep and shallow minima. The periods, defined as the interval between two deep minima, range from 30 to 150 days. The amplitude of light variation may be as much as 3 magnitudes. Many show long-term cyclic variation of 500 to 9000 days. Generally, the spectral classes range from F–G at maximum to K–M at minimum light. Typical representative: R Scuti.

Long-period (Mira Ceti) variables are giants that vary with visual amplitudes from 2.5 to 5 magnitudes or more. They have well-defined periodicity, ranging from 80 to 1000 days. They show characteristic emission spectra of late spectral classes M, C, and S. Typical representative: ο Ceti (Mira).

Semiregular variables are giants or supergiants showing appreciable periodicity accompanied by intervals of irregularities in light variation. The periods range from 30 to 1000 days with visual amplitudes not more than 1 to 2 magnitudes in general. Typical representative: R Ursae Minoris.

(2) Eruptive Variables

Eruptive variables are those with flares occurring in their chromospheres, along with shell mass ejections and other stellar-wind phenomena. The ejected matter can cause brightness increases or drops.

FU Orionis variables are young stars embedded in nebulae. Usually they have large-amplitude fluctuations that may take years to complete. Typical representative: FU Orionis.

T Tauri variables are young stars that have not yet reached the Zero Age Main Sequence. They are characterized by irregular variations of several magnitudes, often accompanied by emission lines and brightness fadings, probably due to dust. Typical representative: T Tauri.

UV Ceti stars are late-type dwarfs that display flare activity. The flares can range from several tenths of a magnitude to many magnitudes in size, lasting a few minutes. Typical representative: UV Ceti.

R Coronae Borealis stars are highly luminous variables that have nonperiodic drops in brightness from 1 to 9 magnitudes due to the formation of "carbon soot" in the star's atmosphere. The duration of minima varies from a few months to years. Members of this group fall into the F–K and R spectral classes. Typical representative: R Coronae Borealis.

Irregular variables are stars that at times show only a trace of periodicity or none at all. Often, poorly studied stars are placed in this category. Typical representative: RX Leporis.

(3) Rotating Variables

Rotating variables are stars with nonuniform surface brightness, caused by star spots, mass outflow, or even shape distortion.

γ Cassiopeiae variables are rapidly rotating B stars with mass outflow, forming equatorial rings or disks that can cause temporary fading episodes. Typical representative: γ Cassiopeiae.

RS Canum Venaticorum variables are rapidly rotating stars, usually close binary systems that undergo small amplitude changes in light that may be due to dark or bright spots on their surface. Eclipses may also be present in such systems (due to binarity). Typical representative: RS Canum Venaticorum.

(4) Binary Systems

Binary systems are composed of two stars or a planet around a star, in which the orbital plane is oriented such that one object crosses the disk of another object. These are usually divided into four main classes: detached, semi-detached, contact, and transitting. The first three relate to whether two stars overfill their Roche lobes or are completely isolated from one another.

Detached systems are those in which the two stars are completely isolated from one another. Light curves usually show constant light between eclipses; eclipse depth can be quite large, depending on the relative brightness of the stellar pair. Typical representative: β Persei (Algol).

Semi-detached systems have one member (the donor) overflowing its Roche lobe, with mass accreting onto the other star. Typical representative: U Cephei.

Contact binaries have both members within a common envelope. These stars often exhibit ellipsoidal variations, with the light curves continuously varying throughout the orbit. Typical representative: β Lyrae.

Transitting systems are a new class of binary, in which a planet crosses the disk of the parent star. These variations are quite small (a few hundredths of a magnitude at best), but give a great deal of information about the host star and about the transitting planet. Typical representative: HD 209458.

(5) Cataclysmic Variables

These are semi-detached binaries that typically show outbursts caused by thermonuclear runaway on either the star surface or on an accretion disk. They are a product of accretion from one star of a binary system onto the other star, usually a compact object such as a white dwarf or neutron star.

Novae consist of a normal star and a white dwarf, whose combined magnitude increases 7 to 16 magnitudes in brightness in one to several hundred days. After the outburst, the star fades slowly, returning to initial brightness in several years or decades. Near maximum brightness, the spectrum is generally similar to A or F giants. Typical representative: CP Puppis (Nova 1942).

Supernovae increase in brightness by 20 or more magnitudes due to a gigantic stellar explosion that destroys the system. The general appearance of the light curve is similar to novae. Typical representative: CM Tauri (supernova of AD 1054, and now the central star of the Crab Nebula).

U Geminorum types are dwarf novae that have long intervals of quiescence at minimum with sudden rises to maximum. Depending upon the star, the amplitude of eruptions ranges from 2 to 6 magnitudes, and the duration between outbursts can be tens to thousands of days. Most of these stars are spectroscopic binaries with periods of a few hours. Typical representative: SS Cygni.

SU Ursae Majoris types are dwarf novae similar to U Gem and Z Cam stars in their physical and spectroscopic properties. They have frequent, faint, and narrow eruptions that last from one to a few days, along with infrequent, bright, and long eruptions—superoutbursts—that last 10 to 20 days. During superoutbursts, there are small-amplitude, periodic variations—superhumps—that are 2% to 3% longer than the orbital period of the system. Typical representative: SU Ursae Majoris.

Z Camelopardalis types are variables similar to U Gem stars in their physical and spectroscopic properties. They show brightness variations interrupted by intervals of constant brightness—standstills—lasting for several cycles, approximately one-third of the way from maximum to minimum. Typical representative: Z Camelopardalis.

VARIABLE STAR OF THE YEAR: T CORONAE BOREALIS

BY ULISSE MUNARI AND ELIZABETH O. WAAGEN

T CrB (HD 143454, Nova CrB 1866 and 1946, SpT M3III, V=2—10, RA 15h 59m 30.16s (J2000), Dec +25° 55′ 12.6″) was first catalogued as an anonymous 9.5-mag. star (BD+26.2765) in the Bonner Durchmusterung (1862 edition) that F. Argelander compiled from his visual survey of the sky with the 78-mm Bonn (Germany) refractor.

★

T CrB rose to world-wide attention on 1866 May 12, when it suddenly jumped to 2nd mag., from which it declined to quiescence in about a month. At that time, it was one of the few known novae, and the brightest in quiescence. On 1946 Feb. 9, T CrB was again in outburst, exactly replicating the 1866 show, and thus becoming a recurrent nova, the fifth such known after T Pyx, U Sco, RS Oph, and CI Aql. In both outbursts, about four months after the primary maximum T CrB displayed a mysterious secondary maximum peaking at about V=8, for which a convincing explanation is still lacking. Such a secondary maximum is unique to T CrB.

Since the 1946 outburst, T CrB has been quiet, with its optical spectrum dominated by emission from an M3III giant in a 227.5-day orbit around a white-dwarf companion near the Chandrasekhar mass limit of 1.4 solar masses, thus probably heading for a Supernova Type Ia explosion. Should that happen, at 1-kpc distance it would become a daylight object at V=–9. The M3III cool giant fills its Roche lobe, and its distorted shape drives the ellipsoidal variability (2 maxima and 2 minima per orbital cycle) that—thanks to the high orbital inclination—dominates the behaviour in quiescence. The amplitude of the ellipsoidal variability is 0.63, 0.49, 0.42, and 0.34 mag. in B, V, R, and I, respectively. At the shortest wavelengths (primarily in U, and to a lesser extent in B), chaotic, short-time scale (hours) and large variability (several tenths of a magnitude) are observed. This flickering is a direct manifestation of the mass transfer from the M giant to the white dwarf, via an accretion disk and associated hot spot.

Since 2015, T CrB has been in an unexpected super-active state, with (i) a spectrum now dominated by bright emission lines of high ionization, (ii) the flickering almost suppressed, and (iii) a large increase in brightness peaking at V=9.2 and B=10.0 mag. in Apr. 2016, a whole magnitude brighter than typical since the 1946 nova outburst. Something most unusual is going on! Very similar behaviour was observed about 70 years after the 1866 outburst, and we are currently 70 years past the 1946 outburst. It is therefore tempting to guess that T CrB may erupt around 2026. A certain degree of unpredictability notoriously affects such predictions, however, so best start immediately keeping a close watch, not only to catch the nova outburst from its earliest beginnings, but also to document the (largely unknown) changes in behaviour on the way to a nova outburst.

Nightly photometric observations of T CrB should be made using standard BVRI filters and transformed to the standard system as long as the current super-active state persists. For comparison with the long record of filtered observations, B and V will be most valuable. During the current super-active state, the B emission is completely dominated by and therefore traces the amount of the M3III giant's wind ionized by energetic radiation from the hot companion. In quiescence, this wind is neutral and B traces the ellipsoidal distortion of the M3III giant and the heating of its side facing the white dwarf, which causes the corresponding minimum to be (much) brighter than the other one. B-band time-series observations would allow investigation of how the amplitude of flickering changes with mean brightness; this flickering is much more evident in U. Because T CrB is so red, be sure your U and/or B filters do not leak at the reddest wavelengths. Visual estimates are valuable too, because they allow direct comparison with the century of T CrB visual data. Finally, valuable low-resolution spectroscopy is within reach of a 10–12 inch telescope, while high resolution able to resolve the profile of emission lines and trace their evolution requires larger instruments.

Please submit observations promptly to the AAVSO via the website **www.aavso.org/WebObs**, especially if T CrB appears brighter than V=9.0.

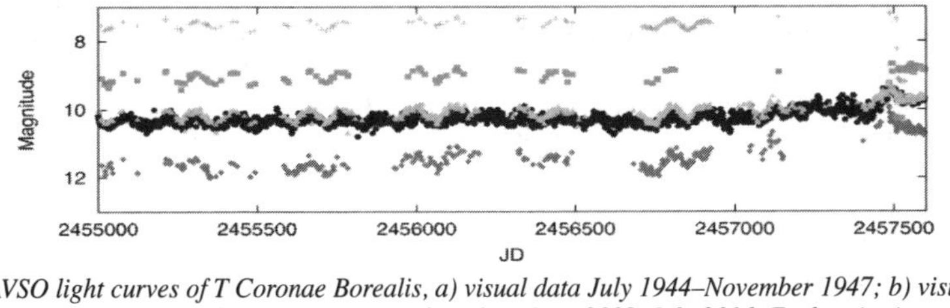

AAVSO light curves of T Coronae Borealis, a) visual data July 1944–November 1947; b) visual, B (diamond), V (triangle), R (square), I (plus) data June 2009–July 2016. Each point is a one-day average of observations in the AAVSO International Database; 387 observers worldwide contributed 20 027 observations to these light curves.

EXPIRED STARS

BY ROY BISHOP

Stars are where the action is, and the action is fuelled by gravitation and thermonuclear fusion. Gravitation, the midwife and undertaker, forms a star, heats it to the temperatures necessary to ignite successive stages of fusion reactions, and when nuclear fuel runs out, crushes the ashes of the star into one of three final states: white dwarf, neutron star, or black hole. Thermonuclear fusion, powered by the strong nuclear interaction between protons and neutrons, merely delays the onset of further collapse and higher temperatures. In the case of our Sun, the first and by far the longest delay, the "hang-up" provided by hydrogen-to-helium fusion, is already half over.

White Dwarfs

Stars comparable to our Sun have insufficient gravity to reach the temperatures necessary to form nuclei heavier than carbon or oxygen. When the thermal support pressure generated by fusion wanes, gravity gradually crushes the central portion of the star. If the mass of this core is less than 1.4 solar masses (a limit discovered by a leading astrophysicist of the 20th century, Subramanyan Chandrasekhar), the collapse halts at a very hot, Earth-sized remnant known as a white dwarf. At this point, the squeeze of gravity is offset by *electron degeneracy pressure*, an intrinsic aspect of the wave–particle nature of matter and the same pressure responsible for the stability and size of an atom. However, in the case of a white dwarf, the pressure is such that the electrons are not tied to individual atomic nuclei but occupy the whole star. In this sense, the star has become a giant atom. In physics jargon: electrons are fermions (i.e. they obey Fermi–Dirac quantum statistics) and hence abide by the Pauli Exclusion Principle, which dictates that no two electrons can occupy the same quantum state. This results in an immense pressure, sufficient to prevent further collapse, provided the mass is less than the Chandrasekhar limit. White-dwarf diameters are about 1% that of our Sun, which has a nearly water-like average density (1 g/cm^3). Thus a cubic centimetre of white-dwarf material has a mass near 100^3 g or one tonne (like a Honda Fit crushed into a sugar cube).

Because of their immense thermal energy and small surface area, white dwarfs cool extremely slowly. The Universe is not yet old enough for any white dwarf to have cooled sufficiently to become a "black dwarf." Also, white dwarfs are intrinsically very faint; thus only those close to the Solar System can be seen.

Only one white dwarf is easily observable with a small telescope: **Omicron 2 Eridani B** (also designated 40 Eridani B), located 16.3 light-years from Earth. Omicron 2 Eridani A, the bright (mag. 4.4) companion to the dim (mag. 9.5) white dwarf, is shown on the JANUARY ALL-SKY MAP on p. 340: o^2 Eri A is the eastern (left-hand) member of the close pair of stars located due west of the word "Rigel." Omicron 2 Eridani B, the white dwarf, is located only 83″ east-southeast of o^2 Eri A (position angle ≈110°). Remarkably, stars A and B are accompanied by a third star, a faint (mag. 11.2) red-dwarf star, o^2 Eri C, which resides only 9″ north of B. (There is a brighter and closer white dwarf, the companion of Sirius, α CMa B, but it is usually lost in the glare of Sirius. See THE NEAREST STARS (p. 286) and DOUBLE AND MULTIPLE STARS (p. 291) for more information on both of these stellar systems.)

For the observer with a small telescope, o^2 Eri B is the only Earth-sized object visible in the depths of interstellar space, the only visible object with a mass density far exceeding that of ordinary matter, the only accessible star no longer powered by nuclear reactions, and the only star that has expired and can still be seen.

Neutron Stars

For a large star of about eight or more solar masses, energy-releasing reactions end in its centre with the fusion of silicon nuclei into iron. Iron has the most tightly bound nucleus (per nuclear particle) and hence is no good as a fuel for further fusion. Electron degeneracy pressure supports the inert iron core until silicon fusion in a surrounding shell supplies enough additional iron to push the inert core over the Chandrasekhar limit. Gravity then overwhelms electron degeneracy pressure, and the core collapses in less than a second, so quickly that, momentarily, the outer layers of the star stay where they were. Gravitation-induced temperatures in the core rise past 10^{10} K, sufficient to disassemble heavy nuclei synthesized over the life of the star. That absorbs energy, accelerating the collapse. Also, electrons attain sufficient energy to combine with protons to form neutrons and neutrinos, another energy-absorbing reaction that also removes electrons, further hastening the collapse.

Provided the infalling mass is less than about three solar masses, like a hammer striking an anvil, when the core reaches a diameter of about 20 km, the infall is violently arrested by a combination of *neutron* degeneracy pressure and the short-range repulsive nature of the strong nuclear force, the same agents that govern the size and structure of the nuclei of atoms of ordinary matter. With a diameter 500 times smaller than that of a white dwarf, the density at this stage is 500^3 larger, 100 million tonnes per cubic centimetre (like an aircraft carrier crushed to the size of the ball of a ballpoint pen). That is the density of ordinary atomic nuclei. The star's core has effectively become a gigantic nucleus, composed primarily of neutrons.

The abrupt rebound of the nearly rigid central core reverses the infall of the adjacent layers, turning the implosion into a spectacular explosion, a Type II supernova. The explosion mechanism is complex and not yet well understood, but appears to involve interactions with the immense numbers of neutrinos generated in the neutron production, and possibly acoustic waves generated by vibrations of the core as it is pummeled by infalling material within a second of its formation. The gravitational energy released in the sudden collapse of the couple of solar masses now locked in the central neutron star is about 10^{46} J. That is far more energy than our Sun will produce in its entire 10-billion-year lifetime.

Over the next several thousand years, the remnants of the outer layers of the star form an expanding, glowing cloud of gas and dust, seeding interstellar space with the heavy chemical elements (oxygen, silicon, iron, uranium, etc.) synthesized in its outer layers both before and during the supernova explosion. The potassium ions moving in the neurons of your brain as you read these words emerged from such a conflagration some 5 billion years ago.

No neutron stars are visible in a small telescope, although one is *indirectly* visible in the **Crab Nebula**, M1. The Crab supernova was a bright, naked-eye star in the skies of Earth in the year 1054 AD, although it had taken 6000 years for the light of the explosion to reach our planet. The nebula we see today is the expanding debris cloud as it was nearly 1000 years after the initial explosion.

The Crab Nebula glows across the electromagnetic spectrum, from radio waves to gamma rays, powered by the rapid but decreasing spin of the neutron star at its centre. The glow of the debris cloud is like the glow of a red-hot disk brake slowing the spin of a wheel. The visible light from the cloud is *synchrotron radiation* emitted by electrons as they spiral in the tangled magnetic field of the neutron star. Nowhere else in the heavens is such an exotic light visible in a small telescope, polarized light with the brilliance of a thousand suns, emitted not by atoms but by free electrons being flung about by a spinning neutron star. The neutron star itself is known as a *pulsar* because it flashes (30 times per second!) in step with its spin. Even if the Crab pulsar were bright enough to be visible in a small telescope, the flashing would not be apparent because, as in a motion picture or cathode-ray-tube monitor, the flicker is too rapid for the eye to follow.

Colour photographs of the Crab Nebula reveal a celestial gift: a package of bluish synchrotron radiation wrapped in the loops of a tattered red ribbon—fragments of the shattered star, fluorescing in hydrogen-alpha light. Unfortunately, the luminance of the fluorescence is below the threshold for vision in the red part of the spectrum. Thus all we see is the ghostly cloud of synchrotron radiation.

The Crab Nebula is located 1° northwest of the star ζ Tau, at the tip of the east horn of Taurus. In the JANUARY ALL-SKY MAP on p. 340, the nebula is the tiny circle of dots 5 mm to the right of the cross marking the summer solstice (SS). In a telescope, the nebula appears merely as a small glowing cloud, but to the knowledgeable observer, this synchrotron radiation brake of a spinning neutron star is an object for profound contemplation.

Black Holes

Stars whose masses are greater than about 20 solar masses likely retain more than 3 solar masses in their imploding cores. This is sufficient that gravitation will overwhelm not only the degeneracy pressure of electrons, but also the highly incompressible nature of nuclear matter. Within seconds, spacetime itself closes around the imploding stellar core, removing all but the core's gravitational field from the observable Universe. The star has become a black hole.

The earliest and best candidate for a stellar black hole is **Cygnus X-1**. Discovered by Dr. Tom Bolton of the University of Toronto, using the 1.88-m telescope at the David Dunlap Observatory (see p. 11), it is one of the strongest galactic X-ray sources in the sky. Cygnus X-1 is the invisible companion of a star that can be seen in a small telescope: HDE 226868, an O9.7Iab star, a very luminous, very hot supergiant located about 8000 ly from the Sun. It orbits its nearby, unseen companion with a 5.6-day period. The mass of the companion is between 10 and 16 solar masses, far too large for it to be a white dwarf or neutron star. X-rays are generated as material from the supergiant falls toward the invisible companion. The X-rays extend to energies of 100 keV and vary on time scales as short as milliseconds, indicative of a very compact companion.

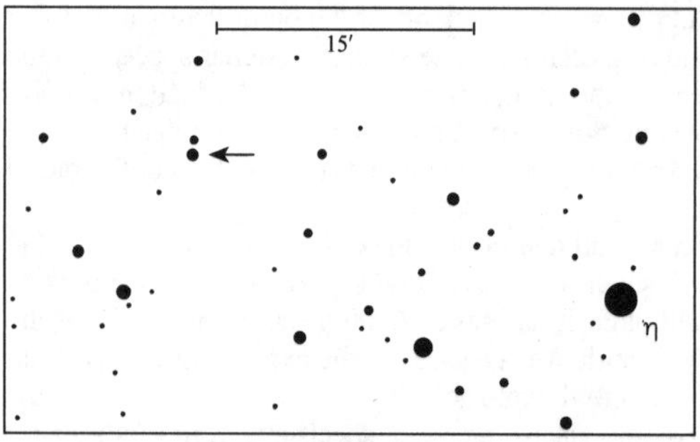

At 9th magnitude, the supergiant HDE 226868 is visible in any small telescope. It is less than half a degree from the 4th-magnitude star η Cygni, which is the star in the neck of the swan, next to the "C" in CYGNUS on the SEPTEMBER ALL-SKY MAP on p. 344. Any low magnification will more than encompass the field shown in the **finder chart** above. North is upward, η Cygni is at the lower right, and HDE 226868 is indicated by the small arrow. The chart magnitude limit is about 13. Although HDE 226868 is a blue supergiant, in telescopes of sufficient aperture this star appears orange because of interstellar dust between us and the star.

All that is to be seen is the hot supergiant, but the view will be worth the search if you know that at this same location in the field of your telescope lurks one of the most likely candidates for a black hole, a knot in the fabric of spacetime where a giant star has vanished. No painting, computer simulation, or Hollywood movie can match this observation.

THE DEEP SKY

THE DEEP SKY—FROM NEAR TO FAR

BY LOUISE O.V. EDWARDS

From the blinding light of city streets, obscuring our view, we barely make out the brightest stars; however, the view of the sky from a dark park or an isolated campsite is truly striking and awe-inspiring. From there, we see the swath of the Milky Way and—from the corners of our eyes—we begin to notice fainter stars, including a few "fuzzy" objects. These celestial wonders were familiar to ancient astronomers the world over: every clear, moonless night, naked eyes gazed into the dark night, unpolluted by artificial light. As part of many Australian aboriginal oral traditions, the diffuse glow from the impressive Magellanic Clouds was seen as distant campfires; dark patches in the Milky Way traced outlines of animals known to the Inca, who imagined "dark-cloud constellations"; Inuit skygazers tell stories interpreting the "fuzzy star" in Orion as fur carried by children of the Hunters (Orion's three belt stars, *Ullaktut*). Greek and Arab astronomers called these diffuse celestial objects "clouds," a concept passed down to us as we use the Latin word *nebula*, meaning mist or cloud.

Since the advent of the telescope (c. 1610), astronomers have been able to peer deeper into the Universe, and thousands of nebulae were soon counted and catalogued (c. 1750–1800). As telescopes and instrumentation continued to improve, astronomers began to distinguish one type of nebulosity from another. Some nebulae resolved into clusters of stars, while others remained truly cloud-like in nature, being composed of gas and dust. Many turned out to be galaxies in their own right, separate and quite outside the Milky Way (c. 1920). Today, amateur astronomers loosely gather these disparate and often far-flung nebulae into the category "deep-sky objects," a term popularized by *Sky & Telescope* magazine since the 1940s.

But why is the nebular glow so diffuse? The reasons vary, and a key factor is the vast range of distances involved. Looking up into the sky from the Earth, the three-dimensional Universe is projected onto the two-dimensional celestial sphere: we specify sky positions with just two directional coordinates, RA and Dec. Although the third dimension—distance—can be difficult to establish, it is critical to our understanding of the physical nature of the objects we observe. Specifically, without knowing the distance to an object, its linear dimensions become impossible to determine from its angular size, since it may be intrinsically large and far away, or intrinsically small and relatively close. The deep-sky selection tabled overleaf is sorted by increasing distance from Earth, which roughly correlates with physical size; the smallest objects, normally giving off less light, are only visible if they are close.

Let's classify the astrophysics of nebulae into three categories: (1) those associated with the birth of stars, (2) those displaying the late evolutionary stages and deaths of stars, and (3) those so distant that their intrinsic morphology is difficult to determine, as they truly appear to be diffuse clouds. In reality, these last are the combined light from thousands to billions of distant individual stars and associated nebulae belonging to the previous categories. In the table, note that the nearest objects (those within a few thousand light-years) are mostly open clusters (**OC**), reflection nebulae (**RN**), emission nebulae (**EN**), giant molecular clouds (**GMC**), or dark nebulae (**DN**). Observing these objects, we see giant clouds of gas and dust (GMC) from which hot, young individual stars or open clusters of stars (OC) are just forming. We are witnessing sites of stellar birth—this starlight reflects from clouds of dust (RN) and can activate the clouds of gas (EN) to emit radiation. Occasionally, cold, dark nebulae (DN) are seen in silhouette against bright backgrounds.

As our Sun is located in a region of the Milky Way with an abundance of the gas and dust necessary to form new stars, the above category of objects can be seen very close by. On the other hand, globular clusters (**GC**) of very old stars are found all the way out to the stellar halo of the galaxy, beyond the dusty disk. (For more about GCs and OCs, see STAR CLUSTERS, p. 310.) Note how GCs are found much further down in the table, out to almost 100 kly. These groups of aging stars appear fuzzy because they are too far away for our eyes—even when aided by small telescopes—to resolve the stars as individual objects; everything gets blurred together. However, when observed in larger telescopes, the individual stars of a globular cluster can be discerned and the "nebula" is revealed to be a dense clump of point sources, not a diffuse cloud.

Other systems associated with the end stages of stellar life are the planetary nebulae and supernova remnants, typically observed up to thousands of light-years distant (see EXPIRED STARS, p. 304). We are no longer seeing star formation or star clusters, but observing the remains of a single star once it has finished its main-sequence life. After a *low-mass* star (like the Sun) enlarges into a red giant, and before it becomes a white dwarf, it goes through a phase where it blows off its outer layers into a surrounding sphere of gas and dust that appears to us as a cloud with a gorgeous symmetric shape: a planetary nebula (**PN**). A supernova remnant (**SNR**) is also the end product of a star, but in this case a massive star. Again, the outer gaseous layers of the ex-star have been blown into a shell around the centre. The SNRs within our galaxy stay visible for millennia, and recent ones are more compact and spherical than those formed long ago, which eventually extend, twist, and fade into the background interstellar medium.

The final category of deep-sky objects is very different. Many nebulae thought to lie within our own galaxy were discovered to be in fact distinct and distant galaxies (**G**) (see GALAXIES: BRIGHTEST AND NEAREST, p. 332). All galaxies contain old and young stars (alone or in clusters), the ingredients for stellar birth, and the remnants of stellar death. Notice that the galaxies in the table are vastly more distant than the other deep-sky objects: millions to hundreds of millions of light-years. Like globular clusters, galaxies appear diffuse because of their incredible distance; even the largest telescopes on Earth and in orbit cannot resolve all the individual stars and contained nebulae! (Some bright galaxies, including the Large and Small Magellanic Clouds, M33, and M101, contain nebulae that are included in the classic deep-sky catalogues.) Finally, the one tabled quasar (**Q**) is the bright core of a galaxy discovered using radio telescopes, yet so distant that its appearance is quasi-stellar in visible light.

RASC OBSERVING PROGRAMS AND CERTIFICATES

The RASC offers four observing certificates for **members** who observe all objects in each of the following observing lists in this chapter:

THE MESSIER CATALOGUE (p. 314),

THE FINEST NGC OBJECTS (p. 318),

THE DEEP-SKY CHALLENGE OBJECTS (p. 322).

DEEP-SKY GEMS (p. 324),

See www.rasc.ca/observing/certificate-programs for details and contact the RASC Observing Committee Chair at rasc.ca/contact/observing for further information.

The RASC also offers the **Explore the Universe Certificate** for novice observers (who do not have to be RASC members) and the **Isabel Williamson Lunar Observing Certificate** for intermediate to advanced observing members.

A DEEP-SKY SELECTION—FROM NEAR TO FAR

NGC	M	Type[A]	Con	RA h	OH List[B]	Size[C] ′	S[C] mag/arcsec²	m[D]	Distance	Remarks
	45	OC	Tau	3	M, OC	100	20	(1.4)	0.44 kly	Pleiades Cluster
1435		RN	Tau	3	DSCO	20×15	21.6	4	0.44	Merope Nebula in above
ρ Oph area		GMC	Oph	16	WFW[E]	5.5°			0.46	EN+DN complex
6726–7		E/RN	CrA	19	SHS	2		11v	0.5	complex region
		DN	Cru	12	SHS	7°×5°	—	—	0.6	Coalsack
7293		PN	Aqr	22	FNGC	16×12	20.8	14.6	0.7	Helix Nebula
ζ Ori		GMC	Ori	5	various[F]	2°		2	1.2	Flame, Horsehead, etc.
6853	27	PN	Vul	19	M	8×6	20.8	13	~1.2	Dumbbell Nebula
1976	42	EN	Ori	5	M	65	15–22	4	1.34	Orion Nebula
6960		SNR	Cyg	20	FNGC	70×6	23.2		1.5	Veil Nebula (west)
2068	78	RN	Ori	5	M	8×6	20.8	10	1.6	many young var. stars
7000		EN	Cyg	20	FNGC	100	23.6		~1.9	North America Nebula
3132		PN	Vel	10	SHS	1.4	17.6	10	2.0	Eight-Burst Nebula
B142–3		DN	Aql	19	DN	80×50	—	—	2	Barnard's "E"
6720	57	PN	Lyr	18	M	1.5×1	17.9	14.8	2.3	Ring Nebula
2261		E/RN	Mon	6	FNGC	2	20.1	11v	2.5	Hubble's Variable Nebula
3587	97	PN	UMa	11	M	2.5	21.6	13	~2.8	Owl Nebula
2392		PN	Gem	7	FNGC	0.7	16.2	10	2.9	Clown Face (Eskimo)
7009		PN	Aqr	21	FNGC	0.4	14.6	12	3.0	Saturn Nebula
7129		RN	Cep	21	FNGC	7	22.5	10	3.3	small OC imbedded
6514	20	EN	Sgr	18	M	28	24.4		~4.7	Trifid Nebula
188		OC	Cep	0	OC	15	24.5	(10)	5.0	oldest OC
IC 443		SNR	Gem	6	DSCO	50×40			5	Jellyfish Nebula
2237–9		EN	Mon	6	FNGC	80×60	26.8	5	5.2	Rosette Nebula
2244		OC	Mon	6	OC	40	22.1	(4.8)	5.2	OC in above
1952	1	SNR	Tau	5	M, RS	5×3	20.6	16v	6.5	Crab and central pulsar
4755		OC	Cru	12	SHS, OC	10	17.8	(4.2)	6.8	Jewel Box
3372		EN	Car	10	SHS	85×80		4.5v	8	Carina Nebula
6838	71	GC	Sge	19	M	6	21.5	(9)	13	looks like OC
5139		GC	Cen	13	SHS, GC	30	19.6	(3.6)	17	ω Centauri GC
6205	13	GC	Her	16	M, GC	23	21.1	(5.7)	21	Hercules Cluster
6715	54	GC	Sgr	18	M, GC	6	21.5	(9)	89	core of Sgr Dwarf Gal.?
2070		EN	Dor	5	SHS	20	20	13	160	Tarantula Nebula in LMC
		G	Dor	5	SHS, G	6°×5°	22.4	(1)	163	Large Magellanic Cloud
224	31	G	And	0	M, G	150×50	22.3	(4)	2.6 Mly	Andromeda Galaxy
598	33	G	Tri	1	M, G	60	22.8	(5.3)	2.8	Triangulum Galaxy
3031	81	G	UMa	9	M, G	18×10	22.3	(8)	12	paired with M82
5128		G	Cen	13	SHS, RS	10×8	20.6	(7.2)	12	Centaurus A radio source
5236	83	G	Hya	13	M, G	10×8	21.4	(8)	15	Southern Pinwheel
5427		G	Vir	14	DSG	2.0×1.7	22.0	(12.0)	110	interacting with 5426
Abell 1367		G	Leo	11	DSCO	1°		(13–16)	380	Leo Galaxy Cluster
3C 273		Q	Vir	12	DSCO, RS	stellar		(12.8)	2440	brightest quasar

[A] **DN**–dark nebula, **EN**–emission nebula (HII), **G**–galaxy, **GC**–globular cluster, **GMC**–giant molecular cloud, **OC**–open cluster, **PN**–planetary nebula, **Q**–quasar, **RN**–reflection nebula, **SNR**–supernova remnant

[B] **DN**–DARK NEBULAE, **DSG**–DEEP SKY GEMS, **DSCO**–DEEP-SKY CHALLENGE OBJECTS, **FNGC**–THE FINEST NGC OBJECTS, **G**–GALAXIES: BRIGHTEST AND NEAREST, **GC**–GLOBULAR CLUSTERS, **M**–THE MESSIER CATALOGUE, **OC**–OPEN CLUSTERS, **RS**–RADIO SOURCES, **SHS**–SOUTHERN HEMISPHERE SPLENDOURS, **WFW**–WIDE-FIELD WONDERS (*Use a combination of* **NGC** *or* **M** *catalogue number,* **Con**, *and* **RA** *hour to locate an object in one of the lists in this chapter.*)

[C] Approximate observable **Size** and surface brightness (***S***) from R.N. Clark, *Visual Astronomy of the Deep Sky* (Sky Publishing, 1990) available online at www.clarkvision.com. These values are not definitive!

[D] ***m*** is the mag. of the associated star for nebulae; v = variable; (***m***) is the total mag. for G, GC, OC, and Q.

[E] 1° south of ρ Oph, RA 16h 28m, Dec –24° 3.3′, star cloud and several ICs, see WIDE-FIELD WONDERS

[F] See FNGC (2024), DSG (2023), DSCO (IC 434), WFW, and DN (B33)

STAR CLUSTERS

BY ANTHONY MOFFAT AND PETER JEDICKE

The study of star clusters is crucial to the understanding of stellar structure and evolution. For most purposes, it can be assumed that the stars in a given cluster formed nearly simultaneously from the same parent cloud of gas and dust. Thus the basic factor that distinguishes one star in a cluster from another is the quantity of matter each contains. When comparing clusters, it is essentially only the age and the chemical composition of their stars that differ. But what makes one cluster *appear* different from another is mainly the degree of concentration and regularity, the spread in magnitude and colour of the member stars (all of which vary mainly with age), and the total number of stars. Extremely young clusters are often irregular in shape, with clumps of newly formed stars pervaded by lanes of obscuring dust and bright nebulosity (e.g. the Orion Nebula around the Trapezium Cluster). The oldest clusters, which have not yet dissipated and have not been torn apart by external forces, tend to be symmetrical in shape, with only the slower-burning, low-mass stars remaining visible; the massive stars will have spent their nuclear fuel and passed to the degenerate graveyard of white dwarfs, neutron stars, or black holes, depending upon their original mass.

The star clusters in the following tables were selected as the most conspicuous. Two types can be recognized: *open* and *globular*. Open clusters often appear as irregular aggregates of tens to thousands of stars, sometimes barely distinguishable from random fluctuations of the general field. Ranging in age from very young to very old, open clusters are concentrated toward the disk of the Milky Way and generally contain stars of chemical abundance similar to the Sun.

Sometimes we observe loose, extended groups of very young stars. Using precise methods of photometry, spectroscopy, and kinematics, we see that these stars often have a common, but not necessarily strictly coeval, origin. Such loose concentrations are called *associations*. Dynamically, both open clusters and associations are generally unbound over time scales of the order of 10 million years, being subject to the strong tidal forces of passing clouds and the background Milky Way Galaxy. Often, associations contain subconcentrations of young open clusters (e.g. the double cluster h and χ Persei of slightly different ages despite their proximity, in the association Per OB1, which stretches over 6° of the sky), with a strong gradient in age as the star-formation process rips through them from one edge to another. In view of their sparse nature, we do not include any of the 100-plus catalogued Milky Way associations.

Globular clusters, on the other hand, are highly symmetric, extremely old and rich agglomerations of up to several million stars, distributed throughout the galactic halo but concentrated toward the centre of the galaxy. Compared to the Sun and other disk stars, they tend to be much less abundant in elements heavier than hydrogen and helium. For the larger and brighter globular clusters, the observer's goal is to see them well enough to distinguish a generous sprinkling of individual stars against a diffuse glowing background. Large telescope apertures and good skies will help resolve globular clusters. Higher powers are helpful for identification of smaller, more distant globular clusters.

The following table lists all well-defined open clusters in the Milky Way Galaxy with angular diameters* greater than 40′ and/or integrated magnitudes brighter than 5.0, as well as the richest clusters and some of special interest. The apparent integrated photographic magnitude (**m_{pg}**) is from Collinder, the angular diameter (**Diam.**) is generally from Trumpler, and the photographic magnitude of the fifth-brightest star (**m_5**) is from Shapley, except where in *italics*, which are new data. The distance (**Dist.**) is mainly from Becker and Fenkart (*Astr. Astrophys. Suppl. 4* (1971), p. 241). The earliest spectral type

* Note that the apparent angular diameter of a cluster may underestimate the full cluster diameter and may be closer to the nuclear diameter, excluding the corona (see David Turner, tinyurl.com/3uaulcb).

of cluster stars (**Sp**) is a measure of the age as follows: expressed in millions of years, O5 = 2, B0 = 8, B5 = 70, A0 = 400, A5 = 1000, F0 = 3000, and F5 = 10 000. Complete source lists of open clusters can be found at www.univie.ac.at/webda/navigation.html.

OPEN CLUSTERS

NGC/ other†	RA (2000) h m	Dec ° ′	Mag. m_{pg}	Diam. ′	m_5	Dist. 10^3 ly	Sp	Remarks
188	0 44.0	+85 21	9.3	14	14.6	5.0	F2	Oldest known
752	1 57.8	+37 41	6.6	45	9.6	1.2	A5	
869	2 19.0	+57 10	4.3	30	9.5	7.0	B1	h Per
884	2 22.4	+57 07	4.4	30	9.5	8.1	B0	χ Per, M supergiants
Perseus	3 22	+48 36	2.3	240	5	0.6	B1	Moving cl.; α Per
Pleiades	3 47.1	+24 08	1.6	120	4.2	0.41	B6	M45, best known
Hyades	4 20	+15 38	0.8	400	*3.9*	0.15	A2	Moving cl. *, in Taurus
1912	5 28.6	+35 50	7.0	18	9.7	4.6	B5	M38
1976/80	5 35.4	−5 23	2.5	50	*5.5*	1.3	O5	Trapezium, very young
2099	5 52.4	+32 32	6.2	24	9.7	4.2	B8	M37
2168	6 08.8	+24 21	5.6	29	9.0	2.8	B5	M35
2232	6 26.5	−4 45	4.1	20	7	1.6	B1	
2244	6 32.4	+4 52	5.2	27	*8.0*	5.3	O5	Rosette, very young
2264	6 41.0	+9 53	4.1	30	*8.0*	2.4	O8	S Mon
2287	6 47.1	−20 44	5.0	32	*8.8*	2.2	B4	M41
2362	7 18.8	−24 56	3.8	7	9.4	5.4	O9	τ CMa
2422	7 35.6	−14 30	4.3	30	9.8	1.6	B3	
2437	7 41.8	−14 49	6.6	27	10.8	5.4	B8	M46**
2451	7 45.4	−37 58	3.7	37	6	1.0	B5	
2516	7 58.3	−60 54	3.3	50	10.1	1.2	B8	
2546	8 12.5	−37 39	5.0	45	7	2.7	B0	
2632	8 40.1	+20 00	3.9	90	7.5	0.59	A0	Praesepe, M44
IC 2391	8 40.3	−53 03	2.6	45	3.5	0.5	B4	
IC 2395	8 41.0	−48 11	4.6	20	10.1	2.9	B2	
2682	8 50.4	+11 50	7.4	18	10.8	2.7	F2	M67, very old
3114	10 02.6	−60 07	4.5	37	7	2.8	B5	
IC 2602	10 43.3	−64 23	1.6	65	6	0.5	B1	θ Car
Tr 16	10 45.2	−59 42	6.7	10	10	9.6	O3	η Car and Nebula
3532	11 06.4	−58 39	3.4	55	8.1	1.4	B8	
3766	11 36.1	−61 37	4.4	12	8.1	5.8	B1	
Coma	12 25.1	+26 06	2.9	300	5.5	0.3	Al	Very sparse
4755	12 53.6	−60 20	5.2	12	7	6.8	B3	κ Cru, "Jewel Box"
6067	16 13.3	−54 13	6.5	16	10.9	4.7	B3	Classic Cepheids
6231	16 54.0	−41 48	3.5	16	7.5	5.8	O9	O supergiants, WR stars
Tr 24	16 57.0	−40 40	3.5	60	*7.3*	5.2	O5	
6405	17 40.1	−32 13	4.6	26	8.3	1.5	B4	M6
IC 4665	17 46.7	+5 44	5.4	50	7	1.1	B8	
6475	17 53.9	−34 48	3.3	50	7.4	0.8	B5	M7
6494	17 56.9	−19 01	5.9	27	10.2	1.4	B8	M23
6523	18 03.1	−24 23	5.2	45	*7*	5.1	O5	M8, Lagoon Nebula
6611	18 18.9	−13 47	6.6	8	10.6	5.5	O7	M16, nebula
IC 4725	18 31.7	−19 15	6.2	35	9.3	2.0	B3	M25, Cepheid U Sgr
IC 4756	18 39.3	+5 27	5.4	50	8.5	1.4	A3	
6705	18 51.1	−6 17	6.8	12.5	12	5.6	B8	M11, very rich
Mel 227	20 11.2	−79 19	5.2	60	*9*	0.8	B9	
IC 1396	21 38.9	+57 30	5.1	60	*8.5*	2.3	O6	Tr 37
7790	23 58.4	+61 13	7.1	4.5	11.7	10.3	B1	Cepheids CEa, CEb, and CF Cas

†IC = Index Catalogue, Tr = Trumpler, Mel = Melotte. * Basic for distance determination
** Appears to contain planetary nebula NGC 2438, but this is not a cluster member.

The table below lists all the globular clusters in the Messier list and most of the globular clusters with a total apparent visual magnitude brighter than about 8.0. A table of Milky Way Galaxy globular-cluster data is available on W.E. Harris's website physwww.mcmaster.ca/~harris/WEHarris.html. The apparent diameter (**Diam.**) is from Cragin, Lucyk, and Rappaport (*Deep Sky Field Guide To Uranometria 2000.0*, Willmann-Bell, 1993). The concentration class (**CC**) is from I to XII, where I is the most compact and XII the least. The integrated spectral type (**Int. Sp. T.**) varies mainly with the abundances. An observer who can see stars down to the magnitude given in the ***V*(HB)** ("horizontal-branch" magnitude) column has a good chance of being able to resolve the globular cluster; this information is from Djorgovski and Meylan (*Structure and Dynamics of Globular Clusters*, Astronomical Society of the Pacific, 1993, p. 341).

GLOBULAR CLUSTERS

NGC	M/ other	RA (2000) h m	Dec ° ′	Mag. m_V	Diam. ′	CC	Int. Sp. T.	Dist. 10^3 ly	*V*(HB)
104	47 Tuc	0 24.0	−72 04	3.95	30.9	III	G4	15	14.06
288		0 52.8	−25 35	8.09	13.8	X		29	15.44
362		1 03.2	−70 50	6.40	12.9	III	F9	28	15.40
1851		5 14.0	−40 02	7.14	11.0	II	F7	46	16.10
1904	79	5 24.1	−24 31	7.73	8.7	V	F5	42	16.20
2808		9 11.9	−64 51	6.20	13.8	I	F7	30	16.19
3201		10 17.6	−46 24	6.75	18.2	X	F6	17	14.75
4590	68	12 39.5	−26 44	7.84	12.0	X	F2	33	15.60
4833		12 59.5	−70 52	6.91	13.5	VIII	F3	20	15.45
5024	53	13 12.9	+18 10	7.61	12.6	V	F6	60	16.94
5139	ω Cen	13 26.8	−47 28	3.68	36.3	VIII	F5	17	14.52
5272	3	13 42.2	+28 22	6.19	16.2	VI	F6	35	15.65
5904	5	15 18.5	+2 04	5.65	17.4	V	F7	26	15.11
6093	80	16 17.0	−22 58	7.33	8.9	II	F6	33	15.86
6121	4	16 23.6	−26 31	5.63	26.3	IX	F8	14	13.35
6171	107	16 32.5	−13 03	7.93	10.0	X	G0	21	15.70
6205	13	16 41.7	+36 27	5.78	16.6	V	F6	21	14.95
6218	12	16 47.1	−1 56	6.70	14.5	IX	F8	24	14.90
6254	10	16 57.1	−4 05	6.60	15.1	VII	F3	20	14.65
6266	62	17 01.2	−30 06	6.45	14.1	IV	F9	22	15.90
6273	19	17 02.6	−26 16	6.77	13.5	VIII	F7	28	16.95
6333	9	17 19.2	−18 30	7.72	9.3	VIII	F5	27	16.10
6341	92	17 17.1	+43 08	6.44	11.2	IV	F2	26	15.05
6356		17 23.6	−17 49	8.25	7.2	III	G4	50	17.50
6388		17 36.3	−44 44	6.72	8.7	III	G2	37	16.90
6397		17 40.7	−53 40	5.73	25.7	IX	F4	9	12.90
6402	14	17 37.6	−3 14	7.59	11.7	VIII	F4	29	17.50
6541		18 08.0	−43 42	6.30	13.1	III	F6	13	15.10
6626	28	18 24.5	−24 52	6.79	11.2	IV	F8	19	15.68
6637	69	18 31.4	−32 20	7.64	7.1	V	G2	28	16.20
6656	22	18 36.3	−23 54	5.10	24.0	VII	F5	10	14.15
6681	70	18 43.2	−32 17	7.87	7.8	V	F5	29	15.60
6715	54	18 55.0	−30 28	7.60	9.1	III	F7	89	17.71
6752		19 10.9	−59 58	5.40	20.4	VI	F4	17	13.85
6779	56	19 16.6	+30 11	8.27	7.1	X	F5	33	16.20
6809	55	19 40.1	−30 57	6.32	19.0	XI	F4	20	14.35
6838	71	19 53.8	+18 46	8.19	7.2	†	G1	13	14.44
6864	75	20 06.0	−21 55	8.52	6.0	I	F9	61	17.45
6981	72	20 53.5	−12 32	9.27	5.9	IX	F7	55	16.99
7078	15	21 30.1	+12 10	6.20	12.3	IV	F3	34	15.86
7089	2	21 33.5	−0 50	6.47	12.9	II	F4	40	16.05
7099	30	21 40.4	−23 10	7.19	11.0	V	F3	26	15.10

† Originally thought to be an open cluster; never assigned a concentration class

FEATURE CLUSTER—TW HYDRAE STELLAR ASSOCIATION

A stellar association is not a cluster, because an open star cluster is normally taken to be a relatively dense concentration of stars bound by their mutual gravity. In contrast, a stellar association is a much looser group, whose members move around the galaxy on paths that are nearly parallel. The tidal force of the rest of the galaxy is enough to disrupt such a group rather quickly, in less than one-tenth the time it takes for the galaxy to make a single rotation. Real open clusters also eventually dissipate, due to close gravitational encounters among pairs of stars, and it takes many tens of millions of years. Nevertheless, some associations contain subclustering.

The idea that a stellar association has a rather different structure—although similar content—than an open cluster was first put forward by Soviet astronomer Viktor Ambartsumian in the late 1940s. He noticed that a number of stars in Orion had similar spectral classification and similar space motions. By space motion an astronomer refers to the vector of a star's actual motion in the galaxy, calculated by combining observations of the radial motion and the proper motion across the celestial sphere, as long as the distance is also known. In the 1950s and 1960s, the study of stellar evolution made it clear that the stars in any particular association were also much the same age, and strikingly young. On the other hand, clusters can have any age from just-formed to billions of years, the latter only applying if the cluster was dense enough to avoid dissipation.

The Handbook does not have a separate section for stellar associations, because it isn't clear how we might enjoy observing such vague conglomerations. There are about 100 associations known in the Milky Way, containing anywhere from fewer than a dozen to barely 100 stars.

What's really important, however, is that a stellar association can be expected also to have additional—and sometimes *only*—members that are less massive, less brilliant, and that burn their nuclear fuel less furiously. Even *HIPPARCOS* didn't have an aperture large enough to discover many of these, so much recent progress relies on data from the near-infrared 2MASS survey, taken with a pair of 1.3-m telescopes. In fact, some of the newly discovered sources are not massive enough to become nuclear crucibles at all. These brown dwarfs are not stars, even though they start off much the same way. So to what catalogue does a brown dwarf belong? Can it be a massive planet if it moves with a stellar association, not in orbit around a host star? Being in orbit around a star was, after all, one of the requirements set out by the International Astronomical Union when adopting a formal definition of a planet. This was the process that led to the outcry over Pluto's "demotion." Once the distance and temperature of a brown dwarf is known, it becomes obvious that it's neither a star nor a planet, so what to call it is not a hollow issue.

Many of the 1000 known brown dwarfs are members of stellar associations, and have been the focus of much research in recent years. In 2016, a group that includes Plaskett Medal winner Jonathan Gagné, along with Kendra Kellogg and Stan Metchev from Western University, announced the discovery of what they diplomatically call a "Jupiter analogue" that was widely reported in the mainstream media. The object, designated "2MASS J11193254-1137466" but known familiarly as 1119 for now, is one of those troublesome objects that does not revolve around a star.

But it is a member of the TW Hydrae Stellar Association. The designation includes its RA and Dec, so you can plot it on a star map in the constellation Crater. To give an idea of how widely spread an association is, the star TW Hydrae itself is more than 20° away from 1119, near the border between Centaurus and Hydra. Shining at a mere 12th mag., TW Hydrae is nonetheless the brightest member of the association. About 30 other members of the TW Hydrae Association have been confirmed, and 1119 is now the closest known, about 82 light-years from our Solar System. There are some closer brown dwarfs around the sky, but they are not part of the association. As for 1119, it's between 4 and 8 times as massive as Jupiter, and its glow is so very, very red that your eye wouldn't see much, even if you were close enough to discern its disk. As a result, most of its total light energy and spectral features are in the near-infrared part of the spectrum. That makes it a challenging but fascinating target for scientific study.

THE MESSIER CATALOGUE

BY ALAN DYER

Charles Messier's Catalogue provides a selection of the best and brightest deep-sky wonders for Northern Hemisphere viewers. Messier compiled his list in the late 1700s to aid prospective comet hunters. Some of these objects he discovered himself, some were first seen by other astronomers of the day, while a few (the Pleiades and the Beehive) were known since antiquity. The Messier numbers do not follow an ordered sequence across the sky. Rather, they are numbered in the order he discovered and catalogued them. Although he intended to, Messier never did publish a list with entries renumbered in order of right ascension.

In our version of THE MESSIER CATALOGUE, we've listed the objects by season *for the evening observer*, grouping the objects within their respective constellations. The constellations are then listed roughly in order of increasing right ascension, that is, constellations farther to the east and that rise later in the night are farther down the list. This is to help plan the sequence of an evening's Messier hunt.

The identity of some Messier objects is controversial. There is evidence that M91 and M102 are mistaken observations of M58 and M101, respectively. M104 and M109 were found by a colleague, Pierre Mechain, and reported to Messier for inclusion in his Catalogue. NGC 205, one of the companion galaxies to M31, the Andromeda Galaxy, was apparently found by Messier but never included in his catalogue. Modern-day observers have dubbed this object M110. In our list, we have included 110 entries, including two objects that some have suggested as alternative candidates for M91 and M102.

Modern-day Messier hunters often wonder what telescopes Messier used. The largest were 190-mm and 200-mm reflectors. However, their speculum metal mirrors would have had the equivalent light-gathering power of a modern 80-mm to 100-mm reflector. He also used a number of 90-mm refractors. Today, a dark site and a good 80-mm refractor or 100-mm reflector should be sufficient for completing the entire list. Objects M6 and M7 are the most southerly, while M74 and M76 are often considered the faintest and most difficult. M83's low altitude and diffuse appearance make it a challenge for Canadian observers north of 50° latitude.

The columns contain the Messier number, the equivalent NGC (New General Catalogue) number, the constellation, the type (see below), the equinox J2000.0 coordinates, the visual magnitude m_V, the angular size in arcminutes (arcseconds for planetary nebula), and observing remarks. Entries marked "!!" are showpiece objects. Data are taken from *The Deep Sky Field Guide to Uranometria 2000.0* (Willmann-Bell, Inc., 1993), compiled by Murray Cragin, James Lucyk, and Barry Rappaport from a variety of contemporary catalogues. Some sizes have been rounded to two significant figures. Also recommended as an excellent guide is *The Messier Objects*, by Stephen James O'Meara (Cambridge University Press, 1998).

MESSIER AND NGC OBJECT TYPES

OC = open cluster	GC = globular cluster
EN = emission nebula	RN = reflection nebula
E/RN = EN + RN	
PN = planetary nebula	SNR = supernova remnant
G-SA *or* G-S = spiral galaxy	G-SB = barred spiral galaxy
G-E = elliptical galaxy	G-S0 = lenticular galaxy
G-I = irregular galaxy	(alphanumeric suffixes denote galaxy sub-types)

NUMERICAL LISTING OF MESSIER OBJECTS

M#	Sky	Con	M#	Sky	Con	M#	Sky	Con	M#	Sky	Con	M#	Sky	Con
1	WIN	Tau	23	SUM	Sgr	45	WIN	Tau	67	SPR	Cnc	89	SPR	Vir
2	AUT	Aqr	24	SUM	Sgr	46	WIN	Pup	68	SPR	Hya	90	SPR	Vir
3	SPR	CVn	25	SUM	Sgr	47	WIN	Pup	69	SUM	Sgr	91	SPR	Com
4	SUM	Sco	26	SUM	Sct	48	WIN	Hya	70	SUM	Sgr	92	SUM	Her
5	SPR	Ser	27	SUM	Vul	49	SPR	Vir	71	SUM	Sge	93	WIN	Pup
6	SUM	Sco	28	SUM	Sgr	50	WIN	Mon	72	AUT	Aqr	94	SPR	CVn
7	SUM	Sco	29	SUM	Cyg	51	SPR	CVn	73	AUT	Aqr	95	SPR	Leo
8	SUM	Sgr	30	AUT	Cap	52	AUT	Cas	74	AUT	Psc	96	SPR	Leo
9	SUM	Oph	31	AUT	And	53	SPR	Com	75	SUM	Sgr	97	SPR	UMa
10	SUM	Oph	32	AUT	And	54	SUM	Sgr	76	AUT	Per	98	SPR	Com
11	SUM	Sct	33	AUT	Tri	55	SUM	Sgr	77	AUT	Cet	99	SPR	Com
12	SUM	Oph	34	AUT	Per	56	SUM	Lyr	78	WIN	Ori	100	SPR	Com
13	SUM	Her	35	WIN	Gem	57	SUM	Lyr	79	WIN	Lep	101	SPR	UMa
14	SUM	Oph	36	WIN	Aur	58	SPR	Vir	80	SUM	Sco	102	SPR	Dra?
15	AUT	Peg	37	WIN	Aur	59	SPR	Vir	81	SPR	UMa	103	AUT	Cas
16	SUM	Ser	38	WIN	Aur	60	SPR	Vir	82	SPR	UMa	104	SPR	Vir
17	SUM	Sgr	39	SUM	Cyg	61	SPR	Vir	83	SPR	Hya	105	SPR	Leo
18	SUM	Sgr	40	SPR	UMa	62	SUM	Oph	84	SPR	Vir	106	SPR	CVn
19	SUM	Oph	41	WIN	CMa	63	SPR	CVn	85	SPR	Com	107	SUM	Oph
20	SUM	Sgr	42	WIN	Ori	64	SPR	Com	86	SPR	Vir	108	SPR	UMa
21	SUM	Sgr	43	WIN	Ori	65	SPR	Leo	87	SPR	Vir	109	SPR	UMa
22	SUM	Sgr	44	SPR	Cnc	66	SPR	Leo	88	SPR	Com	110	AUT	And

SEASONAL LISTING OF MESSIER OBJECTS

M#	NGC	Con	Type	RA (2000) h m	Dec ° ′	m_V	Size ′	Remarks
The Winter Sky								
1	1952	Tau	SNR	5 34.5	+22 01	8.4	6 × 4	!! famous Crab Neb. supernova remnant
45	—	Tau	OC	3 47.0	+24 07	1.2	110	!! Pleiades; look for subtle nebulosity
36	1960	Aur	OC	5 36.1	+34 08	6.0	12	bright but scattered group; use low pow.
37	2099	Aur	OC	5 52.4	+32 33	5.6	20	!! finest of three Auriga clusters; very rich
38	1912	Aur	OC	5 28.7	+35 50	6.4	21	look for small cluster NGC 1907 0.5° S
42	1976	Ori	E/RN	5 35.4	−5 27	—	65 × 60	!! Orion Nebula; finest in northern sky
43	1982	Ori	E/RN	5 35.6	−5 16	—	20 × 15	detached part of Orion Nebula
78	2068	Ori	RN	5 46.7	+0 03	—	8 × 6	bright featureless reflection nebula
79	1904	Lep	GC	5 24.5	−24 33	7.8	8.7	200-mm telescope needed to resolve
35	2168	Gem	OC	6 08.9	+24 20	5.1	28	!! look for sm. cluster NGC 2158 0.25° S
41	2287	CMa	OC	6 47.0	−20 44	4.5	38	4° south of Sirius; bright but coarse
50	2323	Mon	OC	7 03.2	−8 20	5.9	16	between Sirius & Procyon; use low mag
46	2437	Pup	OC	7 41.8	−14 49	6.1	27	!! contains planetary nebula NGC 2438
47	2422	Pup	OC	7 36.6	−14 30	4.4	29	coarse cluster 1.5° west of M46
93	2447	Pup	OC	7 44.6	−23 52	≈6.2	22	compact, bright cluster; fairly rich
48	2548	Hya	OC	8 13.8	−5 48	5.8	54	former "lost" Messier; large, sparse cl.

SEASONAL LISTING OF MESSIER OBJECTS (continued)

M#	NGC	Con	Type	RA (2000) h m	Dec ° ′	m_v	Size ′	Remarks
The Spring Sky								
44	2632	Cnc	OC	8 40.1	+19 59	3.1	95	!! Beehive or Praesepe; use low power
67	2682	Cnc	OC	8 50.4	+11 49	6.9	29	one of the oldest star clusters known
40	—	UMa	2 stars	12 22.4	+58 05	8.0	—	double star Winnecke 4; separation 50″
81	3031	UMa	G-SAab	9 55.6	+69 04	6.9	24 × 13	!! bright spiral visible in binoculars
82	3034	UMa	G-I0	9 55.8	+69 41	8.4	12 × 6	!! the "exploding" galaxy; M81 0.5° S
97	3587	UMa	PN	11 14.8	+55 01	9.9	194″	!! Owl Nebula; distinct grey oval
101	5457	UMa	G-SABcd	14 03.2	+54 21	7.9	26 × 26	!! Pinwheel Gal.; diffuse face-on spiral
108	3556	UMa	G-SBcd	11 11.5	+55 40	10.0	8.1 × 2.1	nearly edge-on; paired with M97 0.75° SE
109	3992	UMa	G-SBbc	11 57.6	+53 23	9.8	7.6 × 4.3	barred spiral near γ UMa
65	3623	Leo	G-SABa	11 18.9	+13 05	9.3	8.7 × 2.2	!! bright elongated spiral
66	3627	Leo	G-SABb	11 20.2	+12 59	8.9	8.2 × 3.9	!! M65 and NGC 3628 in same field
95	3351	Leo	G-SBb	10 44.0	+11 42	9.7	7.8 × 4.6	bright barred spiral
96	3368	Leo	G-SABab	10 46.8	+11 49	9.2	6.9 × 4.6	M95 in same field
105	3379	Leo	G-E1	10 47.8	+12 35	9.3	3.9 × 3.9	bright elliptical near M95 and M96
53	5024	Com	GC	13 12.9	+18 10	7.5	12.6	150-mm telescope needed to resolve
64	4826	Com	G-SAab	12 56.7	+21 41	8.5	9.2 × 4.6	!! Black Eye Gal.; eye needs big scope
85	4382	Com	G-SA0+	12 25.4	+18 11	9.1	7.5 × 5.7	bright elliptical shape
88	4501	Com	G-SAb	12 32.0	+14 25	9.6	6.1 × 2.8	bright multiple-arm spiral
91	4548	Com	G-SBb	12 35.4	+14 30	10.2	5.0 × 4.1	some lists say M91 = M58, not NGC 4548
98	4192	Com	G-SABab	12 13.8	+14 54	10.1	9.1 × 2.1	nearly edge-on spiral near star 6 Com. B.
99	4254	Com	G-SAc	12 18.8	+14 25	9.9	4.6 × 4.3	nearly face-on spiral near M98
100	4321	Com	G-SABbc	12 22.9	+15 49	9.3	6.2 × 5.3	face-on spiral with starlike nucleus
49	4472	Vir	G-E2	12 29.8	+8 00	8.4	8.1 × 7.1	very bright elliptical
58	4579	Vir	G-SABb	12 37.7	+11 49	9.7	5.5 × 4.6	bright barred spiral; M59 and M60 1° E
59	4621	Vir	G-E5	12 42.0	+11 39	9.6	4.6 × 3.6	bright elliptical paired with M60
60	4649	Vir	G-E2	12 43.7	+11 33	8.8	7.1 × 6.1	bright elliptical with M59 and NGC 4647
61	4303	Vir	G-SABbc	12 21.9	+4 28	9.7	6.0 × 5.9	face-on two-armed spiral
84	4374	Vir	G-E1	12 25.1	+12 53	9.1	5.1 × 4.1	!! w/ M86 in Markarian's Chain
86	4406	Vir	G-E3	12 26.2	+12 57	8.9	12 × 9	!! w/ many NGC galaxies in Chain
87	4486	Vir	G-E0-1	12 30.8	+12 24	8.6	7.1 × 7.1	the one with famous jet and black hole
89	4552	Vir	G-E	12 35.7	+12 33	9.8	3.4 × 3.4	elliptical; resembles M87 but smaller
90	4569	Vir	G-SABab	12 36.8	+13 10	9.5	10 × 4	bright barred spiral near M89
104	4594	Vir	G-SA	12 40.0	−11 37	8.0	7.1 × 4.4	!! Sombrero Galaxy; look for dust lane
3	5272	CVn	GC	13 42.2	+28 23	5.9	16.2	!! contains many variable stars
51	5194/5	CVn	G-SAbc	13 29.9	+47 12	8.4	8 × 7	!! Whirlpool Galaxy; superb in big scope
63	5055	CVn	G-SAbc	13 15.8	+42 02	8.6	14 × 8	!! Sunflower Galaxy; bright, elongated
94	4736	CVn	G-SAab	12 50.9	+41 07	8.2	13 × 11	very bright and comet-like
106	4258	CVn	G-SABbc	12 19.0	+47 18	8.4	20 × 8	!! superb large, bright spiral
68	4590	Hya	GC	12 39.5	−26 45	7.7	12	150-mm telescope needed to resolve
83	5236	Hya	G-SABc	13 37.0	−29 52	7.6	16 × 13	large and diffuse; superb from far south
102	5866?	Dra	G-SA0+	15 06.5	+55 46	9.9	6.6 × 3.2	or is M102 = M101? (look for 5907)
5	5904	Ser	GC	15 18.6	+2 05	5.7	17.4	!! one of the sky's finest globulars
The Summer Sky								
13	6205	Her	GC	16 41.7	+36 28	5.7	16.6	!! Hercules Cluster; NGC 6207 0.5° NE
92	6341	Her	GC	17 17.1	+43 08	6.4	11.2	9° NE of M13; fine but often overlooked
9	6333	Oph	GC	17 19.2	−18 31	7.6	9.3	smallest of Ophiuchus globulars
10	6254	Oph	GC	16 57.1	−4 06	6.6	15.1	rich globular cluster; M12 is 3° NW
12	6218	Oph	GC	16 47.2	−1 57	6.8	14.5	loose globular cluster near M10
14	6402	Oph	GC	17 37.6	−3 15	7.6	11.7	200-mm telescope needed to resolve
19	6273	Oph	GC	17 02.6	−26 16	6.7	13.5	oblate globular; M62 4° S
62	6266	Oph	GC	17 01.2	−30 07	6.7	14.1	asymmetrical; in rich field

SEASONAL LISTING OF MESSIER OBJECTS (continued)

M#	NGC	Con	Type	RA (2000) h m	Dec ° ′	m_v	Size ′	Remarks
Summer Sky (cont)								
107	6171	Oph	GC	16 32.5	−13 03	8.1	10.0	small, faint globular
4	6121	Sco	GC	16 23.6	−26 32	5.8	26.3	bright globular near Antares
6	6405	Sco	OC	17 40.1	−32 13	4.2	33	!! Butterfly Cluster; best at low power
7	6475	Sco	OC	17 53.9	−34 49	3.3	80	!! excellent in binocs or rich-field scope
80	6093	Sco	GC	16 17.0	−22 59	7.3	8.9	very compressed globular
16	6611	Ser	EN + OC	18 18.6	−13 58	—	35 × 28	Eagle Neb. w/ open cl.; use neb. filter
8	6523	Sgr	EN	18 03.8	−24 23	—	45 × 30	!! Lagoon Nebula w/ open cl. NGC 6530
17	6618	Sgr	EN	18 20.8	−16 11	—	20 × 15	!! Swan or Omega Nebula; use neb. filter
18	6613	Sgr	OC	18 19.9	−17 08	6.9	10	sparse cluster; 1° south of M17
20	6514	Sgr	E/RN	18 02.3	−23 02	—	20 × 20	!! Trifid Nebula; look for dark lanes
21	6531	Sgr	OC	18 04.6	−22 30	5.9	13	0.7° NE of M20; sparse cluster
22	6656	Sgr	GC	18 36.4	−23 54	5.1	24	spectacular from southern latitude
23	6494	Sgr	OC	17 56.8	−19 01	5.5	27	bright, loose open cluster
24	—	Sgr	starcloud	18 16.5	−18 50	4.6	95 × 35	rich star cloud; best in big binoculars
25	IC 4725	Sgr	OC	18 31.6	−19 15	4.6	32	bright but sparse open cluster
28	6626	Sgr	GC	18 24.5	−24 52	6.8	11.2	compact globular near M22
54	6715	Sgr	GC	18 55.1	−30 29	7.6	9.1	not easily resolved
55	6809	Sgr	GC	19 40.0	−30 58	6.4	19.0	bright, loose globular cluster
69	6637	Sgr	GC	18 31.4	−32 21	7.6	7.1	small, poor globular cluster
70	6681	Sgr	GC	18 43.2	−32 18	8.0	7.8	small globular 2° east of M69
75	6864	Sgr	GC	20 06.1	−21 55	8.5	6	small and distant; 59 000 ly away
11	6705	Sct	OC	18 51.1	−6 16	5.8	13	!! Wild Duck Cl.; the best open cluster?
26	6694	Sct	OC	18 45.2	−9 24	8.0	14	bright, coarse cluster
56	6779	Lyr	GC	19 16.6	+30 11	8.3	7.1	within a rich starfield
57	6720	Lyr	PN	18 53.6	+33 02	8.8	>71″	!! Ring Nebula; an amazing smoke ring
71	6838	Sge	GC	19 53.8	+18 47	8.0	7.2	loose globular; looks like an open cluster
27	6853	Vul	PN	19 59.6	+22 43	7.3	>348″	!! Dumbbell Nebula; a superb object
29	6913	Cyg	OC	20 23.9	+38 32	6.6	6	small, poor open cluster 2° S of γ Cygni
39	7092	Cyg	OC	21 32.2	+48 26	4.6	31	very sparse cluster; use low power
The Autumn Sky								
2	7089	Aqr	GC	21 33.5	−0 49	6.4	12.9	200-mm telescope needed to resolve
72	6981	Aqr	GC	20 53.5	−12 32	9.3	5.9	near the Saturn Nebula, NGC 7009
73	6994	Aqr	OC	20 59.0	−12 38	8.9p	2.8	group of four stars only; an "asterism"
15	7078	Peg	GC	21 30.0	+12 10	6.0	12.3	rich, compact globular
30	7099	Cap	GC	21 40.4	−23 11	7.3	11	toughest in one-night Messier marathon
52	7654	Cas	OC	23 24.2	+61 35	6.9	12	young, rich cl.; faint Bubble Neb. nearby
103	581	Cas	OC	1 33.2	+60 42	7.4	6	three NGC open clusters nearby
31	224	And	G-SAb	0 42.7	+41 16	3.4	185 × 75	!! Andromeda Gal.; look for dust lanes
32	221	And	G-E2	0 42.7	+40 52	8.1	9 × 7	closest companion to M31
110	205	And	G-S0/E5 pec	0 40.4	+41 41	8.1	22 × 11	more distant companion to M31
33	598	Tri	G-SAcd	1 33.9	+30 39	5.7	67 × 42	large, diffuse spiral; requires dark sky
74	628	Psc	G-SAc	1 36.7	+15 47	9.4	11 × 11	faint, elusive spiral; tough in small scope
77	1068	Cet	G-SABab	2 42.7	−0 01	8.9	8.2 × 7.3	a Seyfert galaxy; with starlike nucleus
34	1039	Per	OC	2 42.0	+42 47	5.2	35	best at low power
76	650/51	Per	PN	1 42.4	+51 34	10.1	>65″	Little Dumbbell; faint but distinct

THE FINEST NGC OBJECTS

BY ALAN DYER

Those looking for an observing project beyond THE MESSIER CATALOGUE turn to the New General Catalogue (NGC). The NGC contains 7840 entries and forms the core database of today's computerized backyard telescopes. To match THE MESSIER CATALOGUE, this list contains 110 of the finest NGC objects visible from mid-northern latitudes. The seasonal order is similar to that used in THE MESSIER CATALOGUE, and there is no overlap. While the brightness of the best NGCs rivals many Messier targets, at least a 200-mm telescope is required to see all 110 objects on this list. Most are easy; a few are challenging.

The NGC was originally published by J.L.E. Dreyer in 1888, a work that expanded upon Sir John Herschel's 1864 "General Catalogue." Supplementary "Index Catalogues" were published by Dreyer in 1895 and 1908. The first IC extends the NGC with another 1529 objects discovered visually between 1888 and 1894. Most are faint, elusive targets. (To provide a flavour of this extension to the NGC, one entry from the first IC is included on this list, IC 289.) The Second Index Catalogue contains 3857 entries, most discovered photographically between 1895 and 1907.

The *Sky Atlas 2000.0*, the sets of index card charts called *AstroCards*, *The Night Sky Observer's Guide Vols. 1 and 2* by Kepple and Sanner, and the *Uranometria 2000.0 Deep Sky Atlas* are recommended finder aids. Most planetarium and deep-sky charting computer programs, as well as computerized telescopes, include all the objects on this list and many more.

Notation below is as in THE MESSIER CATALOGUE. Magnitudes (**m_v**) are visual, with the exception of those marked "p," which are photographic, or blue, magnitudes. Most galaxies appear smaller than the sizes listed. For open clusters, the number of stars (*) is also given. Data are taken from *The Deep Sky Field Guide to Uranometria 2000.0* (see the introduction to THE MESSIER CATALOGUE), with some sizes rounded to two significant figures.

SEASONAL LISTING OF FINEST NGC OBJECTS

#	NGC	Con	Type	RA (2000) h m	Dec ° ′	m_v	Size ′	Remarks
The Autumn Sky								
1	7009	Aqr	PN	21 04.2	−11 22	8.3p	>25″	!! Saturn Nebula; small bright oval
2	7293	Aqr	PN	22 29.6	−20 48	7.3	>769″	!! Helix Nebula; large, diffuse; use filter
3	7331	Peg	G-SAb	22 37.1	+34 25	9.5	10 × 4	!! large, bright spiral galaxy
4	7635	Cas	EN	23 20.7	+61 12	—	15 × 8	Bubble Neb.; very faint; 0.5° SW of M52
5	7789	Cas	OC	23 57.0	+56 44	6.7	15	!! 300*; faint but very rich cluster
6	185	Cas	G-E3	0 39.0	+48 20	9.2	14 × 12	companion to M31; small and faint
7	281	Cas	EN	0 52.8	+56 37	—	35 × 30	!! large faint nebulosity near η Cas
8	457	Cas	OC	1 19.1	+58 20	6.4	13	80*; rich; one of the best Cas. clusters
9	663	Cas	OC	1 46.0	+61 15	7.1	16	80*; look for NGCs 654 and 659 nearby
10	IC 289	Cas	PN	3 10.3	+61 19	13.3	>34″	dim oval smudge; use a nebular filter!
11	7662	And	PN	23 25.9	+42 33	8.3	>12″	!! Blue Snowball; annular at high power
12	891	And	G-SAb	2 22.6	+42 21	9.9	13 × 3	!! faint, classic edge-on with dust lane
13	253	Scl	G-SABc	0 47.6	−25 17	7.6	30 × 7	!! very large and bright but at low altitude
14	772	Ari	G-SAb	1 59.3	+19 01	10.3	7.3 × 4.6	diffuse spiral galaxy
15	246	Cet	PN	0 47.0	−11 53	10.9	225″	large and faint with mottled structure
16	936	Cet	G-SB	2 27.6	−1 09	10.2	5.7 × 4.6	near M77; NGC 941 in the same field

SEASONAL LISTING OF FINEST NGC OBJECTS (continued)

#	NGC	Con	Type	RA (2000) h m	Dec ° ′	m_v	Size ′	Remarks
Autumn Sky (continued)								
17	869/884	Per	OC	2 21.0	+57 08	≈5	30/30	!! Double Cluster; 315*; use low power
18	1023	Per	G-SB0⁻	2 40.4	+39 04	9.3	8.6 × 4.2	bright lens-shaped galaxy near M34
19	1491	Per	EN	4 03.4	+51 19	—	25 × 25	visually small and faint emission nebula
20	1501	Cam	PN	4 07.0	+60 55	11.5	52″	faint; dark centre; look for NGC 1502
21	1232	Eri	G-SABc	3 09.8	−20 35	10.0	6.8 × 5.6	face-on spiral; look for NGC 1300 nearby
22	1535	Eri	PN	4 14.2	−12 44	9.6p	>18″	bright planetary with blue-grey disk
The Winter Sky								
23	1514	Tau	PN	4 09.2	+30 47	10.9	>114″	faint glow around 9.4^m central star
24	1931	Aur	E/RN	5 31.4	+34 15	—	4 × 4	haze surrounding four close stars
25	1788	Ori	RN	5 06.9	−3 21	—	5 × 3	fairly bright but diffuse reflection nebula
26	1973+	Ori	E/RN	5 35.1	−4 44	—	≈20 × 10	NGC 1973-5-7 just N. of M42 and M43
27	2022	Ori	PN	5 42.1	+9 05	11.9	>18″	small, faint & distinct with annular form
28	2024	Ori	EN	5 41.9	−1 51	—	30 × 30	bright but masked by glow from ζ Ori
29	2194	Ori	OC	6 13.8	+12 48	8.5	8	80*, fairly rich; look for 2169 nearby
30	2371/2	Gem	PN	7 25.6	+29 29	11.3	>55″	faint double-lobed planetary; use filter
31	2392	Gem	PN	7 29.2	+20 55	9.2	>15″	!! Clown Face or Eskimo Nebula
32	2237+	Mon	EN	6 32.3	+5 03	—	80 × 60	!! Rosette Nebula; very large; use filter
33	2261	Mon	E/RN	6 39.2	+8 44	var	3.5 × 1.5	Hubble's Variable Nebula; comet-shaped
34	2359	CMa	EN	7 18.6	−13 12	—	9 × 6	bright; look for 2360 & 2362 nearby
35	2440	Pup	PN	7 41.9	−18 13	9.4	>14″	almost starlike; irregular at high power
36	2539	Pup	OC	8 10.7	−12 50	6.5	21	50*; rich cluster; near M46 and M47
37	2403	Cam	G-SABc	7 36.9	+65 36	8.5	26 × 13	!! very large & bright; visible in binocs.
38	2655	Cam	G-SAB0	8 55.6	+78 13	10.1	6.0 × 5.3	bright ellipse with starlike nucleus
The Spring Sky								
39	2683	Lyn	G-SAb	8 52.7	+33 25	9.8	8.4 × 2.4	nearly edge-on spiral; very bright
40	2841	UMa	G-SAb	9 22.0	+50 58	9.2	6.8 × 3.3	!! classic elongated spiral; very bright
41	3079	UMa	G-SBc	10 02.2	+55 41	10.9	8.0 × 1.5	edge-on spiral; NGC 2950 nearby
42	3184	UMa	G-SABc	10 18.3	+41 25	9.8	7.8 × 7.2	large, diffuse face-on spiral
43	3877	UMa	G-SAc	11 46.1	+47 30	11.0	5.1 × 1.1	edge-on; same field as χ UMa
44	3941	UMa	G-SB0°	11 52.9	+36 59	10.3	3.7 × 2.6	small, bright. and elliptical
45	4026	UMa	G-S0	11 59.4	+50 58	10.8	4.6 × 1.2	lens-shaped edge-on near γ UMa
46	4088	UMa	G-SABbc	12 05.6	+50 33	10.6	5.4 × 2.1	nearly edge-on; NGC 4085 in same field
47	4157	UMa	G-SABb	12 11.1	+50 29	11.3	7.1 × 1.2	a thin sliver; NGC 4026 and 4088 nearby
48	4605	UMa	G-SBcp	12 40.0	+61 37	10.3	6.4 × 2.3	bright, distinct edge-on spiral
49	3115	Sex	G-S0⁻	10 05.2	−7 43	8.9	8.1 × 2.8	Spindle Galaxy; bright and elongated
50	3242	Hya	PN	10 24.8	−18 38	7.8	>16″	!! Ghost of Jupiter; small but bright
51	3003	LMi	G-Sbc?	9 48.6	+33 25	11.9	5.2 × 1.6	faint elongated streak
52	3344	LMi	G-SABbc	10 43.5	+24 55	9.9	6.9 × 6.4	diffuse face-on barred spiral
53	3432	LMi	G-SBm	10 52.5	+36 37	11.2	6.9 × 1.9	nearly edge-on; faint flat streak
54	2903	Leo	G-SABbc	9 32.2	+21 30	9.0	12 × 6	!! very large, bright elongated spiral
55	3384	Leo	G-SB0⁻	10 48.3	+12 38	9.9	5.5 × 2.9	same field as M105 and NGC 3389
56	3521	Leo	G-SAb	11 05.8	−0 02	9.0	12 × 6	very large, bright spiral
57	3607	Leo	G-SA0°	11 16.9	+18 03	9.9	4.6 × 4.1	NGC 3605 & 3608 in same field
58	3628	Leo	G-Sb pec	11 20.3	+13 36	9.5	14 × 4	large edge-on; same field as M65 & M66
59	4111	CVn	G-SA0⁺	12 07.1	+43 04	10.7	4.4 × 0.9	bright lens-shaped edge-on spiral
60	4214	CVn	G-I AB	12 15.6	+36 20	9.8	10 × 8	large irregular galaxy
61	4244	CVn	G-SAcd	12 17.5	+37 49	10.4	17 × 2	!! large distinct edge-on spiral

SEASONAL LISTING OF FINEST NGC OBJECTS (continued)

#	NGC	Con	Type	RA (2000) h m	Dec ° ′	m_V	Size ′	Remarks
Spring Sky (continued)								
62	4449	CVn	G-I Bm	12 28.2	+44 06	9.6	5.5 × 4.1	bright with odd rectangular shape
63	4490	CVn	G-SBd p	12 30.6	+41 38	9.8	6.4 × 3.3	Cocoon Gal.; bright spiral; 4485 in field
64	4631	CVn	G-SBd	12 42.1	+32 32	9.2	16 × 3	!! large edge-on; with companion 4627
65	4656/7	CVn	G-SBm p	12 44.0	+32 10	10.5	20 × 3	!! in field with 4631; NE end curves up
66	5005	CVn	G-SABbc	13 10.9	+37 03	9.8	5.8 × 2.8	bright elongated spiral near α CVn
67	5033	CVn	G-SAc	13 13.4	+36 36	10.2	10 × 5	large bright spiral near NGC 5005
68	4274	Com	G-SBab	12 19.8	+29 37	10.4	6.7 × 2.5	NGCs 4278/83/86 in same field
69	4414	Com	G-SAc	12 26.4	+31 13	10.1	4.4 × 3.0	bright spiral with starlike nucleus
70	4494	Com	G-E1-2	12 31.4	+25 47	9.8	4.6 × 4.4	small bright elliptical
71	4559	Com	G-SABc	12 36.0	+27 58	10.0	12 × 5	large spiral with coarse structure
72	4565	Com	G-SAb	12 36.3	+25 59	9.6	14 × 2	!! superb edge-on spiral with dust lane
73	4725	Com	G-SABab	12 50.4	+25 30	9.4	10 × 8	very bright, large spiral
74	4038/9	Crv	G-SB/IB	12 01.9	−18 52	≈10.4	≈5 × 3 ea.	"Antennae" interacting galaxies
75	4361	Crv	PN	12 24.5	−18 48	10.9	>45″	small and bright; with 13^m central star
76	4216	Vir	G-SABb	12 15.9	+13 09	10.0	7.8 × 1.6	nearly edge-on; with NGC 4206 and 4222
77	4388	Vir	G-SAb	12 25.8	+12 40	11.0	5.7 × 1.6	with M84 and M86 in Markarian's Chain
78	4438	Vir	G-SA0/a	12 27.8	+13 01	10.2	8.9 × 3.6	paired w/ NGC 4435 to form the "Eyes"
79	4517	Vir	G-Scd	12 32.8	+0 07	10.4	9.9 × 1.4	faint edge-on spiral
80	4526	Vir	G-SAB0°	12 34.0	+7 42	9.7	7.1 × 2.9	between two 7^m stars
81	4535	Vir	G-SABc	12 34.3	+8 12	10.0	7.1 × 6.4	near M49 and 0.75° N of NGC 4526
82	4567/8	Vir	G-SAbc	12 36.5	+11 15	≈11	≈3 × 2 ea.	"Siamese Twins" interacting galaxies
83	4699	Vir	G-Sab	12 49.0	−8 40	9.5	4.4 × 3.2	small & bright; look for NGC 4697 3°N
84	4762	Vir	G-SB0°?	12 52.9	+11 14	10.3	9.1 × 2.2	flattest galaxy known; 4754 in same field
85	5746	Vir	G-SA?b	14 44.9	+1 57	10.3	6.8 × 1.0	fine edge-on near 109 Virginis
86	5466	Boo	GC	14 05.5	+28 32	9.0	11	loose class XII; like rich open cl.; faint
87	5907	Dra	G-SAc	15 15.9	+56 20	10.3	12 × 2	!! fine edge-on with dust lane; near 5866
88	6503	Dra	G-SAcd	17 49.4	+70 09	10.2	7.3 × 2.4	bright elongated spiral
89	6543	Dra	PN	17 58.6	+66 38	8.1	>18″	Cat's Eye Nebula; with 10.9^m central star
The Summer Sky								
90	6210	Her	PN	16 44.5	+23 49	8.8	>14″	blue starlike planetary
91	6369	Oph	PN	17 29.3	−23 46	11.4	>30″	"Little Ghost"; look for 6309 nearby
92	6572	Oph	PN	18 12.1	+6 51	8.1	8″	tiny bright blue oval
93	6633	Oph	OC	18 27.7	+6 34	4.6	27	sparse wide field cluster; IC 4756 nearby
94	6712	Sct	GC	18 53.1	−8 42	8.2	7.2	small globular; look for IC 1295 in field
95	6781	Aql	PN	19 18.4	+6 33	11.4	>109″	pale version of the Owl Nebula, M97
96	6819	Cyg	OC	19 41.3	+40 11	7.3	9.5	150*; faint but rich cluster in Milky Way
97	6826	Cyg	PN	19 44.8	+50 31	8.8	>25″	!! Blinking Planetary; 10.6^m central star
98	6888	Cyg	EN	20 12.0	+38 21	—	18 × 13	Crescent Nebula; faint; use nebular filter
99a	6960	Cyg	SNR	20 45.7	+30 43	—	70 × 6	!! Veil Nebula west half; use filter!
99b	6992/5	Cyg	SNR	20 56.4	+31 43	—	72 × 8	!! Veil Nebula east half; use filter!
100	7000	Cyg	EN	20 58.8	+44 20	—	120 × 100	!! North America; use filter & low power
101	7027	Cyg	PN	21 07.1	+42 14	8.5	15″	unusual protoplanetary nebula
102	6445	Sgr	PN	17 49.2	−20 01	11.2	>34″	small, bright and annular; near M23
103	6520	Sgr	OC	18 03.4	−27 54	7.6p	6	60*; small; dark nebula B86 in same field
104	6818	Sgr	PN	19 44.0	−14 09	9.3	>17″	"Little Gem"; annular; NGC 6822 0.75°S
105	6802	Vul	OC	19 30.6	+20 16	8.8	3.2	50*, at east end of Brocchi's Cluster
106	6940	Vul	OC	20 34.6	+28 18	6.3	31	60*; fairly rich cluster in Milky Way
107	6939	Cep	OC	20 31.4	+60 38	7.8	7	80*; very rich; NGC 6946 in same field
108	6946	Cep	G-SABcd	20 34.8	+60 09	8.8	13 × 13	faint, diffuse face-on spiral near 6939
109	7129	Cep	RN	21 42.8	+66 06	—	7 × 7	faint reflection neb. around sparse cluster
110	40	Cep	PN	0 13.0	+72 32	12.4	>37″	unusual red planetary; 11.6^m central star

DARK NEBULAE

BY PAUL GRAY

Dark nebulae, often appearing as "holes in the sky," are fascinating to observe. The following is a representative selection of visually observable dark nebulae. The **minimum aperture** in millimetres is what observers have found to be necessary to see each nebula; however, many may be observable with smaller apertures under excellent skies. Quality of optics, the observer's experience, and full dark adaptation are often more important than the aperture. Some objects will also benefit from the use of a filter because they are superimposed upon a bright nebula.

Nebulae are listed in order of RA. Column **B** lists the *Barnard Catalogue* number; two objects (L 889 and L 906) are from the *Lynds Catalogue*, one (LG 3) is from the *Le Gentil Catalogue*, and one is uncatalogued. The column **Chart #** lists the chart in *Uranometria 2000.0 Deep Sky Atlas* (2nd Ed., 2001) that contains the object; *italic* numbers indicate that the object is not actually marked on the given chart. The **opacity** is based on a scale of 1 to 6, with 6 being the easiest to observe; no objects of opacity 1 or 2 are listed, since these objects are very difficult to observe visually. Showpiece objects are marked "**!!**". For further information, including finder charts, images, and observation reports, visit www.rasc.ca/handbook/supplements.

#	B	Con	RA (2000) h m	Dec ° ′	Chart #	Size ′	Opa-city	Min. Aper. mm	Remarks
1	5	Per	3 48	+32 54	60	22 × 9	5	200	1° NE of o Per
2	211/3	Tau	4 17.2	+27 48	78	12×110	3	200–250	narrow NW–SE lanes, faint bkgd starfield
3	33	Ori	5 40.9	−2 28	116	6 × 4	4	100–150	Horsehead Nebula; use Hβ filter
4	34	Aur	5 43.5	+32 39	59	20	4	200	2° W of M37; spider-like appearance
5	35	Ori	5 45.5	+9 03	96	20×10	5	150–200	near FU Ori and bright nebula Ced 59
6	37	Mon	6 33	+1100	96	3°	5	150 RFT	near NGC 2245, 2247; try binoculars
7	40	Sco	16 14.7	−18 59	147	15	3	250	in bright nebula IC 4592; 50′ NE of ν Sco
8	44	Oph	16 40	−24 04	146	35×300	6	10×70	large dark rift; naked-eye in superb sky
9	59	Oph	17 11.4	−27 29	146	60	6	10×70	3° SW of θ Oph; part of stem of Pipe Nebula
10	64	Oph	17 17.2	−18 32	146	20	6	150–200	30′ W of M9; causes darkening of M9
11	68	Oph	17 22.6	−23 44	146	3	6	200	small; near B72; region rich in dark nebulae
12	70	Oph	17 23.6	−23 58	146	4	4	200	small; near B72; region rich in dark nebulae
13	72	Oph	17 23.6	−23 38	146	30	6	80–125	!! the Snake; "S" shape; 1.5° N of θ Oph
14	78	Oph	17 33	−26 00	146	3°	6	eye	!! Pipe bowl, "Prancing Horse" hindquarters
15	84A	Sgr	17 57.5	−17 40	146	16	5	150–200	1.5° N of M23; try for extensions to S
16	85	Sgr	18 02.6	−23 02	145	5	4	100	!! dark lanes inside Trifid Nebula (M20)
17	86	Sgr	18 02.7	−27 50	145	4	5	200	!! Ink Spot; nice pair with NGC 6520 5′ E
18	87	Sgr	18 04.3	−32 30	163	12	4	200	Parrot's Head; 2° S of γ Sgr
19	88	Sgr	18 04.4	−24 07	145	2	4	200	on edge of M8; *not* Burnham's "Dark Comet"
20		Sgr	18 04.5	−24 14	*145*	2×1	4	200	Burnham's "Dark Comet"; use filter
21	303	Sgr	18 09.5	−24 00	145	1	5	200–250	inside IC 4685; use filter; challenging
22	92/3	Sgr	18 15.5	−18 11	145	12×6	6	7×50	!! on NW edge of Small Sgr Star Cloud, M24
23	103	Sct	18 39.2	−6 37	126	40×40	6	10×0	on NW side of Scutum star cloud
24	104	Sct	18 47.3	−4 32	105	16×1	5	150–200	20′ N of β Sct; a checkmark shape
25	108	Sct	18 49.6	−6 19	125	3	3	200	30′ W of M11; rich region
26	112	Sct	18 51.2	−6 40	125	20	4	200	30′ S of M11; also look for B114, B118
27	133	Aql	19 06.1	−6 50	125	10×3	6	100	on Scutum star cloud; very dark spot!
28	142/3	Aql	19 40.7	+10 57	85	80×50	6	10×50	!! Barnard's famous "E" cloud
29	145	Cyg	20 02.8	+37 40	48	6×35	4	200	triangular shape
30	L 889	Cyg	20 24.8	+40 10	48	100×20	–	7×50	within γ Cygni Nebula, IC 1318
31	L 906	Cyg	20 37	+42 00	48	6°	–	eye	"Northern Coalsack"
32	150	Cep	20 00.6	+60 18	20	60×3	5	250	curved filament 1.6° S of η Cep
33	353	Cyg	20 57.1	+45 32	32	20×10	5	100	in N of North America Nebula; B352 in field
34	LG 3	Cyg	21 00	+53 00	*32*	12°	–	eye	!! "Funnel Cloud Nebula"; best after Coalsack
35	361	Cyg	21 12.9	+47 22	32	20	4	100	cluster IC 1369 to N; try for 1° tendril to W
36	365	Cep	21 34.9	+56 43	19	22×3	4	200	in IC 1396; indistinct "S" shape; use filter
37	163	Cep	21 42.2	+56 42	19	4	4	200	in IC 1396; use filter
38	168	Cyg	21 49	+47 29	31	100×20	5	7×50	large E–W lane; Cocoon Nebula at E end

DEEP-SKY CHALLENGE OBJECTS

BY ALAN DYER AND ALISTER LING

The beauty of the deep sky extends well past the best and brightest objects. The attraction of observing is not the sight of an object itself but our intellectual contact with what it *is*. A faint, stellar point in Virgo evokes wonder when you try to fathom the depths of this quasar billions of light-years away. The eclectic collection of objects below is designed to introduce some "fringe" catalogues while providing challenging targets for a wide range of apertures. Often more important than sheer aperture are factors such as the quality of sky, quality of the optics, use of an appropriate filter, and the observer's experience. Don't be afraid to tackle some of these with a smaller telescope.

Objects are listed in order of right ascension. Abbreviations are the same as in THE MESSIER CATALOGUE and THE FINEST NGC OBJECTS, with the addition of DN = dark nebula and Q = quasar. **Chart #** indicates the chart in which the object can be found in *Uranometria 2000.0 Deep Sky Atlas* (2nd Ed., 2001). The last column suggests the minimum aperture, in millimetres, needed to see that object. Most data are taken from *Sky Catalogue 2000.0, Vol. 2*. Some visual magnitudes are from other sources.

#	Object	Con	Type	RA (2000) h m	Dec ° ′	m_v	Size ′	Chart #	Minimum Aperture mm
1	**NGC 7822**	Cep	E/RN	0 03.6	+68 37	—	60 × 30	8	300
	large, faint emission nebula; rated "eeF"; also look for E/R nebula Ced 214 (associated w/ star cluster Berkeley 59) 1° S								
2	**IC 59**	Cas	E/RN	0 56.7	+61 04	—	10 × 5	18	200–250
	faint emission/reflection nebula paired with IC 63 very close to γ Cas.; requires clean optics; rated as "pF"								
3	**NGC 609**	Cas	OC	1 37.2	+64 33	11.0	3.0	17	250–300
	faint patch at low power; high power needed to resolve this rich cluster (also look for Trumpler 1 cluster 3° S)								
4	**IC 1795**	Cas	EN	2 24.7	+61 54	—	27 × 13	29	200
	brightest part of a complex of nebulosity that includes IC 1805 and IC 1848; use a nebular filter								
5	**Maffei I**	Cas	G-E3	2 36.3	+59 39	≈14	5 × 3	29	300
	heavily reddened galaxy; very faint; requires large aperture and black skies; nearby Maffei II for extremists								
6	**NGC 1049**	For	GC	2 39.7	−34 29	11.0	0.6	175	250–300
	Class V globular in dwarf "Fornax System" Local Group galaxy 630 000 ly away; galaxy itself invisible?								
7	**Abell 426**	Per	G cl.	3 19.8	+41 31	12–16	≈30	43, A4	200–400
	Perseus galaxy cluster 300 million ly away; mag. 11.6 NGC 1275 Perseus A at centre; see close-up chart A4								
8	**NGC 1432/35**	Tau	RN	3 46.1	+23 47	—	30 × 30	78, A12	100–150
	Pleiades nebulosity (also includes IC 349); brightest around Merope; requires transparent skies and clean optics								
9	**IC 342**	Cam	G-SBc	3 46.8	+68 06	≈12	17 × 1	16	200–300
	large and diffuse face-on spiral; member of UMa–Cam cloud (Kemble's Cascade of stars also on this chart)								
10	**NGC 1499**	Per	EN	4 00.7	+36 37	—	145 × 40	60	80–125 RFT
	California Nebula; very large and faint; use a wide-field telescope or big binoculars plus Hβ filter								
11	**IC 405**	Aur	E/RN	5 16.2	+34 16	—	30 × 19	59	200
	Flaming Star Nebula associated with runaway star AE Aurigae; see Burnham's Handbook p. 285 (also look for IC 410)								
12	**HH 1**	Ori	E	5 36.3	−06 45	≈14.5	8″	136	250
	Herbig–Haro 1; best with no filter at 250 × or more; bipolar jets from forming star; not plotted; 2.5′ SW NGC 1999								
13	**IC 434 / B 33**	Ori	E/DN	5 40.9	−2 28	—	60 × 10	116	100–150 in dark sky!
	B 33 is the Horsehead Nebula, a dark nebula superimposed on a very faint emission nebula IC 434; use Hβ filter								
14	**Sh 2-276**	Ori	EN	5 48.0	+1 —	—	600 × 30!	116	100–150 RFT
	Barnard's Loop; SNR or interstellar bubble? difficult to detect due to size; use filter and sweep with wide field								
15	**Abell 12**	Ori	PN	6 02.4	+9 39	≈13	37″	96	250–300
	plotted in *Uranometria* as PK 198.6–6.3; on NW edge of μ Orionis; OIII filter required								
16	**IC 443**	Gem	SNR	6 16.9	+22 47	—	50 × 40	76	250–300
	faint supernova remnant very close to η Gem.; use filter (also look for NGC 2174 and Sh 2–247 on this chart)								
17	**J 900**	Gem	PN	6 25.9	+17 47	12.2	8″	76	200
	Jonckheere 900; bright starlike planetary; plotted as PK 194.2+2.5 in *Uranometria*; use OIII filter & high power								
18	**IC 2177**	Mon	E/RN	7 05.1	−10 42	—	120 × 40	135	200–300
	Seagull Nebula; large, faint; contains bright patches Gum 1 (−10°28′), NGC 2327 (−11°18′) & Ced 90 (−12°20′)								

DEEP-SKY CHALLENGE OBJECTS (continued)

#	Object	Con	Type	RA (2000) h m	Dec ° ′	m_v	Size ′	Chart #	Minimum Aperture mm
19	**PK 205 +14.2**	Gem	PN	7 29.0	+13 15	≈13	≈700″	95	200–250
	Medusa Nebula or Abell 21; impressive in large aperture w/ OIII filter								
20	**PK 164 +31.1**	Lyn	PN	7 57.8	+53 25	≈14	400″	26	250
	Jones–Emberson 1; faint with two small components; use OIII filter; sometimes confused with nearby NGC 2474–75								
21	**Leo I**	Leo	G-E3	10 08.4	+12 18	9.8	10.7×8.3	93	300
	dwarf elliptical; satellite of Milky Way; very low surface brightness; 0.3° N of Regulus! requires clean optics								
22	**Abell 1367**	Leo	G cl.	11 44.0	+19 57	13–16	≈60	72, A11	300–400
	cluster of some 30 or more galaxies within a 1° field near 93 Leonis; Copeland's Septet nearby								
23	**NGC 3172**	UMi	G-Sb	11 50.2	+89 07	13.6	0.7×0.7	1	250
	"Polarissima Borealis"—closest galaxy to the north celestial pole; small, faint, and otherwise unremarkable								
24	**NGC 4236**	Dra	G-SBb	12 16.7	+69 28	9.6	18.6×6.9	13	200–250
	very large, dim barred spiral; a diffuse glow (NGC 4395 on Chart #54 a similar large diffuse face-on)								
25	**Mrk 205**	Dra	Q	12 21.6	+75 18	14.5	stellar	5	300
	Markarian 205; a faint star on SW edge of NGC 4319; centre of redshift controversy								
26	**3C 273**	Vir	Q	12 29.1	+2 03	12–13	stellar	111	250–300
	at 2–3 billon ly away, one of the most distant objects visible in amateur telescopes; magnitude variable								
27	**NGC 4676**	Com	G cl.	12 46.2	+30 44	14.lp	2×1	53	250
	"The Mice" or VV 224—two classic interacting galaxies; very faint double nature detectable at high power								
28	**Abell 1656**	Com	G cl.	13 00.1	+27 58	12–16	≈60	71, A8	250–300
	Coma Berenices galaxy cluster; very rich; 400 million ly away; brightest member NGC 4889; see close-up chart A8								
29	**NGC 5053**	Com	GC	13 16.4	+17 42	9.8	10.5	71	100–200
	faint and very loose globular 1° SE of M53; requires large aperture to resolve; difficult in hazy skies; class XI								
30	**NGC 5897**	Lib	GC	15 17.4	−21 01	8.6	12.6	148	150–200
	large and loose; easily hidden in hazy skies at higher latitude; brightest stars mag. 13.3, main branch mag. 16.3								
31	**Abell 2065**	CrB	G cl.	15 22.7	+27 43	≈16	≈30	69	500 in superb sky!
	Corona Borealis galaxy cluster; perhaps the most difficult object for amateur telescopes; 1.5 billion ly away								
32	**NGC 6027**	Ser	G cl.	15 59.2	+20 45	≈15	2×1	69	400
	Seyfert's Sextet (6027 A–F); compact group of 6 small and very faint galaxies; see Burnham's Handbook p. 1793								
33	**B 72**	Oph	DN	17 23.5	−23 38	—	30	146	80–125 RFT
	Barnard's dark S-Nebula or "The Snake"; opacity of 6/6; 1.5° NNE of θ Ophiuchi; area rich in dark nebulae								
34	**NGC 6791**	Lyr	OC	19 20.7	+37 51	9.5	16	48	200–250
	large, faint but very rich open cluster with 300 stars; a faint smear in smaller instruments; Type II 3 r								
35	**PK 64 +5.1**	Cyg	PN	19 34.8	+30 31	9.6	8″	48	200
	Campbell's Hydrogen Star; very bright but very starlike; also catalogued as star BD +30°3639								
36	**M 1-92**	Cyg	RN	19 36.3	+29 33	11.0	12″×6″	48	250–300
	Minkowski 1-92 or Footprint Nebula; bright, starlike reflection nebula; double at high mag; associated star invisible								
37	**NGC 6822**	Sgr	G-I	19 44.9	−14 48	≈11	10.2×9.5	125	100–150
	Barnard's Galaxy; member of the Local Group; large but very low surface brightness; requires transparent skies								
38	**Palomar 11**	Aql	GC	19 45.2	−8 00	9.8	3.2	125	200–300
	brightest of 15 heavily reddened GCs found on Sky Survey; magnitude is misleading; 11 Terzan GCs more challenging								
39	**IC 4997**	Sge	PN	20 20.2	+16 45	10.9	2″	84	200
	bright but starlike planetary; the challenge is to see the disk! blink the field with and without a nebular filter								
40	**IC 1318**	Cyg	EN	20 26.2	+40 30	—	large	32, A2	80–150 RFT
	complex of nebulosity around γ Cygni; multitude of patches in rich starfield; use a very wide field plus filter								
41	**PK 80 −6.1**	Cyg	PN?	21 02.3	+36 42	13.5	16″	47	250
	the "Egg Nebula"; a very small proto-planetary nebula; can owners of large telescopes detect polarization?								
42	**IC 1396**	Cep	EN	21 39.1	+57 30	—	170×140	19	100–125 RFT
	extremely large and diffuse area of emission nebulosity; use nebular filter and very wide-field optics in dark sky								
43	**IC 5146**	Cyg	E/RN	21 53.5	+47 16	—	12×12	31	200–250
	Cocoon Nebula; faint and diffuse; use Hβ filter; at the end of the long filamentary dark nebula Barnard 168								
44	**NGC 7317–20**	Peg	G cl.	22 36.1	+33 57	13–14	≈1 ea.	46	250–300
	Stephan's Quintet; 0.5° SSW of NGC 7331; easy to pick out 3 or 4 (also look for "companions" to 7331)								
45	**Jones 1**	Peg	PN	23 35.9	+30 28	12.1	332″	45	250–300
	plotted as PK 104.2 −29.6 in *Uranometria*; large dim glow; OIII filter required								

DEEP-SKY GEMS

BY DAVID H. LEVY

The 154 objects in this personal list are selected from nearly 400 deep-sky objects that I assembled over forty-plus years of comet-hunting. My observing program, called CN-3, began on 1965 Dec. 17 and has continued without interruption since then (see www.rasc.ca/david-h-levy-logbooks). The objects are numbered chronologically (**L#**) in the order I first located them in the night sky, and these numbers match those in my book, *Deep Sky Objects: The best and brightest from four decades of comet chasing* (Prometheus Books, New York, 2005, 262 pp). **UI** refers to the charts in *Uranometria 2000.0*. **UII** refers to charts in *Uranometria 2000.0 Deep Sky Atlas* (the 2nd edition of **UI**). Chart numbers in parentheses indicate unlabelled objects.

This selection complements the other Handbook deep-sky observing lists. Specifically, the following objects are not included here: all objects that appear in THE MESSIER CATALOGUE, THE FINEST NGC OBJECTS, and THE DEEP-SKY CHALLENGE OBJECTS; also, several double stars and variable stars, a few asterisms, some photographic objects, and the gegenschein are not included, though observing them is strongly encouraged; finally, several objects with southern declinations are left out to ensure that the Deep-Sky Gems observing certificate can be earned without travel by the typical RASC member. Levy 384 deserves special note: Just as the terms "Plaskett's Star" and "Kemble's Cascade" recognize Canadian astronomers from the past, "Levy 384" has become the recognized name for a previously unnamed asterism.

On a final, personal note, the late Leo Enright deserves great credit and thanks for the amount of time and effort he invested since he originated this project in 2007. A dear and special friend, Leo devoted his life to inspiring people to take up skywatching. He was one of my closest friends and I miss him deeply.

The main list is grouped by season and ordered by RA. The list below is a cross-reference aid.

NUMERICAL LISTING OF DEEP-SKY GEMS

L#	Sky RA	L#	Sky RA	L#	Sky RA	L#	Sky RA	L#	Sky RA	L#	Sky RA	L#	Sky RA
5	Spr 14	**59**	Aut 1	**133**	Spr 9	**171**	Spr 12	**205**	Sum 16	**239**	Aut 0	***279***	*Sum 18*
6	Sum 16	**62**	Aut 2	**134**	Spr 12	**172**	Spr 12	**206**	Sum 16	**240**	Aut 0	**280**	Aut 23
8	Win 4	**64**	Aut 1	**135**	Spr 12	**178**	Spr 12	**207**	Sum 17	**243**	Sum 17	**281**	Aut 23
19	Sum 16	**81**	Aut 0	**136**	Spr 11	**181**	Spr 11	**208**	Sum 17	**247**	Aut 22	**282**	Aut 22
27	Spr 13	**82**	Spr 14	**137**	Spr 11	**182**	Spr 12	**209**	Spr 9	**249**	Aut 23	**284**	Aut 1
28	Spr 14	**83**	Spr 14	**138**	Spr 11	**183**	Spr 12	**210**	Spr 12	**255**	Spr 13	**286**	Win 3
29	Spr 14	**95**	Win 5	***140***	*Spr 12*	**184**	Spr 13	**211**	Spr 12	**256**	Win 8	**296**	Win 7
31	Aut 1	**96**	Win 8	**145**	Spr 12	**185**	Spr 13	**212**	Spr 12	**257**	Spr 12	**300**	Spr 10
34	Aut 1	**98**	Sum 18	**147**	Sum 18	**186**	Spr 13	**213**	Spr 12	**259**	Spr 12	**315**	Spr 13
35	Win 7	**99**	Aut 2	**149**	Sum 18	**187**	Spr 13	**214**	Spr 12	**260**	Spr 12	**317**	Spr 15
36	Sum 17	**110**	Sum 19	**156**	Sum 20	**188**	Spr 12	**215**	Spr 12	**261**	Spr 13	***324***	*Win 3*
37	Spr 9	**112**	Aut 21	**158**	Win 7	**189**	Spr 13	**217**	Spr 11	**262**	Sum 19	**326**	Spr 12
38	Aut 23	**114**	Win 4	**159**	Win 6	**190**	Spr 13	**219**	Spr 10	**263**	Aut 21	**331**	Spr 10
41	Spr 11	**116**	Win 6	**160**	Win 6	**191**	Spr 12	**220**	Sum 20	**266**	Spr 15	**334**	Sum 17
42	Spr 12	***120***	*Sum 17*	**161**	Win 6	**192**	Spr 12	**223**	Aut 0	**267**	Spr 13	**337**	Spr 10
44	Win 3	**121**	Spr 15	**162**	Win 6	**193**	Spr 12	**224**	Aut 2	**268**	Spr 14	**338**	Aut 2
50	Win 4	**123**	Win 4	**163**	Spr 9	**195**	Win 7	**225**	Win 3	**270**	Sum 18	**340**	Aut 2
51	Spr 9	**124**	Win 6	**164**	Spr 11	**196**	Spr 14	**226**	Win 8	**271**	Sum 17	**341**	Aut 2
53	Aut 1	**125**	Win 5	**165**	Spr 10	**201**	Spr 11	**231**	Spr 13	**273**	Win 5	**342**	Aut 0
55	Aut 23	**129**	Spr 10	**167**	Spr 10	**202**	Spr 14	**232**	Spr 13	**276**	Aut 0	**367**	Aut 1
56	Aut 0	**130**	Spr 10	**169**	Spr 9	**203**	Spr 14	**236**	Sum 16	**277**	Aut 22	**382**	Spr 11
57	Aut 23	**131**	Spr 9	**170**	Spr 12	**204**	Spr 15	**238**	Aut 1	**278**	Aut 1	**384**	Win 8

Editor's note: for certificate purposes, this list was revised in late 2011 by introducing Levy 120, 140, 279, and 324 (see entries in italics) in place of previous duplicates Levy 1, 245, 325, and 381.

DEEP-SKY GEMS (continued)

L#	NGC	RA (2000) h m	Dec ° ′	m_v	Size (′)	UI	UII	Remarks
The Autumn Sky								
112	7023	21 00.5	+68 10	7.0	10 × 8	32	9	Unusual-looking nebula in Cepheus
263	7006	21 01.5	+16 11	10.5	2.8	209	83	Globular cluster in Delphinus
277	7184	22 02.7	–20 49	11.2	6.5 × 1.4	346	142	Very elongated galaxy in Aquarius
247	7217	22 07.9	+31 22	10.1	3.5 × 3.0	122	46	Round galaxy in Pegasus
282	7314	22 35.8	–26 03	10.9	4.2 × 1.7	347	142	Elongated galaxy in Piscis Austrinus
249	7457	23 01.0	+30 09	11.2	4.1 × 2.5	124	46	Elongated galaxy in Pegasus
55	7664	23 26.6	+25 04	12.7	3.0 × 1.7	169	63	Galaxy in Pegasus
57	7723	23 38.8	–12 58	11.2	2.8 × 1.9	304	121	Galaxy in Aquarius
280	7721	23 38.8	–06 31	11.6	3.3 × 1.3	304	121	Elongated galaxy in Aquarius
281	7727	23 39.9	–12 18	10.6	5.6 × 4.0	304	121	Round galaxy in Aquarius
38	7753	23 47.1	+29 20	12.0	3.2 × 1.7	89	45	Slightly elongated galaxy in Pegasus
276	7814	00 03.3	+16 09	10.6	6.0 × 2.5	170	81	Elongated galaxy in Pegasus
342	91	00 21.8	+22 25	13.7	2.2 × 0.8	126	63	Galaxy in And, in galaxy cluster
81	147	00 33.2	+48 30	9.5	15.0 × 9.4	60	30	Comet-like galaxy; satellite of M31
223	150	00 34.3	–27 48	11.3	3.4 × 1.6	306	141	Elongated galaxy in Sculptor
240	157	00 34.8	–08 24	10.4	4.0 × 2.4	261	121	Elongated "Amoeba Galaxy" in Cetus
239	247	00 47.1	–20 46	9.2	19.0 × 5.5	306	158	Very elongated galaxy in Cetus
56	270	00 50.6	–08 39	12.1	2.0 × 1.7	262	140	Galaxy in Cetus
64	404	01 09.4	+35 43	10.3	6.1 × 6.1	91	62	Round galaxy near β Andromedae
278	474	01 20.1	+03 25	11.5	10.0 × 9.2	217	120	Galaxy near NGC 470 in Pisces
34	488	01 21.8	+05 15	10.3	5.5 × 4.0	217	100	Elongated galaxy in Pisces
31	514	01 24.1	+12 55	11.7	3.9 × 2.9	173	100	Easily seen galaxy in Pisces
59	524	01 24.8	+09 32	10.2	3.5 × 3.5	173	100	Round galaxy in Pisces
238	578	01 30.5	–22 40	11.0	3.9 × 2.2	308	158	Elongated galaxy in Cetus
367	613	01 34.3	–29 25	10.0	5.2 × 2.6	352	158	Special galaxy in Sculptor
284	718	01 53.2	+04 12	11.7	2.4 × 2.0	218	119	Round galaxy in Pisces
341	755	01 56.4	–09 04	12.6	2.8 × 1.1	264	139	Elongated galaxy in Cetus
53	752	01 57.8	+37 41	5.7	50	92	61	Very large open cluster in Andromeda
62	898	02 23.3	+41 57	12.9	1.8 × 0.5	91	43	Elongated galaxy in Andromeda
99	949	02 30.8	+37 08	11.8	3.3 × 2.1	93	61	Very cometary galaxy in Triangulum
224	IC 1830	02 39.1	–27 27	11.9	1.9 × 1.5	310	157	Galaxy in Fornax
338	1042	02 40.4	–08 26	11.0	4.2 × 3.3	215	139	Galaxy in Cetus
340	1134	02 53.6	+13 00	12.1	2.3 × 0.8	175	99	Round galaxy in Aries
The Winter Sky								
225	1187	03 02.6	–22 52	10.7	5.2 × 3.0	311	157	Round galaxy in Eridanus
44	1333	03 29.2	+31 25	—	6 × 3	94	60	A weird reflection nebula in Perseus
286	1360	03 33.3	–25 51	9.4	6.5	312	156	Beautiful planetary nebula in Fornax
324	*Tom*5*	03 47.8	+59 03	8.4	14.0	28	39	*Open cluster in Camelopardalis*
50	1579	04 30.2	+35 16	—	12 × 8	96	60	Reflection nebula in Perseus
123	1600	04 31.7	–05 05	10.9	2.3 × 1.5	223	117	Round, diffuse galaxy in Eridanus
8	1624	04 40.4	+50 27	13.0	5 × 5	40	42	Cluster with nebulosity in Perseus
114	1637	04 41.5	–02 51	10.8	3.4 × 2.6	224	117	Comet-like round galaxy in Eridanus
273	1746	05 03.6	+23 49	6.1	42	134	77	Beautiful open cluster in Taurus
95	1999	05 36.5	–06 42	10.0	2 × 2	271	136	Diffuse nebula in Orion
125	2023	05 41.6	–02 14	—	10 × 10	226	116	Nebula near ζ Orionis
116	2158	06 07.5	+24 06	8.6	5	136	76	Compact cluster near M35 in Gemini
124	2174	06 09.7	+20 30	—	40 × 30	137	76	Large field of dust in Orion
161	2245	06 32.7	+10 10	—	5 × 4	182	95	Comet-like bright nebula in Mon
162	2252	06 35.0	+05 23	7.7	20	227	95	Open cluster like rope of stars, in Mon
160	2254	06 36.6	+07 40	9.1	4	182	95	Open cluster and star chain in Mon
159	2264	06 41.1	+09 53	3.9	20	183	95	"Christmas Tree Cluster" in Mon
296	2362	07 18.8	–24 57	4.1	8	319	153	Open cluster in Canis Major
158	IC2194/6/7	07 33.7	+31 19	(12.5)	—	(100)	57	Three of the "Castor Cluster" galaxies
195	2419	07 38.1	+38 53	10.3	4.1	100	95	"Intergalactic Wanderer" in Lynx
35	2420	07 38.5	+21 34	8.3	10	139	75	Open cluster in Gemini

* "Tom" refers to the catalogue of 5 open clusters discovered by Clyde Tombaugh, better known as the discoverer of Pluto.

DEEP-SKY GEMS (continued)

L#	NGC	RA (2000) h m	Dec ° ′	m_V	Size (′)	UI	UII	Remarks
The Winter Sky (continued)								
384	Levy384	08 15.6	−13 58	—	2	(275)	(134)	Compact asterism in Puppis (special!)
256	IC2367	08 24.2	−18 46	12.5	2.3 × 0.5	321	153	Galaxy in Puppis
226	2613	08 33.4	−22 58	10.5	7.6 × 1.9	321	153	Edge-on galaxy in Pyxis
96	2681	08 53.5	+51 19	10.3	5.3 × 3.5	44	39	Galaxy in Ursa Major
The Spring Sky								
163	2775	09 10.3	+07 02	10.1	4.6 × 3.7	187	93	Round galaxy in Cancer
51	Arp321	09 38.9	−04 52	(12.5)	—	(233)	113	"Larry, Moe, & Curly" galaxies in Hya
131	2964	09 42.9	+31 51	11.3	3.2 × 1.8	103	56	Galaxy contains Mrk 404 in Leo
169	2986	09 44.3	−21 17	10.6	4.1 × 3.4	323	152	Round galaxy in Hydra
209	3049	09 54.8	+09 16	12.1	2.3 × 1.5	188	93	Comet-like galaxy in Leo
37	3055	09 55.3	+04 16	12.1	2.0 × 1.1	234	113	Comet-like galaxy in Sextans
133	3070	09 58.0	+10 22	12.3	1.6 × 1.6	189	93	Round galaxy near NGC 3069, in Leo
129	U5373	10 00.0	+05 20	11.3	5.5 × 3.7	234	113	Sextans B galaxy; Local Group member
337	0957	10 01.3	+55 54	15.5	—	45	25	Famous double quasar in Ursa Major
	+561A/B							(gravitational lens; distinct in 16″ scope)
130	3198	10 19.9	+45 33	10.3	9.2 × 3.5	72	39	Very elongated galaxy in Ursa Major
300	3226	10 23.4	+19 54	11.4	2.5 × 2.2	144	73	Galaxy in Leo
165	3245	10 27.3	+28 30	10.8	2.9 × 2.0	105	73	Elongated galaxy in Leo Minor
219	3309	10 36.6	−27 31	11	4.4 × 3.1	325	151	Hydra I galaxy cluster (five members)
	+ 3311	10 36.7	−27 32	10.9	4.0 × 3.6			
	+ 3312	10 37.0	−27 34	11.8	3.4 × 1.1			
	+ 3314	10 37.4	−27 41	12.8	1.5 × 0.8			(actually two spirals!!)
	+ 3316	10 37.6	−27 36	12.6	1.4 × 1.2			
167	3310	10 38.7	+53 30	10.8	3.5 × 3.2	46	25	Round galaxy in Ursa Major
331	3319	10 39.2	+41 41	11.1	6.9 × 4.0	72	38	Graceful spiral galaxy in Ursa Major
164	3486	11 00.4	+28 58	10.5	6.6 × 4.7	106	73	Round galaxy in Leo Minor
382	U6253	11 13.5	+22 10	12	15.0 x12.5	146	73	Galaxy in Leo
137	3718	11 32.6	+53 04	10.8	10.0x 4.7	47	24	Elongated galaxy in Ursa Major
136	3738	11 35.8	+54 31	11.7	3.2 × 2.8	47	24	Galaxy near M97 in Ursa Major
41	3810	11 41.0	+11 28	10.8	3.8 × 2.6	192	91	Round galaxy in Leo
201	3865	11 44.9	−09 14	12.0	2.0 × 1.6	282	131	Diffuse galaxy in Crater
181	3887	11 47.1	−16 51	10.6	3.5 × 2.4	292	131	Round galaxy in Crater
217	3923	11 51.0	−28 48	9.6	6.9 × 4.8	368	150	Elongated galaxy in Hydra
138	3953	11 53.8	+52 20	10.1	6.0 × 3.2	47	24	Very elongated galaxy in Ursa Major
193	4129	12 08.9	−09 02	12.5	2.3 × 0.7	283	131	Elongated galaxy in Virgo
135	4256	12 18.7	+65 54	11.9	4.1 × 0.8	25	13	Edge-on galaxy in Draco
134	4319	12 21.7	+75 19	11.9	2.8 × 2.1	9	5	Galaxy near 4291 & 4386 in Draco
42	4340	12 23.0	+16 43	11.2	3.7 × 3.1	193	91	Galaxy near NGC 4350 in Coma
171	4450	12 28.5	+17 05	10.1	5.0 × 3.4	148	72	Elongated galaxy in Coma
145	4473	12 29.8	+13 26	10.2	3.7 × 2.4	193	91	Very elongated galaxy in Coma
140	*4485*	12 30.5	+41 42	11.9	2.0 × 1.3	37	75	*Elong. galaxy N of NGC 4490 in CVn*
260	4519	12 33.5	+08 39	11.8	3.5 × 2.3	194	90	Galaxy in Virgo
192	4536	12 34.5	+02 11	10.6	6.4 × 2.6	239	110	Very elongated galaxy in Virgo
326	4570	12 36.9	+07 15	10.9	4.3 × 1.3	194	90	Comet-like elongated galaxy in Virgo
188	4591	12 39.3	+06 01	13.0	1.6 × 0.8	194	90	Elongated galaxy in Virgo
178	4596	12 39.9	+10 11	10.4	4.6 × 4.1	194	90	Elongated galaxy in Virgo
213	4623	12 42.2	+07 41	12.2	2.0 × 0.7	194	90	Very elongated galaxy in Virgo
182	4636	12 42.8	+02 41	9.5	7.1 × 5.2	239	110	Galaxy with bright core in Virgo
170	4651	12 43.7	+16 24	10.8	3.5 × 2.3	194	90	Round galaxy in Coma
210	4685	12 47.1	+19 28	12.6	1.5 × 0.9	149	71	"Winking Galaxy" in Coma
172	4689	12 47.8	+13 46	10.9	3.7 × 3.2	194	90	Elongated galaxy in Coma
215	4688	12 47.8	+04 20	11.9	4.0 × 4.0	239	110	Very large galaxy in Virgo
214	4713	12 50.0	+05 19	11.7	2.9 × 1.8	194	90	Elongated galaxy in Virgo
259	4722	12 51.5	−13 19	12.9	1.5 × 0.7	284	130	Round galaxy in Corvus

DEEP-SKY GEMS (continued)

L#	NGC	RA (2000) h m	Dec ° ′	m_V	Size (′)	UI	UII	Remarks
The Spring Sky (continued)								
191	4772	12 53.5	+02 10	11.0	2.7 × 1.3	239	110	Galaxy in Virgo
211	4779	12 53.8	+09 44	12.4	1.9 × 1.7	194	90	Round galaxy in Virgo
212	4795	12 55.0	+08 04	12.1	1.9 × 1.7	194	90	Round galaxy in Virgo
183	4818	12 56.8	−08 31	11.1	3.4 × 1.4	284	130	Very elongated galaxy in Virgo
257	4866	12 59.5	+14 10	11.2	5.5 × 1.2	194	90	Elongated galaxy in Virgo
190	4956	13 05.1	+35 11	12.4	1.5 × 1.5	109	53	Round galaxy in Canes Venatici
255	5016	13 12.1	+24 06	12.8	1.7 × 1.3	150	71	Round galaxy in Coma
187	5020	13 12.6	+12 36	11.7	3.0 × 2.6	195	90	Elongated galaxy in Virgo
232	5068	13 18.9	−21 02	9.6	7.1 × 6.6	330	149	Very large galaxy in Virgo
189	5127	13 23.8	+31 34	11.9	2.3 × 1.7	109	53	Round galaxy in Canes Venatici
184	5147	13 26.3	+02 06	11.8	1.6 × 1.5	240	110	Round galaxy in Virgo
315	5146	13 26.5	−12 19	12.3	1.8 × 1.2	285	130	Round galaxy in Virgo
185	5248	13 37.5	+08 53	10.3	6.2 × 4.6	196	90	Round galaxy in Boötes
267	5247	13 38.1	−17 53	10.1	5.2 × 3.2	331	130	Beautiful, diffuse spiral in Virgo
261	5350	13 53.4	+40 22	11.3	3.1 × 2.5	76	36	Galaxy in Canes Venatici
186	5371	13 55.7	+40 28	10.6	4.1 × 3.2	76	36	Round galaxy in Canes Venatici
231	5364	13 56.2	+05 01	10.5	6.6 × 5.1	196	89	Elongated galaxy in Virgo
27	5377	13 56.3	+47 14	11.3	4.1 × 2.3	76	36	Galaxy near Big Dipper's handle
202	5427	14 03.4	−06 02	11.4	2.6 × 1.8	286	129	Galaxy, interacting with 5426, in Vir
28	5473	14 04.7	+54 54	11.4	2.2 × 1.7	49	23	Comet-like galaxy near M101 in UMa
29	5474	14 05.0	+53 40	10.8	6.0 × 4.9	49	23	Galaxy near M101 in Ursa Major
82	5634	14 29.6	−05 59	9.4	4.9	287	109	Globular cluster in Virgo
83	5638	14 29.7	+03 14	11.2	2.3 × 2.1	242	109	Comet-like galaxy in Virgo
5	5676	14 32.8	+49 28	11.2	3.7 × 1.6	77	36	Small elliptical galaxy in Boötes
203	5668	14 33.4	+04 27	11.5	3.2 × 2.8	242	109	Comet-like galaxy in Virgo
268	5690	14 37.7	+02 17	11.8	3.3 × 1.0	242	109	Very elongated galaxy in Virgo
196	5694	14 39.6	−26 32	9.2	3.6	332	148	"Tombaugh's Cluster" in Hydra
317	5838	15 05.4	+02 06	10.9	3.5 × 1.6	242	108	Elongated galaxy in Virgo
121	5846	15 06.4	+01 36	10.0	3.0 × 3.0	243	108	Galaxy in Virgo
204	5850	15 07.1	+01 33	10.8	4.6 × 4.1	243	108	Comet-like galaxy in Virgo
266	5962	15 36.5	+16 37	11.3	2.6 × 1.8	199	88	Round galaxy in Serpens
The Summer Sky								
205	6106	16 18.8	+07 25	12.2	2.3 × 1.2	201	87	Galaxy in Hercules
206	6118	16 21.8	−02 17	11.7	4.6 × 1.9	246	107	Galaxy in Serpens
236	6181	16 32.3	+19 50	11.9	2.3 × 0.9	156	69	Galaxy in Hercules
19	6207	16 43.1	+36 50	11.5	3.0 × 1.1	114	50	Spiral galaxy near M13 in Hercules
6	6229	16 47.0	+47 32	9.4	4.5	80	34	Compact globular cluster in Hercules
271	6287	17 05.2	−22 42	9.3	5	337	146	Globular cluster in Ophiuchus
334	6342	17 21.2	−19 35	9.8	3	338	146	Globular cluster near M9 in Ophiuchus
36	6364	17 24.5	+29 24	12.9	1.5 × 1.2	115	50	Comet-like galaxy in Hercules
207	6384	17 32.4	+07 04	10.4	6.4 × 4.3	203	86	Galaxy in Ophiuchus
208	6426	17 44.9	+03 00	11.1	3.2	248	106	Globular cluster in Ophiuchus
243	6440	17 48.9	−20 22	9.1	5.4	338	146	Globular cluster in Sagittarius
120	*6451*	17 50.7	−30 13	8.2	7.0	164	377	*"Tom Thumb Cluster," OC in Scorpius*
279	*6522 + 6528*	18 03.6	−30 02	8.3	16.4	163	377	*"Baade's Window," two faint GCs close to the galactic centre in Sgr*
270	6535	18 03.8	−00 18	10.5	3.6	249	106	Globular cluster in Serpens
149	6553	18 09.3	−25 54	8.1	8.1	339	145	Faint globular cluster in Sagittarius
147	6638	18 30.9	−25 30	9.1	5	340	145	Globular cluster in Sagittarius
98	6709	18 51.5	+10 21	6.7	13	205	85	Open cluster in Aquila
110	6760	19 11.2	+01 02	9.1	6.6	251	105	Globular cluster in Aquila
262	6814	19 42.7	−10 19	11.2	3.0 × 3.0	297	125	Round galaxy in Aquila
220	6910	20 23.1	+40 47	7.4	7	84	32	Open cluster in Cygnus
156	6934	20 34.2	+07 24	8.7	5.9	208	84	Globular cluster in Delphinus

WIDE-FIELD WONDERS

BY CHRIS BECKETT

In recent years, wide-field eyepieces, short-tube refractors, fast (sub-*f*/4) reflectors, and large, imaged-stabilized binoculars have increased in popularity. Dark-Sky Preserves with transparent skies have become attractive observing destinations for amateur astronomers. Such equipment and sites lend themselves to viewing a host of wonderful wide-field deep-sky objects that exceed typical telescopic fields of view. Observing large objects such as star clouds, open clusters, diffuse nebulae, giant molecular clouds, and supernova remnants—often with multiple objects in the same field of view—allows the observer to gain an appreciation for the structure of our home galaxy, the Milky Way. Although many objects in the following list are visible under light-polluted skies, they are best observed from the darkest sites with the aid of a good selection of nebula filters. All you need to begin is a pair of handheld binoculars—try experimenting with a filter taped over one objective. Several objects are visible using this technique in a dark location—in fact, some become invisible once you move to large apertures or high power! In the following list, **RA** and **Dec** identify the brightest portions. Most object types are defined on p. 314; in addition, DN = dark nebula, GMC = giant molecular cloud, and Ast = asterism.

Object	Con	Type	RA (2000) h m	Dec ° ′	Size ′	Remarks
NGC 206	And	starcloud	00 41	+40 49	5	star cloud within dark lanes of M31
best seen in wide fields with M31 dust lanes to SW; use M32 and mag. 7 star to locate						
Collinder 463	Cas	OC	01 47	+71 52	57	Crescent Cluster
4 dozen stars scattered in a crescent						
Stock 2	Cas	OC	02 16	+59 33	60	Mushroom Cluster
try to see the Double Cluster and Stock 2 in same field; note star chain leading to Stock 2						
IC 1805 & 1848	Cas	EN	02 34	+61 29	4.5°	Heart and Soul Nebulae
large complex of nebulae and star clusters; use filter; IC 1795 is brightest part of IC 1805						
Cosmic ? Mark	Cet	Ast	02 37	+06 56	2.5°×1°	asterism known as the "Question Mark"
looks exactly like a large question mark, best seen in binoculars						
Melotte 20	Per	OC	03 25	+49 54	5°	Perseus OB3 Association
large cluster for small binoculars; look for a miniature "Draco" asterism, including 4 stars denoting the head						
Kemble's Cascade	Cam	Ast	03 59	+63 06	3°	asterism: colourful chain of 20+ stars
terminates at NGC 1502; named by Walter Scott Houston in honour of Father Lucian Kemble (1922–1999)						
Taurus Cloud	Tau	GMC	4h–5h	+16–31	25°×15°	part of the Taurus Molecular Cloud
M45, NGC 1435, IC 353/349/1995; many dark nebulae; "haze" over background star field						
NGC 1499	Per	EN	04 02	+36 39	145×40	California Nebula
use magnification of 15× to 30× to detect wave detail and to train your eye for fainter objects						
Sh2-245	Tau	EN	04 03	+03 06	15×90	Eridanus Arc
use Hβ filter; look for brightest section 3° S of ν Tau						
NGC 1647	Tau	OC	04 47	+19 10	40	large binocular cluster, 5° NE of Hyades
bright; often overlooked; telescope reveals many "double" stars; may be glimpsed without aid in a dark sky						
NGC 1746	Tau	OC	05 05	+23 50	42	NGC 1750 and NGC 1758 superimposed
15× binoculars show a nice cluster embedded in a chain of meandering stars						
IC 2118	Eri	RN	05 08	–07 12	3°×1°	Witch Head Nebula
use low-power, wide-field binoculars or telescope on best nights.						
Collinder 65	Tau	OC	05 27	+16 43	6°	Giant Mushroom
binocular cluster, beautiful, but often not marked on charts; large mushroom-shaped arrow						
Sh2-264	Ori	EN	05 36	+09 56	4.5°×4°	Angelfish Nebula
use Hβ filter in vicinity of λ Ori to see this huge nebula						
Collinder 70	Ori	OC	05 36	–01 06	3°	Orion OB1 Association
3-D view of Ori belt stars over distant field; look for S-shaped star chain W of ε Ori						
Simeis 147	Tau	SNR	05 41	+28 06	3.5°	Taurus supernova remnant
look for "Skates Egg" knot, 10′ E of mag. 8 star SAO 77397						

Object	Con	Type	RA (2000) h m	Dec ° ′	Size ′	Remarks
Orion GMC	Ori	GMC	05 42	–02 24	1°×2°	Orion Molecular Cloud bright section
use low-power binoculars and filters; look for wave and gap SW of ε Orionis.						
Collinder 89	Gem	OC	06 19	+23 38	60	
large, loose cluster						
Collinder 132	CMa	OC	07 16	–30 42	80	large cluster
beautiful sprinkling of colourful stars visible even during full Moon						
MW 3	UMa	IFN	09 30	+70 11		Volcano Nebula
Mandel Wilson 3 Integrated Flux Nebula; use low power, dark sky, and luck						
Mel 111	Com	OC	12 26	+26 02	3°	Coma Star Cluster
best with very wide-field binoculars						
ρ Oph Complex	Sco		16 26	–23 27	60×25	star cloud with triple star and nebulae
IC 4604 surrounds ρ Oph (mag. 4.6); IC 4603 at HD147889 (mag. 7.9); IC 4605 at 22 Sco (mag. 4.8)						
Sh2-27	Oph	EN	16 33	–10 08	10°×7°	very large emission nebula
use UHC filter and best sky possible; brightest section NW of M107; some uncertainty over classification						
LBN 1103	Sco	EN	16 34	–28 08	4°×3°	SE of Antares
large sprawling nebula, 15× binoculars give best view in dark sky						
Prancing Horse	Oph	DN	17 30	–24 00	10°×7°	large, delicate, dark nebula
B59, B78, B77, B262, B63, B64, B268; observe dark rift in Cyg to Aql as warmup						
IC 4665	Oph	OC	17 47	+05 43	70	Summer Beehive
overlooked large star cluster; best in binoculars; fuzzy patch with the unaided eye						
NGC 6455	Sco		17 52	–35 20	2°	starcloud often mistaken as small OC
starcloud visible without optical aid; SW of M7, which is possibly superimposed						
Taurus Poniatovii	Oph	Ast	17 57	+05 10	10°×5°	asterism: Poniatowski's Bull in NE Oph
main stars 72, 66, 67, 68, and 70 Oph; extends into Ser; Barnard's Star currently resides here; defunct const.						
NGC 6526	Sgr	EN	18 06	–23 41	40	nebula N of M8
large U-shaped nebula and star cloud N of a dark rift, look for NGC 6546 to NE						
IC 4685	Sgr	EN	18 10	–23 49	60	large complex
use nebular filters; look for: NGC 6559, CR 367, IC 1274/5						
IC 1284	Sgr	EN	18 18	–19 40	17×15	eye of M24
use Hβ filter; sweep SW of IC 1284 to detect 120′×30′ nebulous region						
Sh2-54	Ser	EN	18 19	–11 58	60×30	nebula & starcloud
large nebular haze N of M16; look for open cluster NGC 6604 & Simeis 3-132						
NGC 6633	Oph	OC	18 28	+06 31	27	Circular Cloud
large cluster sitting over top of apparent star cloud						
IC 4756	Ser	OC	18 40	+05 28	52	Graff's Cluster
visible without optical aid with NGC 6633 as "duelling clusters"						
Basel 1	Sct	OC	18 49	–05 49	55	W of M11
small cluster in the bowl of a dipper-shaped asterism						
B111	Sct	DN	18 51	–04 56	2°	Half-Moon Nebula
large kidney-shaped dark nebula N of M11, superimposed on Scutum star cloud						
B138	Aql	DN	19 15	+0 52	140×20	Barnard's Black Lizard
huge dragon-shaped dark nebula below Altair; use binoculars						
NGC 6774	Sgr	OC	19 17	–16 18	60	Ram's Head
a "true cluster"; contains G2 stars; look for star chains running SE and SW						
Collinder 399	Vul	Ast	19 26	+20 15	89	Coathanger or Brocchi's Cluster
3 dozen orange and blue stars in the pattern of a coathanger; look E for NGC 6802						
Stock 1	Vul	OC	19 36	+25 15	52	halfway between β Cyg and Coathanger
50 stars mag. 7 and brighter; best seen in binoculars						
Sh2-119	Cyg	EN	21 17	+43 46	2.5°×2°	NE of North America Nebula complex
use large binoculars or RFT with nebular filter; sweep past 68 Cyg; visible if Pelican can be seen						
IC 1396	Cep	EN	21 40	+57 34	170×140	large emission nebula
locate μ Cep, then add nebular filter; attempt van den Bergh 142, Elephant Trunk Nebula						
Stock 12	Cas	OC	23 37	+52 36	40	
very large, loose, binocular cluster; look for star chain to SE						
Great Rift		DNs/GMCs			120°	overlapping dark nebulae and GMCs
huge naked-eye rift splitting the Milky Way from Cyg, through Aql, Oph, and Sco, to Cen						

SOUTHERN HEMISPHERE SPLENDOURS

BY ALAN WHITMAN

Any serious deep-sky observer yearns to experience the far-southern sky, the home of the finest emission nebula (the Carina Nebula), the most obvious dark nebula (the Coalsack), arguably the best open cluster (NGC 3532), the most impressive globular cluster (47 Tucanae), the biggest and brightest globular cluster (Omega Centauri, although it is likely the core of a small galaxy absorbed by the Milky Way), the galaxy that offers amateur telescopes hundreds of targets within it (the Large Magellanic Cloud), and the closest naked-eye star in the night sky (α Centauri), just to name a few. Here is a checklist of "must-see" splendours, rated with one to three exclamation marks, plus 16 other significant objects. The author has observed all of these objects under fine, dark skies.

Dec −35° was chosen as the northern cutoff for this list. However, three slightly more northerly objects that greatly benefit from being viewed higher in the sky were included, notably M83, because it is one of the finest face-on spiral galaxies in the southern sky, but its three spiral arms are not well seen from Canada. Countries like Australia, Chile, and Namibia offer the best views of these magnificent objects. However, most objects on the list can be viewed from the southern Caribbean; many are visible from Hawaii or from the Florida Keys; some, including Omega Centauri, Centaurus A, and the many glorious clusters in the tail of Scorpius, can be appreciated from the American Southwest. February through April are the preferred months for a southern observing run, since there are no far-southern splendours (those with exclamation marks) located between 20h and 0h of right ascension.

Data for open and globular clusters are from Archinal and Hynes's 2003 reference book *Star Clusters*, with the two noted exceptions. Data for other objects are mostly from Malin and Frew's highly recommended 1995 guidebook *Hartung's Astronomical Objects for Southern Telescopes*, 2nd ed. The dimensions of galaxies and nebulae and a few other numbers are mostly from various lists in the *Observer's Handbook* or from Sinnott's 1988 work, *NGC 2000.0*. Various sources, including private communications, have provided some difficult-to-obtain data.

Notation used below is mostly as defined on p. 314; in addition, * = star or stars, CC = concentration class of a globular cluster (see p. 312), and DN = dark nebula. Numbers without a prefix in the **NGC** column are NGC numbers.

#	NGC	Con	Type	RA (2000) h m	Dec ° ′	m_V	Size″ ′	Remarks
1	55	Scl	G-SBm	0 14.9	−39 12	7.9	32 × 6	! in 100-mm scope: diffuse splinter
2	104	Tuc	GC	0 24.1	−72 5	4	50	!!! 47 Tuc; yellow core in 370-mm scope
3	β	Tuc	Dbl*	0 31.5	−62 58	4.3, 4.5	27″	! both blue-white
4	SMC	Tuc	G-SBm	0 52.7	−72 50	2.3	5° × 3°	!!! many NGCs included
5	362	Tuc	GC	1 3.2	−70 51	6.8	14	! Milky Way GC beside SMC; CC III
6	p	Eri	Dbl*	1 39.8	−56 12	5.8, 5.8	12″	! both yellow-orange dwarfs
7	1097	For	G-SBb	2 46.3	−30 17	9.3	13 × 8	! in 300-mm scope: bar and tough arms
8	θ	Eri	Dbl*	2 58.3	−40 18	3.2, 4.1	8.4″	! both white
9	1313	Ret	G-SBd	3 18.3	−66 30	8.9	9 × 7	in 370-mm scope: bar, one spiral arm
10		For	Gal Cl.	3 22.7	−37 12	—	—	position is for bright 1316, Fornax A
11	1365	For	G-SBc	3 33.6	−36 8	9.5	14 × 10	!! in 300-mm scope: bar with 2 spiral arms
12	f	Eri	Dbl*	3 48.6	−37 37	4.9, 5.4	8.1″	! yellowish stars
13	1566	Dor	G-Sc	4 20	−54 56	9.4	13 × 9	!! in 250-mm scope: two classic spiral arms
14	ι	Pic	Dbl*	4 50.9	−53 28	5.6, 6.5	12.5″	! very nice yellow pair
15	1851	Col	GC	5 14.1	−40 3	7.1	12	! brightest centre of any GC; CC II
16	LMC	Dor	G-SBm	5 23.6	−69 45	0.1	11° × 9°	!!! many nights' work for large apertures
17	2070	Dor	EN/OC	5 38.7	−69 6	5.4	20	!!! Tarantula Nebula; "spider legs" easy
18	γ	Vol	Dbl*	7 8.7	−70 30	3.9, 5.4	14.4″	! gold and light-green pair
19	2451	Pup	OC	7 45.4	−37 57	2.8	50	! two OCs in radial line, 400 ly apart

SOUTHERN HEMISPHERE SPLENDOURS (continued)

#	NGC	Con	Type	RA (2000) h m	Dec ° ′	m_v	Size ′	Remarks
20	2477	Pup	OC	7 52.2	−38 32	5.8	20	!! 300*; arcs of 12th-mag.–13th-mag. stars
21	2516	Car	OC	7 58	−60 45	3.8	22	!! 100*; resembles the Beehive but richer
22	γ	Vel	Dbl*	8 9.5	−47 20	1.8, 4.1	41″	! 4*; 1.8-mag. star is brightest Wolf–Rayet
23	2547	Vel	OC	8 10.2	−49 14	4.7	25	! The Heart Cluster (description by Dyer)
24	IC 2391	Vel	OC	8 40.3	−52 55	2.6	60	! o Vel Cluster; bright stars; fine in binocs
25	2736	Vel	SNR	9 0.4	−45 54	—	20x0.5	! Pencil Nebula, part of Vela SNR; use filter
26	2808	Car	GC	9 12	−64 52	6.2	14	! brightest CC I; like a pile of sand
27	3114	Car	OC	10 2.7	−60 6	4.2	35	! 120*; four arcs of stars in binocs
28	3132	Vel	PN	10 7.7	−40 26	9.2	0.8	Eight-Burst Nebula; colourless
29	3199	Car	EN	10 17.1	−57 55	9	22	! crescent formed by Wolf–Rayet star
30	3201	Vel	GC	10 17.6	−46 25	6.9	20	star chains right through core; CC X
31	3293	Car	OC	10 35.8	−58 14	4.7	5	!! Gem Cluster; EN/RN/DN involved
32	3324	Car	EN	10 37.3	−58 38	6.7	15	two-lobed nebula
33	IC 2602	Car	OC	10 43	−64 24	1.6	100	! θ Car Cl, a.k.a. the Southern Pleiades
34	3372	Car	EN	10 45.1	−59 52	2.5	80	!!! Carina Nebula[A]
35	3532	Car	OC	11 5.5	−58 44	3	50	!!! Football Cluster; finest OC?; 55′ across
36	3699	Cen	PN	11 28	−59 57	11.3	1.1	dark rift visible in 200-mm scope
37	3766	Cen	OC	11 36.3	−61 37	5.3	15	! triangular; 60*; λ Cen Nebula nearby
38	3918	Cen	PN	11 50.3	−57 11	8.1	0.2	! the Blue Planetary; round
39	—	Mus	DN	12 25	−72	—	3° × 12′	! the Dark Doodad; near 4372 and γ Mus
40	4372	Mus	GC	12 25.8	−72 39	7.2	19	! CC XII (size is from NGC 2000.0)
41	α	Cru	Dbl*	12 26.6	−63 6	1.3, 1.6	4.0″	! blue-white pair; 3rd star 4.9 mag. at 90″
42	DY	Cru	Red*	12 47.4	−59 42	9v	—	! Ruby Crucis; 3′ W of β Cru; B−V is 5.8
43	—	Cru	DN	12 51	−63	—	6°	!!! Coalsack; forms head of the Emu DN
44	4755	Cru	OC	12 53.6	−60 21	4.2	10	! Jewel Box; sparse in small apertures
45	4833	Mus	GC	12 59.6	−70 52	6.9	14	! CC VIII (magnitude is from W.E. Harris)
46	4945	Cen	G-SBcd	13 5.5	−49 28	8.4	20 × 4	! in 500-mm scope: dark lane on SW edge
47	5128	Cen	G-S0pec	13 25.5	−43 1	6.8	26 × 20	!! Cen A; merging spiral and elliptical[B]
48	5139	Cen	GC	13 26.8	−47 29	3.9	55	!!! Omega Cen; huge rich oval; CC VIII
49	5189	Mus	PN	13 33.5	−65 59	9.5	2.6	! the Spiral Planetary; use OIII filter
50	M83	Hya	G-SABc	13 37	−29 52	7.6	16 × 13	!! in 200-mm: bar, 1 arm; 370-mm: 3 arms
51	5286	Cen	GC	13 46.4	−51 22	7.4	11	! CC V; bluish PN 5307 nearby
52	5460	Cen	OC	14 7.6	−48 18	5.6	35	25 straggling*; trapezoidal asterism in S
53	α	Cen	Dbl*	14 39.6	−60 50	0.0, 1.3	4.1″	!! rapidly changing yellow pair: 22″–1.7″
54	5822	Lup	OC	15 4	−54 20	6.5	35	! triangular; stars are in discrete clumps
55	5927	Lup	GC	15 28	−50 40	8	6	CC VIII; pair with Nor GC 5946
56	B228	Lup	DN	15 45	−34	—	4° × 20′	! an unknown wonder; opacity 6
57	5986	Lup	GC	15 46.1	−37 47	7.6	10	200-mm resolves large core; CC VII
58	6025	TrA	OC	16 3.6	−60 25	5.1	15	! triangular, in three clumps
59	6067	Nor	OC	16 13.2	−54 13	5.6	15	! 100*; many pairs
60	6087	Nor	OC	16 18.9	−57 54	5.4	15	! 40*; embedded in Norma Star Cloud
61	6124	Sco	OC	16 25.3	−40 40	5.8	40	100*; many trios around circumference
62	6231	Sco	OC	16 54.2	−41 50	2.6	14	!! ζ, 6231, and Tr 24 form the False Comet
63	6242	Sco	OC	16 55.5	−39 28	6.4	9	23*; good for small scopes
64	6259	Sco	OC	17 0.7	−44 39	8	15	like a fainter M11; 120*
65	6281	Sco	OC	17 4.8	−37 53	5.4	8	25*; shines in modest scopes
66	6302	Sco	PN	17 13.7	−37 6	9.6	1.5 × 0.5	Bug Nebula; bright core; knots at tips
67	IC 4651	Ara	OC	17 24.7	−49 55	6.9	10	! loops and chains of 70 equal-mag. stars
68	6388	Sco	GC	17 36.3	−44 44	6.8	10	450-mm scope resolves faint stars; CC III
69	6397	Ara	GC	17 40.7	−53 40	5.3	31	!! easily resolved 10th-mag. stars; CC IX
70	6541	CrA	GC	18 8	−43 42	6.3	15	! huge outer halo; CC III
71	6723	Sgr	GC	18 59.6	−36 38	6.8	13	! CC VII; part of fine complex below
72	6726–7	CrA	RN	19 1.7	−36 54	—	9 × 7	! 7th-mag. stars involved[C]
73	6752	Pav	GC	19 10.9	−59 59	5.3	29	!! easily resolved 11th-mag. stars; CC VI[D]
74	7582	Gru	G-SBb	23 18.4	−42 22	10.2	4 × 1	brightest member of Grus Quartet

[A] Chevron-shaped dark lane, many other DN involved, including Keyhole Nebula; tiny orange mag. 5 (variable) Homunculus Nebula at centre; four OC involved

[B] Prominent broad dark lane; 370-mm scope reveals thin bright streak within the dark lane

[C] Part of !! complex with GC 6723, DN SL 40+41 (55′ long, opacity 6), variable RN 6729 (involved with R CrA), headlight Dbl* Brs 14 (mags. 6.6, 6.8 at 13″), and Dbl* γ CrA (both yellow-white, mags. 4.9, 5.0 at 1.3″ and widening)

[D] Curving star chains converge to a tiny central peak; very tight group of four 12th-mag. galaxies 1° SE

GALAXIES: BRIGHTEST AND NEAREST
BY BARRY F. MADORE AND IAN STEER

External galaxies are generally of such low surface brightness that they often prove disappointing objects for the amateur observer. However, it must be remembered that many of these galaxies were discovered with very small telescopes and that the enjoyment of their discovery can be recaptured. In addition, the central concentration of light varies from galaxy to galaxy, making a visual classification of the types possible at the telescope. Indeed, the *Hubble galaxy classification* (**Type**) given in Table 1 (facing page) is in part based on the fraction of light coming from the central bulge of the galaxy as compared to the contribution from a disk component. Disk galaxies with dominant bulges are classified as **Sa**; as the nuclear contribution declines, types of **Sb**, **Sc**, and **Sd** are assigned until the nucleus is absent at type **Sm**. Often the disks of these galaxies show spiral symmetry, the coherence and strength of which is denoted by Roman numerals **I** through **V**, smaller numbers indicating well-formed global spiral patterns. Those spirals with central bars are designated **SB**, while those with only a hint of a disk embedded in the bulge are called **S0**. A separate class of galaxies that possess no disk component are called ellipticals and can only be further classified numerically by their apparent flattening, with **E0** being apparently round and **E7** being the most flattened.

Environment appears to play an important role in determining the types of galaxies we see at the present epoch. Rich clusters of galaxies, such as the system in Coma, are dominated by ellipticals and gas-free S0 galaxies. The less-dense clusters and groups tend to be dominated by the spiral, disk galaxies. Remarkably, pairs of galaxies are much more frequently of the same Hubble type than random selection would predict. Encounters between disk galaxies may in some cases result in the instabilities necessary to form the spiral structure we often see. M51 (the Whirlpool) and its companion, NGC 5195, are an often-cited example of this type of interaction. In the past, when the Universe was much more densely packed, interactions and collisions may have been sufficiently frequent that entire galaxies merged to form a single large new system; it has been suggested that some elliptical galaxies formed in this way.

Table 1 on the facing page lists the 40 brightest galaxies taken from the *Revised Shapley–Ames Catalog*. As well as their designations, positions, and types, the table lists the total blue magnitudes, major and minor axis lengths (to the nearest minute of arc), the latest estimate of their distances in 10^6 ly, and their radial velocities corrected for the motion of our Sun about the galactic centre. Although the Universe as a whole is in expansion, there are parts that are still bound together (or at the very least,

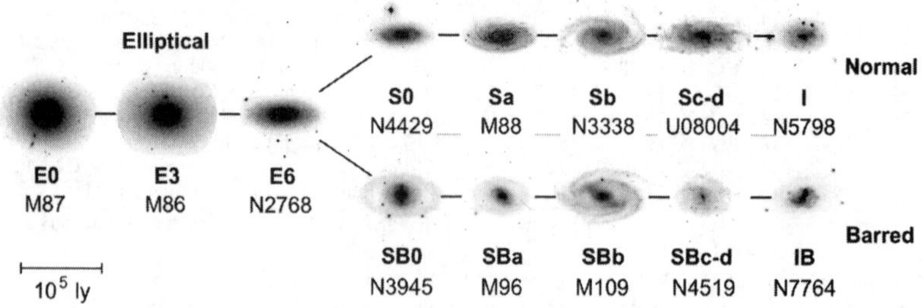

The Hubble "tuning fork" diagram of galaxy classification, using actual galaxy images, with the Messier, NGC (N), or UGC (U) number indicated below the type. (Diagram created by Ian Steer.)

held back in their expansion) by gravity. These groups and clusters are, in essence, representative of the largest material structures in the Universe. Recently, large-scale flows of material have been reported, far in excess of the velocities expected due to the perturbing presence of other galaxies and clusters of galaxies. Either there are exceedingly large concentrations of matter yet to be discovered just beyond our limited view of the world, or the Universe has had a much more interesting history than our present theories indicate. The brightest and nearest galaxies in Table 1 may be moving not only as a result of the universal expansion, but also through very complex interactions with distant parts as yet only postulated but not seen. A selection of nearest galaxies, listed on the following page in Table 2, form what is known as the Local Group of Galaxies. **(Data in Tables 1 and 2 have been updated for 2017.)**

TABLE 1—THE 40 OPTICALLY BRIGHTEST SHAPLEY-AMES GALAXIES

NGC	Other	RA (2000) h m	Dec ° ′	Type	Magnitude B_T	Size ′	Distance 10^6 ly	Rad. Vel. km/s
55		0 14.9	−39 11.8	SBm	8.84	32 × 6	6.29	129
205	M110	0 40.4	+41 41.1	E5 pec	8.92	22 × 11	2.64	−241
221	M32	0 42.7	+40 51.9	E2	9.03	9 × 7	2.51	−200
224	M31	0 42.7	+41 16.2	Sb I–II	4.36	190 × 60	2.54	−300
247		0 47.1	−20 45.6	SBd III–IV	9.86	21 × 7	11.7	156
253		0 47.6	−25 17.3	SBc	7.09	28 × 7	10.3	243
292	SMC	0 52.7	−72 49.7	SBm IV–V pec	2.70	320 × 185	0.196	158
300		0 54.9	−37 41.1	Sd III	8.95	22 × 16	6.39	144
598	M33	1 33.8	+30 39.6	Scd II–III	6.27	71 × 42	2.87	−179
628	M74	1 36.7	+15 47.0	Sc I	9.95	11 × 10	29.1	657
1068	M77	2 42.7	−00 00.8	Sb II	9.61	7 × 6	41.2	1137
1291		3 17.3	−41 06.5	SB0/a	9.39	10 × 8	28.0	839
1313		3 18.3	−66 29.9	SBd III–IV	9.20	9 × 7	12.9	470
1316	Fornax A	3 22.7	−37 12.5	S0 pec	9.40	12 × 9	65.1	1760
	LMC	5 23.6	−69 45.4	SBm III	0.90	645 × 550	0.163	278
2403		7 36.9	+65 36.2	SBcd III	8.11	22 × 12	11.3	131
2903		9 32.2	+21 30.1	SBbc I–III	9.68	13 × 6	28.4	556
3031	M81	9 55.6	+69 03.9	Sab I–II	7.89	27 × 14	12.1	−34
3034	M82	9 55.9	+69 40.8	I0	9.30	11 × 4	13.1	203
3521		11 05.8	−00 02.2	SBbc II–III	9.83	11 × 5	38.6	801
3627	M66	11 20.3	+12 59.5	SBb II	9.65	9 × 4	31.9	727
4258	M106	12 19.0	+47 18.2	SBbc II	8.41	19 × 7	24.3	448
4449		12 28.2	+44 05.6	IBm IV	9.99	6 × 4	12.2	207
4472	M49	12 29.8	+08 00.0	E2	9.37	10 × 8	51.5	997
4486	M87	12 30.8	+12 23.5	E0	9.59	8 × 7	54.2	1307
4594	M104	12 40.0	−11 37.4	Sa	8.98	9 × 4	36.3	1024
4631		12 42.1	+32 32.5	SBd	9.75	16 × 3	19.0	606
4649	M60	12 43.7	+11 33.2	E2	9.81	7 × 6	53.9	1117
4736	M94	12 50.9	+41 07.2	Sab	8.99	11 × 9	16.4	308
4826	M64	12 56.7	+21 41.0	Sab II	9.36	10 × 5	16.8	408
4945		13 05.5	−49 28.1	SBcd	9.30	20 × 4	13.3	563
5055	M63	13 15.8	+42 01.8	Sbc II–III	9.31	13 × 7	26.1	484
5128	Cen A	13 25.5	−43 01.2	S0 pec	7.84	26 × 20	12.0	547
5194	M51	13 29.9	+47 11.7	Sbc I–II pec	8.96	11 × 7	27.9	463
5236	M83	13 37.0	−29 52.0	SBc II	8.20	13 × 12	22.2	513
5457	M101	14 03.2	+54 20.9	SBcd I	8.31	29 × 27	22.2	241
6744		19 09.8	−63 51.5	SBbc II	9.14	20 × 13	27.5	841
6822		19 45.0	−14 48.2	IBm IV–V	9.31	16 × 14	1.63	−57
6946		20 34.9	+60 09.2	SBcd II	8.23	12 × 10	18.5	40
7793		23 57.8	−32 35.5	Sd IV	9.98	9 × 6	12.8	227

TABLE 2—THE NEAREST GALAXIES—OUR LOCAL GROUP

Name	RA (2000.0) h m	Dec ° ′	Type	Magnitude B_T	Distance 10^6 ly
Milky Way Galaxy			Sb/c		
IC 10	0 20.3	+59 18	IBm	11.80	2.90
NGC 147	0 33.2	+48 31	dE5 pec	10.47	2.51
And III	0 35.6	+36 30	dE	15.00	2.41
NGC 185	0 39	+48 20	dE3 pec	10.10	2.41
M110 = NGC 205	0 40.4	+41 41	E5 pec	8.92	2.64
M32 = NGC 221	0 42.7	+40 52	E2	9.03	2.51
M31 = NGC 224	0 42.7	+41 16	Sb I–II	4.36	2.54
And I	0 45.7	+38 02	dE3 pec	13.60	2.51
SMC	0 52.7	−72 50	SBm IV–V pec	2.70	0.196
Sculptor	1 0.2	−33 43	dE	8.60	0.261
LGS 3	1 3.9	+21 53	Irr	14.20	3.91
IC 1613	1 4.8	+02 07	IBm V	9.88	2.41
And II	1 16.5	+33 25	dE	13.50	2.09
M33 = NGC 598	1 33.8	+30 40	Scd II–III	6.27	2.87
Fornax	2 40	−34 27	dE4	9.28	0.456
LMC	5 23.6	−69 45	SBm III	0.90	0.163
Carina	6 41.6	−50 58	dE3	11.30	0.326
Antlia	10 4.1	−27 20	IBm	16.19	4.30
Leo I	10 8.5	+12 18	dE3	11.18	0.815
Sextans	10 13.1	−01 37	dE	10.40	0.261
Leo II	11 13.5	+22 09	dE0	12.60	0.717
Ursa Minor	15 9.1	+67 13	E	11.90	0.228
Draco	17 20.2	+57 55	E pec	10.90	0.261
Sagittarius	18 55.3	−30 33	IBm:	4.50	0.098
NGC 6822	19 45	−14 48	IBm IV–V	9.31	1.63

Editor's Notes:

(1) Aside from those famous companions of the Milky Way Galaxy, the Large Magellanic Cloud (LMC) and the Small Magellanic Cloud (SMC), there is only one galaxy beyond our own that is easily visible to unaided human eyes: M31, the Andromeda Galaxy (2.58 Mly distant). M33, the Triangulum Galaxy, can also be seen, but this is a difficult observation. To locate M31, see the NOVEMBER ALL-SKY MAP on p. 345, where the tiny cluster of six dots above the first "A" of "ANDROMEDA" indicates its location. With modest optical aid (e.g. binoculars) a dozen or more of the galaxies listed in Table 1 can be seen by experienced observers under dark skies. With a 250-mm telescope, the quasar 3C 273, at 1000 times the distance of M31, can elicit a noticeable signal in the visual cortex (see p. 323).

(2) An interesting article by G. Lake entitled "Cosmology of the Local Group" appears in *Sky & Telescope*, December 1992, p. 613.

(3) The National Aeronautics and Space Administration/Infrared Processing and Analysis Center (NASA/IPAC) Extragalactic Database (NED) is a comprehensive compilation of extragalactic data for 215 million distinct extragalactic objects. The database includes most major catalogues and offers references to and abstracts of articles of extragalactic interest that have appeared in most major journals. Also online are 1.9 billion photometric measurements, 5 million redshifts, over 2.6 million images, and more than 400 thousand detailed classifications. It is possible to search the main NED database for objects selected by catalogue prefix, position, type, or redshift. The database is available at ned.ipac.caltech.edu. See ned.ipac.caltech.edu/level5 for a knowledgebase of review articles and basic information.

GALAXIES WITH PROPER NAMES

BY BARRY F. MADORE

Below are the catalogue designations and positions of galaxies known to have proper names, which usually honour the discoverer (e.g. McLeish's Object), identify the constellation in which the galaxy is found (e.g. Andromeda Galaxy), or describe the galaxy in some easily remembered way (e.g. Whirlpool Galaxy).

Galaxy Name	Other Names / Remarks	RA (2000) h m	Dec ° ′
Ambartsumian's Knot	NGC 3561, UGC 06224, ARP 105	11 11.2	+28 42
Andromeda Galaxy	M31, NGC 224, UGC 00454	0 42.7	+41 16
Andromeda I		0 45.7	+38 01
Andromeda II		1 16.5	+33 26
Andromeda III		0 35.3	+36 31
Antennae Galaxy	Ring Tail, NGC 4038/39, ARP 244	12 01.9	−18 52
Antlia Dwarf	AM 1001-270	10 04.0	−27 20
Aquarius Dwarf	DDO 210	20 46.9	−12 51
Arp's Galaxy		11 19.6	+51 30
Atoms For Peace	NGC 7252, ARP 226	22 20.8	−24 41
Baade's Galaxies A & B	MCG+07-02-018/19	0 49.9	+42 35
Barbon's Galaxy	Markarian 328, ZWG 497.042	23 37.7	+30 08
Barnard's Galaxy	NGC 6822, IC 4895, DDO 209	19 44.9	−14 48
Bear's Paw (Claw)	NGC 2537, UGC 04274, ARP 6	8 13.2	+46 00
BL Lacertae		22 02.7	+42 17
Black Eye Galaxy	M64, NGC 4826, UGC 08062	12 56.7	+21 41
Bode's Galaxies	M81/82, NGC 3031/4, UGC 05318/22	9 55.7	+69 23
Burbidge Chain	MCG-04-03-010 to 13	0 47.5	−20 26
BW Tauri	UGC 03087, MCG+01-12-009	4 33.2	+05 21
Carafe Galaxy	Cannon's Carafe, near NGC 1595/98	4 28.0	−47 54
Carina Dwarf		6 41.6	−50 58
Cartwheel Galaxy	Zwicky's Cartwheel, MCG-06-02-022a	0 37.4	−33 44
Centaurus A	NGC 5128, ARP 153	13 25.5	−43 01
Circinus Galaxy		14 13.2	−65 20
Coddington's Nebula	IC 2574, UGC 05666, DDO 81	10 28.4	+68 25
Copeland Septet	MCG+04-28-004/05/07 to 11, UGC 06597, UGC 06602, ARP 320, NGC 3745/46/48/50/51/53/54†	11 37.8	+21 59
Cygnus A	MCG+07-41-003	19 59.4	+40 43
Draco Dwarf	UGC 10822, DDO 208	17 20.2	+57 55
Exclamation Mark Galaxy		0 39.3	−43 06
The Eyes	NGC 4435/8, UGC 07574/5, ARP 120a/b	12 27.7	+13 03
Fath 703	NGC 5892	15 13.7	−15 29
Fornax A	NGC 1316, ARP 154	3 22.7	−37 12
Fornax Dwarf	MCG-06-07-001	2 39.9	−34 32
Fourcade–Figueroa	MCG-07-28-004	13 34.8	−45 33
The Garland	S of NGC 3077 = UGC 05398	10 04.2	+68 40
Grus Quartet	NGC 7552/82/90/99	23 17.8	−42 26
GR 8 (Gibson Reaves)	UGC 08091, DDO 155	12 58.7	+14 13
Hardcastle's Galaxy	MCG-05-31-039	13 13.0	−32 41
Helix Galaxy	NGC 2685, UGC 04666, ARP 336	8 55.6	+58 44
Hercules A	MCG+01-43-006	16 51.2	+04 59
Hoag's Object		15 17.2	+21 35

† Position errors caused these to be historically marked as nonexistent in the NGC and RNGC.

GALAXIES WITH PROPER NAMES (continued)

Galaxy Name	Other Names / Remarks	RA (2000) h m	Dec ° ′
Holmberg I	UGC 05139, DDO 63	9 40.5	+71 11
Holmberg II	UGC 04305, DDO 50, ARP 268	8 19.3	+70 43
Holmberg III	UGC 04841	9 14.6	+74 14
Holmberg IV	UGC 08837, DDO 185	13 54.7	+53 54
Holmberg V	UGC 08658	13 40.6	+54 20
Holmberg VI	NGC 1325a	3 24.9	−21 20
Holmberg VII	UGC 07739, DDO 137	12 34.7	+06 17
Holmberg VIII	UGC 08303, DDO 166	13 13.3	+36 12
Holmberg IX	UGC 05336, DDO 66	9 57.6	+69 03
Horologium Dwarf	Schuster's Spiral	3 59.2	−45 52
Hydra A	MCG-02-24-007	9 18.1	−12 06
Integral Sign Galaxy	UGC 03697, MCG+12-07-028	7 11.4	+71 50
Keenan's System	NGC 5216/16a/18, UGC 08528/9, ARP 104	13 32.2	+62 43
Kowal's Object		19 29.9	−17 41
Large Magellanic Cloud	Nubecula Major	5 23.6	−69 45
Leo I	Regulus Dwarf, UGC 05470, DDO 74, Harrington–Wilson #1	10 08.5	+12 18
Leo II	Leo B, UGC 06253, DDO 93, Harrington–Wilson #2	11 13.4	+22 10
Leo III	Leo A, UGC 05364, DDO 69	9 59.3	+30 45
Lindsay–Shapley Ring	Graham A	6 42.8	−74 15
Lost Galaxy	NGC 4535, UGC 07727	12 34.3	+08 11
McLeish's Object		20 09.7	−66 13
Maffei I	UGCA 34	2 36.3	+59 39
Maffei II	UGCA 39	2 42.0	+59 37
Malin 1		12 37.0	+14 20
Mayall's Object	MCG+07-23-019, ARP 148	11 03.9	+40 50
Mice	NGC 4676a/b, UGC 07938/9, IC 819/20, ARP 242	12 46.1	+30 44
Miniature Spiral	NGC 3928, UGC 06834	11 51.8	+48 41
Minkowski's Object	ARP 133 (NE of NGC 541)	1 25.8	−01 21
Pancake	NGC 2685, UGC 04666, ARP 336	8 55.6	+58 44
Papillon	IC 708, UGC 06549	11 33.9	+49 03
Pegasus Dwarf	UGC 12613, DDO 216	23 28.5	+14 44
Perseus A	NGC 1275/6, UGC 02669	3 19.8	+41 31
Phoenix Dwarf Irregular		1 51.1	−44 26
Pinwheel Galaxy	see also Triangulum Galaxy	1 33.9	+30 39
Pinwheel Galaxy	M99, NGC 4254, UGC 07345	12 18.8	+14 25
Pinwheel Galaxy	M101, NGC 5457, UGC 08981, ARP 26	14 03.3	+54 22
Pisces Cloud	NGC 379/80/82-85, UGC 00682/3/6-9, ARP 331	1 07.5	+32 25
Pisces Dwarf	LGS 3	0 03.8	+21 54
Polarissima Australis	NGC 2573	1 42.0‡	−89 20
Polarissima Borealis	NGC 3172, ZWG 370.002	11 50.3‡	+89 07
Reinmuth 80	NGC 4517a, UGC 07685	12 32.5	+00 23
Reticulum Dwarf	Sersic 040.03	4 36.2	−58 50
Sagittarius Dwarf		19 30.0	−17 41
Sculptor Dwarf	MCG-06-03-015	1 00.2	−33 42
Sculptor Dwarf Irregular		0 08.1	−34 34

‡ The high declination of these objects makes the RA particularly uncertain.

GALAXIES WITH PROPER NAMES (continued)

Galaxy Name	Other Names / Remarks	RA (2000) h m	Dec ° ′
Seashell Galaxy	Companion to NGC 5291	13 47.4	−30 23
Sextans A	UGCA 205, MCG-01-26-030, DDO 75	10 11.0	−04 41
Sextans B	UGC 05373, DDO 70	10 00.0	+05 19
Sextans C	UGC 05439	10 05.6	+00 04
Sextans Dwarf		10 13.1	−01 37
Seyfert's Sextet	Serpens Sextet, NGC 6027/6027a-e, UGC 10116	15 59.2	+20 46
Shapley–Ames 1		1 05.1	−06 13
Shapley–Ames 2	NGC 4507	12 35.1	−39 55
Shapley–Ames 3	MCG-02-33-015	12 49.4	−10 07
Shapley–Ames 4	UGC 08041	12 55.2	+00 07
Shapley–Ames 5	MCG-07-42-001	20 24.0	−44 00
Shapley–Ames 6		21 23.2	+45 46
Siamese Twins	NGC 4567/4568	12 36.5	+11 15
Silver Coin	Sculptor Galaxy, NGC 253, UGCA 13	0 47.6	−25 18
Small Magellanic Cloud	Nubecula Minor	0 52.7	−72 50
Sombrero Galaxy	M104, NGC 4594	12 39.9	−11 37
Spider	UGC 05829, DDO 84	10 42.6	+34 27
Spindle Galaxy	NGC 3115	10 05.2	−07 42
Stephan's Quintet	NGC 7317-20, UGC 12099-102, ARP 319	22 36.0	+33 58
Sunflower Galaxy	M63, NGC 5055, UGC 08334	13 15.8	+42 02
Triangulum Galaxy	Pinwheel, M33, NGC 598, UGC 01117	1 33.9	+30 39
Ursa Minor Dwarf	UGC 09749, DDO 199	15 08.8	+67 12
Virgo A	M87, NGC 4486, UGC 07654, ARP 152	12 30.8	+12 23
Whirlpool Galaxy	Rosse's Galaxy, Question Mark Galaxy, M51, NGC 5194/5, UGC 08493/4, ARP 85	13 29.9	+47 12
Wild's Triplet	MCG-01-30-032 to 34, ARP 248	11 46.8	−03 49
Wolf–Lundmark–Melotte	MCG-03-01-015, DDO 221	0 02.0	−15 28
Zwicky #2	UGC 06955, DDO 105	11 58.4	+38 03
Zwicky's Triplet	UGC 10586, ARP 103	16 49.5	+45 30

Catalogues:

AM *Catalogue of Southern Peculiar Galaxies and Associations*, by H.C. Arp and B.F. Madore, Cambridge University Press (1987).

ARP *Atlas of Peculiar Galaxies*, H. Arp, *Ap. J. Suppl. 14*, 1 (1966).

DDO *David Dunlap Observatory Publ.*, S. van den Bergh, II, No. 5, 147 (1959).

IC *Index Catalogue*, J.L.E. Dreyer, *Mem. R.A.S.* (1895–1910).

MCG *Morphological Catalogue of Galaxies*, B.A. Vorontsov–Velyaminov et al., Moscow State University, Moscow (1961–1974).

NGC *New General Catalogue of Nebulae and Clusters of Stars*, J.L.E. Dreyer, *Mem. R.A.S.* (1888).

RNGC *The Revised New General Catalogue of Nonstellar Astronomical Objects*, J.W. Sulentic and W.G. Tifft, University of Arizona Press (1973).

UGC *Uppsala General Catalogue of Galaxies*, P. Nilson, *Nova Acta Regiae Societatis Scientiarum Upsaliensis*, Ser. V: A, Vol. 1, Uppsala, Sweden (1973).

UGCA *Catalogue of Selected Non-UGC Galaxies*, P. Nilson, Uppsala Astronomical Observatory (1974).

ZWG *Catalogue of Galaxies and Clusters of Galaxies*, F. Zwicky et al., Vol. 1–6, California Institute of Technology (1961–1968).

RADIO ASTRONOMY AND RADIO SOURCES

BY KEN TAPPING & HUGH PETT

Cosmic radio sources fall into two broad classes: "Continuum Sources," which emit over much of the radio spectrum and extend well beyond the frequency band used by any particular radio telescope, and "Spectral Sources," which emit radio spectral lines, such as the 1420.406 MHz (21-cm wavelength) spectral line from cosmic, neutral hydrogen. The continuum emissions are produced by high-energy electrons in magnetic fields, hot plasmas, or by plasma waves. These emissions are broadband but vary with frequency.

Frequency Bands Allocated for Radio Astronomical Use

The list below shows the frequency bands up to 31.5 GHz allocated by international treaty for use by radio observatories.

Band (MHz)	Primary Lines	Band (GHz)	Primary Lines
322.0–328.6	deuterium, D	4.8–5.0	formaldehyde, HCHO
406.1–410.0	continuum-only	10.6–10.7	continuum-only
608–614	continuum-only	14.47–14.50	formaldehyde, HCHO
1400–1427	hydrogen, H (21 cm)	15.35–15.40	continuum-only
1610.6–1613.8	hydroxyl, OH	22.21–22.50	water, H_20
1660–1670	hydroxyl, OH	23.6–24.0	ammonia, NH_3
2670–2700	continuum-only	31.3–31.5	continuum-only

Cosmic Radio Sources

The sources listed below are among those observable using small radio telescopes. Flux densities are given for 0.1, 0.5, 1, and 4 GHz (wavelengths of 3 m, 60 cm, 30 cm, and 7.5 cm, respectively) because equipment for these wavelengths is widely available.

Source	RA (2000) h m	Dec ° ′	Flux Densities (0.1, 0.5, 1, and 4 GHz) Jy	Remarks
Sun			20k/250k/450k/800k	"quiet" values; short, intense emissions from flares
Moon			2/50/210/3350	225 K thermal; plus near-surface emissions at <3 cm
Jupiter				Strong bursts at dekametre wavelengths
W3	2 25.4	+62 06	—/80/150/134	IC 1795; complex, bright HII region; OH emission
Taurus A	5 34.5	+22 01	1450/1250/1000/360	Crab Nebula; remnant of AD 1054 supernova
Orion A	5 35.3	−5 25	90/200/360/330	Orion Neb.; HII star-forming region; OH, IR source
IC 443	6 17.0	+22 34	350/140/80/20	Jellyfish Nebula; supernova remnant
Virgo A	12 30.8	+12 23	1950/150/300/120	M87; elliptical galaxy (E0) with jet; mag. +8.6
Centaurus A	13 25.4	−43 02	8500/5000/1900/200	NGC 5128; galaxy (S0 pec); mag.. +6.8, $z = 0.002$
3C 295	14 11.4	+52 12	95/60/28/10	radio galaxy; mag. +20.5, $z = 0.461$
Galactic centre	17 42.0	−28 50	4400/2900/1800/800	strong, diffuse emission from galactic centre
Sagittarius A*	17 42.5	−28 55	100/250/200/336	compact source at gal. ctr.; assoc. with black hole?
Cygnus A	19 59.5	+40 44	15500/4000/2100/370	strong radio galaxy (E); mag. +16.2, $z = 0.056$
Cygnus X	20 22.6	+40 23	400/150/30/70	complex region
Cassiopeia A	23 23.4	+58 49	25000/4500/2800/810	supernova remnant

Technology is advancing too quickly for printed books to be very useful. However, for background radio astronomy information, see *Radio Astronomy*, by J.D. Kraus (Cygnus-Quasar Books, Powell, Ohio, 1986). A number of small, simple radio telescopes and some projects to try are described in *Radio Astronomy Projects*, by William Lonc, Radio-Sky Publishing, 1997. Organizations focusing on amateur radio astronomy include the Society of Amateur Radio Astronomers—SARA (sara.org) and the UK Amateur Radio Astronomy Network (www.ukaranet.org.uk). The RASC Okanagan Centre (okanagan-radio-astronomy.org/index.html) has an active radio-astronomy group.

MAPS OF THE NIGHT SKY

BY ROY BISHOP

The maps on the following seven pages cover the entire sky. Stars are shown down to a magnitude of 4.5 or 5, that is, those that are readily apparent to the unaided eye on a reasonably dark night.

The first six maps are drawn for latitude 45°N but are useful for latitudes several degrees north or south of this. They show the hemisphere of sky visible at various times of year. Because the aspect of the night sky changes continuously with both longitude and time, while time zones change discontinuously with both longitude and time of year, it is not possible to state simply when a particular observer will find that his or her sky fits exactly one of the six maps. The month indicated above each map is the time of year when the map will match the ***late evening* sky**. On any particular night, successive maps will represent the sky as it appears every four hours later. For example, at 2:00 or 3:00 on a March morning, the May map should be used. Just after mealtime on a January night, the November map will be appropriate. The centre of each map is the *zenith*, the point directly overhead; the circumference is the horizon. To identify the stars, hold the map in front of you so that the part of the horizon you are facing (west, for instance) is downward. (The four letters around the periphery of each map indicate compass directions.)

The southern-sky map is centred on the south celestial pole and extends to Dec 20°S at its periphery. Thus there is considerable overlap with the southern areas of the other maps. Note that the orientation of the various names is generally inverted compared to that on the first six maps, as most users of this Handbook will be residents of the Northern Hemisphere and will make use of the southern-sky map when they make trips to the tropics. Thus in "normal" use this map will be read in an area above its centre, unlike the first six maps, which are normally read below their centres. The months indicated around the edge of the map may be used to orient it to each of the preceding six maps and have the same "late evening" significance as explained above. Tick marks around the edge of the map indicate hours of right ascension, with hours 0, 3, 6, etc., labelled. Starting at the centre of the map, the series of small crosses along RA 0h indicates southern declinations 90°, 80°, 70°,…, 20°. With the aid of a drawing compass, an observer in the Northern Hemisphere can quickly locate a circle, centred on the south celestial pole, that represents the southern limit of his or her sky.

On all seven maps, stars forming the usual constellation patterns are linked by straight lines, constellation names being given in uppercase letters. Three constellations (Horologium, Mensa, and Microscopium) consist of faint stars; hence no patterns are indicated and the names are placed in parentheses. Small clusters of dots indicate the positions of bright star clusters, nebulae, or galaxies. The pair of wavy dotted lines indicates roughly the borders of the Milky Way. Small asterisks locate the directions of the galactic centre (GC), the north galactic pole (NGP), and the south galactic pole (SGP). LMC, SMC, and CS signify, respectively, the Large Magellanic Cloud, the Small Magellanic Cloud, and the Coal Sack. Two dashed lines appear on each of the first six maps. The one with more dashes is the celestial equator. Tick marks along this indicate hours of right ascension, the odd hours being labelled. The line with fewer dashes is the ecliptic, the apparent annual path of the Sun across the heavens. Letters along this line indicate the approximate position of the Sun at the beginning of each month. Also located along the ecliptic are the Northern Hemisphere vernal equinox (VE), summer solstice (SS), autumnal equinox (AE), and winter solstice (WS).

The epoch of the maps is 1950.0. Because of the small scale of the maps, the effect of precession is not yet significant.

JANUARY ALL-SKY MAP

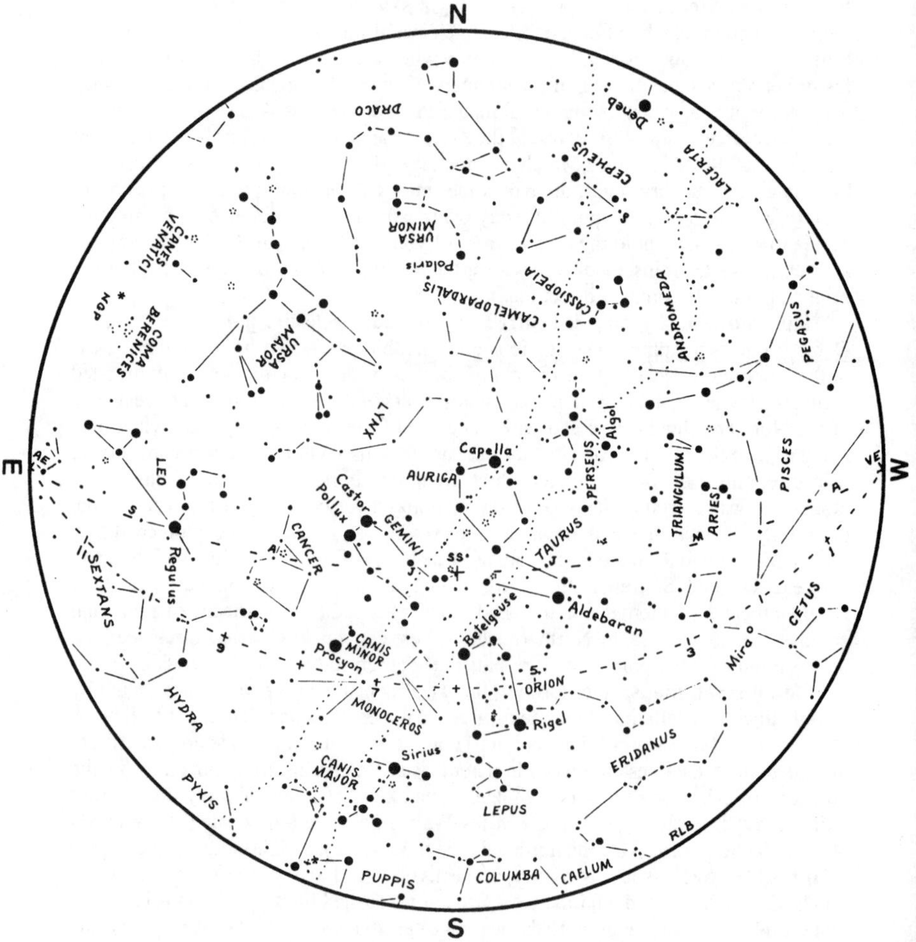

MARCH ALL-SKY MAP

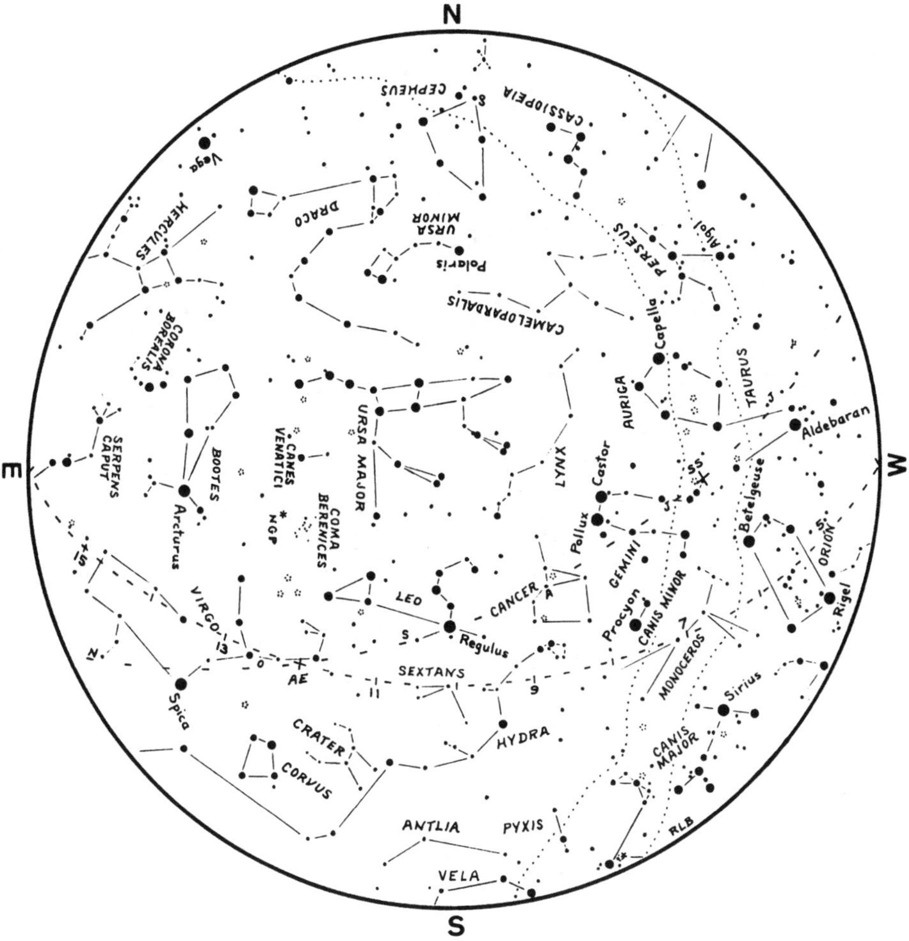

MAY ALL-SKY MAP

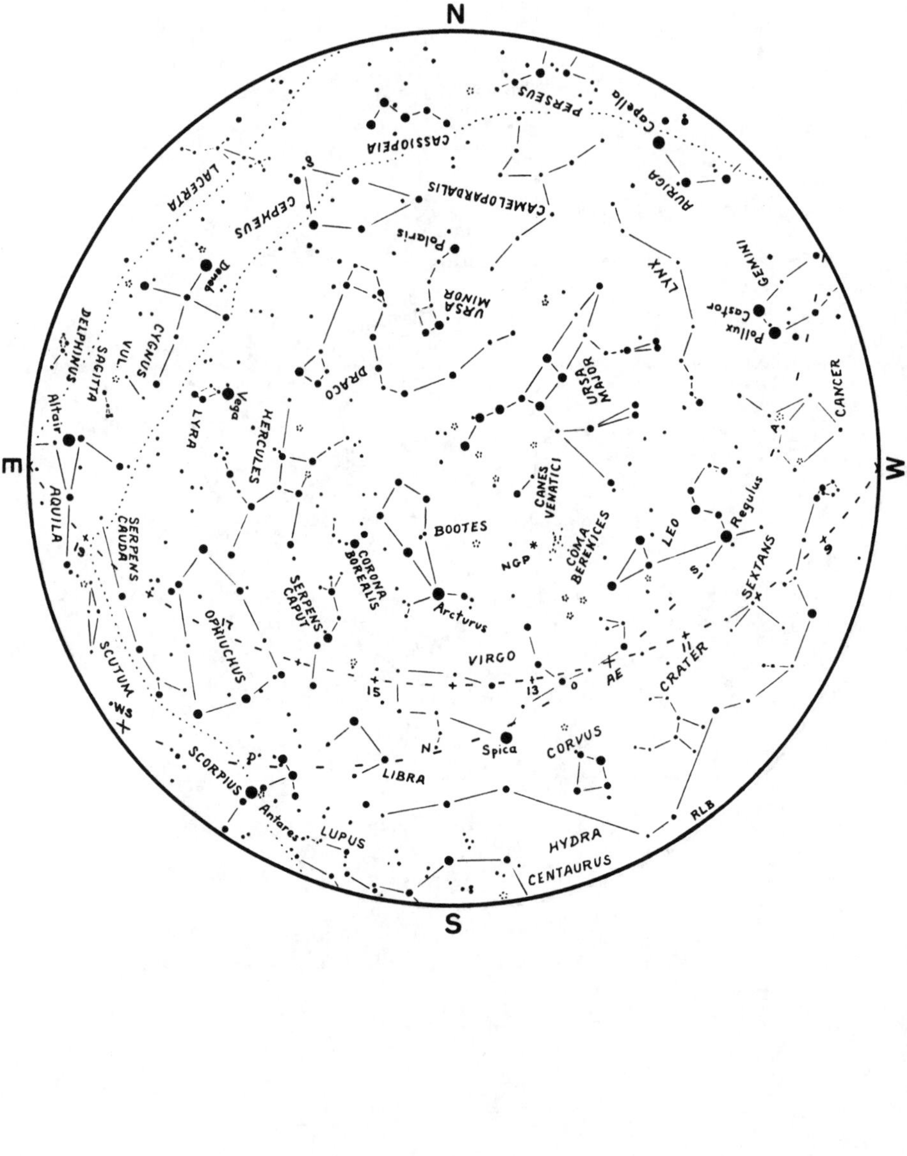

JULY ALL-SKY MAP

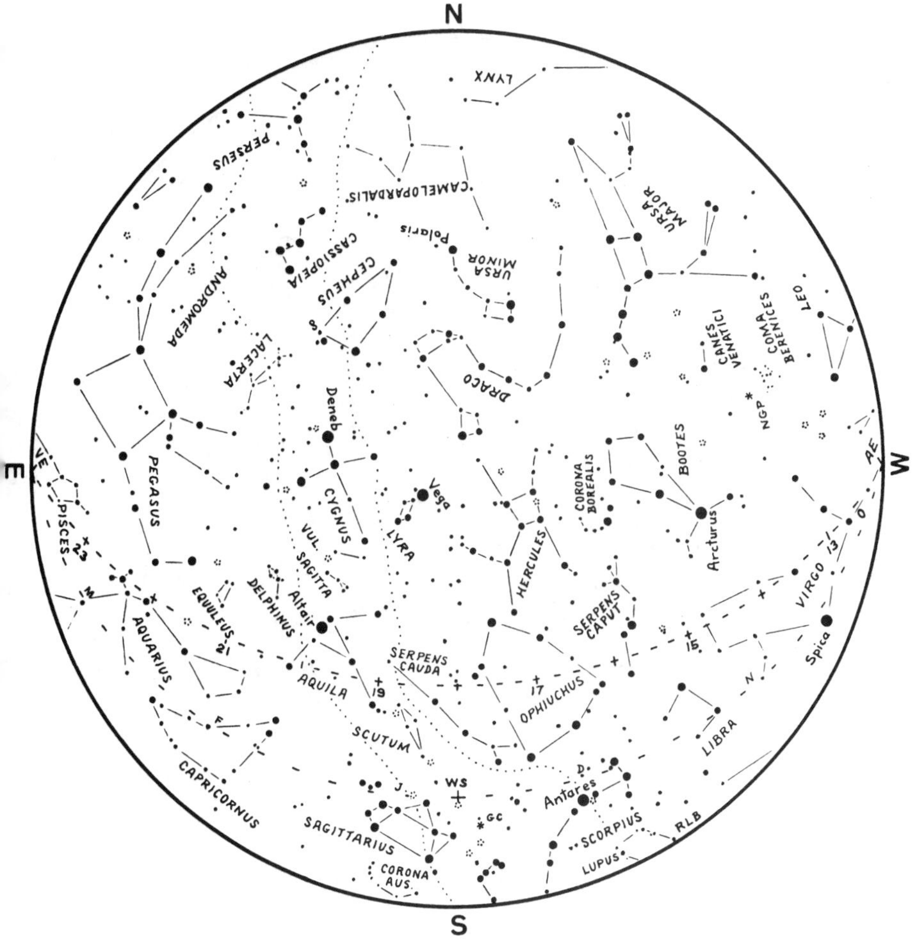

SEPTEMBER ALL-SKY MAP

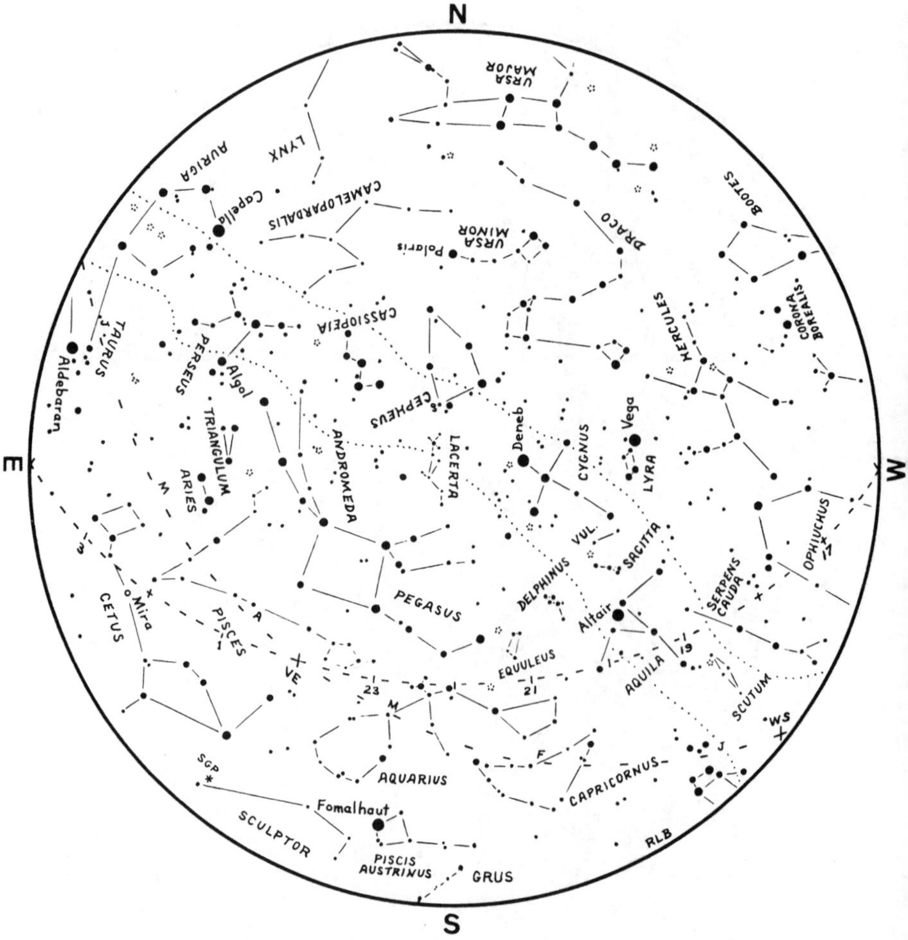

NOVEMBER ALL-SKY MAP

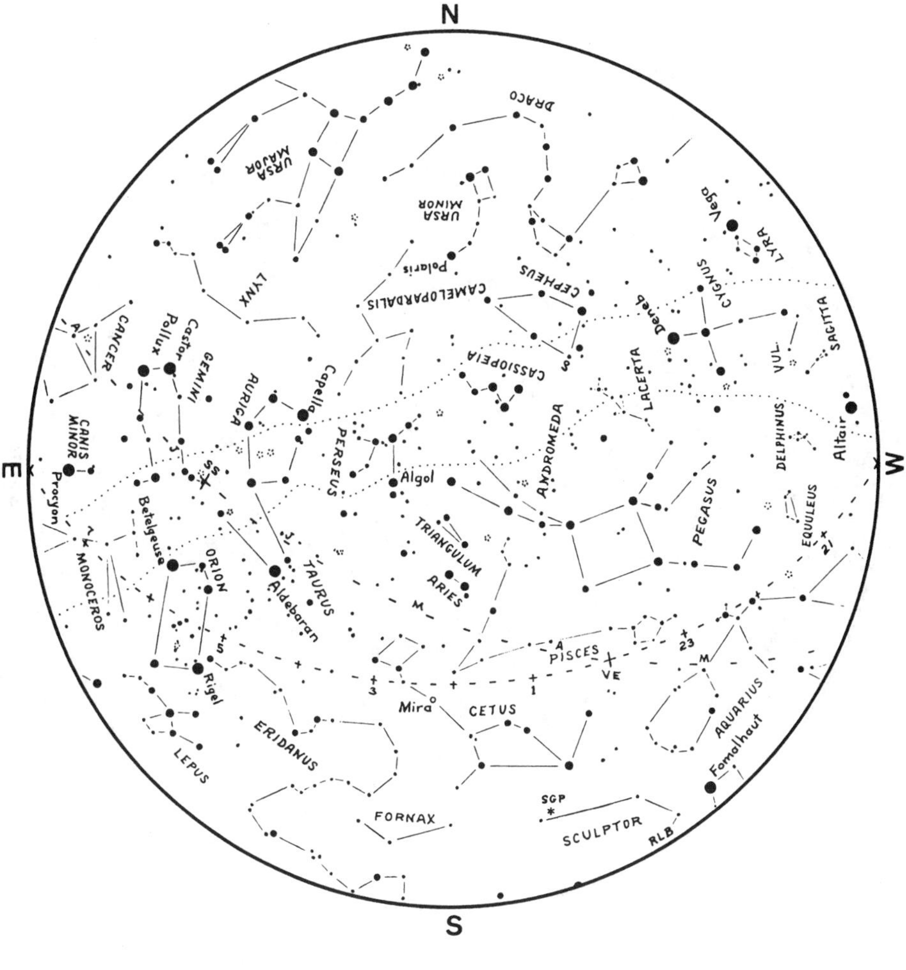

THE SOUTHERN SKY

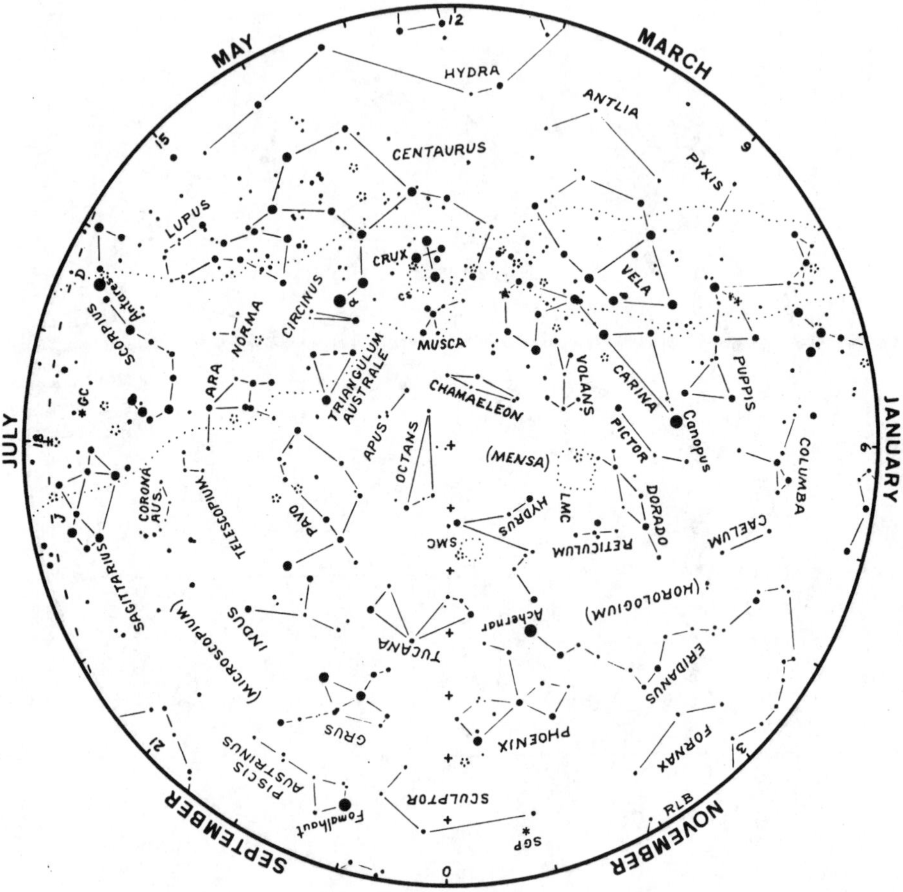

Editor's Note: A Glossary can be found online at www.rasc.ca/handbook/supplements.

INDEX

(**bold** = primary pages)

"MM" denotes the monthly pages of THE SKY MONTH BY MONTH starting on p. 98.

"MM" denotes the monthly pages of THE SKY MONTH BY MONTH starting on p. 98.

"MM" denotes the monthly pages of THE SKY MONTH BY MONTH starting on p. 98.

"MM" denotes the monthly pages of THE SKY MONTH BY MONTH starting on p. 98.

"MM" denotes the monthly pages of THE SKY MONTH BY MONTH starting on p. 98.

2017 HOLIDAYS AND SPECIAL DATES

New Year's Day	Sun. Jan. 1	
Martin Luther King Jr. Day (U.S.)	Mon. Jan. 16	
Chinese New Year (Year of the Rooster)	Mon. Jan. 28	
Winter Star Party, Florida Keys	Mon. Feb. 20	– Sun. Feb. 26
Washington's Birthday / Presidents Day (U.S.)	Mon. Feb. 20	
Ash Wednesday (beginning of Lent)	Wed. Mar. 1	
Daylight Saving Time starts (see p. 45)	Sun. Mar. 12	
Naw Ruz (Bahá'í New Year)*	Mon. Mar. 20	
First Day of Passover*	Sat. Apr. 11	
Good Friday	Fri. Apr. 14	
Easter Sunday	Sun. Apr. 16	
International Astronomy Week	Mon. Apr. 24	– Sun. Apr. 30
International Astronomy Day	Sat. Apr. 29	
Texas Star Party, Fort Davis, Texas	Sun. May 21	– Sun. May 28
Victoria Day (Canada)	Mon. May 22	
RTMC Astronomy Expo, Riverside, California	Thu. May 25	– Mon. May 29
First day of Ramadân*	Tue. May 27	
Memorial Day (U.S.)	Mon. May 29	
CASCA 2017, Edmonton, Alberta	Mon. May 29	– Thu. Jun. 1
National Aboriginal Day (Canada)	Wed. Jun. 21	
Fête nationale (Québec only)	Sat. Jun. 24	
RASC General Assembly, Ottawa, Ontario	Thu. Jun. 29	– Mon. Jul. 3
Canada Day	Sat. Jul. 1	
Independence Day (U.S.)	Tue. Jul. 4	
Starfest, Mount Forest, Ontario	Thu. Jul. 20	– Sun. Jul. 23
Stellafane Convention, Springfield, Vermont	Thu. Jul. 20	– Sun. Jul. 23
Star-B-Q, Eccles Ranch, Alberta	Fri. Jul. 21	– Sun. Jul. 23
Mount Kobau Star Party, Osoyoos, British Columbia	Sat. Jul. 22	– Sun. Jul. 30
Butterpot Star Party, St. John's, Newfoundland	Fri. Jul. 28	– Sat. Jul. 29
Nova East, Smileys Provincial Park, Nova Scotia	Fri. Jul. 28	– Sun. Jul. 30
Civic Holiday (most of Canada)	Mon. Aug. 7	
Kejimkujik Dark Sky Weekend, Caledonia, Nova Scotia	Fri. Aug. 11	– Sun. Aug. 13
Saskatchewan Summer Star Party, Cypress Hills, Sask.	Wed. Aug. 23	– Sun. Aug. 27
Labour Day (Canada and U.S.)	Mon. Sep. 4	
Alberta Star Party, Starland, Alberta	Fri. Sep. 15	– Sun. Sep. 17
Northern Prairie Star Party, near Tofield, Alberta	Tue. Sep. 19	– Sun. Sep. 24
Rosh Hashanah (Jewish New Year)*	Thu. Sep. 21	
Spruce Woods Star Party, Spruce Woods Park, Manitoba	Thu. Sep. 21	– Sat. Sep. 23
Islamic New Year*	Fri. Sep. 22	
Yom Kippur (Day of Atonement)*	Sat. Sep. 30	
Thanksgiving Day (Canada)	Mon. Oct. 9	
Columbus Day (U.S.)	Mon. Oct. 9	
Halloween	Tue. Oct. 31	
Daylight Saving Time ends (see p. 45)	Sun. Nov. 5	
Remembrance Day (Canada) and Veterans Day (U.S.)	Sat. Nov. 11	
Thanksgiving Day (U.S.)	Thu. Nov. 23	
Christmas Day	Mon. Dec. 25	
Boxing Day (Canada)	Tue. Dec. 26	

*Begins at sunset the previous evening.

See p. 11 for websites and geographical coordinates for the listed *star parties*.